BIOGRAPHICAL MEMOIRS
OF FELLOWS
OF THE ROYAL SOCIETY

VOLUME 60

BIOGRAPHICAL MEMOIRS
OF FELLOWS
OF THE ROYAL SOCIETY

2014
VOLUME 60

Published by the Royal Society
6–9 Carlton House Terrace
London SW1Y 5AG

The Royal Society is a Registered Charity (No. 207043)

Published December 2014

Editor: Professor Trevor Stuart

Commissioning: Keith Moore

Editorial Coordinator: Raminder Shergill

Editorial Board

Professor McNeill Alexander

Professor David Buckingham

Professor Christopher Calladine

Professor William Chaloner

Ms Georgina Ferry

Professor Bruce Joyce

Professor David Lilley

Professor Leon Mestel

Professor Tilli Tansey

Publisher: Phil Hurst

Production editor: Kelly Hutchinson

Picture curator: Joanna Hopkins

Typeset by Perfect Page, London

Printed by Henry Ling Limited, The Dorset Press, Dorchester

The Royal Society makes all reasonable efforts to obtain necessary permissions for the use of images which are copyright material. If you are the copyright owner of any images reproduced within any volume of *Biographical Memoirs* (or its forerunner, *Obituary Notices*) and are uncertain as to whether we hold your up-to-date contact information, please contact The Librarian, Library and Information Services of the Royal Society (email: library@royalsociety.org).

ISBN: 978-1-78252-097-9

ISSN: 0080-4606

CONTENTS

EDITORIAL

As is usual, the volumes of *Biographical Memoirs* contain much material of interest to the student of the mathematical, physical, engineering, biological and medical sciences. Often a memoir has been written in collaboration with another Academy or Society. In the present volume the memoir of Shiing-Shen Chern is an expanded version of an obituary notice by Nigel Hitchin that appeared in the *Bulletin of the London Mathematical Society*. Chern was a great geometer, who revolutionized differential geometry and whose mathematical tools are now common currency in geometry, topology and theoretical physics. His proof of the Gauss–Bonnet theorem, which was a pivotal event in the history of differential geometry, led to the importance of the Chern classes. Moreover. S.-S. Chern was extremely influential in the development of mathematics and geometry both in the USA, at the Institute of Advanced Study, Princeton, and Chicago and Berkeley, and in China, in Shanghai and Nankei.

Also on the physical side was the distinguished engineer Maurice Wilkes who, as explained by Martin Campbell-Kelly, led the construction of EDSAC, the world's first practical stored-program computer and then led the team constructing EDSAC 2 and the Titan computers. Moreover, he invented microprogramming, a fundamental technique in computer design. His influence was very great in the development of computing in the UK.

It is rare for a husband and wife both to be Fellows and to have memoirs that appear in the same volume, as is the case with Noreen and Kenneth Murray. Alexander Gann and Jean Beggs have described Noreen as an architect of recombinant DNA who was expert in the genetic manipulation of bacteria and in microbial genetics. As explained by W. J. Brammar and W. B. Gratzer, Kenneth was extremely influential in genetic engineering and biotechnology, and particularly in the discovery and development of a hepatitis vaccine, which has become of tremendous use worldwide. Kenneth started a spin-off company, Biogen, to market the hepatitis vaccine, the royalties from which have been used to set up a fund, the Darwin Trust, in support of young scientists. Both Kenneth and Noreen were hospitable with their generosity to others, not only with the Darwin Trust.

Another scientist who devoted royalties to charitable foundations was Edward Penley Abraham, whose memoir has been written by David S. Jones and John H. Jones. During World War II, Abraham made critical contributions with others, including Ernst Chain FRS, to the purification and structural elucidation of penicillin. In the postwar years he discovered and developed cephalosporin C, the royalties from which he used in setting up charitable trusts in favour of the Royal Society, King Edward VI School, Southampton, the Sir William Dunn School of Pathology at Oxford and Lincoln College, Oxford, all for the benefit of medicine and allied sciences. As with the Murrays, it was an act of great generosity.

I shall continue by treating the memoirs in two groups: (i) those in the physical sciences and (ii) those in the biological sciences, starting with the first group.

http://dx.doi.org/10.1098/rsbm.2014.0022

Two contrasting cases have already been highlighted: those of Maurice Wilkes in computing and Shiing-Shen Chern in mathematics. Three other mathematical cases follow that of Chern, the first being Friedrich Hirzebruch, whose memoir has been written by Michael Atiyah. Hirzebruch was distinguished in Germany for his leadership but was also admired for his fine work, for example the 'signature theorem', and for the impact that his work had not only in mathematics but also in theoretical physics and quantum mechanics. Another mathematician was Philip Saffman, who studied with G. I. Taylor in Cambridge but spent most of his professional life at the California Institute of Technology. Two of his graduate students, Darren Crowdy and Saleh Tanveer, contribute his memoir. He was distinguished both in vortex dynamics and in the theory and bifurcations of water waves, where he significantly extended knowledge of the Benjamin–Feir instability; moreover, stimulated by discussions over the garden fence with his neighbour Max Delbrück ForMemRS (see *Biogr. Mems Fell. R. Soc.* **28**, 58–90 (1982)) during a break from lawn-mowing, he became prominent in the motion of particles in a two-dimensional membrane that has a neighbouring viscous fluid (the Saffman–Delbrück model). A fourth mathematician was Paul Moritz Cohn, whose memoir has been written by George Bergman and me. He came to England by Kindertransport in 1939. His research lay in algebraic rings, especially non-commutative rings, where he made great advances, together with contributions in group theory, Lie groups and semigroups. Ring theory constitutes an important area of mathematics, including the concepts of matrices and tensors. Moreover there are applications in theoretical physics, such as Heisenberg's uncertainty principle. The memoir of Paul Cohn draws attention to his experiences as a refugee. In recent years several Fellows who came into this category have been the subject of memoirs, including Nicholas Kemmer in 2011 and Hans Kosterlitz and Fritz Ursell in 2013, the reasons for migration being varied. This leads to the case of Uli Arndt, a refugee who came to England with his family in 1936. At home in Birmingham, where he was at school, he lived with his family in a semi-detached house, the other half being occupied by Rudolf Peierls (FRS 1945) and his two lodgers Otto Frisch (FRS 1948) and Klaus Fuchs. Uli reflected later that the initial work to establish the feasibility of an atomic bomb may have been carried out there by Peierls and Frisch. He became a distinguished physicist, and his memoir has been contributed by R. A. Crowther and A. G. W. Leslie. Arndt specialized in X-ray crystallography with applications to large biological molecules. Moreover, at the Laboratory of Molecular Biology he developed three-dimensional data sets of crystals, an example of interaction between the physical and biological sciences. In all these cases the UK drew great benefit from the scientific work of these refugees, for whom our country became a safe haven.

I have already discussed one engineer, Maurice Wilkes, but a second engineer whose memoir appears in this volume is John Hadji Argyris, a refugee from occupied Europe; Brian Spalding writes of his contributions to the finite-element method of numerical analysis and also of his early recognition of the great changes that were likely to come from the advent of the digital computer. Argyris had a lively history in Greece, Germany, England from 1943 and then finally back to Germany in the 1960s, but the conflicting historical records made the writing of the memoir somewhat difficult. A third engineer was William Johnson, whose memoir is contributed by Steven Reid. Johnson made very significant developments in the mechanics of solids, in the plasticity of materials and in the topic of dislocations. A fourth engineer was Peter Gray, who was concerned with combustion chemistry and chemical instabilities, his memoir being written by S. K. Scott. For many years he was Head of Physical Chemistry at the University of Leeds, before returning to Cambridge as Master of Gonville and Caius College. Related work was that of John Clarke who, as explained by K. N. C. Bray and N. Riley, was active in research on chemically reacting flows, including flames, ignition processes, shock waves and detonations. Earlier he had served in the Fleet Air Arm, flying Fairey Fireflys. Bruce Bilby, whose memoir was written by G. W. Greenwood, was concerned with the mathematics and physics of crystal defects and dislocations, providing precise descriptions of their form and movement. This led Bilby to the experimentally verifiable interpretation of phenomena such as yield points and strain ageing.

In the biological sciences group, mention has been made already of Kenneth and Noreen Murray and of Edward Abraham. However, I now wish to mention John Monteith who, as explained by Michael H. Unsworth, was educated in physics and meteorology but did important research on the growth and development of living organisms in the environment, whether temperate or tropical. His work on the question of heat balance of animals proved to be of importance for its impact in developing countries. Thus, as in the case of Arndt but in a different way, his research spanned physical and biological aspects. Quite a different researcher was David Jack, who, as the memoir by Alasdair Breckenridge makes clear, was prominent in the development of drugs for treating common diseases of the respiratory, gastrointestinal and cardiovascular systems. Jack was one of the most successful inventors of new medicines in the twentieth century. The memoir of David Walker, which was contributed by Peter Horton, explains his research on photosynthesis, together with the fixation of carbon dioxide by the biochemical transformations of the Benson–Calvin cycle. Moreover, he was given to popularizing the sciences at a time when this activity was less prevalent than it is now and the importance of the public understanding of science was not recognized.

The memoir of James Franklin Crow, who was a Foreign Member, is a slight modification of that published by the US National Academy of Sciences and was written by Daniel L. Hartl and Rayla Greenberg Temin. Professor Crow's research focused on theoretical and experimental population genetics, especially using *Drosophila* as a model organism with later application to human genetics. He was fond of relating that he and the first issue of the journal *Genetics* were scheduled to arrive on the same day, 18 January 1916; he was on time but the journal was several weeks late! Quentin Howieson Gibson, whose memoir is contributed by John S. Olson and H. Gutfreund, also worked for a long time in the USA, although he was born in Aberdeen, studied in Belfast and was a Professor of Biochemistry at Sheffield before moving to the USA in 1963. He became a Member of the National Academy of Sciences. He had many major scientific accomplishments in biochemistry applied to medicine, in flash photolysis and in stopped-flow rapid-mixing spectrometry. He was a remarkable scientist whose publishing career spanned 66 years. Allan Charles Wilson was a New Zealander. As indicated by his biographer, Rebecca L. Cann, Allan was educated in Otago, New Zealand, and at Washington State University before gaining his PhD at the University of California, Berkeley. His professional career was spent mainly in the USA, where he became prominent in the theory of molecular evolution and the use of a molecular clock to measure evolutionary change between living species over time. Indeed, as a result of Wilson's influence the term 'molecular evolution' became common parlance in his lifetime. As explained by Alan Rickinson, the microbiologist Harry Smith was born in Northampton, was educated in the University of Nottingham and spent his professional career at the Chemical Defence Establishment, Porton Down, and then at the University of Birmingham. He was noted for his research work on the pathogenesis of microbial disease. His work on *Bacillus anthracis* led to the discovery of a tripartite toxin that could lead to the death of the host, the first bacterial toxin to be identified. George Bellamy Mackaness came from Sydney, New South Wales, and was educated there before visiting Oxford and meeting and being greatly influenced by Howard Florey FRS. As discussed by Philip Carter, he spent much of his professional career in the USA. Mackaness developed an *in vitro* method of studying macrophage–parasite interactions, showing why some anti-tubercular drugs are ineffective. Moreover, he elucidated the nature of immunity to tuberculosis. Malcolm Clarke was a marine biologist who, as made clear by Peter J. Herring, was educated in University College, Hull, and became distinguished as a world authority on cephalopods (squids), resulting from his study of the contents of the stomachs of their predators, such as sperm whales, where the beaks of cephalopods were readily identified. He was always fascinated by whales and their buoyancy control.

I wish to thank Keith Moore, who is the Librarian of the Royal Society, Raminder Shergill, who is the Editorial Coordinator for the Memoirs, Kelly Hutchinson, who is the Production Manager, Bruce Goatly and all other colleagues in the production of these memoirs. I also express my warm thanks to the authors.

Any reader should feel free to write to me if she or he wished to volunteer to write any particular memoir or to suggest another author. The offer would be gratefully received.

Trevor Stuart FRS
t.stuart@imperial.ac.uk
September 2014

SIR EDWARD PENLEY ABRAHAM CBE

10 June 1913 — 9 May 1999

Biogr. Mems Fell. R. Soc. **60**, 5–22 (2014)

E. P. Abraham

SIR EDWARD PENLEY ABRAHAM CBE

10 June 1913 — 9 May 1999

Elected FRS 1958

By David S. Jones[1] and John H. Jones[2]

[1]*Formerly of Corpus Christi College, Oxford OX1 4JF, UK*
[2]*Balliol College, Oxford OX1 3BJ, UK*

Edward Penley Abraham (Ted Abraham to intimate friends and family, EPA to his students), was a pioneer in antibiotics who made critical contributions to the purification and structural elucidation of penicillin as a young man in wartime, and led the discovery and development of cephalosporin C in his maturity. A kindly, modest and self-effacing private man, he could have amassed great wealth out of cephalosporin patents, but instead chose the path of philanthropy. He established substantial charitable funds in his lifetime for the benefit of medicine and allied subjects, the Royal Society, King Edward VI School, Southampton, and the University of Oxford, especially the Sir William Dunn School of Pathology and Lincoln College.

Early life

Abraham was born on 10 June 1913 at 47 South View Road, Southampton, which now sports a commemorative blue plaque. His parents were Albert Penley Abraham, a customs and excise officer, and Maria Agnes Abraham, *née* Hearne, who was born in Ireland, daughter of a journeyman carpenter. His only sibling, Mary Abraham, was born in 1917. Abraham's paternal family had deep roots in the Southampton area, traceable to the John Abraham who married Mary Heckley at Alverstoke in 1765, and perhaps beyond. The persistent given name Penley came into the family through Elizabeth Penley of St Pancras, who married William Burree there in 1826: she was the paternal grandmother of Abraham's paternal grandmother.

In 1924 Abraham entered King Edward VI School, Southampton (KES), with a Corporation Scholarship, and showed sporting prowess and academic talent right across the board. The heads of both classics and science solicited him to specialize, and the direction he took was a close-run thing, although late in life, typically modest and unconvincing, he said he would have been no good at classics. He was admitted to The Queen's College, University of Oxford

http://dx.doi.org/10.1098/rsbm.2014.0002

(which had already supported him at KES with a Queen's College VIth Form Scholarship), as a Southampton Exhibitioner in 1932, to read chemistry. The elderly F. D. Chattaway FRS was his first tutor. Abraham thought he had been 'a quite well known organic chemist in his day but tended to live in the past', and was glad that he soon gave way to Wilson Baker (FRS 1946), whom he acknowledged as the most important early chemical influence on him; perhaps he was also influential in charitable ways: Baker was a founder of Oxfam.

Abraham was awarded first-class honours in 1936, and did DPhil research from 1936 to 1938 in the Dyson Perrins Laboratory (the DP) on peptide and protein chemistry, under the overall direction of Robert (later Sir Robert) Robinson FRS (PRS 1945–50). Robinson had been stimulated to enter the field by the cyclol hypothesis (Curtis & Jones 2006). Abraham's doctoral work established in him a permanent bias towards biological chemistry. During it he was the first to crystallize hen egg-white lysozyme (1)*, and he was also the first to explore the use of the phthaloyl group for amino-group protection in peptide synthesis, although that work was never published.

Abraham met Asbjørg Harung in mid-1938 while she was visiting Oxford. She returned to Norway soon after that, but he courted her by letter and occasional visits throughout the academic year 1938–39, while working at Hans von Euler-Chelpin's institute in Stockholm. His long and sometimes passionate letters to her are very revealing, fluently written, moving between humour and serious reflection, casually laced with learned classical and literary allusions, and slipping occasionally into French or German. He describes not only his friends, diverse cultural interests and outdoor activities, but also his concerns about the looming war; 'if anything bad should happen suddenly, I will do everything possible to see you before trying to get home to imbibe the bitter doctrine: dulce et decorum est pro patria mori. I am not at all afraid to die, there are worse things than that, but the thought of losing you is something different.'

Euler was a Nobel laureate, but Abraham was not impressed, writing to Asbjørg in January 1939: 'Frankly I am terribly disappointed in Euler and cannot imagine how he has got so far unless it is by having first rate coworkers. At present there is not an atom of inspiration from the top.' While in Euler's laboratory he performed experiments on alloxazine adenine dinucleotide (2) in collaboration with Fritz Schlenk (1910–98); he was grateful to Schlenk for his kindness, which included insisting that he should publish the work alone. He also became very friendly with Holger Erdtman (1902–89), later a very distinguished natural products chemist.

When war broke out, Abraham was prevented from returning home immediately by a serious foot infection that was spreading up his leg. Reminiscing 50 years later with a chuckle about his first experience with antibacterial drugs, he recalled that his Swedish physician had warned him that if he did not rest and take the *p*-aminobenzenesulphonamide prescribed, he would not be going anywhere 'except in a wooden box'. He travelled to Bergen in mid-September, married Asbjørg there on 1 November and rushed back to England alone late in 1939. He had been expected to return to the DP, but by that time the cyclol hypothesis had been discredited and Robinson had made a swift retreat from peptides and proteins. Abraham was instead taken in by H. W. (later Lord) Florey (FRS 1941; PRS 1960–65), just down the road from the DP at the Sir William Dunn School of Pathology. Florey discouraged him from volunteering for military service, which was his inclination. He was assigned to assist E. B. (later Sir Ernst) Chain (FRS 1949), initially to work on wound shock (4).

---

* Numbers in this form refer to the bibliography at the end of the text.

Asbjørg was reluctant to leave Norway in haste, and in April 1940 she was trapped there by the Nazi invasion, after which they could only communicate surreptitiously via Erdtman in neutral Sweden. His last surviving letter to her, in January 1941, shows mutual resignation to more years of separation and concluded 'I try to wait for you with courage'. She escaped on foot over the mountains to Sweden later that year, and was still in Stockholm in mid-1942, but she somehow managed to turn up unannounced at Abraham's parents' house during the blackout, soon after entering the UK at Aberdeen in November. Their only child, Michael Erling Penley Abraham, born in Oxford in July 1943, was severely disabled, a sadness of which Abraham hardly ever spoke.

THE STRUCTURE OF PENICILLIN

When Abraham took up his post in the Dunn School, Florey, Chain and Norman Heatley were already engaged on work with several antibacterial preparations, including 'penicillin', which Alexander (later Sir Alexander) Fleming (FRS 1943) had discovered but not foreseen the importance of. It was at that stage a complex mixture, of which the active agent was a potent but minor (much less than 1%) constituent. Florey performed a historic experiment on 25 May 1940 in which he gave eight mice a potentially fatal streptococcal infection and then treated four of them with penicillin: the controls died overnight, but the treated animals were all alive two days later. This was quickly followed by experiments that consolidated the demonstration that penicillin was a potential miracle cure for bacterial infections—if enough of it could be produced. Abraham's name was not on the first *Lancet* paper (Chain *et al.* 1940) but he was very much involved in its production and purification, his particular contribution being alumina chromatography (6), then a very novel technique, and he was party to the first human toxicity trial on 27 January 1941 (10), telling Asbjørg two days later, 'We are beginning to test our material for possible toxic effects on human patients—choosing those that are bound to die anyhow!' So his name was on the second *Lancet* paper (5).

As soon as enough material approaching homogeneity became available (6), a great deal of effort was invested secretly on both sides of the Atlantic in discovering the structure of the active substance, in the hope that that could be followed by chemical synthesis. The principal Oxford organic chemists on the case were Abraham and Chain in the Dunn School, and Baker, J. W. (later Sir John) Cornforth (FRS 1953) and Robinson in the DP. All of these made important contributions to what was probably the most complex structural problem in organic chemistry tackled and solved up to that time, with few physical aids to call on. The active substance was labile, of questionable purity to start with, and was to turn out eventually to have a completely novel structure. The work was never published in the usual way, and the results were spread over a large number of secret reports that were summarized at the war's end (Clarke *et al.* 1949).

Abraham himself wrote several historical accounts of the penicillin story (10, 32, 43, 45, 47, 48); see also Curtis *et al.* (2008), pp. 65–72, and Curtis & Jones (2007).

Abraham and Chain obtained evidence by September 1942 that acid hydrolysis of penicillin gave an amino acid. Abraham isolated this amino acid, which was named penicillamine, in crystalline form as a hydrochloride. A great leap forward might have been made at this stage if it had been realized that the transient deep blue colour seen on oxidation of penicillamine with ferric chloride was like the characteristic blue seen on the oxidation of cysteine with the same reagent. This was not considered because the analysts had not found any sulphur in penicillin.

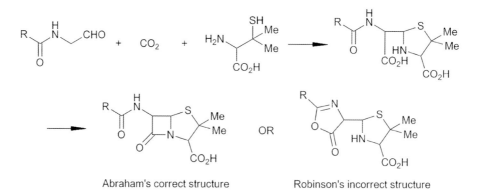

Scheme 1. The notional reconstruction of penicillin from its degradation products. R = pent-2-enyl for the penicillin grown by fermentation in Oxford; R = benzyl for that grown in America. The difference was slightly confusing until clarified in 1943, but it did not affect the structural debates.

Oxidation with bromine water gave a strong dibasic acid, penicillaminic acid, which was formulated in ignorance of the presence of sulphur as $C_5H_{11}O_7N$. Abraham also managed to form a stable crystalline copper salt that seemed to be $[C_5H_{10}O_7N]_2Cu$. In an attempt to explain the high oxygen content it had been suggested that it was hydrated, but it did not release water when strongly heated over a drying agent *in vacuo*.

Baker, now convinced that there had been an analytical oversight, performed a sodium fusion test on a sample of penicillamine hydrochloride in July 1943, and obtained a positive result for sulphur. Up to this point the Oxford team had been working with penicillin as its amorphous but convenient barium salt, which was the origin of the analytical mistake, the sulphur having been lost as insoluble barium sulphate (J. W. Cornforth, personal communication reported in Curtis *et al.* (2008), p. 66). On hearing that the sodium salt of American penicillin (see scheme 1) had been crystallized, Abraham made the sodium salt of the Oxford penicillin, which crystallized easily. These findings removed much confusion, and rapid progress followed. Abraham proved that penicillamine was an α-amino-β-mercapto acid, and obtained a crystalline thiazolidine when attempting to recrystallize it from hot acetone. Cornforth then guessed the presence of a gem-dimethyl group, and proved by synthesis that penicillamine was in fact β,β-dimethylcysteine (= β-mercaptovaline).

In addition to penicillamine, acid hydrolysis of penicillin gave CO_2 and an acylamino-acetaldehyde. Robinson deduced that the CO_2 had resulted from decarboxylation of the corresponding α-carboxy aldehyde, and that penicillin (the correct molecular formula of which was by then known) could be notionally reconstructed from penicillamine by thiazolidine formation between it and the α-carboxy aldehyde, followed by dehydration, and proposed a thiazolidine–oxazolone structure. Abraham, however, had been engaged in performing electrometric titrations on penicillin and was unable to find evidence of a weakly basic group, such as the thiazolidine nitrogen in Robinson's proposed structure. With this in mind he wrote down the isomeric β-lactam structure and showed it to Chain, who received it with enthusiasm. Baker also gave it his support and it was added, in Robinson's absence, to a report that Robinson had drafted. The report (7) was submitted for circulation on 22 October 1943. Robinson was furious, on his return, to discover the amendments made to the final version, going so far as to send in an addendum stating that 'one of us considers the four ring structure above somewhat improbable.'

Robinson was a genius who was rarely wrong, but over penicillin he was blinkered by his own self-confidence. Even when Abraham's structure was proved crystallographically by Dorothy Hodgkin (FRS 1947) in 1945 (Crowfoot *et al.* 1949), he clutched at straws, supposing that the crystal structure did not preclude mobile equilibria with other structures in solution. On the other side of the Atlantic, some, including R. B. Woodward (ForMemFRS 1956) strongly supported Abraham's structure, but others favoured Robinson's until the crystal structure proof. An essentially American view of the history of penicillin by J. C. Sheehan was published in 1982. Abraham contributed a handsome foreword (42) to it, with the gentle closing caveat 'He will scarcely expect that all those who read his book will purr with approval of the contents of every page, for on some topics there may never be a final word.'

THE DISCOVERY, STRUCTURE AND DEVELOPMENT OF CEPHALOSPORIN C

In the immediate postwar years Abraham worked on several antibiotic topics and made a visit to Berkeley, where he was introduced to isotopic labelling techniques and contributed to elucidating the mammalian pathway by which tryptophan is converted to nicotinic acid (9). Two things crucial to his later work happened when he returned to Oxford in 1948. Guy Newton was admitted by Florey to the Dunn School for doctoral work, and Giuseppe Brotzu sent Florey a *Cephalosporium acremonium* culture with antibiotic properties that he had obtained from a sewage outfall in the Bay of Naples.

Abraham himself put modest accounts of the early work on cephalosporin on record a number of times (47, 48), always stressing the joint nature of his collaboration with Newton, which began as that of master and apprentice, but evolved into a partnership of close friends. See also Curtis *et al.* (2008), pp. 80–86, Jones (2008) and Hamilton-Miller (2000).

Florey placed Newton under Abraham's immediate supervision and asked Heatley to make preliminary investigations of Brotzu's antibiotic material, which was shown to be a complex mixture (scheme 2). Larger amounts of it were made in collaboration with the Medical Research Council (MRC) Antibiotics Station at Clevedon in Somerset. It was then passed to Abraham, who investigated the hydrophobic fraction first. The principal component cephalosporin P_1 (P for Gram-positive activity) appeared to have the formula $C_{32}H_{48}O_8$ and was closely related to the known antibiotic helvolic acid (16). When Newton had finished his DPhil work he stayed with Abraham to work on the hydrophilic fraction. The major component of that fraction, cephalosporin N (N for Gram-negative activity), was recognized as probably of the penicillin type, and was therefore judged to be worth exploring in depth. The compound responsible for the activity observed by Brotzu, it did eventually turn out to be a new penicillin, and was renamed penicillin N (10, 13, 14). However, its purification was difficult. In September 1953, with a view to obtaining a more easily purified and characterized derivative, Abraham suggested converting the crude cephalosporin N to the corresponding crude penillic acid by mild acid treatment, which is a general isomerization of penicillins, and purifying the product. When Newton performed this experiment, he was indeed able to isolate the penillic acid pure by ion-exchange chromatography, but he did not stop the column, and in the later fractions he found a minor ninhydrin-reactive component with a λ_{max} of 260 nm that had come through from the crude antibiotic mixture unchanged by the acid treatment. It was found to have some similarities in chemical properties to the penicillins, but also some marked differences; and it had a broad spectrum of relatively low antibiotic activity but was resistant to penicillinase. This compound, which was also later

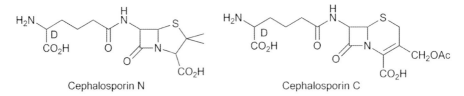

Scheme 2. The principal hydrophilic antibiotics from *Cephalosporium acremonium*. Cephalosporin N = penicillin N.

isolated with difficulty from the original antibiotic mixture, crystallized easily as a sodium salt. It was arbitrarily named cephalosporin C (15, 17).

The inactivity of penicillinase against cephalosporin C was of importance, because bacterial strains causing infections that did not respond to penicillin therapy were evolving and becoming problematic. Further investigation was therefore undertaken, with strong encouragement from Florey, who did the first *in vivo* experiments. He showed it was not toxic to mice, and cured otherwise fatal artificially inflicted streptococcal infections; he reported these results in a lecture delivered on 25 April 1955 (Florey 1955). He remained closely informed thereafter, but he did not put his name on any of the subsequent cephalosporin papers or patents.

After the war it was felt that British ethical reservations about the decency of taking profit from medical discoveries had allowed the American pharmaceutical industry to barge in and reap the financial benefit. This sparked the Development of Inventions Act 1948 and the foundation of the National Research Development Corporation (NRDC), which had a brief to see that inventions in British universities were protected and commercially developed. In return for assignment of rights to the NRDC by inventors, the NRDC would take on the administrative burden and costs of obtaining and commercializing patents, paying the inventors an agreed share of the royalties.

Steps were taken by the NRDC to obtain patent cover for cephalosporin C, and to stimulate industrial interest as soon as its possible potential was appreciated. Several companies in the pharmaceutical industry were interested at an early stage, but Glaxo Laboratories Ltd was the keenest. They were licensed to produce the antibiotic in cooperation with the Oxford and Clevedon workers. Newton was instrumental in helping Glaxo to get going, and made numerous visits to them; in return, Glaxo produced more than 100 g of pure cephalosporin C for work at Oxford. This gave Glaxo a lead in the cephalosporin business and contributed to the continuation of its rise from being a producer of mundane health products to being a sophisticated international drug company, which is now part of GlaxoSmithKline (Jones 2001).

Abraham and Newton's cephalosporin C structural analysis depended on the study of degradation products, careful observation and colour reactions, but infrared, ultraviolet and even (30 MHz) NMR spectroscopy, then in its infancy, were also used—it was probably the first application of NMR to an important natural product problem anywhere. What would now call for a few milligrams of pure material and a few days with advanced instrumentation needed multi-gram quantities and took five years.

Abraham conceived the fused β-lactam-dihydrothiazine structure of cephalosporin C while on a skiing holiday in 1958 (48). Asbjørg had inherited a chalet at Gullsteinhovda near Geilo in Norway. The couple generally went there at Easter for skiing and in August for hiking. The chalet had a wonderful view overlooking the Hallingdal valley. He would often sit outside it in quietness looking down the valley, and he remarked several times that it was a place that inspired many good research ideas.

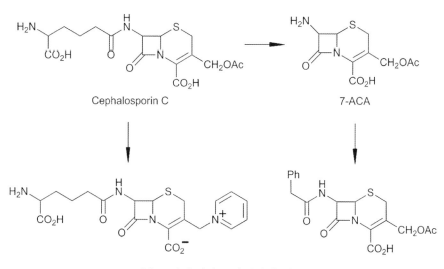

Scheme 3. Cephalosporin C derivatives.

However, it was not until around April 1959 that the structure was established to Abraham's satisfaction, with first public disclosure at a meeting in Australia in August 1960 (18). Having been in disagreement with Robinson over the structure of penicillin, and then eventually been proved right, Abraham had a similar experience over the cephalosporin C structure with Woodward. After disclosing his structure in Canberra, Abraham travelled home via America and called on Woodward, who said to him, 'If I had proposed that structure for a compound with that absorption spectrum I would be very unhappy' (48). Full details were published in 1961 (19), followed immediately by Dorothy Hodgkin's X-ray confirmation (Hodgkin & Maslen 1961). Because Robinson and Woodward were arguably the greatest organic chemists of all time, to have bettered them both in turn was no mean feat.

Abraham and Newton also established in principle that the side chain could be removed, giving 7-aminocephalosporanic acid (7-ACA), and replaced by acyl groups such as phenyl-acetyl with changes in activity (21); and that the acetoxy group was susceptible to displace-ment by heterocyclic nucleophiles (20). These observations, which were also patented under the auspices of the NRDC, opened the way for the pharmaceutical industry to produce diverse cephalosporin C analogues (scheme 3) based on the bicyclic nucleus 7-ACA, for which improved manufacture was soon developed (Morin *et al.* 1962). Cephalosporin C itself had a few medical successes, but attention soon shifted to the next generation such as cephalothin and cephaloridine, which were being marketed by Eli Lilly & Co. and Glaxo, respectively, by late 1964. With the essentials defined, and the pharmaceutical companies vigorously engaged, the development of derivatives was largely left to them. Thousands have been made by now, and many are in regular clinical use.

β-Lactamases

With Chain, Abraham observed in 1940 (3) that penicillin preparations (still grossly impure and not chemically characterized) were inactivated enzymically by an extract from penicillin-resistant *B. coli*, and in 1944 (8) he showed that the enzyme worked by opening the β-lactam ring. Testing new antibiotic preparations with penicillinase became standard practice, and was important for recognizing cephalosporin N as a member of the penicillin family.

When cephalosporin C was isolated, its stability to pure penicillinase was the trigger for accelerating work on it, but crude penicillinase preparations from *B. cereus* did inactivate it, and it was found to be a competitive inhibitor of penicillinase (15, 17). *B. cereus* was later shown to produce two crystallizable β-lactamases designated I and II, the latter being a zinc-dependent glycoprotein and the former being carbohydrate-free and zinc-independent. β-Lactamase I hydrolysed benzylpenicillin but not cephalosporin C; β-lactamase II hydrolysed them both. The zinc was found to be bound to histidine (26, 29, 36, 37). Unravelling the workings of these and related enzymes and the fates of the cephalosporin C degradation products, which were much more complicated than with penicillin (27, 28), were major themes of Abraham's later work.

β-LACTAM ANTIBIOTIC BIOSYNTHESIS

Blackboard dissection of the cephalosporin C structure pointed to its biosynthesis somehow from valine, cysteine and α-aminoadipic acid. Abraham confirmed this (22–25) by showing that radioactivity was efficiently and specifically incorporated into it on adding radiolabelled amino acids to a *Cephalosporium* sp. culture. There was correlation between the amounts of penicillin N and cephalosporin C produced, and it was suggested (23) that they had a common biosynthetic intermediate, α-aminoadipylcysteinylvaline (ACV). It was not so straightforward to put that hypothesis to the test, because when labelled peptides were added to intact cultures, they did not penetrate the cells where antibiotic synthesis took place. However, it was shown in 1976 (35) that L,L,D-ACV (but not its epimers) was incorporated intact by a cell-free system obtained from *Cephalosporium acremonium* into a penicillin that was actually isopenicillin N (38) (scheme 4), and this was directly observed by NMR in 1980 (40). Enzymic epimerization of isopenicillin N to penicillin N was published in 1981 (41). The biotransformation of penicillin N into cephalosporin C (scheme 5) had been established earlier (Kohsaka & Demain 1976), although this was indirect via desacetoxycephalosporin C (Baldwin *et al.* 1981). It was thus possible to map the principal pathways in the formation of the two antibiotic systems by the early 1980s (39).

Abraham was also able to start probing the mechanisms of the five-membered and six-membered ring-forming processes, by feeding *Cephalosporium acremonium* numerous valines with methyl groups that were stereospecifically labelled with ^{13}C, ^{2}H or ^{3}H, or both ^{2}H and ^{3}H (33, 34, 44). The valine skeleton was incorporated intact (scheme 6), the pro-*S* methyl group being the exclusive source of the α-methyl group of penicillin N, so the ring closure there was stereospecific. The same methyl group became the exocyclic methylene of cephalosporin C. By contrast, although conversion of the other methyl group into the endocyclic methylene group of cephalosporin C was correspondingly regiospecific, it was stereochemically random so far as choice between the hydrogen atoms was concerned. This observation and previous literature on peroxide-initiated sulphide rearrangements prompted the suggestion (44) that the ring expansion began by hydrogen abstraction from the β-methyl group to give a primary free radical intermediate with a lifetime enabling free rotation before rearrangement to a tertiary radical (scheme 7). The chemical feasibility of the proposal was later demonstrated in the DP (Baldwin *et al.* 1987), where radicals generated from 2β-bromomethylpenicillin analogues by treatment with triphenyltin hydride were shown to lead to the cephalosporin ring system.

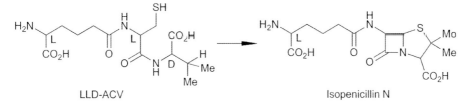

Scheme 4. The biosynthesis of isopenicillin N from L,L,D-ACV.

Scheme 5. The pathway for the biosynthesis of penicillin N and cephalosporin C.

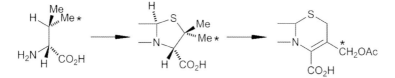

Scheme 6. The biosynthetic incorporation of labelled valine into cephalosporin C.

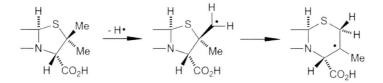

Scheme 7. Possible intermediates in the biosynthetic ring expansion.

Exchanges that soon evolved into a close collaboration on β-lactam biosynthesis between Abraham at the Dunn School and J. E. (now Sir Jack) Baldwin FRS at the DP had begun when Baldwin was installed in Robinson's chair in 1978, a resumption of the interdepartmental relationship that had been so fruitful under pressure over penicillin during the war. Baldwin had entered the field several years previously, recognizing that β-lactam antibiotic biosynthesis posed fundamental problems in mechanistic organic chemistry, because the transformations involved in generating the ring systems of the penicillins and cephalosporins from a tripeptide, whatever they were, were obviously well beyond current textbook explanations. Indeed, Baldwin—then still at Massachusetts Institute of Technology—and American colleagues had obtained results defining the fate of the valine methyl groups at the same time as Abraham's group in Oxford (Neuss *et al.* 1973).

The exquisitely elegant work that ensued was probably due more to Baldwin and his many co-workers in the DP than to Abraham and his much smaller Dunn School group, although Abraham's name is on many joint papers until around 1990. The two leaders reviewed their work magisterially in 1988 (46), acknowledging a special debt to R. M. Adlington.

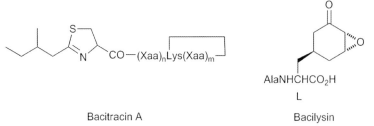

Bacitracin A   Bacilysin

Scheme 8. Bacitracin A and bacilysin.

OTHER SCIENTIFIC WORK

The work outlined above, especially the cephalosporin C discoveries, tends to overshadow Abraham's other scientific work, but he made several other important contributions to peptide antibiotic chemistry involving the recognition of very unusual structural features. For example, with Newton he showed that bacitracin A has a thiazoline ring near the amino terminus (12), and that nisin contains lanthionine and cystathione (11); and with J. E. (now Sir John) Walker (FRS 1995), that bacilysin is a dipeptide with a cyclic epoxy ketone side chain (30, 31) (scheme 8).

PHILANTHROPY

Because the University of Oxford had no policy regarding the patent income of employees, Abraham stood to benefit personally from the cephalosporin patents obtained by the NRDC, but the MRC took the greater part of Newton's share, as he was an MRC employee. After a tussle with the Inland Revenue, Abraham established two charitable funds for most of his share ('with my wife's encouragement') and a third was set up jointly with Newton.

> The Edward Penley Abraham Research Fund. Registered Charity 309659, established 17 March 1967. For research in medicine chemistry and biology in the University and colleges of Oxford especially the Dunn School and Lincoln College.
> The Guy Newton Research Fund. Registered Charity 309696, established 17 March 1967. For research at the Dunn School.
> The EPA Cephalosporin Fund. Registered Charity 309698, established 18 May 1970. For education, and research in medicine chemistry and biology, in the University and colleges of Oxford, KES, and the Royal Society.

In the early years these funds received revenue from Abraham and Newton's work, which of course ran out when the patents did; they now receive only investment income. For 30 years Abraham was able to take a close interest in the funds, which made general support grants, endowed professorships, funded research fellowships, and enabled many eponymous building projects. This work continues on an increasing scale. Despite massive support of their prescribed objectives from the outset, and which is ongoing (in 2011–12 totalling over £5 million, which might have been a below-average year), the three funds now have between them a capital base of well over £150 million.

Figure 1. Sir Edward and Lady Abraham after his investiture, 1980.

HONOURS

Abraham was honoured with a CBE, a knighthood (figure 1), the Royal Society Royal and Mullard Medals, the Scheele Medal of the Swedish Pharmaceutical Society, honorary doctorates from at least four universities, and honorary fellowships of at least seven Oxford colleges. He was a Foreign Honorary Member of the American Academy of Arts and Science, and a Kentucky Colonel. He accepted the adulation accorded him as the elder statesman and philanthropist of the world of antibiotics with modesty and courtesy, but in time he became embarrassed, and he declined with apology at least one Oxford honorary fellowship. He was nominated for a share in a Nobel prize in 1981, apparently without his knowledge, and again in 1983; when approached in 1996 he was gracefully evasive.

POSTWAR PERSONAL LIFE

A student who joined Abraham at the Dunn School soon after Newton's premature death in 1969, which was a great personal as well as professional loss to Abraham, writes:

Figure 2. Sir Edward Abraham CBE by Daphne Todd OBE, 1991. Commissioned by KES, where it hangs. The molecular model in the background is 7-aminocephalosporanic acid. (Photographed by Graham Piggott, Head of Art at KES; reproduced with permission.) (Online version in colour.)

I have very happy and positive memories of my student days with EPA, as he was known. The group was busy and highly productive. Although in my day I never remember him doing any serious 'hands on' bench work, he was very attuned to his students' projects and was rigorous in his scientific approach to them. His students received much insightful encouragement, but at the same time he expected 100% commitment from them.

After the war, Florey, a Fellow of Lincoln College, obtained a benefaction from Lord Nuffield to establish fellowships at Lincoln commemorating the penicillin work. Abraham was elected to a non-voting Nuffield (Penicillin) Research Fellowship in 1948. He enjoyed participating in college life, and played an active role on the college's governing body (especially its finance committee) from 1960, when he was elected to a professorial fellowship with full voting rights. As he was elected to an honorary fellowship when he retired, his close connection to Lincoln continued for the rest of his life. His affection for it is amply demonstrated by the fact that he set up the first and largest of his Trust Funds so that Lincoln would be especially favoured and the Rector of Lincoln was a Trustee *ex officio*.

He seems to have enjoyed the affectionate respect of all who knew him, and even got on well with Chain, a volatile and difficult character who fell out with most of his colleagues.

Abraham retired from his university post at the then statutory age of 67 years in 1980, but was active in the Dunn School and a great traveller to international conferences for another decade or so. And the regular visits to Norway (usually three weeks at Easter, six weeks in the summer) with Asbjørg, which had been a major part of their lives since soon after the war, continued until 1994.

In retirement (figure 2) he had more time to act on the gratitude he felt to KES for his start in life (Darby 2004). President of the Old Edwardians for many years, he made numerous visits with Asbjørg, and they became friends of successive Heads. When in 1977 the Governors were facing the need to decide between independence and fitting into a state system in which selective admission by academic ability was frowned on, Abraham had written out of the blue to offer to give major assistance through the EPA Cephalosporin Fund if the school became independent, and this he did. New laboratories were funded, and scholarships and bursaries in chemistry and biology for sixth-formers joining from the state-maintained sector were established. In 1985 he became Patron of a KES Appeal, and in commending it he wrote, 'When I was myself a pupil at the School I was impressed by the opportunities it offered to boys from a wide range of family backgrounds, many of them by no means wealthy', and continued that he was proud to have played his part in helping 'to keep the school open to pupils of limited means'.

But from around 1990 the Abrahams mostly lived in quiet retirement at Badgers Wood, the substantial Boars Hill house and garden just outside Oxford which they loved. The house was in fact almost the only outward sign of wealth; he bought a nice car in 1984, but it aged with him, and he still owned it when he died. He had a serious bout of Guillain–Barré syndrome in 1993, and joked when he came out of hospital that, having ridden his bike into the Cherwell and survived the resulting Weil's disease many years before, he had beaten not one but *two* rare diseases. His last scientific paper (49) was published in 1996, and his last trip abroad was in mid 1997: after hesitation about being away from Asbjørg, who was unwell, he travelled to Massachusetts and back in little over 48 hours to receive an honorary degree from Harvard. He died at St Luke's Hospital in Headington on 9 May 1999. Asbjørg entered a care home shortly afterwards and died on 20 May 2001. The Abrahams had made linked wills in the 1980s; the end results were that the wooded grounds of Badgers Wood (now known as Abraham Wood) passed to the Oxford Preservation Trust and that the greater part of their £10 million estate was distributed to Abraham's Trust Funds and other charities, including direct bequests totalling about £1 million between Lincoln College, KES and the Royal Society.

ACKNOWLEDGEMENTS

This memoir has been developed from a 2011 Oxford Chemistry Part II thesis by D.S.J., 'The life and work of Sir Edward Abraham 1913–1999', an electronic copy of which has been deposited with the Royal Society Library. We have had assistance from many archivists and individuals, whom we thank collectively. Andrew Mussell (Archivist of Lincoln College), Julian Thould (Headmaster of KES) and Bill Cox (sometime chairman of the KES Governors) have been especially helpful, Theresa Mayes (Abraham's niece) kindly made Abraham's 1938–41 letters to Asbjørg available, and Tor Harung (his nephew by marriage) provided photographs and further family information.

We are heavily indebted to those who catalogued Abraham's very extensive papers in the Bodleian Library, and to the summary of his life and work that opens the catalogue. He prepared a few autobiographical notes for the Royal Society, which survive in the Bodleian Abraham Papers at A.1, and his many historical notes, forewords, book reviews, conference introductions, biographical memoirs and suchlike are, no doubt unintentionally, often partly autobiographical. The long video interview that he recorded under the auspices of the Biochemical Society in 1990 was also very illuminating.

We also found three biographies of Howard Florey (Bickel 1972; Macfarlane 1979; Williams 1984) and the article by Jeremy Hamilton-Miller (Hamilton-Miller 2000) especially useful for general background.

The frontispiece photograph was taken in about 1958.

REFERENCES TO OTHER AUTHORS

Baldwin, J. E., Keeping, J. W., Singh, P. D. & Vallejo, C. A. 1981 Cell-free conversion of isopenicillin N into deacetoxycephalosporin C by *Cephalosporium acremonium* mutant M-0198. *Biochem. J.* **194**, 649–651.

Baldwin, J. E., Adlington, R. M., Kang, T. W., Lee, E. & Schofield, C. J. 1987 Ring expansion of penams to cephams: a possible biomimetic process. *J. Chem. Soc. Chem. Commun.* **1987**, 104–106.

Bickel, L. 1972 *Rise up to life. A biography of Howard Walter Florey who gave pencillin to the world*. London: Angus & Robertson.

Chain, E., Florey, H. W., Gardner, A. D., Heatley, N. G., Jennings, M. A., Orr-Ewing, J. & Sanders, A. G. 1940 Penicillin as a chemotherapeutic agent. *Lancet* i, 226–228.

Clarke, H. T., Johnson, J. R. & Robinson, R. (eds) 1949 *The chemistry of penicillin*. Princeton University Press.

Crowfoot, D. [Hodgkin, D. C.], Bunn, C. W., Rogers-Low, B. W. & Turner-Jones, A. 1949 The X-ray crystallographic investigation of the structure of penicillin. In *The chemistry of penicillin* (ed. H. T. Clarke, J. R. Johnson & R. Robinson), ch. 11, pp. 313–367. Princeton University Press.

Curtis, R. & Jones, J. 2006 Peptide chemistry at Oxford before the second world war. *J. Peptide Sci.* **12**, 563–568.

Curtis, R. & Jones, J. 2007 Robert Robinson and penicillin: an unnoticed document in the saga of its structure. *J. Peptide Sci.* **13**, 769–775.

Curtis, R., Leith, C., Nall, J. & Jones, J. 2008 *The Dyson Perrins Laboratory and Oxford organic chemistry 1916–2004*. Oxford: John Jones. ISBN 978-0-9512569-4-7.

Darby, G. 2004 *King Edward VI School* [Southampton] *1553–2003*. Southampton: KES.

Florey, H. W. 1955 Antibiotic products of a versatile fungus. *Ann. Intern. Med.* **43**, 480–490.

Hamilton-Miller, J. M. T. 2000 Sir Edward Abraham's contribution to the development of the cephalosporins: a reassessment. *Int. J. Antimicrob. Agents* **15**, 179–184.

Hodgkin, D. C. & Maslen, E. N. 1961 The X-ray analysis of the structure of cephalosporin C. *Biochem. J.* **79**, 393–402.

Jones, E. 2001 *The business of medicine. The extraordinary history of Glaxo, a baby food producer, which became one of the world's most successful pharmaceutical companies*. London: Profile Books.

Jones, J. 2008 The life and work of Guy Newton (1919–1969). *J. Peptide Sci.* **14**, 545–555.

Kohsaka, M. & Demain, A. L. 1976 Conversion of penicillin N to cephalosporin(s) by cell-free extracts of *Cephalosporium acremonium. Biochem. Biophys. Res. Commun.* **70**, 465–473.

Macfarlane, G. 1979 *Howard Florey: making of a great scientist*. Oxford University Press.

Morin, R. B., Jackson, B. G., Flynn, E. H. & Roeske, R. W. 1962 Chemistry of cephalosporin antibiotics. I. 7-Aminocephalosporanic acid from cephalosporin C. *J. Am. Chem. Soc.* **84**, 3400–3401.

Neuss, N., Nash, C. H., Baldwin, J. E., Lemke, P. A. & Grutzner, J. B. 1973 Incorporation of (2*RS*, 3*S*)-[4-^{13}C]-valine into cephalosporin C. *J. Am. Chem. Soc.* **95**, 3797–3798.

Williams, T. I. 1984 *Howard Florey: penicillin and after*. Oxford University Press.

ABRAHAM & NEWTON CEPHALOSPORIN C PATENTS

The principal British cephalosporin patents obtained by the NRDC with Abraham & Newton as coequal lead inventors are listed below, but there were numerous others in different jurisdictions, or following on. Cephalosporin N (= penicillin N) patents are not listed, but can be located easily. Dates are those for publication of the complete specifications.

Cephalosporin C. GB 810196, 1959.

A process for the production of derivatives of cephalosporin C. GB 847375, 1960.

(With C. W. Hale) *Cephalosporin C$_c$, a transformation product of cephalosporin C*. GB 912360, 1962.

(With C. W. Hale). *Cephalosporin C compounds*. GB 912541, 1962.

(With B. Boothroyd) *Derivatives of cephalosporin C*. GB 953695, 1964.
Improvements in and relating to antibiotics. GB 953696, 1964.
N acyl derivatives of 7-aminocephalosporanic acid and related compounds. GB 966221, 1964.
(With P. W. Trown) *Process for purification of cephalosporin C*. GB 1036125, 1966.

BIBLIOGRAPHY

The following publications are those referred to directly in the text. A full bibliography is available as electronic supplementary material at http://dx.doi.org/10.1098/rsbm.2014.0002 or via http://rsbm.royalsocietypublishing.org. His principal papers are nearly all in *Biochemical Journal* and freely available online.

(1)   1937   (With R. Robinson) Crystallization of lysozyme. *Nature* **140**, 24.
(2)   1939   Experiments relating to the constitution of alloxazine-adenine-dinucleotide. *Biochem. J.* **33**, 543–548.
(3)   1940   (With E. Chain) An enzyme from bacteria able to destroy penicillin. *Nature* **146**, 837.
(4)   1941   (With G. M. Brown, E. Chain, H. W. Florey, A. D. Gardner & A. G. Sanders) Tissue autolysis and shock. *Exp. Physiol.* **31**, 79–100.
(5)   (With E. Chain, C. M. Fletcher, H. W. Florey, A. D. Gardner, N. G. Heatley & M. A. Jennings) Further observations on penicillin. *Lancet* **ii**, 177–189.
(6)   1942   (With E. Chain) Purification and some physical and chemical properties of penicillin. *Br. J. Exp. Path.* **23**, 103–115.
(7)   1943   (With E. Chain, W. Baker & R. Robinson) *Further studies of the degradation of penicillin. Formation of penilloaldehyde. Its oxidation to acid $C_8H_{13}O_3N$. Structure of penilloaldehyde. Structure of penillic acid. Structures for penicillin (oxazolone-thiazolidine and β-lactam structures)* (British Ministry of Supply Penicillin Production Committee Report no. 103, 23 October.)
(8)   1944   (With E. Chain, W. Baker & R. Robinson) *Mechanism of action of penicillinase* (Medical Research Council Committee on Penicillin Synthesis Report no. 21, 2 February).
(9)   1949   (With C. Heidelberger & S. Lepkovsky) Tryptophan metabolism II. Concerning the mechanism of the mammalian conversion of tryptophan into nicotinic acid. *J. Biol. Chem.* **179**, 151–155.
(10) 1951   (With H. W. Florey) The work on penicillin at Oxford. *J. Hist. Med.* **6**, 302–317.
(11) 1953   (With G. G. F. Newton & N. J. Berridge) Sulphur-containing amino acids of nisin. *Nature* **171**, 606.
(12)   (With G. G. F. Newton) Observations on the nature of bacitracin A. *Biochem. J.* **53**, 604–613.
(13) 1954   (With G. G. F. Newton & C. W. Hale) Purification and some properties of cephalosporin N, a new penicillin. *Biochem. J.* **58**, 94–102.
(14)   (With G. G. F. Newton) Degradation, structure and some derivatives of cephalosporin N. *Biochem. J.* **58**, 103–111.
(15) 1955   (With G. G. F. Newton) Cephalosporin C, a new antibiotic containing sulphur and D-α-aminoadipic acid. *Nature* **175**, 548.
(16) 1956   (With H. S. Burton & H. M. E. Cardwell) Cephalosporin P_1 and helvolic acid. *Biochem. J.* **62**, 171–176.
(17)   (With G. G. F. Newton) Isolation of cephalosporin C, a penicillin-like antibiotic containing D-α-aminoadipic acid. *Biochem. J.* **62**, 651–658.
(18) 1960   (With G. G. F. Newton) Degradation of cephalosporin C. *Abstracts of Papers, IUPAC International Symposium on the Chemistry of Natural Products, Canberra, Australia.* Presentation on 22 August 1960 at session CS3 of the Symposium. Abraham's annotated copies of the Symposium Handbook and Abstracts Book are in Bodleian Abraham Papers, F.2; the text he prepared for the presentation is in E.37.
(19)   (With G. G. F. Newton) The structure of cephalosporin C. *Biochem. J.* **79**, 377–393.
(20)   (With C. W. Hale & G. G. F. Newton) Derivatives of cephalosporin C formed with certain heterocyclic tertiary bases. *Biochem. J.* **79**, 403–408.
(21)   (With B. Loder & G. G. F. Newton) The cephalosporin C nucleus (7-aminocephalosporanic acid) and some of its derivatives. *Biochem. J.* **79**, 408–416.
(22) 1963   (With P. W. Trown & B. Smith) Biosynthesis of cephalosporin C from amino acids. *Biochem. J.* **86**, 284–291.

(23) 1967 (With B. Smith, S. C. Warren & G. G. F. Newton) Biosynthesis of penicillin N and cephalosporin C. Antibiotic production and other features of the metabolism of a *Cephalosporium* sp. *Biochem. J.* **103**, 877–890.

(24)   (With S. C. Warren & G. G. F. Newton) Use of α-aminoadipic acid for the biosynthesis of penicillin N and cephalosporin C by a *Cephalosporium* sp. *Biochem. J.* **103**, 891–901.

(25)   (With S. C. Warren & G. G. F. Newton) The role of valine in the biosynthesis of penicillin N and cephalosporin C by a *Cephalosporium* sp. *Biochem. J.* **103**, 902–912.

(26) 1968 (With S. Kuwabara) Some properties of two cell-bound β-lactamases from *Bacillus cereus* 569/H. *Biochem. J.* **115**, 859–861.

(27) 1970 (With J. M. T. Hamilton-Miller & G. G. F. Newton) Products of aminolysis and enzymic hydrolysis of the cephalosporins. *Biochem. J.* **116**, 371–384.

(28)   (With J. M. T. Hamilton-Miller & E. Richards) Changes in proton-magnetic-resonance spectra during aminolysis and enzymic hydrolysis of cephalosporins. *Biochem. J.* **116**, 385–395.

(29)   (With S. Kuwabara & E. P. Adams) The composition of β-lactamase I and β-lactamase II from *Bacillus cereus* 569/H. *Biochem. J.* **118**, 475–480.

(30)   (With J. E. Walker) Isolation of bacilysin and a new amino acid from culture filtrates of *Bacillus subtilis*. *Biochem. J.* **118**, 557–561.

(31)   (With J. E. Walker) The structure of bacilysin and other products of *Bacillus subtilis*. *Biochem. J.* **118**, 563–570.

(32) 1971 Howard Walter Florey, Baron Florey of Adelaide and Marston. *Biogr. Mems Fell. R. Soc.* **17**, 255–302.

(33) 1973 (With H. Kluender, C. H. Bradley, C. J. Sih & P. Fawcett) Synthesis and incorporation of (2*S*,3*S*)-[4-^{13}C]valine into β-lactam antibiotics. *J. Am. Chem. Soc.* **95**, 6149–6150.

(34) 1974 (With H. Kluender, F. C. Huang, A. Fritzberg, H. Schnoes, C. J. Sih & P. Fawcett) Studies on the incorporation of (2*S*,3*R*)-[4,4,4-^{2}H$_3$]valine and (2*S*,3*S*)-[4,4,4-^{2}H$_3$]valine into β-lactam antibiotics. *J. Am. Chem. Soc.* **96**, 4054–4055.

(35) 1976 (With P. A. Fawcett, J. J. Usher, J. A. Huddleston, R. C. Bleaney & J. J. Nisbet) Synthesis of δ-(α-aminoadipyl)cysteinylvaline and its role in penicillin biosynthesis. *Biochem. J.* **157**, 651–660.

(36) 1978 (With G. S. Baldwin, A. Galdes, H. A. O. Hill, B. E. Smith & S. G. Waley) Histidine residues as zinc ligands in β-lactamase II. *Biochem. J.* **175**, 441–447.

(37) 1979 (With G. S. Baldwin & S. G. Waley) Identification of histidine residues that act as zinc ligands in β-lactamase II by differential tritium exchange. *Biochem. J.* **179**, 459–463.

(38)   (With J. O'Sullivan, R. C. Bleaney & J. A. Huddleston) Incorporation of ^{3}H from δ-(L-α-amino[4,5-^{3}H]adipyl-L-cysteinyl-D-[4,4-^{3}H]valine into isopenicillin N. *Biochem. J.* **184**, 421–426.

(39) 1980 (With J. O'Sullivan & J. A. Huddleston) Biosynthesis of penicillins and cephalosporins in cell-free systems. *Phil. Trans. R. Soc. Lond.* B **289**, 363–365.

(40)   (With J. E. Baldwin, B. L. Johnson, J. J. Usher, J. A. Huddleston & R. L. White) Direct NMR observation of cell-free conversion of (L-α-amino-δ-adipyl)-L-cysteinyl-D-valine into isopenicillin N. *J. Chem. Soc. Chem. Commun.* **1980**, 1271.

(41) 1981 (With G. S. Jayatilake & J. A. Huddleston) Conversion of isopenicillin N into penicillin N in cell-free extracts of *Cephalosporium acremonium*. *Biochem. J.* **194**, 645–647.

(42) 1982 Foreword to *The enchanted ring—the untold story of penicillin*, by J. C. Sheehan. Cambridge, MA: MIT Press.

(43) 1983 Ernst Boris Chain. *Biogr. Mems Fell. R. Soc.* **29**, 43–91.

(44) 1984 (With C.-P. Pang, M. Lutstorf, A. E. Derome, R. L. White, D. H. G. Crout & P. J. Morgan) Stereochemistry of the incorporation of valine methyl groups into methylene groups in cephalosporin C. *Biochem. J.* **222**, 777–788.

(45) 1987 Sir Robert Robinson and the early history of penicillin. *Nat. Prod. Rep.* **4**, 41–46.

(46) 1988 (With J. E. Baldwin) The biosynthesis of penicillins and cephalosporins. *Nat. Prod. Rep.* **5**, 129–145.

(47) 1990 Selective reminiscences of β-lactam antibiotics. Early research on penicillins and cephalosporins. *BioEssays* **12**, 601–606.

(48)   Reflections on the development of the penicillins and cephalosporins. *Sartoniana* **3**, 17–35.

(49) 1996 (With P. A. Whiteman) Phenoxymethylpenicillin amidohydrolases from *Penicillium chrysogenum*. *FEBS Lett.* **394**, 31–33.

JOHN HADJI ARGYRIS

19 August 1913 — 2 April 2004

John Rogers

JOHN HADJI ARGYRIS

19 August 1913 — 2 April 2004

Elected FRS 1986

By D. Brian Spalding FRS

Concentration, Heat and Momentum Limited (CHAM), Bakery House,
40 High Street, Wimbledon, London SW19 5AU

Contents

John Argyris was born in Greece; he was educated there and in Germany, made his scientific reputation in England, and spent the last part of his career in Germany, where he died at the age of 90 years.

Arguably his greatest contribution was in the computer analysis of stresses and strains in solid structures. He was certainly one of the first to recognize that the development of the electronic digital computer not only vastly increased the quantitative predictive capabilities of engineers but also demanded the invention of novel methods of exploitation, especially including general-purpose computer software.

His early work concerned stresses and strains in aircraft structures; but he later applied his mind and methods to:

© 2014 The Author(s)
Published by the Royal Society

(i) more general structural problems, then to
(ii) the finite-element method,
(iii) fluid mechanics, and in his later years to
(iv) the theory of chaos.

It is primarily in respect of topics (i) and (ii) that he will be remembered.

Overview

The institutions with which he was mainly associated were, first, the Royal Aeronautical Society (RAeS); second, Imperial College, London; and finally, the Technical University of Stuttgart.

Assessment of Argyris's contributions to the advancement of knowledge has been rendered unusually difficult by two distinct accidents. The first of these is that he worked at a time in which his field was in turmoil, resulting from the hard-to-digest arrival of the digital computer, and the second is that the author has not found a satisfactory and universally accepted account of his past history.

Therefore, although some unverified items are included in this memoir, the situation has been clarified by placing them in the special section headed 'Apocryphal material'; in which respect the author of this memoir has been greatly helped by consultation with the persons listed in the acknowledgements section. Unfortunately no one could be found who could advise with certainty on events before Argyris's arrival in England, even though the World Innovation Foundation (2004) published an obituary that included details of that period. However, the source of its information is unclear.

Early years

John Argyris was born Ioannis Hatziargyris, son of Nikolaos, on 19 August 1913, in the Greek city of Volos, 300 km from Athens. The Hatziargyris family members were prominent landowners in the plains of Thessaly; Hatziargyris Street, which runs through Volos, was named after a close relative, also called Ioannis Hatziargyris, sometime mayor of the city. John's mother was Loukia Karatheodoris, the daughter of an engineer and diplomat who had been the Prince of Samos before the union of that island with Greece in 1912. Her family members were prominent in Greek society within the Ottoman Empire; one of these, Constantin Caratheodory, had achieved international fame as a mathematician. Loukia was a person of considerable personal talent who had a strong influence on her two sons, the younger of whom, Kostas Hatziargyris, became a prominent journalist and active member of the Greek Communist Party. She later divorced his (and John's) father, and subsequently married Themistoklis Sofoulis, who later became Prime Minister of Greece.

The Hatziargyris family moved to Athens when John was six years old; however, according to his own account, he went to no school, being educated at home until the age of 13 years on the insistence, it has been said, of his 'authoritarian father'. According to another account of his, he attended the third Classical High School for Boys.

University education

Whatever schooling he had evidently enabled him to enter the National Technical University of Athens, where he studied civil engineering. However, it seems that he did not complete his studies, because antipathies between his family and one of the professors (it may be remarked that such antagonisms played a significant part in Argyris' career from the start) purportedly led to his departure in 1934 for Germany, and specifically for the Technische Hochschule of Munich. There he obtained his Dipl.Ing. qualification in 1936 and worked for some time as a Scientific Assistant, after which he found employment in a private consulting company (Firma J. Golnow & Sohn, of Stettin). He also married Elmina Ragavis, the daughter of the Greek ambassador to Germany, of whom he has said (Papadrakakis 2001): 'I felt sorry for my wife; she was completely lost. Our world in Germany was collapsing around us, and she was desperate. Her despair tormented me'. It seems that the marriage ended in divorce; but *Who's Who* gives no details.

How long he stayed with the company is not clear; but at least one publication (1)* resulted. Also unclear is how he came to leave Germany (but see the section on apocryphal material) and enrol in a one-year course for flight engineers at the Eidgenössiche Technische Hochschule of Zürich, Switzerland, according to the records of which he stayed only from October 1941 until March 1942 (see the section on apocryphal material).

The Royal Aeronautical Society

By 29 May 1943 'Mr Hadji-Argyris' had reached England, where he entered the employment of the RAeS in London. His task was to work on the checking and creation of the 'data sheets' that the Society issued for the guidance of designers of aircraft structures. This employment lasted until March 1949.

The minutes of the RAeS's Stressed Skin Data Sheets Committee (A. Quilter, personal communication, 2006), chaired by Professor A. G. (later Sir Alfred) Pugsley (FRS 1952), which supervised his work, make interesting reading. We find the following:

(i) On 10 July 1943, 'the committee placed on record their appreciation of the work done by Mr. Hadji-Argyris in the preparation of this sheet and asked Mr. Pribham to have the work written up … .'

(ii) On 10 December 1943, 'The Secretary drew attention to the wording of a note by Mr. Argyris which had been passed, through the Technical Officer, to the Committee. He explained that there appeared to be a misunderstanding on Mr. Argyris's part of his position and work for the committee.'

(iii) On 3 March 1944, 'A paper on shear-flow and shear-centre of thin-walled cylinders, with special reference to asymmetrical wing cells, by J. Hadji-Argyris, was considered from the point of view of data sheets. It was agreed that the form was not suitable, as given, for data sheets and Mr. Argyris agreed to prepare his paper in a suitable form for publication.'

(iv) On 19 January 1945, 'Mr. Hadji-Argyris was invited to be present …', and 'It was decided that Mr. Argyris and Mr. Cox should prepare an abridged version of the theory underlying these data sheets … .'

* Numbers in this form refer to the bibliography at the end of the text.

(v) On 16 February 1945, 'The Committee agreed in view of the special difficulties created by the war situation, a temporary expenses allowance of £40 per annum should be paid to Mr. Argyris as from February 1st, 1945.'

(vi) On 16 March 1945, 'In attendance: Mr. Pribham, Mr. Argyris (part-time)', which form of name appears in most of the subsequent minutes. The 'Hadji-' had by now been almost entirely dropped. (The subject of this memoir will therefore henceforth be referred to simply as JHA.)

(vii) At the same meeting, JHA presented a new data sheet, which was approved, with amendments, and he was asked to produce several more.

(viii) On 30 August 1945, the name of the committee having been changed to the Structures Committee, 'Mr. Argyris stated that two further data sheets on … would be ready for the next meeting … .'

(ix) On 12 October 1945, 'JHA attended, for the first time, the whole of the meeting.'

(x) On 26 October 1945, it was agreed 'that Mr. Argyris's salary should be increased and that the present arrangement by which he received a certain sum for expenses would be terminated'.

(xi) On 30 November 1945, 'Mr. Pollicutt … inquired whether it would be possible for Mr. Argyris to pay them a visit. It was agreed that this would afford Mr. Argyris a good opportunity to visit a firm, and that when he returned from Greece, he should get in touch with Mr. Pollicutt.'

(xii) On 19 December 1945, ' Mr. Argyris was ill, but would get in touch with Mr. Pollicutt when he recovered.'

This continued until March 1949, with 'Mr. Argyris' evidently enjoying increasing respect.

An interesting entry is that for 30 October 1946, where it is stated: 'Mr. Argyris and Mr. Dunne … outlined a new theory which enables a completely arbitrary cross-section and a very wide range of … to be considered'. However, this is nowhere mentioned in later minutes, but see below.

Publications bearing Argyris's name, and emanating from his work at the RAeS, include 'Diffusion of load into flat stiffened panels of varying cross-section' (2), co-authored with H. L. Cox, which dealt with panels stiffened by stringers kept apart by sheets that resisted only compression and shear. The method was already known in 1936 as the 'finite-stringer' method in early papers on which Cox was a co-author. It was also sometimes called the 'stringer-sheet' method and involved assumptions about the stress distributions within the sheets, in particular that the shear stresses were uniform.

Another paper, submitted to *Journal of the Royal Aeronautical Society* in October 1946 by JHA and P. C. Dunne, was entitled 'General theory of cylindrical and conical tubes under torsion and bending loads' (3). This was probably the 'new theory' mentioned in the minutes of 30 October above. P. C. Dunne was a stress analyst from the Boulton-Paul company who had joined the RAeS's technical staff in October 1945. So he and JHA had evidently not taken long to interact fruitfully.

JHA's experience of working at the RAeS proved to be of immense importance to his subsequent career. It established him in a new country and in a new field of technology; it acquainted him with the (perhaps irksome) ways of business; and it enabled him to collaborate with, and to learn from, men who had already achieved much.

Even if later accounts of its war-winning consequence cannot be fully substantiated (see the section on apocryphal material), his time at the RAeS certainly laid the foundations for the next—and perhaps most creative—segment of his professional life, namely his sojourn at the Imperial College of Science and Technology.

IMPERIAL COLLEGE, LONDON

On 1 October 1949 JHA was appointed Senior Lecturer in the Department of Aeronautics, headed until 1951 by Professor (later Sir Arnold) A. A. Hall (FRS 1953). JHA was promoted to a readership in 1950 and to a professorship in 1955. He gave his inaugural lecture in May 1956.

In 1953 he married Inge-Lisa Johansson from Sweden who, with his son Holger, survived him. So they were able to celebrate 50 years together.

Freed from the constraints of the RAeS, which took seriously its mission to be directly useful to the UK aircraft industry, JHA flourished. The following summary account of the activities of the group that he established is based on kind contributions in a personal communication from his assistant from 1959 onward, Mr P. C. Gasson.

Argyris's main interests during 1949–52 and after included:

(i) local instability and stress coefficients of struts and stiffened panels;

(ii) load diffusion and shear lag—a topic that led him to investigate the warping and constraint stresses in short open tubes loaded in torsion;

(iii) *Structural principles and data*, an RAeS publication in its fourth edition, published by Pitman in 1952 (4). A co-contributor to this compendium of aeroelasticity and structural analysis was P. C. Dunne.

Sydney Kelsey joined the department from English Electric Aviation in 1952, to begin 15 years of close collaboration with JHA.

It was at this time that JHA began to consider the difficulty of analysing thin low-aspect-ratio delta-type wings by energy-theorem methods; which led to his early recognition of the need to computerize the whole process of structural design and analysis. Numerous articles were published in *Aircraft Engineering* (5).

By 1959 JHA was already spending some time in Stuttgart, where he had been invited to set up a new aeronautical department, later known as the Institute for Statics and Dynamics of Aircraft and Aerospace Structures (ISD) in the mid to late 1950s. He thus managed two leading but separately governed university research groups, dividing his time equally between the two for several years.

In 1959 the Imperial College Aero-Structures section employed four lecturers, including JHA, a technical assistant/designer/demonstrator and four or five workshop technicians. The lecturers were Sydney Kelsey, Kevin Thomas and Stan Kochanski (replaced by Anthony Chan in 1961). Apart from the short open tube, a main focus was on a cranked low-aspect-ratio wing box with honeycomb skins. Kevin Thomas was in charge of fatigue, and Stan Kochanski covered kinetic heating, but all else was geared to the advancement of matrix methods.

AERONAUTICAL STRUCTURES LABORATORY, IMPERIAL COLLEGE, CA. 1959–65

All design and experimental work during about 1955–65 was under the direction of Sydney Kelsey, who acted as JHA's second-in-command.

As a consultant to the Boeing Aircraft Corporation, JHA provided more than 30 research reports, which covered most of the experimental work done. Several papers relating to the theoretical work being done were published, one such in 1962 being entitled 'Matrix methods of structural analysis: a precis of recent developments', co-authored by JHA, Kelsey and H. A. Kamel (6).

Of JHA as a person, and as a lecturer, P. C. Gasson has written (personal communication):

(1)   The Professor had a great command of language—Greek (his mother tongue), German, English, French and Swedish. He spoke with a noticeable German accent. He wrote concise technical and elegant English and was a highly competent user of classical engineering mathematics. All his writings were an education and a pleasure to read. 'General theory of cylindrical and conical tubes under torsion and bending loads', Argyris and Dunne (3), was perhaps his most important early work.

(2)   The Professor made copious use of alphabets, Gothic included, in his technical writings and he seemed to delight in testing the printer's patience and type-setting skills. Subscripts and superscripts were always fitted in wherever they were appropriate.

(3)   Be his audience undergraduate students or eminent engineers, the Professor was always able to captivate, educate and entertain. But once inadvertently, in his 1956 inaugural lecture, a creep-buckling demonstration had been set in motion earlier in the lecture, which was nearing its conclusion when the tubular aluminium Euler strut became critical (in a double sense); it suddenly bent more than expected and touched the live element of the electrical heater.

(4)   All who attended the RAeS Lanchester lecture (8) entitled 'The impact of the digital computer on engineering science', delivered by the Prof in 1969, saw Argyris, the actor, at his best. A truly Oscar-winning performance, some would say.

(5)   I am proud to have known and served the Professor, a perceptive intellectual, a trend-setter and a most remarkable, charismatic man.

Publications during this period were indeed numerous; and when Huebner & Thornton (1982) came to review the history of the finite-element method in their book entitled *The finite-element method for engineers*, they drew attention to the flurry of publications by Argyris and Kelsey (5), which greatly augmented the stream of innovations that, in the engineering community, had started to flow in the 1950s.

Sydney Kelsey, whom some see as the 'unsung innovator' of these exciting times, was clearly an important contributor to JHA's research, as was recognized by many. JHA became excited by and involved in the working-out of the implications of novel ideas that emerged from his collaboration with Kelsey. However, relations with collaborators were not always smooth, and in some cases they broke down irreparably.

THE FINITE-ELEMENT METHOD

At this point it is necessary to refer to a matter of central importance in assessing JHA's achievements. First some essential facts should be recited.

(i) The finite-element method (FEM) exists today as a widely used technique for predicting the distributions of stresses and strains in solid continua, and to a much lesser extent, distributions of velocity and pressure in fluids, and distributions of temperature in both.

(ii) Its use is dependent, in practice, on the existence of computer software that performs the necessary computations.

(iii) FEM involves the replacement of differential equations by algebraic equations that would be equivalent to them if numerous enough. These are obtained by integrating the differential equations.

(iv) The differential equations are those that express the well-established laws of conservation of mass, momentum and energy (such as Navier–Stokes), but practitioners of FEM distinguish themselves from others in multiplying these equations by non-unity 'weighting functions' before integrating them. This is of course legitimate, but its utility is debatable.

(v) 'Discretization'—the shift of attention from continuous variations to discontinuous variations whose discontinuities occur at the surfaces of arbitrarily defined pieces of the continua—is therefore essential to the FEM approach.

(vi) It differs from the 'finite-difference method' (FDM) and 'finite-volume method' (FVM), which also employ discretization, mainly in respect of the algebraic forms of the weighting functions and the shapes of the pieces. FDM and FVM use, in FEM parlance, unity weighting functions, which amounts to no weighting at all!

(vii) FEM was given its name by Turner *et al.* (1956).

(viii) Since that time it has undergone continuous refinement and simplification, in the course of which those features which at first seemed to set it apart from the FDM and FVM methods have almost completely disappeared.

(ix) In its early years, when it appeared more *sui generis* than it does now, the question of who was its originator was much debated; in this debate, JHA's name was not at first much mentioned.

Numerical stress analysis before finite elements

To put into perspective the finite-element 'tsunami', as it has been called, it is useful to recall the following:

(i) finite-difference equations had first been applied to torsional solid-stress problems by Runge (1908);

(ii) L. F. Richardson (FRS 1926) solved such equations to compute the stresses in a dam (Richardson 1910);

(iii) A. Thom developed the 'method of squares' before 1939 (Thom & Apelt 1961);

(iv) R. V. (later Sir Richard) Southwell FRS published a particularly convenient solution procedure, the 'relaxation method' (Southwell 1944);

(v) the second edition of S. P. Timoshenko's magisterial *Theory of elasticity* (Timoshenko & Goodier 1951) already included an appendix devoted to such methods, and its third edition, published in 1970, added a section devoted to their implementation by means of digital computers.

The final paragraph of the latter appendix is worth quoting:

The finite-difference equations to be solved by the computer can be derived in various ways. Article 1 of this Appendix illustrates the mathematical conversion from the partial differential equations of a continuum. Variational methods can also be used. For instance, in the problem of Fig. 29 the potential energy was expressed as a sum involving the nodal point displacement, then minimized. Article 3 of this Appendix illustrates the 'physical' conversion from the continuum (membrane) to a net of uniformly stressed strings. The finite-difference equations are then derived as the physical equations for a finite element of the net. Similar procedures for more elaborate problems are included in what is now called the finite-element method.

This is all very factual, consequential and sober. Timoshenko, one can be sure, did not regard FEM as possessing the revolutionary new-ground-breaking quality that its enthusiasts increasingly claimed for it.

JHA's CONTRIBUTIONS TO FEM

The contribution of JHA and Kelsey to the development of the finite-element method can be regarded as peripheral, because they were not dealing with discretized continua in the true sense but with frameworks and structures of the 'panel and stringer' kind, about which JHA may have learned from Cox in his RAeS years.

The word 'discretization' does not appear in their papers, either explicitly or as synonyms; instead the papers focused more on the 'energy theorems' that the equations embodied, on their formulation in terms of matrices, and on whether it was better to concentrate on 'forces' or 'displacements'.

However, the 'matrix methods' that they developed for handling the resulting algebraic equations proved to be ideal also for the equations to which the *discretized* continua gave rise. This was generously recognized by R. W. Clough (1960), a true discretizer, who wrote enthusiastically of his whole-hearted adoption of the 'Argyris method'. These words of Clough may have misled many, including perhaps JHA himself, into believing that JHA was the inventor of FEM, at least in Clough's view. However, Clough himself regarded publications by Hrennikoff (1941) and McHenry (1943) as expressing and using the essential ideas, even though the term 'finite element' was not coined until more than a decade later. Others recognized R. Courant (Courant 1943) as a contemporaneous and independent innovator.

THE ROLE OF THE DIGITAL COMPUTER

A more clearly original contribution that JHA made at this time was to recognize, during his Imperial College years, the following:

(i) that the coming of the digital computer had immensely enlarged the potential capabilities of the engineering designer; and

(ii) that the potential could become real only through the entrepreneurial creation, and distribution, of general-purpose software packages that embodied the appropriate scientific and mathematical principles.

His creation, with Kamel, of the ASKA (Automatic System for Kinematic Analysis) computer program (7), and his finding of successful ways in which to distribute it commercially, was truly a pioneering step. It created an example that many followed and has transformed the way in which engineers design not only aircraft but also structures of all kinds.

It was indeed followed, notably by the MacNeal Schwendler Corporation in the USA, which released its first FEM-based commercial software package, Nastran, in 1971. That program, developed with lavish NASA research funding and widely adopted by the American aerospace industry, soon pushed ASKA to the fringes of the market, where it finally subsided.

Other such packages also entered the market, and some survived. Nevertheless, JHA's pioneering efforts deserve recognition.

OTHER INFLUENCES

That having been said, it must be admitted that current software packages bear little resemblance to ASKA, either outwardly (which is understandable in view of advances in computer graphics) or inwardly. They all use iterative methods of solution, of which JHA was scornful; probably none of the particular 'elements' that he and his later colleagues introduced remain in use.

JHA's influence is thus not to be compared with that of Olgierd Zienkiewicz (FRS 1978), even though both JHA in 1985 and Zienkiewicz in 1990 were awarded Royal Medals, with rather similar citations of FEM. Zienkiewicz, without claiming to have invented FEM has, through his publications (Zienkiewicz 1965, 1967) and the school that he created at the University of Swansea, significantly influenced the development and spread of the finite-element methodology. Too significantly, some would say, because the advantages claimed by the Swansea school for the superiority of FEM over FVM for solving fluid mechanics have proved not to outweigh the concomitant disadvantages. Although several commercial FEM codes were launched in the hopes prevailing over, or at least coexisting with, the FVM-based computational fluid dynamics (CFD) codes, almost none remain in the market. All this raises the question: is FEM truly better even for problems of stress analysis in solids? It is hard to find any well-argued reasons for a positive answer.

In short, the view of the superiority of FEM, as expressed by the Swansea group, JHA and others, seems perhaps to have been ill-founded.

TECHNISCHE HOCHSCHULE, STUTTGART

Hard though it is to understand now, Imperial College was slow to equip itself with digital computers; as a consequence, JHA had to use one at University College London, and later at North London Polytechnic. It is therefore not surprising that he was open to offers that were accompanied by the prospect of substantial computer power.

In the late 1950s, JHA was invited by the German Federal State of Baden-Württemberg to create a new institute within the Technische Hochschule of Stuttgart, to be called the ISD. When its new building in Stuttgart-Vaihingen was opened, according to the obituary by Bryan Spooner (Spooner 2004), who worked there, 'It was Professor Argyris's particular pleasure to commission a work of art … and selected an eminent Swedish sculptor to create and erect the Icarus Needle, a beautiful edifice of layered glass, symbolising man's endeavours in mastering flight.'

Equally close to his heart, however, one must suppose, was the succession of ever more powerful computers for which he was now able to obtain funding, a resource that he had felt starved of at Imperial College. It was this that enabled him in 1963 to develop ASKA, and to market it through the agency of the Norwegian firm IKOSS, which opened an office in Vaihingen close to Stuttgart.

Two other activities should be mentioned: first, the foundation of the journal *Computer Methods in Applied Mechanics and Engineering*, published first by North-Holland and now by Elsevier; and second, the application of the finite-element method to problems of fluid flow. The first filled a notable gap; and this journal, which JHA edited for many years, still flourishes. The motive for the second was not perfectly clear. Fluid-mechanical simulations were already being satisfactorily handled by finite-volume methods, as they still are. That finite-element methods could be used for fluid flow had been demonstrated by the Swansea group and others. Perhaps JHA had a desire to improve on the work of others and to solve new problems.

JHA would have been 70 years old in August 1983, which must have precipitated the end of his position at ISD. The Institute for Computer Applications in Stuttgart is said to have been founded by the Technische Hochschule specifically to allow him to continue his much-valued activities.

JHA's last field of interest was the theory of chaos (9), his views on which are apparent from his answers in April 2001 to questions posed in a newspaper interview (Papadrakakis 2001):

> Q. What is the place of Chaos in science today?
> A. Well, 20th Century science will be remembered for three great scientific revolutions: Relativity, Quantum Mechanics and Chaos. Of the three, Chaos can be applied to the whole of the universe, both as we perceive it in its enormity and as it manifests itself on a human scale. … The exploration of Chaos will be the driving force behind the mainframe of scientific thought in the 21st Century … .
> Q. What attracted you to Chaos?
> A. My chaotic personality! One needs an equal measure of imagination and folly to explore the complexity of systems, determinism, free will, and the nature of conscious intelligence … .

The interview ended with an exchange that throws light on another aspect of his personality:

> Q. Recently you were awarded a CBE?
> A. Indeed; and I have to mention how nice the Queen Mother was at the award ceremony.

APOCRYPHAL MATERIAL

A generous supplier of advice to the writer of this memoir, himself a Greek, explained that hyperbole is not only a word of Greek origin: it is also commonly used in Greek communication. It therefore seems allowable to mention here that, in addition to the ascertainable facts about JHA, anyone who searches for information about him, on the Internet for example, is bound to encounter material whose origin is difficult to ascertain. Examples are to be found in Hughes *et al.* (2004), an obituary notice written in a US engineering journal by three distinguished engineer-scientists; in an interview with JHA printed in the newspaper *Thessalia* (J. Vlachopoulos, personal communication, 2006), where JHA's memory may have been faulty; and in the appreciation published in 2004 by the World Innovation Foundation, of which JHA was chairman. It is, for example, unclear how he came to leave Germany for Switzerland, and then to leave ETH Zürich for England. It is also doubtful that JHA's work had the war-winning consequences alluded to in some of these references.

Apocryphal stories accumulate around many prominent people, and the more their accent, ethnic origin and behaviour differ from the norm, as did those of JHA, the more readily are the stories credited. Certainly, such stories do abound about JHA, and the interview in *Thessalia* may well have contributed to the apochrypha.

Honours and awards

JHA was far from indifferent to the esteem in which he and his work were held, and he was not afraid to let it be known that he enjoyed having honours awarded to him. The following are some of the many honours that JHA received.

1955   Fellow of the RAeS, UK
1970   Honorary Dott.Ing., Genoa, Italy
1971   Silver Medal of the RAeS, UK
1972   Honorary Dr.Tech., Trondheim, Norway
1975   Von Karman Medal of the American Society of Civil Engineers, USA
1979   Copernicus Medal of the Polish Academy of Sciences, Poland
1980   Honorary Professor of the Northwestern Polytechnic University, Xi'an, China
1981   Timoshenko Medal of the American Society of Mechanical Engineers, USA
1983   Honorary Professor of the Technical University of Beijing, China
      Fellow of the American Institute of Aeronautics and Astronautics, USA
      Member of Academico Italia, Italy
1984   Honorary Professor of Qinghua University, Beijing, China
1985   Fellow of the American Association for the Advancement of Science, USA
      Honorary Fellow of the Aeronautical Society of India, India
      Royal Medal of the Royal Society
1986   Foreign Associate Fellow of the US National Academy of Engineering
      Honorary Fellow of the RAeS, UK
      Honorary TekDr, Swedish Technical University, Sweden
      Fellow of the Royal Society
1989   Honorary DSc, University of Athens, Greece
      Grand Cross of Merit with Star, Federal Republic of Germany
1990   Fellow of the Royal Academy of Engineering, UK
1991   Fellow of the American Society of Civil Engineers, USA
1992   Honorary Fellow of the Romanian Academy, Romania
1993   Honorary DSc, Technical University of St Petersburg, Russia
      Honorary DSc, Technical University of Timisoara, Romania
1994   Honorary Member of the Greek Association of Computational Mechanics, Greece
1995   Honorary DSc, Technical University of Athens, Greece
      Honorary DSc, University of Ioannina, Greece
1996   Honorary DSc, University of Thessaly, Greece
      Prince Philip Medal, UK
2000   Einstein Award of the Einstein Foundation, USA
      Commander of the British Empire (CBE), UK

Acknowledgements

I am grateful to the following persons who have allowed me to consult them: Professor K.-J. Bathe (MIT), Ms Sonja Blum (ETH), Professor Glyn Davies (Imperial College), Mr Peter C. Gasson (formerly of Imperial College), Dr Davis S. Hill (World Innovation Foundation), Professor Sydney Kelsey (Notre Dame University), Mr Adam Quilter (Engineering Sciences Data Unit, RAeS), Professor John Vlachopoulos (McMaster University), Ms Claire Westgate

(Imperial College) and Professor Olgierd C. Zienkiewicz (Swansea University). They do not, of course, necessarily agree at all with any of the views expressed in the memoir.

The Editor of *Biographical Memoirs* consulted Professor T. R. Hughes, Professor J. T. Oden and Professor M. Papadrakakis, together with J. H. Argyris's son, Holger Argyris, and thanks each of them. He also thanks Brian Riddle (National Aerospace Library) and Professor Peter Bearman (RAeS) for help with references. The Editor would also like to thank Anne Barrett, the Archivist of Imperial College, for her great help in locating the frontispiece and arranging for permission for the Royal Society to use it in this way, and for help with the bibliography

The frontispiece photograph is reproduced courtesy of National Academy of Engineering USA.

References to other authors

Clough, R. W. 1960 *The finite element method in plane stress analysis. Proc. 2nd ASCE Conference on Electronic Computation, Pittsburg, PA, September 1960*. Reston, VA: American Society of Civil Engineers.

Clough, R. W. 1965 The finite element method in structural mechanics. In *Stress analysis* (ed. O. C. Zienkiewicz & G. S. Hollister), pp. 85–119. New York: John Wiley & Sons.

Courant, R. 1943 Variational methods for the solution of problems of equilibrium and vibration. *Bull. Am. Math. Soc.* **49**, 1–23.

Huebner, K. H. & Thornton, E. A. 1982 *The finite-element method for engineers*. New York: Wiley-Interscience.

Hrennikoff, A. 1941 Solution of problems in elasticity by the framework method. *J. Appl. Mech.* **8**, A169–A175.

Hughes, T. R., Oden, J. T. & Papadrakakis, M. 2004 In Memoriam to Professor John H. Argyris. *Computer Methods Appl. Mech. Engng* **193**, 3763–3766.

McHenry, D. 1943 A lattice analogy for the solution of plane stress problems. *J. Inst. Civil Engrs*. **21**, 59–82.

Papadrakakis, I. 2001 International interview for Lambrakis Publishing, Greece. *Vimamagazino* of the Sunday newspaper *TO VIMA*, 15 April.

Richardson, L. F. 1910 The approximate arithmetical solution by finite differences of physical problems involving differential equations, with an application to the stresses in a masonry dam. *Phil. Trans. R. Soc. Lond.* A **210**, 307–357.

Runge, C. 1908 Über eine Methode, die partielle Differentialgleichung $\Delta u = $ constant numerisch zu integrieren. *Z. Math. Phys.* **56**, 225–232.

Southwell, R. V. 1944 *Relaxation methods in engineering physics*. Oxford University Press.

Spooner, B. 2004 Professor John H. Argyris. *Aerosp. Prof.* (August), 11.

Thom, A. & Apelt, C. J. 1961 *Field computations in engineering and physics*. London: Van Nostrand.

Timoshenko, S. P. & Goodier, J. N. 1951 *Theory of elasticity*, 2nd edn. New York: McGraw-Hill.

Turner, M. J., Clough, R. W., Martin, H. C. & Topp, L. J. 1956 Stiffness and deflection analysis of complex structures. *J. Aeronaut. Sci.* **23**, 805 823 and 854.

World Innovation Foundation 2004 John H. Argyris. See http://www.thewif.org.uk/version2/nlett/27/page3.html.

Zienkiewicz, O. C. 1965 Finite-element procedures in the solution of plate and shell problems. In *Stress analysis* (ed. O. C. Zienkiewicz & G. S. Hollister), ch. 8, pp. 120–144. New York: John Wiley.

Zienkiewicz, O. C. 1967 *The finite-element method*. New York: McGraw-Hill.

Bibliography

The following publications are those referred to directly in the text. A more complete bibliography (up to 1955) is available as electronic supplementary material at http://dx.doi.org/10.1098/rsbm.2013.0003 or via http://rsbm.royalsocietypublishing.org.

(1) 1940 On the stress analysis of wireless pylons. *Der Stahlbau*.

(2) 1944 (With H. L. Cox) Diffusion of load into flat stiffened panels of varying cross-section. Aeronautical Research Council R&M no. 1969.

(3) 1947 (With P. C. Dunne) General theory of cylindrical and conical tubes under torsion and bending loads. *J. R. Aeronaut. Soc.* **51**, 199–168, 757–784, 884–930.

(4) 1952 (With P. C. Dunne) *Structural analysis* (**Part II** of *Handbook of Aeronautics*, vol. 1). London: Pitman.

(5) 1959–61 (With S. Kelsey) Energy theorems and structural analysis. *Aircraft Engng* **31**, 62–74, 101–112, 133–143, 169–180, 182–203, 244–256, 272–283; **33**, 34–45, 71–83, 103–114, 154–174, 193–200, 227–238. (Later republished under this title in 1960, 1963 and 1967 by Butterworths, London.)

(6) 1964 (With S. Kelsey & H Kamel) Matrix methods of structural analysis; a precis of recent developments. *AGARDograph* **72**, 1–164.

(7) 1965 (With H. Kamel) *Automatic System for Kinematic Analysis*. Research Report no. 8, ISD Stuttgart, October.

(8) 1970 The impact of the digital computer on engineering sciences, parts 1 and 2. (12th Lanchester Memorial Lecture.) *J. R. Aeronaut. Soc.* **74**, 13–41, 111–127.

(9) 1994 (With G. Faust & M. Haase) *An exploration of chaos: an introduction for natural scientists and engineers* (*Texts on Computational Mechanics*, vol. 7). Amsterdam: North-Holland.

ULRICH WOLFGANG ARNDT

23 April 1924 — 24 March 2006

Biogr. Mems Fell. R. Soc. **60**, 39–55 (2014)

U. W. Arndt

ULRICH WOLFGANG ARNDT

23 April 1924 — 24 March 2006

Elected FRS 1982

By R. A. Crowther FRS FMedSci and A. G. W. Leslie FRS

Medical Research Council Laboratory of Molecular Biology, Francis Crick Avenue, Cambridge Biomedical Campus, Cambridge CB2 0QH, UK

Ulrich (Uli) Arndt was a physicist and engineer whose contributions to the development of a wide range of instrumentation for X-ray crystallography played an important part in our ability to solve the atomic structure of large biological molecules. Such detailed information about protein structures has for the past 50 years underpinned the huge advances in the field of molecular biology. His innovations spanned all aspects of data generation and collection, from improvements in X-ray tubes, through novel designs for diffractometers and cameras to film scanners and more direct methods of X-ray detection. When he started in the field, the intensities of individual X-ray reflections were often estimated by eye from films. By the end of his career the whole process of collecting from a crystal a three-dimensional data set, possibly comprising hundreds of thousands of measurements, was fully automated and very rapid.

EARLY YEARS

Ulrich Wolfgang Arndt, always known as Uli, was born in Berlin in 1924. His father was born and brought up in St Petersburg; he then lived and worked in the USA before he married. His mother, although raised in Hamburg, grew up speaking fluent English and French as well as German. This combination of backgrounds gave Uli strong pan-European feelings for the rest of his life. In 1930 the family moved to Darmstadt, and Uli made good progress with his schooling despite the growing political unrest. In 1933 he transferred to the Gymnasium but found that much of the teaching amounted to National Socialist indoctrination, a process that was counteracted on long weekend walks with his parents in the Odenwald, away from prying ears. He was already learning Latin at school and began private lessons in English and French. This both gave him a facility with languages and also prepared him for the possible moves ahead. Reading poetry with his mother started an enduring love of literature. Uli was the only child in his class not to be a member of the Hitler Youth, but he avoided the worst of

© 2014 The Author(s)

http://dx.doi.org/10.1098/rsbm.2014.0003   41   Published by the Royal Society the harassment this might have entailed by allowing his exercise books to be cribbed by less talented students.

His father was by now the commercial director of a company that made weighing, testing and dynamic balancing machines. His parents' position with foreign connections and with suspected left-wing sympathies was becoming increasingly untenable. So in 1936 his father appointed himself head of a British subsidiary of the company and thus could move the family's complete household to London, any further delay making their exit increasingly problematical. In his autobiography (19)* Uli describes the complicated route that they took to minimize costs and conserve foreign currency. They flew from Frankfurt to Berlin in a Lufthansa JU 52, the civilian version of the plane that was to become the mainstay of the Luftwaffe, took the 'Flying Hamburger' train to Hamburg, transferred to Bremerhaven and then boarded the transatlantic liner *Bremen* for the journey to Southampton.

After some coaching, Uli passed the entrance examination to Dulwich College, where he enrolled on the classical side and obtained credits at School Certificate in all subjects except Greek. However, influenced by a family friend, Uli decided to switch from classics to science. Schooling was disrupted by the Munich crisis and in 1939, as had been hoped, his father's company was taken over by a British company. This entailed a move to Birmingham and enrolment for Uli at King Edward's School. The family lived in a semi-detached house the other half of which was occupied by Professor (later Sir) Rudolf Peierls (FRS 1945), whose lodgers included Otto Frisch (FRS 1948) and Klaus Fuchs. In later years Uli realized that the first studies, drafted by Peierls and Frisch, on the feasibility of an atomic bomb had perhaps been produced next door.

Uli did sufficiently well in his Higher School Certificate to win an entrance scholarship to Birmingham University and spent a year there before getting a place at Emmanuel College, Cambridge. He went up in October 1942 to read Natural Sciences, specializing in physics and electronics, and took the Part II Physics Tripos in just two years, the maximum time allowed in World War II. He recalled taking his final practical examination set by the professor, Sir Lawrence Bragg FRS, on D-Day in 1944. Only six people took Part II, and although Uli gained a lower second-class honours degree, the other man got only a third and the women were not then members of the university, so Uli could claim the best physics result in the university that year.

STARTING RESEARCH

The practical aspects of the physics courses had interested Uli most, and an outstanding performance in the final practical encouraged him to approach Bragg about the possibility of a research position in the Cavendish Laboratory. He was offered a project in the Department of Crystallography, headed at that time by Henry Lipson (FRS 1957), who became his PhD supervisor. Financed by the Electrical Research Association, the work involved crystallographic and magnetic measurements on iron–copper–nickel alloys thought suitable as improved materials for permanent magnets. Uli quickly decided that the photographic methods in use at the time were too tedious and inaccurate, so he set out to build a new X-ray tube and an X-ray spectrometer of a then quite novel type. It was thus right at the beginning of his

---

* Numbers in this form refer to the bibliography at the end of the text.

research career that he started to design and construct equipment for X-ray crystallography, an endeavour he was to pursue for the rest of his life. When Lipson moved to Manchester, the new Head of Department, Will Taylor, became Uli's research supervisor.

By the time his grant ran out in 1948, his instrument was far from complete and he had made only one set of highly dubious measurements. Fortunately he had established contact with Alan Wheeler and Wally Hall in the Department of Metallurgy in Birmingham University. They invited him to join them as a Research Fellow to collaborate with them on the construction of an X-ray powder spectrometer for the investigation of metal structures. They were quickly able to assemble a precision Geiger counter spectrometer, which was a world first as far as publication was concerned (1). The description of the instrument and a discussion of the results obtained with it gave Uli sufficient material to complete his PhD thesis, which was successfully examined in November 1949.

At the Royal Institution, 1950–63

Shortly after this, Uli bumped into Dennis Riley, a former Cambridge colleague from the Department of Mineralogy and Petrology, who was by now working at the Royal Institution (RI) in London. He was trying to build a small team in the Davy–Faraday Laboratory to work on the structure of proteins and he offered Uli a job. When Uli arrived at the RI he found a laboratory steeped in history but in practical terms overwhelmed by it. The 50 kW X-ray tube dating from the 1930s in the basement, a room previously used by Michael Faraday and Sir James Dewar, was believed to be the largest in the world but proved unreliable and difficult to use. Moreover, Uli soon showed, by using one of his Geiger counter detectors, that the high-power X-ray source delivered less intensity at the sample than did a conventional sealed-off commercial tube. Uli managed to persuade those in authority to replace the tube with a compact 5 kW rotating-anode X-ray tube that he had designed. He also produced some of the first proportional counters, which had a greater dynamic range for X-ray detection than the Geiger counters he had been using. By continuously flowing the appropriate gas mixture through the counter, he avoided the need for high-vacuum techniques, so the apparatus could be constructed from the bits and pieces in the RI store cupboards left over from Dewar's gas liquefaction experiments.

At that time in the early 1950s little was known about the structure of proteins, and it was not clear that the crystallographic efforts of Max Perutz (FRS 1954) and others would yield useful information. It had been known for many years that hydrated protein crystals diffracted X-rays sufficiently well for their detailed structure to be determined in principle. The diffracted beams from a crystal can be thought of as spots lying on a regular three-dimensional so-called reciprocal lattice, and given an appropriate method of recording they can be seen as such (figure 1a). However, an X-ray diffraction experiment yields only the intensities of the diffracted beams and not their relative phases, which are essential if a three-dimensional molecular structure is to be computed by Fourier synthesis. It was not until 1953 that Perutz and colleagues demonstrated the feasibility of isomorphous phasing for protein crystals (Green *et al.* 1954). In this technique heavy atoms are bound to specific sites in the protein crystal without otherwise changing the structure, hence the epithet isomorphous. The bound heavy atoms lead to changes in intensity of the diffracted beams, which can then be used to determine the missing phases and hence the structure of the protein. The first protein structure

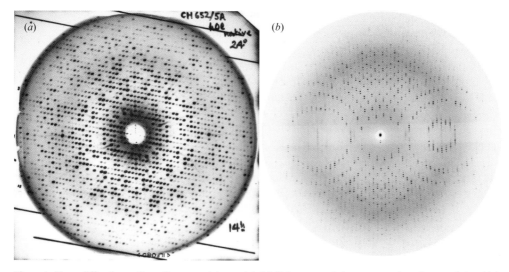

Figure 1. X-ray diffraction patterns from a protein crystal. (*a*) Pattern recorded as a precession photograph in which the spots lie on a regular lattice. (*b*) Pattern recorded as a rotation photograph in which the spots lie on more complex arcs.

to be determined in atomic detail was myoglobin by J. S. (later Sir John) Kendrew FRS and colleagues in 1960 (Kendrew *et al.* 1960).

Against this background Arndt and Riley, using the X-ray equipment that Uli had just developed, collected diffraction data on many different non-crystalline biological materials. In 1951 Linus Pauling ForMemRS and colleagues had published their model of the α helix as a common constituent of proteins and had shown the radial distribution function calculated from their structure (Pauling & Corey 1951). At the RI they were now well set up to determine such distribution functions from their experimental X-ray scattering curves for amorphous freeze-dried proteins and synthetic peptides. The very first distribution they obtained from bovine serum albumin agreed very well with the prediction from the Pauling model (2). Indeed, there was surprisingly good agreement for most globular proteins with the α helix but not for the β proteins such as silk fibroin (3). In the light of later knowledge the agreement was largely fortuitous, because they predicted a high α-helical content for proteins that sometimes turned out to contain no α helices.

However, the arrival in 1954 of Sir Lawrence Bragg as Director of the Davy Faraday Laboratory at the RI and the departure of Dennis Riley led to a switch of Uli's interests from low-angle scattering to the study of single crystals of proteins, an ultimately far more powerful technique. The switch to single crystals was reinforced by the arrival at the RI in 1955 of David (later Lord) Phillips (FRS 1967), and a fruitful collaboration ensued. To collect X-ray diffraction data, the protein crystal and X-ray detector have to be oriented appropriately for each reflection in turn. This is achieved by mounting the crystal on an instrument called a diffractometer. Uli constructed a hand-operated three-circle counter diffractometer (figure 2), but the difficulty in those days of computing the required crystal and counter settings (4) was such that it was awkward to use, the nearest available computer being EDSAC II in Cambridge. However, the instrument was used by Perutz and colleagues to collect data for the initial 5.5 Å map of haemoglobin (Perutz *et al.* 1960).

Figure 2. Uli adjusting his first three-circle diffractometer; photograph taken probably in about 1958.

These difficulties led Arndt and Phillips to a completely different approach to data collection and to the invention of the linear diffractometer (5). The instrument was partly designed by air-mail exchanges, because Uli was spending an otherwise scientifically not very productive sabbatical year in Madison, Wisconsin. This was the first fully automatic diffractometer and it was manufactured under licence by Hilger & Watts Ltd, who sold about 100 of the machines worldwide. The machine in effect incorporated an analogue computer by means of which the settings of crystal and counter were generated by the instrument itself, given only the cell parameters of the crystal under investigation. The 'computer' comprised a mechanical model of the reciprocal lattice composed of three slides representing the reciprocal-lattice axes to which the motions of the crystal and counter were linked. Once the crystal had been correctly oriented with respect to the slide system, any reflection could be found by setting the appropriate positions on the three slides, and the crystal and counter would automatically take up their correct positions. This facility made the automatic operation of the diffractometer for measurement of the complete diffraction pattern a relatively simple matter. Various schemes of automatic operation were possible, none of which required the preliminary calculation of angular settings, as was necessary for the three-circle diffractometer. In particular it was possible with the slides to measure the X-ray intensity distribution along lines in reciprocal space—hence the name 'linear diffractometer'—either continuously or in sequence at the points of the most densely populated reciprocal lattice rows. Uli describes how he once demonstrated the instrument to P. P. Ewald (FRS 1958), well known for his introduction of the Ewald sphere construction to describe the diffracting conditions from a crystal. Uli presented the diffractometer as a child of the Ewald sphere and therefore as Ewald's grandchild, but the great man objected to being credited with the ancestry of such an ugly grandchild! The instrument was used to collect some of the data used in Kendrew's initial 6 Å map of myoglobin, the first protein crystal structure to be solved (Kendrew *et al.* 1958).

However, the linear diffractometer did not have a long life: digital computers were becoming increasingly available and could be used for automatic shaft-setting procedures on the axes of three-circle or four-circle diffractometers, thereby enabling greater flexibility in data collection. One of Uli's first home-built automatic three-circle instruments was controlled by a Ferranti machine tool controller, which was fed with setting information via five-hole paper tape and produced the results of intensity measurements via a paper tape punch. A collaboration with B. T. M. Willis at the Atomic Energy Research Establishment in Harwell, who was doing neutron diffraction, resulted in a much better engineered diffractometer, which was also run by Ferranti three-axis controllers (6). The mechanical design of this neutron diffractometer was adapted by Hilger & Watts Ltd to produce an X-ray version that was for many years a workhorse in protein crystallography. In the end it achieved adequate reliability when the tape input and output were replaced by direct links to digital computers. The collaboration with Willis also led to the publication in 1966 of a monograph entitled *Single crystal diffractometry* (7), which remained a standard work on the subject for many years.

LABORATORY OF MOLECULAR BIOLOGY, CAMBRIDGE

Uli's pioneering work in instrumentation and automation had not gone unnoticed, and in 1962 he was invited by Perutz to join the newly opened Medical Research Council Laboratory of Molecular Biology (LMB). The family moved to Cambridge in early 1963. This was an exciting time because Perutz and Kendrew had recently been jointly awarded the Nobel Prize in Chemistry for their development of protein crystallography to the point at which structures could be solved. However, the process was still very labour intensive, because automation was still in its infancy. It was to be Uli's job to improve this situation by instrument development.

The relatively large size of the unit cell in protein crystals, compared with small-molecule crystals, means that when a crystal is in a diffracting condition for one reflection many other reflections are simultaneously excited. On a diffractometer with a counter, only one of these reflections can be measured at a time, meaning that the process is inefficient and takes a long time, but more importantly that the crystal suffers excessive radiation damage because only a few of the diffracted X-rays are being detected. An alternative is to record the diffraction pattern on film, which acts as an area detector that simultaneously records all the diffracted beams falling on the film. A camera such as the Buerger precession camera has a mechanical linkage and a layer-line screen arrangement that allows the user to record a section of the three-dimensional diffraction pattern in a way that shows the diffracted beams on a regular two-dimensional lattice of spots (figure 1*a*). It is convenient to have the reflections of a single layer recorded as a so-called precession photograph in this regular manner, but the use of a layer-line screen still means that not all diffracted beams are recorded. The degree of blackness in each spot corresponds to the intensity of that diffracted beam, and the integrated optical density of each spot has to be measured to solve the crystal structure.

When Uli came to the LMB, the process of measuring such films was performed laboriously with a Joyce–Loebl scanning densitometer. This involved manually setting the densitometer to run accurately along each line of spots in turn to produce an ink trace showing the optical density at each point along the scan, from which the peak height could be measured with a ruler. On the assumption that the spot shape was invariant, this peak height was proportional to diffracted intensity. The indices and intensity of each spot then had to be punched onto a computer card for further processing. The whole process was labour intensive and potentially prone to error.

A Ferranti Argus process control computer had been installed at the LMB in 1964 to run the diffractometers. A high-resolution cathode ray tube (CRT) plotter was included as part of the installation, with the idea that it could be used for plotting contour maps of sections of electron density maps once a protein structure had been solved. Previously this had been done by hand from printed computer output. Once the plotter was running, the idea arose that it could be used as a light source for a flying-spot microdensitometer to automate the measurement of X-ray films. Uli was closely involved in the design and construction of such a device, the first of its kind (8).

The basic principle is that the spot of light on the CRT is imaged onto the film and the intensities of the incident and transmitted beams are measured by photomultipliers (figure 3). The optical density at that point on the film can be estimated from the logarithm of the ratio of these intensities. As the spot is moved by computer to successive points across the face of the CRT, the sampling spot moves correspondingly across the film, thus enabling the optical density to be read out at any point on the film. Because the set-up can give random access to any point on the film, much of the processing of the data can be done on the fly, unlike a mechanical drum scanner where a complete scan has to be made before subsequent processing. The light output from the phosphor on the CRT varied from point to point, so it was necessary to use a split-beam arrangement for photomultipliers to measure incident and transmitted light simultaneously. The outputs were fed to a novel logarithmic analogue-to-digital converter, for which a patent application was made by Uli and Frank Mallett. The computer program to measure precession films was designed to make small rasters over each diffraction spot in turn, with other smaller rasters to estimate the local background. The integrated background-corrected density of each spot, together with its indices, was then written to magnetic tape for further processing. The whole process was much faster than the manual method, and the data produced were also more accurate.

Although fast and convenient for measuring the well-defined X-ray spots from single crystals, the CRT-based scanner was limited in its spatial accuracy, sampling spot size and optical density range. Accordingly, Uli was involved in the design of a completely different kind of scanner (9), which was intended for measuring X-ray diffraction patterns from fibres, such as tobacco mosaic virus. The scanner was based on a manual projection microscope in which the micrometer table was replaced by a computer-controlled coordinate table with lead screws driven by stepping motors. The logarithmic analogue-to-digital converter was similar to that used for optical density measurement in the CRT-based scanner. This scanner had a greater linear optical density range, better positional accuracy and a smaller sampling spot than the CRT scanner but was considerably slower.

A modified version of the CRT-based scanner was used by D. J. DeRosier and A. (later Sir Aaron) Klug (FRS 1969) for the digitization of electron micrographs for the first three-dimensional maps made from micrographs (DeRosier & Klug 1968), thus starting the whole field of three-dimensional electron microscopy. The mechanical scanner was subsequently also used extensively for scanning micrographs, so developments in X-ray technology had a major impact in a different area of structural biology.

The availability of flexibly programmable film scanners raised the question as to the most efficient ways of collecting X-ray diffraction data. For small-molecule crystals with small unit

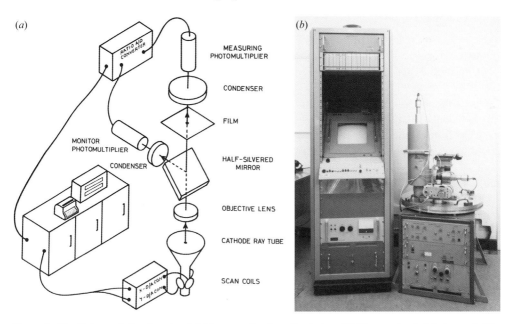

Figure 3. The flying-spot densitometer. (*a*) The overall schematic design. (*b*) The constructed instrument. The densitometer and film cameras sit on the right on the turntable above the high-resolution CRT; the large viewing CRT and control electronics are in the rack on the left.

cells, few diffracted beams are excited at any one position of the crystal; however, for proteins the unit cells are much larger and many reflections are simultaneously excited. Thus for small unit cells the single-counter diffractometer provides an efficient way of collecting data, but for protein crystals with large unit cells an area detector such as film provides a better approach. Uli records that he was giving a seminar at the LMB about these matters when Francis Crick (FRS 1959) asked him at what cell size the cross-over took place. This led Uli to make a more detailed quantitative analysis, which was published as an optimum strategy for measuring structure factors (10). In the acknowledgements Uli thanked some colleagues for helpful discussions but later regretted that he had not mentioned Francis Crick, whose question had triggered his investigation in the first place.

Analysis of the type just described, coupled with the advent of programmable film scanners, led to the idea of using screenless oscillation photography for collecting data from crystals with large unit cells. In the late 1960s Uli's PhD student Paul Phizackerley investigated the potential of this method and, with Alan Wonacott, an instrument was designed and constructed (12). There was now no need for the diffraction spots to be recorded on a regular lattice as produced by the precession camera. It was more efficient to record the diffraction pattern (figure 1*b*) by small, contiguous, oscillations of the crystal about an axis without the use of a layer-line screen, so that all diffracted X-rays at a given crystal setting could be recorded, thus maximizing the speed of recording and minimizing the radiation damage to the crystal.

The design adopted was chosen to make the mechanical arrangements as simple as possible, so that high precision and reproducibility of crystal movement could be achieved (figure 4). There was thus a single axis for rotation of the crystal, with the incident X-ray beam normal to this axis. Introduction of an inclination axis would give a minimal increase in the

Figure 4. Uli demonstrating the rotation camera to Peder Kierkegaard, taken probably in about 1974.

amount of the diffraction pattern that could be measured from a single crystal but required a more complex design because the additional axis would have to intersect the rotation axis with great precision. A flat film format was chosen, because with a cylindrical film the crystal axis would have to be accurately positioned along the axis of the cylinder, which would be difficult to achieve with an automatic system for changing films. With large unit cells many contiguous oscillations are required to collect a complete set of data, so automatic changing of film between successive exposures is very desirable. In any screenless method the crystal movement corresponding to one exposure must be kept small to prevent the superposition of diffraction spots. This means that an appreciable proportion of the spots on any one exposure will be only partly recorded, because the whole of the spot will not have passed through the diffracting condition. The high potential efficiency of screenless photography can thus only be realized if it is possible to add the parts of a diffraction spot recorded on successive exposures to create an integrated intensity. For this to be possible the crystal rotation must be reproducible and sufficiently free from backlash, so great care was taken in mimizing backlash and eccentricity in the shafts. A variety of film holders could be used, but the standard one consisted of a turntable, which permitted the automatic recording of up to eight exposures. Holes drilled at identical positions in the backs of the various cassettes with an extra X-ray exposure provided fiducial marks for subsequent densitometry of the films. The demands on speed and accuracy for measuring the large numbers of films being generated led to the development of a hybrid film scanner that combined the speed of the old flying-spot densitometer for local scanning and spot integration with a mechanical stage for accuracy of positioning (Mallett *et al*. 1977). Uli was not directly involved in this part of the project. With further developments from the laboratory prototype, the Arndt–Wonacott camera was produced commercially by N.V. Enraf-Nonius, Delft, The Netherlands, and many instruments were sold for use with laboratory sources and at synchrotrons.

An international meeting on the use of the rotation method was organized by David Blow FRS in 1975; the proceedings were published in 1977 as a monograph entitled *The rotation method in crystallography*, edited by Uli and Wonacott (13). Besides acting as editors they both made major contributions to the contents, which described the use of the instrument and the ways of processing the resulting data. The monograph rapidly became the authoritative work on the subject and is Uli's most cited publication. Even today the rotation method of data collection remains the standard approach in protein crystallography and represents Uli's most lasting scientific legacy.

When Uli developed the film-based oscillation camera, he originally intended it to be only a temporary solution. He foresaw that electronic detectors would provide a far superior system, eliminating the requirement for time-consuming film loading, development and subsequent densitometry. He made the decision to base this new instrument on commercially available sensors, and after careful review of the field opted for the use of a television camera as the detector (11). This led to the development of the X-ray TV detector, a venture that occupied Uli for the next 20 years. It also led to Uli and his family spending the year 1972–73 at the Institut Laue–Langevin in Grenoble, where he was invited to turn his expertise to neutron detectors. However, the institute had only a minor interest in biological problems, so after a year Uli decided to return to Cambridge.

From the beginning, progress was largely dictated by the technical limitations of the camera tubes, the image intensifiers and the computers controlling the detector. The limited size and sensitivity of commercially available camera tubes led to a design in which a phosphor faceplate was coupled to an image intensifier (to provide the required sensitivity), which in turn was optically coupled by a fibre-optic bundle to a silicon intensifier target (SIT) camera tube (14). De-magnification was provided both electron-optically in the image intensifier and by the use of a tapered fibre-optic cone, and allowed the 64 mm by 48 mm active area to be matched to the 18 mm diameter SIT tube. The camera operated with the interlaced 625-line standard, and produced a digitized image of 512×512 pixels with a frame period of 40 ms. Individual frames were summed in a mass store unit before being written out to computer storage. Uli characteristically considered the optimum design for every component of the detector, from the phosphor to the camera tube. This involved a detailed analysis of the many potential sources of noise and allowed him to predict the best values for operational parameters such as the voltages applied to the image intensifier and the SIT tube, and the reference voltage for the analogue-to-digital converter. The importance of temperature stabilization, ideally at a temperature below ambient, was also realized and the instrument was modified accordingly.

All of the initial development was performed on a prototype instrument constructed with Uli's colleague David Gilmore entirely at the LMB, but in the early 1980s an agreement was reached with N.V. Enraf-Nonius to produce a commercial version of the detector, marketed under the name FAST, which was mounted on their CAD4 diffractometer with a kappa goniostat. The first of these was delivered to the LMB in 1983 and gave a substantial improvement in performance.

The use of an image intensifier and the SIT tube introduced significant spatial distortions in the images, and the sensitivity of the detector also varied across the active area. It was therefore necessary to develop spatial and non-uniformity corrections, and Uli's PhD student David Thomas played a major role in developing the procedures and particularly the software for achieving this. However, the sensitivity of the image intensifier to local magnetic fields required

Figure 5. Uli with the prototype microfocus X-ray tube. (Online version in colour.)

the spatial distortion correction to be recalibrated every time that the detector position was changed, which was a drawback. Providing the software to process the resulting images was also a significant challenge, and again David Thomas, by then a staff scientist, played a central role.

By 1990 there were more than 25 of these instruments in use for protein crystallography. This included one at the synchrotron radiation source at the Brookhaven National Laboratory in New York and another at the Daresbury synchrotron, UK, which must have been particularly satisfying for Uli; the potential use of synchrotron radiation for protein crystallography had been a serious consideration from the early days of the FAST development (15) and was one of the reasons that Uli had focused on a system based on a TV tube rather than on a multiwire proportional counter, because the global count rate limitations of the latter made it unsuitable for the high photon fluxes at synchrotron sources. However, the use of the TV camera tube also resulted in inherent limitations in performance, including stability issues and poor signal-to-noise ratios for weakly diffracting samples. As a result, by the mid 1990s the FAST had been largely superseded, first by image plate scanners and then by charge-coupled device (CCD) detectors, in spite of the fact that both of these had significantly longer readout times.

After Uli's official retirement in 1989, he returned to the area of X-ray generators, a topic that had formed a large part of his PhD thesis 40 years earlier. Having seen a variety of X-ray focusing optics at synchrotron sources, Uli started thinking about whether similar devices could be used to improve the performance of laboratory-based X-ray sources. His basic idea was for an X-ray source with a very small focal spot size combined with special X-ray mirrors that would be able to capture a much larger fraction of the emitted X-rays than conventional generators. This design would produce a beam of almost the same intensity for a fraction of the input power. With his characteristic rigour, Uli laid out the ground rules for such a system in his 1990 paper (16), considering a variety of different optical elements and the implications for the construction of the X-ray tube (figure 5).

He then embarked on a very fruitful collaboration with Ladislav Pina and Adolf Inneman in Prague, who had experience in making similar mirrors for X-ray telescopes in Russian satellites. Using an electroforming technique, they were able to produce the very small ellipsoidal mirrors that were required, with internal diameters of a fraction of a millimeter. Uli prepared plans on paper for the X-ray tube itself, but fortuitously (through his wife Valerie) he renewed an old friendship with Jim Long and Peter Duncumb FRS, whom he had much earlier taught at Cambridge University and who were experts in electron optics and X-ray generation. Together they were able to produce a tube–mirror combination that gave an X-ray intensity at the sample that was similar to that of a conventional generator running at 100 times the power (17). This design was manufactured under licence by Bede Scientific Instruments, and one of the first devices was tested in 1998 by Uli and Anne Bloomer at the LMB. The Bede Microsource, running at the conservative power rating of 24 W, gave an intensity that was 25% of that achieved from a Rigaku generator (equipped with double Franks mirrors) running at 5 kW (18).

Despite the promising beginnings for the Microsource, it was destined to be always chasing but never reaching the performance of the larger generators. Perhaps as a result of the influence of Uli's published work, commercial manufacturers were also developing generators operating with much smaller focal spot sizes. The development of multilayer focusing X-ray optics, particularly when used in combination with these generators, resulted in very significant improvements in intensity that could not be matched even by an upgraded Microsource. For biological crystallography, in which intensity is more important than efficiency of the generator, the Microsource was never an attractive alternative. As a result the sales were restricted to more specialist applications such as non-destructive testing. At one point there was interest in using the Microsource in the International Orbiting Space Laboratory to test the quality of protein crystals grown in microgravity, but these plans never materialized.

Legacy

The scientific career of an instrument developer such as Uli Arndt represents a continual struggle to develop new systems with current barely adequate technology, only to see a completely new approach become viable. This happened many times in Uli's career. Thus many of his instruments became obsolete soon after becoming successful. However, Uli seemed to have the knack of conceiving and planning the next instrument while the current one was being completed, and in this way often managed to stay ahead of the game. One of the major changes during his career was the rapid development of digital computers and advanced electronics, which transformed the way in which scientific instruments were planned and constructed. His expertise was often called on more widely, and he was a member of the Crystallographic Apparatus Commission of the International Union of Crystallography from 1962 to 1964. Uli sometimes described himself as a 'tinkerer' but always regarded himself as supremely fortunate to be paid to do something he loved in an outstandingly supportive and stimulating environment. His contributions, recognized by the award in 2000 of the Dorothy Hodgkin Prize by the British Crystallographic Association, certainly helped to make macromolecular crystallography an indispensable and efficient technique for structural biologists.

Figure 6. Uli and Valerie returning from the skiing holiday in Lech on which they first met in 1955.

PERSONAL LIFE

Uli was very much a feature of life at the LMB. With his trademark bow tie and, until smoking was finally banned, his pipe, he was often to be seen in the canteen, explaining his latest ideas and designs, frequently with the aid of a diagram scribbled on a paper napkin or chocolate wrapper. He was also an excellent storyteller with a range of amusing anecdotes, many of which appear in his autobiography (19). He read widely from an early age and was particularly interested in history and the biographies of statesmen and politicians. Second-hand bookshops proved a happy hunting ground for some of the more obscure titles. He always enjoyed languages and was fluent in German and French and, at one time, had a working knowledge of Norwegian and Dutch, as well as understanding some Italian. Uli was a keen theatregoer, and a lively discussion of the latest play he had seen would often form the background to a coffee or tea break. As a bachelor Uli did a good deal of sailing, mostly in chartered boats on the south coast and in the Channel. With the family he tried dinghy sailing but never took to the competitive aspects that this entailed. He was a keen walker and many holidays were spent in the Lake District, usually staying on Buttermere. He also did quite a lot of skiing, which he continued with his family. As he became older and less physically active he enjoyed sketching and painting in watercolours.

It was on a skiing holiday in Austria in 1955 that he first met Valerie Hilton-Sergeant, who was to become his wife (figure 6). They married in 1958 and spent 46 very happy years together. They had three daughters, Elizabeth, Caroline and Annabel, who became respectively a lawyer, a doctor and a university lecturer, and seven grandchildren. Valerie died in 2004 and Uli in 2006. In the months before his death Uli wrote his scientific and personal autobiography *Personal X-ray reflections* (19) and saw the page proofs, though not the final publication, just before he died. Much of this memoir has drawn on his writing.

ACKNOWLEDGEMENTS

We are most grateful to Elizabeth Arndt for her helpful comments on and corrections to an earlier draft of this article and also for providing copies of figures 2, 4 and 6. Every effort has been made to trace the copyright holders, but where this has not been possible we apologize for any omission. For all the other pictures, the copyright belongs to the Laboratory of Molecular Biology, Cambridge. We also thank our colleagues Dr R. Henderson FRS and Dr R. M. Sweet for helpful suggestions on an earlier draft of the memoir, and the LMB archivist, Annette Faux, for tracing materials for us.

The frontispiece photograph was taken in about 1963 and is reproduced with permission from the Medical Research Council Laboratory of Molecular Biology.

REFERENCES TO OTHER AUTHORS

DeRosier, D. J. & Klug, A. 1968 Reconstruction of three dimensional structures from electron micrographs. *Nature* **217**, 130–134.

Green, D. W., Ingram, V. & Perutz, M. F. 1954 The structure of haemoglobin. IV. Sign determination by the isomorphous replacement method. *Proc. R. Soc. Lond.* A **225**, 287–307.

Kendrew, J. C., Bodo, G., Dintzis, H. M., Parrish, R. G. Wyckoff, H. W. & Phillips, D. C. 1958 A three-dimensional model of the myoglobin molecule obtained by X-ray analysis. *Nature* **181**, 662–666.

Kendrew, J. C., Dickerson, R. E., Strandberg, B. E., Hart, R. G., Davies, D. R., Phillips, D. C. & Shore, V. C. 1960 Structure of myoglobin. A three-dimensional Fourier synthesis at 2 Å. resolution. *Nature* **185**, 422–427.

Mallett, J. F. W., Champness, J. N., Faruqi, A. R. & Gossling, T. H. 1977 A new automatic flat-bed microdensitometer for use in X-ray crystallography. *J. Phys.* E **10**, 351–358.

Pauling, L. & Corey, R. B. 1951 Atomic coordinates and structure factors for two helical configurations of polypeptide chains. *Proc. Natl Acad. Sci. USA* **37**, 235–240.

Perutz, M. F., Rossmann, M. G., Cullis, A. F., Muirhead, H., Will, G. & North, A. C. T. 1960 Structure of haemoglobin. A three-dimensional Fourier synthesis at 5.5-Å. resolution, obtained by X-ray analysis. *Nature* **185**, 416–422.

BIBLIOGRAPHY

The following publications are those referred to directly in the text. A full bibliography is available as electronic supplementary material at http://dx.doi.org/10.1098/rsbm.2014.0003 or via http://rsbm.royalsocietypublishing.org.

(1)	1949	(With W. H. Hall & R. A. Smith) A Geiger-counter spectrometer for the measurement of Debye–Scherrer line shapes. *Proc. Phys. Soc.* A **62**, 631–638.

(2)	1952	(With D. P. Riley) New type of X-ray evidence on the molecular structure of globular proteins. *Nature* **169**, 138–139.

(3)	1955	(With D. P. Riley) The structure of some proteins as revealed by an X-ray scattering method. *Phil. Trans. R. Soc. Lond.* A **247**, 409–439.

(4) 1957 (With D. C. Phillips) On the determination of crystal and counter settings for a single crystal X-ray diffractometer. *Acta Crystallogr*. **10**, 508–510.

(5) 1961 (With D. C. Phillips) The linear diffractometer. *Acta Crystallogr*. **14**, 807–818.

(6) 1963 (With B. T. M. Willis) Automatic neutron diffractometer for three-dimensional structure-factor determination. *Rev. Sci. Instrum*. **34**, 224–230.

(7) 1966 (With B. T. M. Willis) *Single crystal diffractometry*. Cambridge University Press.

(8) 1968 (With R. A. Crowther & J. F. W. Mallet) A computer-linked cathode-ray tube microdensitometer for X-ray crystallography. *J. Sci. Instrum*. (2) **1**, 510–516.

(9) 1969 (With J. Barrington Leigh, J. F. W. Mallet & K. E. Twinn) A mechanical microdensitometer. *J. Sci. Instrum*. (2) **2**, 385–387.

(10) The optimum strategy in measuring structure factors. *Acta Crystallogr*. B **24**, 1355–1357.

(11) 1970 (With D. J. Gilmore) A television system for the direct analysis of X-ray diffraction patterns. *IEEE Trans. Nucl. Sci*. **NS-17**, 318–321.

(12) 1973 (With J. M. Champness, R. P. Phizackerley & A. J. Wonacott) A single-crystal oscillation camera for large unit cells. *J. Appl. Crystallogr*. **6**, 457–463.

(13) 1977 (Ed., with A. J. Wonacott) *The rotation method in crystallography*. Amsterdam: North-Holland/Elsevier.

(14) 1982 (With D. J. Thomas) A high speed single crystal television X-ray diffractometer. *Nucl. Instrum. Methods* **201**, 21–25.

(15) 1984 Area detectors for protein crystallography at storage rings. *Nucl. Instrum. Methods* **222**, 252–255.

(16) 1990 Focusing optics for laboratory sources in X-ray crystallography. *J. Appl. Crystallogr*. **23**, 161–168.

(17) 1998 (With J. V. P. Long & P. Duncumb) A microfocus X-ray tube used with focusing collimators. *J. Appl. Crystallogr*. **31**, 936–944.

(18) 1999 (With A. C. Bloomer) Experiences and expectations of a novel X-ray microsource with focusing mirror. *Acta Crystallogr*. D **55**, 1672–1680.

(19) 2006 *Personal X-ray reflections*. London: Athena Press. (Publication now taken over by G2Rights.)

BRUCE ALEXANDER BILBY

3 September 1922 — 20 November 2013

BRUCE ALEXANDER BILBY

3 September 1922 — 20 November 2013

Elected FRS 1977

By G. W. Greenwood FRS FREng

*Department of Materials Science and Engineering, The University of Sheffield,
Mappin Street, Sheffield S1 3JD, UK*

Emeritus Professor Bruce Bilby, who died in November 2013 at the age of 91 years, was among the few pioneers who made great contributions to the understanding of crystal defects, notably of dislocations, in providing precise geometrical descriptions of their form, arrangement, interaction and movement. This has led to a clear and experimentally verifiable interpretation of phenomena that include the occurrence of yield points, strain ageing, mechanisms of twinning and martensitic transformations, and the characteristics of atomic separation that lead to fracture. Bruce's approach often made use of areas of pure mathematics, whose relevance had not previously been suspected, in elegant descriptions of defected crystal structures. Much of his work is related to the role of defects in metals and alloys in their influence on mechanical properties. It assists in considerations of safety assurance of large structures. It links macroscopic behaviour with phenomena on an atomic scale and has underpinned technological judgements.

Early years, education and war service

Bruce was born in Edmonton, London, the eldest of three children. His father, George, had entered the Civil Service by taking the examination for boy clerks and was employed as an Officer of Customs and Excise. George had once hoped to become a government chemist and maintained a keen amateur interest in chemistry. He also built primitive crystal radio receivers and erected a tall mast in his garden to assist in wireless reception. Bruce's mother, Jean (*née* Telfer), was a shorthand typist before marriage and had first met George at a cycling club. They became keen gardeners and kept chickens. In winter they enjoyed skating when a nearby lake was frozen and in summer extended their travels to the countryside in an old Austin Seven. Bruce inherited many of the interests and practical abilities of his parents.

When Bruce was 10 years old the family moved to Dover, where he attended the Dover County (later Grammar) School for Boys. New interests arose there, especially in the sea and ships, which were to become an abiding fascination. He particularly valued a huge, though obsolete, copy of *Lloyds register of shipping*, handed down by a relative, which added to his interest in 'ship spotting'. Bruce liked to construct various objects and machines with his Meccano set but also enjoyed energetic pursuits, including cycling, roller skating and table tennis. He excelled at swimming, later winning his school's cup and playing water polo for the Dover Swimming Club. During his school days Bruce made extensive use of his small Hercules cycle, which had no gears. After various local expeditions, he prepared himself for longer journeys with several rides to Chatham and back, a round trip of some 80 miles, before riding to Westcliff-on-sea via the Gravesend ferry to visit his cousins. With thoughts of war approaching and the anticipation of shortages, his parents bought him a full size Rudge–Whitworth machine with Sturmey–Archer three-speed gear. This cycle was later to carry him several times between Cambridge, South Wales and South Devon when he was a university student.

At school his fascination with chemistry was gradually overshadowed by physics and mathematics, largely through the inspirational physics teaching of the senior physics master, W. E. Pearce. The start of the war had initially little influence on the pattern of life, but this changed suddenly. At one week's notice in June 1940 the Dover schools were evacuated. Bruce's school was relocated in Ebbw Vale with a substantially different environment from that which was previously familiar. Nevertheless, Bruce adapted to the changes and the school did all that was possible to provide continuity. There were some interesting and memorable new experiences. One of these was a visit to the South Wales steelworks of Richard Thomas and Baldwin, in which the huge industrial scale of operations involved in the melting, casting and mechanical working of steel made a lasting impression.

Bruce was awarded a state scholarship on the results of his Higher School Certificate Examination, but he took advice to remain at school for a further term and sit the Open Scholarship Examinations in natural sciences at Cambridge in December 1940. His decision was partly influenced by the example of J. W. (later Sir James) Menter (FRS 1966), who had taken similar advice in the previous year. Bruce was successful in being awarded an Open Minor Scholarship within the Peterhouse group of colleges. Because of wartime conditions, he was able to start immediately at the university and, supported by his college scholarship, he entered Peterhouse in January 1941.

He had very much looked forward to studying physics at university level, but was aware that, within the Part 1 Natural Sciences Tripos, additional subjects must be chosen. A decision was not easy when he noted, with some apprehension, that a course on mineralogy was unavoidable in his preferred combination. Surprisingly, in the presentation of this subject, he found its emphasis on crystallographic aspects and on x-ray diffraction much more to his liking than he had expected. With the excellent treatment of crystallography, the course was to have decisive influence on his future career. He completed Part 1 of the Tripos in June 1942 with a college prize and Andrew Perne Senior Scholarship. He went on to take Part 2 in Physics, finishing his degree course in June 1943.

In parallel with academic studies, the nation's state of war required additional commitments, and Bruce served in the Signals Section of the University Senior Training Corps. Previous experience in his school's Cadet Corps, where he had risen to the rank of corporal, helped in his adaptation. Subsequently he joined the Home Guard and this required him to do some work on the land during vacations as an agricultural labourer, assisting in food production to meet the country's wartime needs. With his strong physique, one of his allocated tasks was to assist in wheat threshing by throwing sheaves to the top of the machine with a pitchfork. Very tired towards the end of the day, he failed to release the pitchfork from one of the sheaves and both were swept together into the machine. Fortunately, despite a loud rasping and the emergence of wood splinters and tangled metal from the exit port, the machine was largely undamaged. That was the last time this activity was included in his agricultural work! Back at the university, a totally contrasting duty was to spend long nights on college roofs undertaking fire-watching duty.

After his completion of Part 2 Physics, Bruce was interviewed by the Central Register Committee set up in wartime to allocate the employment of scientists graduating at that time. He was recruited into the Radiography Section of the Naval Construction Department of the Admiralty formed under the initiative of the Superintendent of Welding Development. There were brief induction periods for training, which involved works experience in the Royal Dockyards at Portsmouth and Chatham, Woolwich Arsenal, Kent Alloys and the X-ray Department of Bristol General Hospital, and attendance in London at the Kodak School of Industrial and Engineering Radiography. Work in dockyards provided valuable experience of industrial conditions. Bruce was commissioned as Lieutenant (Sp) in the Royal Naval Volunteer Reserve and sent to Germany immediately after the war had ended to investigate what might be learned from corresponding work and equipment in the former enemy country. After completing the required period of three years' Admiralty Service he was free to leave.

BIRMINGHAM

In 1946 Bruce took up a new post as a Science Research Council Research Assistant in the Department of Metallurgy at the University of Birmingham. The department had a distinguished record, extending over several decades, in its contributions to metallurgical practice. Its head, Professor D. Hanson, was keen to introduce and build on many of the impressive new concepts currently emerging from studies in metal science. Bruce endorsed such an approach and was ready for further changes in his life. At this time he married his first wife, Hazel Casken, a radiographer who had worked in the firm of David Brown at Penistone, South Yorkshire. They had met three years previously while on the course at the Kodak School of Radiography they both attended.

At the university, Bruce joined the team led by A. H. (later Sir Alan) Cottrell (FRS 1955) with interests centred on plasticity and the strength of metals and alloys. After a year of experimental work, involving the construction of an extensometer and a furnace for growing single crystals, Bruce moved on to study dislocation theory and its possible implications. At that time very few people were interested in the concept of dislocations: there was no direct experimental evidence for their existence and there had been few publications in the field. Studies in this area were, however, beginning at several places in the USA, Japan and Germany, but particularly in the UK with groups working under Ergon Orowan (FRS 1947) at Cambridge and in the Department of Physics at Bristol University, under N. F. (later Sir Nevill) Mott FRS, that included F. C. (later Sir Charles) Frank (FRS 1954), F. R. N. Nabarro (FRS 1971) and J. F. Nye (FRS 1976). The Department of Metallurgy at Birmingham developed close links with physicists at Bristol.

Bruce's initial interest was in Cottrell's theory of the elastic interaction of solute atoms with dislocations to explain yield point phenomena and strain ageing in steels containing small amounts of carbon or nitrogen. Experimental evidence had shown that the yield point could be removed by small amounts of plastic deformation but it would return after the steel was aged for a time depending on temperature. Bruce deduced (1)* that, after dislocation/solute separation caused by the plastic deformation, the yield point would return depending on the time raised to the power 2/3. This agreed with experimental results on several systems as well as carbon or nitrogen in iron, for which the effect was strongest. As a related effect, it was also known that carbon and nitrogen could diffuse sufficiently rapidly at about 200 °C in iron for this to occur during plastic deformation. The stress–strain curves would then show serrations and the ductility would be reduced (2). Cottrell had provided approximate values of the dislocation/solute interaction energy by an essentially intuitive approach. With Cottrell's encouragement, Bruce went to greater depth and, using the Rayleigh–Betti reciprocal theorem, was able to produce rigorous mathematical analysis (3).

At that time, many metallurgists were still sceptical about the reality of dislocations in the absence of more direct experimental evidence of their existence. Bruce gave lectures in different parts of the country to several regional branches of the Institute of Metals on the subject 'What is a dislocation?' One of the objectives was to familiarize those working in industry with the latest developments in the theory of the strength and plasticity of metals. The lectures were generally received with interest and enthusiasm, although they provoked some tongue-in-cheek reactions. One of these was from W. Hume-Rothery FRS, who commented 'a dislocation is an invention of a mathematician who cannot understand the properties of metals'. But the science moved on. Over the next three decades, P. B. (later Sir Peter) Hirsch (FRS 1963), Hume-Rothery's successor as Isaac Wolfson Professor of Metallurgy at Oxford, was a leading figure among those who provided direct and irrefutable evidence of the existence of dislocations and of their properties that verified mathematical predictions. They also went on to show that knowledge of the characteristics and behaviour of dislocations is important in the design, manufacture and performance of solid state electronic devices. Previously, Hume-Rothery had not been the only eminent scientist to doubt the value of dislocation concepts. His opinion was shared by several others, including E. N. da C. Andrade FRS, Quain Professor of Physics at University College London, who had provided, in his wide-ranging and well-respected experimental research, much new information on metal plasticity and creep but remained doubtful that dislocation theory would prove capable of providing viable explanations.

Aware of these views, prevalent in the mid twentieth century, and of the necessity of a wider understanding and appreciation of the potential importance of dislocations, Bruce recognized the need first for improved visualization of their geometrical character. To assist in this (4), through demonstrating the location of atomic positions, he created models from wooden balls connected by curtain wire by which three-dimensional aspects could be more widely understood. These creations made a strong impact for students and others in their understanding of crystal defects.

Such a model is illustrated in figure 1, although details in the photograph are far less easy to decipher than those provided by a complete all-round view of the actual object. The models were to prove especially valuable, even to those with relatively little mathematical experience, in the elucidation of screw dislocations and in the operation of Frank–Read sources

---

* Numbers in this form refer to the bibliography at the end of the text.

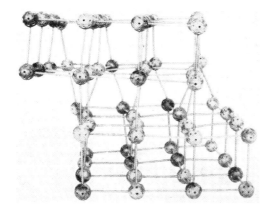

Figure 1. A wire-and-ball model of a crystal containing a screw dislocation.
(From (4), with kind permission of the Institute of Metals.)

through which dislocations could be generated. Such visualization in three dimensions was essential to an understanding of the significant geometrical features. This led on to dynamical considerations, which could be demonstrated by systematic uncoupling and rejoining of wire and balls in new positions. The models were used extensively in lecture demonstrations, not only by Bruce but also by others including Sir Laurence Bragg FRS in a Royal Institution Lecture. A greatly enlarged photograph of a model of a crystal containing a crossed grid of screw dislocations was placed over the entrance to the Crystallography Section at the 1951 Festival of Britain Exhibition. Bruce realized that its selection was due to its decorative properties rather than its scientific revelation. Although he was pleased to have this recognition of the model's photographic qualities, he preferred to see more instructive examples of the models in use. Nevertheless, such examples found their way elsewhere and, for those with more mathematical appreciation, the demonstrations assisted in recognizing the importance of adopting vectorial representation (5), through which the significance and usefulness of the dislocation concept then became clearer. With agreed sign conventions, it was shown that displacements could be represented unambiguously by a single vector analogous to the vector that determines the direction of motion of a wire in relation to the electric current and magnetic field in a dynamo.

After five years at Birmingham, which included conferment of his PhD in 1949 and subsequently a University Research Fellowship there, Bruce moved to Sheffield in the autumn of 1951.

SHEFFIELD

Bruce joined the Department of Metallurgy at Sheffield University to which, a year previously, A. G. Quarrell had been appointed Professor of Physical Metallurgy. Aided by industrial and government support supplemented by its own resources, the university was substantially expanding in this area. Simultaneously with Bruce's joining, the department was further reinforced by the arrival of Dr R. W. K. (later Sir Robert) Honeycombe (FRS 1981), G. B. Greenough, D. W. Wakeman and A. R. Entwisle.

Bruce's appointment was to the Royal Society Sorby Research Fellowship, and the University of Sheffield was to become the base for the remainder of his working life. On completion of the tenure of this post and, after a brief period as J. H. Andrew Research Fellow, he became a permanent member of the academic staff of the university. The title of Reader in Theoretical Metallurgy was conferred upon him in 1958 and this was followed by promotion to a personal chair in 1962.

Sheffield was delighted to have the opportunity, and now the basis, for the exploration of dislocation concepts with consideration of their promise in explaining much that had remained obscure. Bruce had brought his dislocation models with him, and their value was soon realized. This was reflected at a Christmas party, in a light-hearted way soon after his arrival, by research students in their adapting and ascribing to him the song 'When I was a lad' from Gilbert and Sullivan's operetta *HMS Pinafore*:

> When I was a lad I was always a trier,
> I used a lot of balls and curtain wire.
> I fastened them up with the greatest glee
> in complicated patterns like a Christmas tree.
> Then I painted them red and I painted them yellow
> and that's how I came to be a Sorby Fellow.

Dislocation theory at Sheffield

Bruce began work with his first research student, R. Bullough (FRS 1985), on aspects of mechanical twinning and of martensitic transformations, initially examining the hypothesis that mechanical twin formation was influenced by the large local stresses set up around inhomogeneities of various kinds during deformation and fracture. By calculating stresses around a moving crack, certain asymmetries (6) in twin formation on cleaved surfaces of zinc single crystals were explained.

Following with a broader programme, increasing attention was given to the dislocation description of boundaries in crystals as in twins and of boundaries between different crystal structures occurring in martensitic transformations. E. Smith (FRS 1996) was soon to join in the work as a research student, and the three of them studied general geometrical relationships in dislocated crystals in ways that could be linked usefully with continuum mechanics.

Development of the work was strongly influenced by researches in Bristol, particularly by Nye, concerning the description of deformed crystals. Bruce wanted to place on a more formal basis the mathematical representation of a crystal containing dislocations everywhere (7, 8, 13). (One of these (7) includes a preliminary account of some of the work with his research students R. Bullough and E. Smith on continuous distributions of dislocations and surface dislocations.) This was an ambitious task. It required finding a way of defining a continuously dislocated crystal. To enable a correspondence of lattice directions to be specified in such a crystal, a matrix of nine functions, together with its reciprocal, was defined at each point. Around any closed circuit of steps in the dislocated crystal the corresponding steps in a reference crystal could now be executed, the associated Burgers vector calculated and a general expression for the dislocation tensor found. With dislocations arranged so that they produce no far-reaching stress, the local crystal lattice is generated from the reference lattice at each point by matrices representing rotations. These results verified relationships between dislocation geometry and curvature tensors previously proposed by Nye, who had also considered the behaviour of a line scribed on the surface of a crystal subject to uniform bending. This scribed line is indicative of the shape change of the crystal, which results from a combination of the deformation of the lattice (in this case pure rotation) and another deformation due to plasticity through slip by dislocation movement. This resolution of the total shape strain into the shape changes produced by the lattice strain and that due to slip was discussed in several papers from the Sheffield group.

The problems of giving a dislocation description of interfaces in twins and in martensitic transformations (10), together with experimental work on the motion of simple tilt boundaries, provided further stimulus for workers at Sheffield. Suggestions were made by the group at Bristol of the possibility of deducing a formula for the dislocation content of a crystal boundary by regarding the boundary as a surface distribution of dislocation density. This led Bruce and his co-workers to introduce the concept of a surface dislocation. In slip processes, a dislocation line bounds an area over which there has been a local slip defined by the Burgers vector. The motion of a dislocation line causes slip over the region swept out. A surface dislocation is a surface separating volumes where the lattice deformation differs, in the simplest case, by a rotation. Such a surface dislocation also causes plastic deformation by its motion. It corresponds to an array of line dislocations. Ascribing tensor notation to the surface dislocation, a formal mathematical approach could then be applied to analyse a variety of experimental results. Later, it was used to discuss the discontinuities both of stress and of rotation occurring across general arrays of dislocations and, as a particular case, to confirm Frank's formula for the dislocation content of a general grain boundary. The concept of the surface dislocation was also to prove useful in discussions of the theory of the crystallography of martensitic transformations (15, 16).

Bruce considered further the geometry of the dislocated crystal and, in particular, the problem of following a prescribed crystallographic direction in it. This invoked the principal elements in a generalized space: the metric tensor, giving the length of any small vector, and the coefficients of connection, giving a law of parallelism. Calculated from the metric tensor, the connections are asymmetric, which brings in the requirement of a geometry that is non-Riemannian. In non-Riemannian space, the antisymmetric part of the connection is called the torsion tensor and the space is said to have torsion. In space with torsion, infinitesimal parallelograms do not exist. Bruce was intrigued to find that such a relatively remote mathematical structure was applicable to a practical subject that had arisen quite separately from the need to understand the deformation and strength of materials. These connections of pure mathematics with demonstrable phenomena indicated the importance of this link. The relevance was to give impetus to a revival of interest in the foundations of mechanics and the relationship with other areas. Bruce further introduced these new ideas in applying them to the theory of folding. The usefulness was established of the extensive theory of non-Riemannian spaces in its employment in, and relationship to, the theorems of dislocation theory. L. M. Brown (FRS 1982) noted a comment from J. D. Eshelby (FRS 1974) that Bruce's work cast a shaft of light on the theory of general relativity with its similar mathematical basis.

Work on generalized continuum mechanics did not prevent Bruce from pursuing his interests in problems more immediately relevant to metallurgical practice. With others he wrote several papers on martensitic transformations (9), on more practical aspects of dislocation theory (11, 12, 14) and on the role of hydrogen in the cracking of steel (17, 25). With A. G. Crocker, Bruce ventured into an early use of the Ferranti Pegasus computer, which had been purchased by the United Steel Companies for their Cybernetics Department and on which the university was to be allowed limited time each week. Indeed, he made, with Crocker, a visit to the machine at Ferranti in London to test programs before the machine was delivered.

After Bruce's appointment to his personal chair in 1962, he gave his Inaugural Lecture with the title 'Mathematics and materials'. It was not published, but its main theme was that, on the one hand, pure scientists would find interesting problems of pattern in technology and, on the other, that technologists should welcome the support and interest of the pure scientist. He noted that, according to the dictionary, a material was a thing from which something was made. This perhaps epitomized the difference in viewpoint of the pure and applied sciences. However, striking analogies of pattern between mathematical ideas and the real world had almost philo-sophical implications, and there were plenty of interesting problems to be found in practice. A quotation from Bruce's summing up found its way into a local newspaper: 'Do not look only from your high towers at a distant prospect of Attercliffe [an industrial area in the Don valley within Sheffield], but go down sometimes and see what actually happens there.'

In the following year Bruce was the recipient of the Rosenhain Medal of the Institute of Metals.

Research on fracture

Looking for further practical applications of the new dislocation concepts and continuing to benefit from discussions with Cottrell, Bruce's small but powerful research group directed much of their attention to problems of fracture, its characteristics and its avoidance. These problems were crucial in the design of nuclear reactors for power generation.

Importantly, Cottrell had proposed a simple model to allow for the plasticity at a crack tip. A crack that spreads throughout a large structure before the regions remote from it show that any sign of plastic deformation presents an engineering catastrophe. To prevent such occur-rences, particularly recalling problems that had arisen from the spectacular failures in welded 'Liberty' ships during the war, considerable attention was already being devoted in numerous places to the understanding of fracture mechanics. The importance of plasticity in the material was widely recognized, but problems remained in evaluating the respective roles of elasticity and plasticity (18, 19). Cottrell, in his lecture on 'Why some brittle solids are strong', stated:

> to develop this idea [the propagation of a brittle fracture] an elastic–plastic theory was needed. I soon wrote down the mathematical equations representing this situation and equally quickly real-ized that I could not solve them. And so I approached my old friend and research collaborator, B. A. Bilby, a much better mathematician, at the University of Sheffield.

Bruce was able to deal with this and, with input from his research student K. H. Swinden, arrived at analytical solutions that had practical implications. A series of material parameters characterizing crack advance were identified. These could be estimated or measured in a struc-ture and an appropriate system of inspection and testing could be set up to reduce catastrophic occurrences to a minimum.

Procedures involved an assessment of the size of plastic zones and the effect of the mode of loading in relation to specimen size and geometry. Among the parameters characterizing the advance of a crack, an important feature is the opening displacement that occurs at the crack tip if it blunts through the onset of plastic deformation in that region. Another parameter intro-duced to discuss tougher materials exhibiting such plasticity and some crack growth is the *J* parameter, which can be calculated from the elastic–plastic field along a path remote from the crack. In fracture mechanics it is usual to think of three idealized modes of remote loading of a crack, the actual loading usually being a combination of these. Bruce and Swinden considered the simplest case, in which the crack plane is under shear in a direction parallel to the crack line. They showed that the relative displacement due both to the crack and to the plasticity beyond its tip can then be represented (20) by continuous distributions of dislocations in the crack plane. The distributions are determined so that under remote loading there is no stress over the region representing the crack but a finite stress (representing a plastic yield stress) in the plane beyond the crack tip. As a result there is a relative displacement at the crack tip due to the dislocations that have spread against finite resistance into the region representing plasticity. Thus the model provides an estimate of the crack opening displacement.

At this stage, an earlier paper by D. S. Dugdale was noted on 'Yielding in steel sheets containing slits', in which the slits were perpendicular to the stress. Here the approach was from a somewhat different mathematical viewpoint, not using dislocation theory. The two different approaches, however, were complementary and led to the Dugdale, Bilby, Cottrell, Swinden (DBCS) or 'strip yield' model, which has had widespread application in the interpretation of fracture and fatigue. Its power lies in its provision of simple analytical relations between important parameters governing crack behaviour, particularly between the remote load, the elastic modulus, the relative displacement that occurs at the crack tip and the stress resisting dislocation motion beyond it. This work was also valuable in assessing the importance of notches in fatigue (22, 24). Cottrell made immediate use of the key results in the derivation of a criterion of notch sensitivity. From it he was able to discuss a wide range of fractures, from the purely brittle to the fully ductile fast failures that could occur in pipelines and plate structures. The general model and its implications were reviewed by Bruce and Eshelby (23). The value of this work has been increasingly appreciated, as exemplified in its underpinning of procedures developed by workers in the Central Electricity Generating Board in their preparation of Code R6 for risk assessment of failure.

Other academic involvements at Sheffield

Within the university, Bruce was active in teaching as well as research and gave lectures to both undergraduate and postgraduate students. A general view of these students was that the lectures were not always easy to comprehend immediately but, in looking back at their content at a later time, the students came to realize their rigour and value in enhancing understanding of many of the new, exciting and significant developments that were then transforming and greatly accelerating progress in metallurgy. Additionally, Bruce had a major role in establishing a postgraduate course in conjunction with the Department of Applied Mathematics on 'Theory of deformation, flow and fracture'.

The early 1960s were a difficult time for Bruce, going through divorce in 1964, with the three children continuing their education in Sheffield and visiting their mother in Nottingham at weekends and during school holidays. Happily, in 1966, he was again married, this time to Lorette Thomas, an independent research worker in the Department of Community Medicine at Sheffield, and they had two children. At his work in the university there were upheavals through disagreements over Faculty policy and the allocation of new posts. This led to changes in Faculty structure in 1966 and the creation of a small new department, named the Department of the Theory of Materials, with Bruce at its head with his title changed to Professor of the Theory of Materials. It was housed in space made available in the Elmfield Building of the Department of Glass Technology that had joined the Faculty of Metallurgy in 1962. There were some benefits in this departmental independence, but the location was some distance from other departments of pure and applied science with consequent drawbacks in making more difficult the informal association with others that could have been of mutual benefit. There was little in common between the Theory of Materials staff, with their focus of attention on faulted crystals, and the interests of their only neighbours, the glass technologists; however, some mutual concerns were found. Bruce was able to demonstrate that Eshelby's earlier study of stresses around ellipsoidal inclusions in stressed solids could be extended to determine the conditions under which bubbles within, and in relative motion with, viscous liquids would remain ellipsoidal. This became of interest to geologists as well as those concerned with glass manufacture.

From its foundation in 1966, the new department soon began to flourish and establish its own reputation. Eshelby was looking for a new appointment at that time (as Bruce was aware) and joined the staff as Reader. Five years later he was promoted to a personal chair. Dr C. Atkinson (FRS 1998) (later to become Professor of Applied Mathematics at Imperial College, London) was appointed Lecturer. There was a secretary and a junior programmer to link with the support available from the University's Computer Services. Soon afterwards, the department was strengthened by the appointments of I. C. Howard as Lecturer (later becoming Professor) and G. E. Cardew, with extensive previous experience, as Senior Programmer. The department addressed a wide range of important problems. These were often difficult conceptually and mathematically but the staff worked effectively, both individually and collectively, and were always were quick to get to the fundamentals. An output of highly significant research was maintained and a steady flow of research students continued. Atkinson, as well as collaborating with Eshelby in solving important problems in the dynamics of fracture, was able to provide the first analysis of the interaction of a dislocation with a crack in an anisotropic medium.

Acknowledging the increasing complexity of his subject area and believing that understanding was necessary if theoretical results were to be used intelligently, Bruce wrote elementary accounts of dislocation theory (21) to aid in its comprehension. He also wrote a valuable review on developments in the theory of fracture (26). Concurrently, he made further advances, notably in the systematic study of shuffling movements in deformation twinning and in the use of the slip field model in notch fatigue.

The department suffered a severe blow with the sudden death of Eshelby in 1981. As a tribute to him, the International Union of Theoretical and Applied Mechanics held the Eshelby Memorial Symposium in Sheffield in April 1984, and Bruce played a large part in its planning. The event was a great success, with a high proportion of world leaders in the field of deformation and fracture in attendance. The proceedings, entitled *Fundamentals of deformation and fracture*, were edited by Bruce in collaboration with K. J. Miller, then Head of the Department of Mechanical Engineering at Sheffield, and J. R. Willis (FRS 1992) of the University of Bath; the volume was published by Cambridge University Press. Bruce presented an excellent introductory lecture and review (28) at the Symposium focused on the contributions that Eshelby had made.

Bruce gave several memorable and much-valued lectures at major institutions and at conferences throughout his career, although he rarely sought such opportunities. When invitations came along he sometimes preferred that his collaborators present papers rather than himself. This was not due to shyness but to a genuine wish that his colleagues and students should get both the experience in paper presentation and an appropriate share of the credit for the work done. For Bruce, much of his interaction with others came from innumerable requests from people elsewhere to visit Sheffield to have discussions with him. Most of the visitors found such interactions highly rewarding and were delighted to have contact in this way. Many were surprised by, but admiring of, his selfless attitude where problems and not personalities were always the focus of attention.

The long tradition of metallurgical work at Sheffield had given metallurgy the status of a Faculty within the university, initially comprising only the one department, the Department of Metallurgy. The number of departments that this Faculty contained gradually extended with incorporation by transfer in 1962 of the already well-established Department of Glass Technology and with new departments, the Department of Ceramics and the Department of Theory of Materials, joining on their formation. The Faculty name was later changed to become, more appropriately, the Faculty of Materials, and the departments within it concerned with non-metallic materials were combined and extended to form the Department of Ceramics, Glasses and Polymers. The post of Dean was rotated between the senior members of staff, and Bruce served as Dean on two occasions, each for the allocated period of three years. Although not seeking roles that were largely administrative, Bruce was nevertheless effective as Dean and it gave him more opportunity for contact with staff throughout the university. He served diligently on several committees that this post required. In these, he was widely respected by staff in all disciplines for his thorough academic approach and fairness. He suggested improvements that he felt might be effective in minor changes in several areas but understood that it was never easy to predict the outcome of the Senate's debate. Although appreciating the need for specialization to achieve academic depth, Bruce nevertheless felt that university staff should not feel too restricted in their range of study. One small disappointment was the Senate's declining his proposal to alter the name of the Department of Biblical Studies to the Department of Religious Studies.

Approaching and after formal retirement, Bruce continued to look at problems within the university's Department of Mechanical Engineering, aiding their research in studies on fatigue. The extension of earlier work (29) gave opportunity for improved predictions of the conditions leading to fracture and fatigue. For such evaluation, extensive numerical work was essential. Fortunately computer support continued to be available from G. E. Cardew, and the contribution paved ways to further progress (27). Bruce also continued to benefit from his long and fruitful collaboration with I. C. Howard, who had moved from Bruce's former department to the Department of Mechanical Engineering. Along with use of finite element computer programs developed at other institutions, a program, TOMECH, was formulated at Sheffield and first used to examine the effect of specimen geometry on the stress and strain at the tips of stationary cracks. It was also used in alternative approaches to fracture problems, notably those based on the concepts of 'damage theory'. In this, the gradual failure of the material ahead of the crack is explicitly modelled so that in this region the load-bearing capacity gradually decreases with consequent crack advance. The approach assisted in the extrapolation of results on relatively small specimens to predict the behaviour of much larger engineering components. It also proved valuable in its predictions of the conditions of failure in the walls of cylinders rapidly rotated about their axes (30), thus linking with experimental data relevant to the design and performance of pressure vessels.

The growth in computer power progressively allowed more extensive use of finite element programs and an increasing number of workers to enter the field of fracture assessment. More procedures were devised and some were incorporated into codes of practice. Bruce made a detailed study resulting in a better understanding of the relation between the *R*-curve procedure originating in the USA and the R6 and PD6493 procedures devised in the UK. This was a complex area but provided the opportunity to introduce further variables. Bruce's final series of papers, on failure assessment diagrams, showed how such variables (31) could be incorporated. The value of this work was recognized by his being awarded the Griffith Medal by the European Structural Integrity Society in 1994.

Figure 2. Bruce playing a game of croquet in his garden. (Online version in colour.)

A colleague once asked some of his former research students (two of whom became FRS), who had worked with him on the continuum of dislocations, why they had not continued working on it afterwards. They replied that it was too hard! This never stopped Bruce from continuing to study erudite subjects long after his early retirement in 1984.

ACTIVITIES OUTSIDE THE UNIVERSITY

In parallel with his working life, Bruce greatly enjoyed activities with his family. They had interests indoors in music and literature as well as pursuits in outdoor life. In music, Bruce took piano lessons late in life. He never claimed a high level of competence and declined public performances, though he prepared for examinations extending to Grade 6. His receipt of professional music tuition and his dedication to serious study were further indications of his perpetual desire to aim at accuracy and precision in all he undertook.

Over a long period, croquet remained an enjoyable activity, regulated by Bruce's knowledge of the rules, which was so thorough that decisions were rarely challenged by his opponents. His large garden was excellently adapted for pursuit of the game, and many visitors recall their enjoyment there and the challenges presented. Bruce continued to play (figure 2) until shortly before his death. His wife felt that his physically active lifestyle, starting in his early years and involving swimming and cycling over long distances, had contributed to a long and healthy life.

Figure 3. Bruce on his yacht *Lady Be' Ann* in the North Sea. (Online version in colour.)

Bruce's prime interest was in the sea and ships, inspired by his schooldays and the environment in Dover. In 1969 this was revived to become a practical and time-consuming involvement when the family purchased a small seagoing wooden yacht, *Ocean Baby*, moored on the river Humber at Grimsby. Such a location, with complex tidal conditions, required considerable seamanship but Bruce enjoyed the challenges it created. After a trip on the Dutch canals in 1976, during which *Ocean Baby* got a rope around her propeller just as she was about to pass under the huge Maastricht Bridge raised for her at rush hour, the decision was taken to replace her by a 29-foot fibreglass Bermudian sloop *Lady Be' Ann* (figure 3). In 1978 she was taken from Grimsby into the French canals at Saint-Valery-sur-Somme. Finally, in 1986 a long voyage was planned over three summers during which the boat was taken via the French canals and on to the Greek island of Lefkas.

In retirement Bruce and Lorette were great companions for one another, and family gatherings gave much pleasure to them both. They encouraged their children, grandchildren and great-grandchildren in a wide range of activities, and took much pride in their development and progress.

Bruce's only daughter, Elisabeth, died in 2009, and his eldest son, John, died in 2011. Bruce is survived by his wife, Lorette, and three sons, Tom, Richard and Nicholas, together with their wives and Elisabeth's husband, Marcel, and John's wife, Lesley. They and the twelve grandchildren and three great-grandchildren will miss Bruce greatly but remember him with much love, respect and affection.

Concluding notes

At the university, Bruce's work was always characterized by deep thought, clarity and precision. This made him appear sometimes remote, but not to his closer colleagues and many friends, who valued his thoroughness, extensive knowledge and wide interests. The members of staff who worked with him and all his research students held Bruce in high esteem. It is notable that their beginning in his research group almost invariably led to their achievement of high-ranking appointments: some of them remained in academic research, some moved to high-technology companies and consultancy, and others attained managerial leadership. Although Bruce was regarded mainly as a theoretician, much of his work and that of his group provided results that had practical applications. The work demonstrated the continuing importance of continuum mechanics while emphasizing the value of understanding defects in materials on an atomic scale. Linking the microscopic scale with the macroscopic was a major feature.

There is now widespread recognition of the immense value of dislocation theory in understanding the properties of crystalline materials. Bruce's work contributed greatly to the provision of a firm mathematical basis for this situation. Throughout, Bruce's work demonstrated that a concentration on what may first seem to be of purely academic interest can have profound technological benefits.

Honours and awards

1963   Rosenhain Medal, Institute of Metals, London
1977   Fellowship of the Royal Society
1994   Griffith Medal, European Structural Integrity Society

Acknowledgements

I am most grateful to Mrs Lorette Bilby for showing me notes that Bruce had compiled and, with their son, Richard, for providing additional information about his life. I have further had valuable comments from Professor C. Atkinson FRS and Professor L. M. Brown FRS. My account is also helped by my having had the pleasure and privilege of knowing Bruce in various capacities over many years.

The frontispiece photograph was taken in 1992 by Bruce's daughter.

Bibliography

The following publications are those referred to directly in the text. A full bibliography is available as electronic supplementary material at http://dx.doi.org/10.1098/rsbm.2014.0015 or via http://rsbm.royalsocietypublishing.org.

(1)   1949   (With A. H. Cottrell) Dislocation theory of the yielding and strain ageing of iron. *Proc. Phys. Soc. Lond.* A **62**, 49–62.
(2)   1950   On the theory of the discontinuous yield point. *Sheet Metal Indust.* (August), 707–718.
(3)   Interactions of dislocations and solute atoms. *Proc. Phys. Soc. Lond.* A **63**, 191–200.
(4)   Static models of dislocations. *J. Inst. Metals* **76**, 613–627.

(5)   1952   A rule for determining the displacements caused by the motion of a dislocation line. *Research* **4**, 387–388.

(6)   1954   (With R. Bullough) The formation of twins by a moving crack. *Phil. Mag.* **45**, 631–646.

(7)   1955   Types of dislocation source. In *Defects in crystalline solids. Report of the Conference of the International Union of Physics, Bristol*, pp. 124–133. London: The Physical Society.

(8)   (With R. Bullough & E. Smith) Continuous distributions of dislocations. A new application of the methods of non-Riemannian geometry. *Proc. R. Soc. Lond.* A **231**, 263–273.

(9)   1956   (With J. W. Christian) Martensitic transformations. In *Mechanism of phase transformations in metals* (Institute of Metals Monograph and Report Series no. 18), pp. 121–172. London: Institute of Metals.

(10)   (With R. Bullough) Continuous distributions of dislocations: surface dislocations and the crystallography of martensitic transformations *Proc. Phys. Soc. Lond.* B **69**, 1276–1286.

(11)   (With A. R. Entwisle) Dislocation arrays and rows of etch pits. *Acta Metall.* **4**, 257–261.

(12) 1957   (With L. R. T. Gardner & A. N. Stroh) Continuous distributions of dislocations and the theory of plasticity. In *IX International Congress of Applied Mechanics, Brussels, Actes*, vol. 8, pp. 35–44.

(13) 1958   (With R. Bullough, L. R. T. Gardner & E. Smith) Continuous distributions of dislocations. IV. Single glide and plane bending. *Proc. R. Soc. Lond.* A **244**, 538–557.

(14) 1960   Continuous distributions of dislocations. *Prog. Solid Mech.* **1**, 331–398.

(15) 1961   (With A. G. Crocker) On the theory of martensite crystallography. *Acta Metall.* **9**, 992–995.

(16)   (With J. W. Christian) The crystallography of martensitic transformations. *J. Iron Steel Inst.* **197**, 122–131.

(17) 1962   (With J. Hewitt) Hydrogen in steel—the stability of microcracks. *Acta Metall.* **10**, 587–600.

(18) 1963   (With A. H. Cottrell & K. H. Swinden) The spread of plastic yield from a notch. *Proc. R. Soc. Lond.* A **272**, 304–314.

(19) 1964   (With A. H. Cottrell, E. Smith & K. H. Swinden) Plastic yielding from sharp notches. *Proc. R. Soc. Lond.* A **279**, 1–9.

(20) 1965   (With K. H. Swinden) Representation of plasticity at notches by linear dislocation arrays. *Proc. R. Soc. Lond.* A **285**, 22–33.

(21) 1967   The modern theory of plasticity. In *Modern theory in the design of alloys: Lectures delivered at the Institution of Metallurgists Refresher Course, April 1966*, pp. 1–45. London: Iliffe Books for the Institution of Metallurgists.

(22) 1968   (With P. T. Heald) Crack growth in notch fatigue. *Proc. R. Soc. Lond.* A **305**, 429–439.

(23)   (With J. D. Eshelby) Dislocations and the theory of fracture. In *Fracture, an advanced treatise* (ed. H. Liebowitz), vol. 1, pp. 99–182. New York: Academic Press.

(24) 1970   (With P. T. Heald) Propagation of cracks from notches under repeated loading. In *Fracture toughness of high-strength materials: theory and practice* (Iron and Steel Institute publication 120), pp. 63–65. London: Iron and Steel Institute.

(25) 1975   (With D. M. Allen-Booth & C. Atkinson) A numerical analysis of the diffusion equation resulting from the void theory of the trapping of hydrogen in iron and steel. *Acta Met.*, **23**, 371–376.

(26)   The theory of fracture. In *Conference on the mechanics and physics of fracture, Cambridge, Institute of Physics and the Metals Society*, January, pp. 1/1 – 1/10.

(27) 1977   (With G. E. Cardew & I. C. Howard) Stress intensity factors at the tips of kinked and forked cracks. In *Fracture 1977: Proceedings of the Fourth International Congress on Fracture (ICF4), Waterloo, Canada* (ed. D. M. R. Taplin), vol. 3, pp. 197–200. University of Waterloo Press.

(28) 1984   Introductory lecture. In *Fundamentals of deformation and fracture. The Eshelby Memorial Symposium, IUTAM* (ed. B. A. Bilby, K. J. Miller & J. R. Willis), pp. 11–32. Cambridge University Press.

(29) 1988   (With M. R. Goldthorpe, I. C. Howard & Z. H. Li) Size and constraint effects in ductile fracture. In *Materials and Engineering Design, Institute of Materials Symposium, London, 9–13 May*, pp. 205–212. London: Institute of Materials.

(30) 1993   (With I. C. Howard & Z. H. Li) Prediction of the first spinning cylinder test using ductile damage theory. *Fatigue Fract. Engng Mater. Struct.* **16**, 1–20.

(31) 1994   (With I. C. Howard & Z. H. Li) Failure assessment diagrams. III. Mappings and failure assessment lines when the crack driving force is a functional. *Proc. R. Soc. Lond.* A **444**, 497–508.

SHIING-SHEN CHERN

26 October 1911 — 3 December 2004

S. S. Chern

SHIING-SHEN CHERN

26 October 1911 — 3 December 2004

Elected ForMemRS 1985

By Nigel J. Hitchin FRS

Mathematical Institute, Radcliffe Observatory Quarter, Woodstock Road, Oxford, OX2 6GG, UK

Shiing-Shen Chern was a towering figure in mathematics, both for his contributions to differential geometry and as a source of inspiration and encouragement for all mathematicians, and particularly those in China. Born in the final year of the Qing dynasty, and educated at a time when China was only beginning to set up Western-style universities, he lived to preside over the 2002 International Congress of Mathematicians in Beijing. He was a co-founder of the Mathematical Sciences Research Institute in Berkeley and its first Director in 1981; he also set up the Nankai Institute for Mathematics in 1985. His contributions to differential geometry were of foundational importance for the global viewpoint that developed in the postwar years, and the mathematical tools he introduced are now the common currency in geometry, topology and even aspects of theoretical physics.

Early life

Shiing-Shen Chern was born on 26 October 1911 in Jia Xin, Chekiang Province, in China. His father practised law and worked for the government. At Fu Luen Middle School in Tsientsin he first showed his mathematical ability by doing all the exercises in classical English textbooks on algebra and trigonometry, and then went at the age of 15 years to Nankai University—a one-man department run by Li-Fu Chiang, a student of Julian Coolidge. As a result he studied a great deal of geometry, reading Coolidge, George Salmon FRS, Guido Castelnuovo and Otto Staude. He then became a postgraduate in 1930 at Tsinghua University in Beijing (or Peiping as it was then called) and came under the influence of Dan Sun, one of the few mathematicians in China writing research papers. During this period he became seriously interested in Sun's subject, projective differential geometry, and studied in detail the works of Wilhelm Blaschke.

This memoir is based on an obituary that appeared in *Bull. Lond. Math. Soc.* **38**(3), 507–519 (2006).

It was also at Tsinghua that he met his wife, Shih-Ning, the daughter of a professor. After Blaschke paid a visit to Tsinghua in 1932 and lectured on differential-geometric invariants, Chern won a fellowship to study with him in Hamburg for two years. In 1936 he received his DSc there for work on the theory of webs. While in Hamburg he also attended the lectures of Erich Kähler on what is now called Cartan–Kähler theory, and he spent the following year in Paris studying with Elie Cartan ForMemRS himself.

The year in Paris was formative, because his interaction with Cartan introduced Chern to notions that are now standard in differential geometry but which few people understood then. As he later remarked: 'Without the notation and terminology of fibre bundles, it was difficult to explain these concepts in a satisfactory way', but clearly Chern absorbed Cartan's methods, as his papers of the time show. Cartan lectured on exterior differential systems, and Chern visited him at his home every other week for discussions. The Julia seminar that year was also devoted to Cartan's work, and Chern there met André Weil ForMemRS and other young French mathematicians.

In the summer of 1937 he crossed the Atlantic, the USA and the Pacific to take up the position of professor at Tsinghua, only to be faced with the outbreak of the Sino-Japanese war. His university had moved, together with the universities of Peking and Nankai, to Kunming. There, despite the deprivations of war and the lack of communication with the outside world, he found the time to pore over Cartan's work and form his own vision of where geometry should be going. He also taught many students who later made substantial contributions in mathematics and physics—one such was Chen Ning Yang ForMemRS of Yang–Mills fame. He was already known internationally when in 1943 he was able, via a chain of military flights through India, Africa, Brazil and Central America, to make his way to the Institute for Advanced Study in Princeton.

PRINCETON

In Princeton, Hermann Weyl ForMemRS and Oscar Veblen were well aware of his papers. It was a quiet place at the time because of the absences due to war work, but he made contact with Claude Chevalley and Solomon Lefschetz ForMemRS and also with Weil in nearby Lehigh University. They had a common background in having studied Cartan and Kähler and, in Weil's words (Weil 1992, p. 74):

> we seemed to share a common attitude towards such subjects, or towards mathematics in general; we were both striving to strike at the root of each question while freeing our minds from preconceived notions about what others might have regarded as the right or the wrong way of dealing with it.

Discussions with Weil revealed the properties of characteristic classes, all expressed in terms of sphere bundles, because vector bundles were as yet unheard of. Weil explained to Chern the Todd–Eger classes, derived in the spirit of Italian geometry. These discussions provided the foundation of Chern's most famous work on characteristic classes, and at the time they emerged in his new intrinsic proof (6)* of the general Gauss–Bonnet theorem—by his own account, one of his favourite theorems (Jackson 1998).

---

* Numbers in this form refer to the bibliography at the end of the text.

CHINA AND CHICAGO

When the war ended in 1945, Chern began his return to China but only reached Shanghai in March 1946. There he was given the task of setting up an Institute of Mathematics as part of the Academia Sinica. He did this very successfully, nurturing several outstanding mathematicians, but Nanjing, where the institute was located, was getting more and more dangerous in the turmoil of the civil war. Weil, now in Chicago, and Veblen and Weyl in Princeton, were becoming concerned about his fate, and both Chicago and the Institute offered him visiting positions, and then a full professorship at Chicago. So in 1949 he returned to the USA, this time with his family, to spend most of his working life there.

Chern's work in Nanjing and Chicago became quite topological, there being several papers on the topology of fibre bundles, some with E. H. Spanier, as well as differential geometric applications. His talk at the 1950 International Congress (13) shows how far the interaction of differential geometry and topology had come by this time. This is a thoroughly modern statement, a million miles from the work of 15 years earlier. Chern's students in Chicago included K. Nomizu, L. Auslander and J. Wolf.

BERKELEY

In 1960 Chern took up a professorship in Berkeley—an expanding department and a milder climate made the move attractive. He immediately started a differential geometry seminar (which of course continues to this day), and he attracted visitors both young and old. P. A. Griffiths started his collaborations as a graduate student 'sent to learn from Chern', as did J. Simons, M. do Carmo and many others. His own PhD students included S.-T. Yau, A. Weinstein, P. Li and J. Millson.

Chern was known for being open and welcoming to visitors and students alike. His diplomatic, statesmanlike demeanour was a valuable commodity in the department and he was often encouraged to accompany the Chairman in his dealings with the administration to smooth the path to an agreement. He made a particular impression on a young undergraduate, Robert Uomini, who was inspired by Chern's lectures and, although uncertain about his future, was encouraged by Chern to pursue a PhD in mathematics, which he gained in 1976. Twenty years later he won US$22 million in the state lottery and endowed a visiting professorship in Chern's name, in gratitude.

Although approaching retirement, in 1978 Chern, together with I. M. Singer and C. Moore, prepared a response to the National Science Foundation's request for proposals for a Mathematical Institute to reflect the 'need for continued stimulation of mathematical research' in an environment that regarded American mathematics to be in a 'golden age'. There was considerable opposition to this in the mathematical community, fearing that funding would be taken away from individual investigators and that Berkeley would have an unfair advantage over other departments. But Chern and his colleagues, drawing on his experience with the Academia Sinica and the Institute for Advanced Study, won the argument and approval came in 1981. Chern became the first Director of MSRI, as the Mathematical Sciences Research Institute became known. It was of course a huge success, but Chern continuously supported it in many ways, not least from the proceeds of his 2004 Shaw prize. A recent building at MSRI is naturally named Chern Hall, and a statue was erected in 2011 on the occasion of a conference celebrating the centenary of his birth.

CHINA

Chern's interest in Chinese mathematicians continued throughout his years in the USA. He had an aim: 'Chinese mathematics must be on the same level as its Western counterpart, though not necessarily bending its efforts in the same direction.' During the 1980s he initiated three developments in China: an International Conference on Differential Geometry and Differential Equations, the Summer Education Centre for Postgraduates in Mathematics, and the Chern Programme, aimed at organizing Chinese postgraduates in mathematics for further study in the USA. In 1984 he was invited by China's Ministry of Education to return to his alma mater, Nankai University, to create the Nankai Research Institute of Mathematics. A residence, 'The Serene Garden', was built by the university for Chern, and he and his wife lived there every time they returned to China. While he was the Director, he invited many overseas mathematicians to visit and donated more than 10000 books to the institute, and his $50000 Wolf Prize to Nankai University.

In 1999 he finally returned to China permanently and the MSRI held a farewell party for him, at which Chern said:

> The study of mathematics should be an undertaking of youngsters. There's nobody else my age that's still working on frontier research in mathematics around the world. I have a simple belief: it's that I still want to do something for the development of mathematics during the remainder of my life.

In fact he did continue to do mathematics, and just before his death was grappling with an old problem about the existence or otherwise of a complex structure on the 6-sphere, but perhaps the best testament to his achievement in his final years was sitting next to President Jiang Zemin in the Great Hall of the People, at the opening of the 2002 International Congress of Mathematicians.

Chern received many awards for his work, including the US National Medal of Science in 1975, the Wolf Prize in Mathematics in 1983 and the Shaw Prize in 2004.

Shiing-Shen Chern died in Tianjin, China, on 3 December 2004, aged 93 years. His wife of 61 years, Shih-Ning, had died four years earlier. He is survived by a son, Paul, and a daughter, May Chu.

MATHEMATICAL WORK

Characteristic classes

Chern's proof of the general Gauss–Bonnet theorem (6) was a pivotal event in the history of differential geometry, not just for the theorem itself but for what it led to—in particular the Chern classes. The classical theorem of the same name for a closed surface in Euclidean space states that the integral of the Gaussian curvature is 2π times the Euler characteristic. This link between curvature and topology has several features: one is Gauss's *theorema eregium*, which says that the Gauss curvature, although ostensibly defined by the second fundamental form which measures the way in which the surface sits in Euclidean space, is in fact intrinsic and determined by the first fundamental form, or metric, and its derivatives. So, clearly, whatever its integral is depends only on the intrinsic geometry. However, there is a very natural and useful extrinsic interpretation of this integral as the degree of the Gauss map: the unit normal to the surface at each point defines a map to the 2-sphere, and its topological degree is the invariant. The problem was to extend this result to (even-dimensional) manifolds in higher dimension. Hopf (1926) had generalized the Gauss map approach to hypersurfaces in n-dimensional space, but to put the intrinsic problem in context one should recall that even the definition of a manifold was only formulated correctly by Hassler Whitney (Whitney 1936), and even in 1946 Cartan considered that 'the general notion of manifold is quite difficult to define with precision' (Cartan 1946, p. 56). Basic properties such as embedding in Euclidean space, or the existence of triangulations, had not been established. Allendoerfer (1940) and Allendoerfer & Weil (1943) had given a proof for manifolds embedded in Euclidean space with higher codimension: this used Weyl's formula for the volume of tubes: in modern language this can be interpreted as a generalization of the Gauss map from the unit normal bundle to a sphere. It was still an extrinsic proof, but the integrand was recognized to be intrinsic.

Chern's proof was entirely intrinsic—he used the unit tangent sphere bundle of the manifold and identified a natural differential form α on it. Its exterior derivative dα has a number of terms, one of which is the correct curvature integrand on the manifold itself. He then applies Hopf's theorem relating the index of a vector field to the Euler characteristic—the vector field in modern language gives a section of the sphere bundle outside the singular points, and Chern shows that the extra terms in dα do not contribute in the integral.

The novel content came from studying the intrinsic tangent sphere bundle, and from using the exterior differential calculus that Chern had learned at the hands of Cartan. It provided a link between topology and differential geometry at a time when the very basics of the topology of manifolds were being laid down. In fact, he wrote several papers on the geometry and topology of fibre bundles (8–12), at the same time and often independently of topologists such as N. Steenrod, but he was always interested in geometrical interpretations. Given the focus over the past 30 years in four-dimensional Riemannian geometry it is interesting to see Chern introducing 'a new topological invariant' for four-manifolds (7), without knowing that it is the signature and, later (14), discussing the formula relating this invariant and the Euler characteristic in what is now called the self-dual case.

The successful attack on the Gauss–Bonnet theorem led him to study the other invariants of sphere bundles, to see whether curvature could represent them. He started with Stiefel–Whitney classes but their mod 2 property 'seemed to be a mystery' (Weil 1992), and Pontryagin classes were not known then, so he moved into Hermitian geometry and discovered the famous Chern classes (8), whose importance in algebraic geometry, topology and index theory cannot be overestimated.

Chern consistently wrote about connections and curvature, absorbing the Weil approach through invariant polynomials on the Lie algebra to generalize to principal bundles, and once vector bundles had replaced sphere bundles he gave perhaps the cleanest description of covariant derivatives and characteristic classes, at the same time as solving problems in higher dimensional complex geometry (21).

Throughout his work on characteristic classes and curvature, Chern was always concerned with the geometry of forms living on fibre bundles. Perhaps this came from the recognition that his early work with Cartan was really concerned with this, although the language had not been available then. In any event he recognized that there was more than just the topological characteristic class to be obtained, and this emerged in a strong form in his work on Chern–Simons invariants with J. Simons. Nowadays the Chern–Simons functional is an everyday tool for theoretical physicists. Simons himself was initially interested in a combinatorial formula for the signature of a four-dimensional manifold, and a particular differential form appeared in a natural way in attempting to do this. Chern enthusiastically seized on the idea of generalizing it using invariant polynomials on Lie algebras and elevating its status beyond its original motivation.

Geometrical structures, connections and differential equations

Chern's early work was influenced by Blaschke and Cartan, and involved the consideration of differential geometries more general than Riemannian geometry, often associated with distinguished families of submanifolds. Some of this was motivated by attempts to extend general relativity, for example Weyl geometry and path geometry. The latter considers a manifold that has a distinguished family of curves on it which behave qualitatively like geodesics: given a point and a direction there is a unique curve of the family passing through the point and tangent to the direction. Veblen and his school in Princeton had worked on this, and it was through this work that they probably first heard of Chern. There is a close relation with projective structures, and there are curvature-type local invariants. Cartan studied the differential equation $y'' = F(x, y, y')$, where F is a polynomial in y' of degree three, by these methods, using a natural projective connection over a two-dimensional space, but the general case, and a higher-order equation studied by Chern (1, 2), involved a connection over a fibre bundle. Chern's papers follow Cartan very closely, with the then terminology of 'infinitesimal displacement of elements', which makes the subject difficult to understand nowadays.

Families of submanifolds of higher dimension were considered and particularly 'webs', which was Blaschke's subject when he originally visited China. In modern language a web is a family of foliations in general position, but there are again local diffeomorphism invariants of curvature type. Later in his career, Chern collaborated with Griffiths (23–25) on a web-related problem in algebraic geometry—an algebraic curve of degree d in projective n-space meets a generic hyperplane in d points. By duality this gives a d-web of hyperplanes in the dual space.

Curvature invariants in another aspect of holomorphic geometry came up in his work with J. Moser (22) on the geometry of real hypersurfaces of complex n-dimensional space, picking up on a problem once considered by Cartan.

These higher-order connections are only gradually being understood nowadays, but they were undoubtedly formative in Chern's mathematical development, in particular in formalizing geometrical objects as connections on intrinsically defined bundles far more general than the tangent bundle.

The study of these connections, especially when formulated in the language of exterior differential systems, leads continuously into the Cartan–Kähler theory, and Chern wrote several papers on this (30, 32, 33). When, in the mid 1970s, soliton equations such as the Korteweg–de Vries (KdV) equation, together with its Bäcklund transformations, began to be studied in this way he was well prepared to apply these methods (26, 27, 29, 31). His knowledge of classical differential geometry, not unexpectedly, also enabled him to recognize the geometrical origins of the sinh–Gordon equation (28).

Euclidean geometry

The classical differential geometry of surfaces in Euclidean space still carries unsolved problems, and most differential geometers are attracted to some aspect of this; Chern was no exception. His main interest was in global properties, and in particular the use of holomorphic methods. It is well known that any metric in two dimensions can, by choosing isothermal coordinates (x, y), be written in the form $h(dx^2 + dy^2)$, and then the complex parameter $z = x + iy$ gives a surface in Euclidean space the structure of a Riemann surface. The proof of this, with appropriate regularity conditions, was somewhat obscure until Chern gave an elementary proof using the Cauchy kernel (15, 16) and then put the method to use in globally characterizing the sphere among surfaces where there is a functional relationship between the mean curvature and the Gaussian curvature (17).

The holomorphic aspect came to the fore also in his proof (20) that the Gauss map of a minimal surface in n dimensions (which goes into the Grassmannian $G(2, n)$, a complex manifold) is antiholomorphic. Using this, he generalized to higher dimensions the Bernstein theorem, which says that a globally defined minimal graph $z = f(x, y)$ must be a plane.

Another Euclidean area of research linking curvature and topology is the generalization by Chern and Lashof (18, 19) of Fenchel's theorem (Fenchel 1929) that the integral of the curvature of a closed curve is at least 2π. They use the same Gauss map as Allendoerfer and Weil for a manifold in Euclidean space and pull back the *absolute value* of the volume form. In this case they obtain a lower bound for the integral in terms of the sum of the Betti numbers and discuss the cases where equality holds. This generated a whole area of study of *taut* and *tight* submanifolds.

Other contributions

In a life as long and full as Chern's, there are many more highly significant contributions—on holomorphic mappings, minimal submanifolds, G-structures and Hodge theory. He also returned to some favourite themes over the decades. One was Blaschke's use of integral geometry and generalizations of the attractive Crofton's (M. Crofton FRS) formula, which measures the length of a curve by the average number of intersections with a line (3–5).

Another was the subject of Finsler metrics. In a retrospective millennial paper 'Back to Riemann' (35), he pointed out: 'In 1948 I published a paper solving the problem of equivalence of Finsler manifolds … the paper was summarized in Rund's book and has been otherwise completely ignored.' Riemann had originally suggested an arbitrary norm on the tangent space but decided to consider only one coming from an inner product because the calculations were simpler. Chern's exposure to other types of geometries and connections other than the Levi-Civita connection (T. Levi-Civita ForMemRS) led to several papers exploring this geometrical structure, and, together with Bao and Shen, to the book *An introduction to Riemann–Finsler geometry* (34). There is indeed a certain resurgence in the area, and it demonstrates once again the breadth of Chern's view of geometry, and his ability to isolate new and interesting developments.

ACKNOWLEDGEMENT

The frontispiece photograph was taken at Professor Chern's signing of the Charter Book on his admission to the Royal Society on 9 September 1985. (Online version in colour.)

REFERENCES TO OTHER AUTHORS

Allendoerfer, C. B. 1940 The Euler number of a Riemann manifold. *Am. J. Math.* **62**, 243–248.

Allendoerfer, C. B. & Weil, A. 1943 The Gauss–Bonnet theorem for Riemannian polyhedra. *Trans. Am. Math. Soc.* **53**, 101–129.

Cartan, E. 1946 *Leçons sur la géométrie des espaces de Riemann*, 2nd edn. Paris: Gauthier-Villars.

Fenchel, W. 1929 Über Krümmung und Windung geschlossener Raumkurven. *Math. Annln* **101**, 238-252.

Hopf, H. 1926 Über die Curvatura integra geschlossener Hyperflächen. *Math. Ann.* **95**, 340–367.

Jackson, A. 1998 Interview with Shiing Shen Chern. *Not. Am. Math. Soc.* **45**, 860–865.

Weil, A. 1992 S. S. Chern as geometer and friend. In *Chern—a great geometer of the 20th century* (ed. S.-T. Yau), pp. 72–78. Hong Kong: International Press.

Whitney, H. 1936 Differentiable manifolds. *Ann. Math.* **37**, 645-680.

BIBLIOGRAPHY

The following publications are those referred to directly in the text. A full bibliography is available as electronic supplementary material at http://dx.doi.org/10.1098/rsbm.2014.0018 or via http://rsbm.royalsocietypublishing.org.

(1)   1937   Sur la géomètrie d'une equation différentielle du troisième ordre. *C. R. Acad. Sci. Paris* **204**, 1227–1229.

(2)   1940   The geometry of the differential equation $y''' = F(x, y, y', y'')$. *Sci. Rep. Nat. Tsing Hua Univ.* **4**, 97–111.

(3)   Sur une généralisation d'une formule de Crofton. *C. R. Acad. Sci. Paris* **210**, 757–758.

(4)   Generalization of a formula of Crofton. *Wuhan Univ. J. Sci.* **7**, 1–16.

(5)   1942   On integral geometry in Klein spaces. *Ann. Math.* **43**, 178–189.

(6)   1944   A simple intrinsic proof of the Gauss–Bonnet formula for closed Riemannian manifolds. *Ann. Math.* **45**, 747–752.

(7)   1945   On Riemannian manifolds of four dimensions. *Bull. Am. Math. Soc.* **51**, 964-971.

(8)   1946   Characteristic classes of Hermitian manifolds. *Ann. Math.* **47**, 85–121.

(9)   1948   On the multiplication in the characteristic ring of a sphere bundle. *Ann. Math.* **49**, 362–372.

(10) 1949   (With Y.-F. Sun) The imbedding theorem for fibre bundles. *Trans. Am. Math. Soc.* **67**, 286–303.

(11)   (With S.-T. Hu) Parallelisability of principal fibre bundles. *Trans. Am. Math. Soc.* **67**, 304–309.

(12) 1950   (With E. H. Spanier) The homology structure of sphere bundles. *Proc. Natl Acad. Sci. USA* **36**, 248–255.

(13) 1952   Differential geometry of fiber bundles. In *Proceedings of the International Congress of Mathematicians, Cambridge, Massachusetts, 30 August—6 September 1950* (ed. L. M. Graves, P. A. Smith, E. Hille & O. Zariski), vol. 2, pp. 397–411. Providence, RI: American Mathematical Society.

(14) 1953   Relations between Riemannian and Hermitian geometries. *Duke Math. J.* **20**, 575–587.

(15) 1954   (With P. Hartman & A. Wintner) On isothermic coordinates. *Comment. Math. Helv.* **28**, 301–309.

(16) 1955   An elementary proof of the existence of isothermal parameters on a surface. *Proc. Am. Math. Soc.* **6**, 771–782.

(17)   On special *W*-surfaces. *Proc. Am. Math. Soc.* **6**, 783–786.

(18) 1957   (With R. Lashof) On the total curvature of immersed manifolds. *Am. J. Math.* **79**, 306–318.

(19) 1958   (With R. Lashof) On the total curvature of immersed manifolds. II. *Michigan Math. J.* **5**, 5–12.

(20) 1965   Minimal surfaces in an Euclidean space of *N* dimensions. In *Differential and combinatorial topology (a symposium in honor of Marston Morse)* (ed. S. S. Cairns), pp. 187–198. Princeton University Press.

(21)   (With R. Bott) Hermitian vector bundles and the equidistribution of the zeroes of their holomorphic sections. *Acta Math.* **114**, 71–112.

(22) 1974 (With J. K. Moser) Real hypersurfaces in complex manifolds. *Acta Math.* **133**, 219–271. (Erratum: *Acta Math.* **150**, 297 (1983).)

(23) 1978 (With P. A. Griffiths) Abel's theorem and webs. *Jber. Dt. Math.-Verein.* **80**, 13–110. (Corrections and addenda: *Jber. Dt. Math.-Verein.* **83**, 78–83 (1981).)

(24)   (With P. A. Griffiths) An inequality for the rank of a web and webs of maximum rank. *Annli Scuola Norm. Sup. Pisa Cl. Sci.* **5**, 539–557.

(25)   (With P. A. Griffiths) Linearization of webs of codimension one and maximum rank. In *Proceedings of the International Symposium on Algebraic Geometry, Kyoto University, Kyoto, 1977* (ed. Masayoshi Nagata), pp. 85–91. Tokyo: Kinokuniya Book Store.

(26) 1979 (With C. K. Peng) Lie groups and KdV equations. *Manuscr. Math.* **28**, 207–217.

(27) 1980 (With C. L. Terng) An analogue of Bäcklund's theorem in affine geometry. *Rocky Mountain J. Math.* **10**, 105–124.

(28) 1981 Geometrical interpretation of the sinh-Gordon equation. *Annls Polon. Math.* **39**, 63–69.

(29)   (With C. K. Peng) On the Bäcklund transformations of KdV equations and modified KdV equations. *J. China Univ. Sci. Tech.* **11**, 1–6.

(30) 1982 (With R. Bryant & P. A. Griffiths) Exterior differential systems. In *Proceedings of the 1980 Beijing Symposium on Differential Geometry and Differential Equations, Beijing, 1980* (ed. S.-S. Chern & W.-T. Wu), pp. 219–338. Beijing: Science Press.

(31) 1986 (With K. Tenenblat) Pseudospherical surfaces and evolution equations. *Stud. Appl. Math.* **74**, 55–83.

(32)   (With P. A. Griffiths) Pffafian systems in involution. In *Proceedings of the 1982 Changchun Symposium on Differential Geometry and Differential Equations* (ed. S.-S. Chern, R.-H. Wang & M.-Y. Chi), pp. 233–256. Beijing: Science Press.

(33) 1991 (With R. L. Bryant, R. B. Gardner, H. L. Goldschmidt & P. A. Griffiths) *Exterior differential systems* (Mathematical Sciences Research Institute Publications, no. 18). New York: Springer-Verlag.

(34) 2000 (With D. Bao & Z. Shen) *An introduction to Riemann–Finsler geometry* (Graduate Texts in Mathematics, no. 200). New York: Springer-Verlag.

(35)   Back to Riemann. In *Mathematics: frontiers and perspectives* (ed. V. Arnold, M. Atiyah, P. Lax & B. Mazur), pp. 33–34. Providence, RI: American Mathematical Society.

JOHN FREDERICK CLARKE

1 May 1927 — 11 June 2013

John F. Clarke

JOHN FREDERICK CLARKE

1 May 1927 — 11 June 2013

Elected FRS 1987

By K. N. C. Bray[1] FRS and N. Riley[2]

[1] 23 De Freville Avenue, Cambridge CB4 1HW, UK
[2] School of Mathematics, University of East Anglia, Norwich NR4 7TJ, UK

Flying, and an enthusiasm for aviation, motivated John Clarke's early career choices: he flew Fairey Fireflys in the Fleet Air Arm, worked in the Gas Turbine Division of Armstrong Siddeley Motors, and studied aeronautical engineering at Queen Mary College, where he graduated with first-class honours. He stayed on there to do a PhD, and then worked at English Electric, before moving to Cranfield in 1958. John Clarke's many important publications, mainly in the general area of chemically reacting flows, cover a wide range of topics including flames, ignition processes, shock waves and detonations, the dynamics and physics of burning gases and internal ballistics, to name but a few. In all of his contributions to his subject it is perhaps too easy to overlook the individual. He had a delightful sense of humour, wore his distinctions lightly and was a most generous and friendly man.

EARLY YEARS

John Clarke, one of the UK's most distinguished combustion scientists of the twentieth century, was born and brought up in Warwickshire. His father, Frederick, was also a Warwickshire man, born in 1886. He was apprenticed to the Alfred Herbert Machine Tool Company and, during World War I, served as an Armourer Staff Sergeant in France. Subsequently he had a variety of posts in the Midlands motor and motorcycle industry. For some time he and his brother-in-law ran their own company building bicycles and motorcycles. The engines for the latter were sourced from another manufacturer; they proved to be unreliable and the company failed in the late 1920s. Subsequently he became Works Engineer at the Brice Piston Ring Co. in Warwick.

John's mother, Clara (*née* Nauen), was of German origin, born in Krefeld in 1888. She and her two sisters were educated, in their early teens, at a convent school in The

Netherlands. Her family came to England when she was 18 years old so that her father could establish a dye works in Bridgenorth, Shropshire. The family moved to Coventry before World War I, and she was working as a secretary there when she met John's father. They were married in 1924.

Because his mother had been brought up in the Roman Catholic faith (his father was indifferent to religion), John's first two schools were Roman Catholic primary schools first in Coventry and then Warwick, to where the family had moved. These schools proved to be unsatisfactory and he was quickly removed to a County Council Elementary School in Westgate, a district of Warwick close to home. From there he won a scholarship to Warwick School, where he went as a day boy for the remainder of his school days. He enjoyed most academic subjects and sports. In the School Certificate (the forerunner of GCSEs) he attained the highest award in art. In subsequent years he often wondered why no one had ever suggested that a career in art was worth considering. Many can attest that in later years he was indeed an accomplished artist. His subjects for the Higher School Certificate (today's A-level), taken in 1944, were physics, chemistry and mathematics. Two teachers who influenced him greatly at school were K. Wardle (mathematics) and F. A. Fisher (physics). It was the latter who prevented sixth-form scientists from becoming 'illiterate mechanics' via lessons in music, English literature and English language.

FLEET AIR ARM, 1945–49

With a boyhood interest in aeroplanes, John was a member of the newly formed Air Training Corps while at Warwick School, gaining the highest rank of Flight Sergeant. This rank guaranteed entry to nearby Royal Air Force (RAF) airfields with the attendant possibility of gaining a flight in, for example, an Airspeed Oxford or Vickers Wellington. This served to convince him that a career in flying was to be pursued. However, the war in Europe had ended before he was able to enlist, and the RAF was no longer recruiting. But the Royal Navy was, and so he joined the Fleet Air Arm. Initial training as a Navy pilot was on de Havilland Tiger Moths and subsequently the so-called North American Harvard. He gained his 'wings' in 1948. During this initial period he joined the Royal Aeronautical Society as a student member, and sat and passed examinations held by it, enabling him to become a graduate of that institution.

After this initial period of training, actually with the RAF, he was transferred to the then Naval Air Station at Lossiemouth, where training for some was on Seafires; for others, including John, it was on Fairey Fireflys (see figure 1). During this time he realized that his reactions were not quick enough for carrier-borne landings, and he opted to leave the Service; it was his choice. To leave the Navy was a rather protracted business and he spent some time at home on paid leave before working for a few months at the Armstrong Siddeley Motors Gas Turbine Division in Coventry. During this period he continued to fly Tiger Moths with the Coventry Aero Club, on more than one occasion with Eric Franklin, Armstrong Whitworth's chief test pilot, doing blind take-offs and landings. One highlight he recalls was a promise to local cricket-playing friends to carry out a brief display of aerobatics over their game. A loop and barrel-roll were accomplished, but unfortunately, as it transpired, over the wrong cricket match!

During this latter period a return to academic training was becoming increasingly attractive with, unsurprisingly, aeronautical engineering a prominent feature, and he was accepted

Figure 1. John with the Fairey Firefly at Lossiemouth.

for a first-degree course in Aeronautical Engineering at Queen Mary College, University of London, to begin in October 1949.

QUEEN MARY COLLEGE, 1949–55

John always claimed that it was this first-degree course that taught him what the word 'aerodynamics' actually meant. Students on the course at that time considered themselves fortunate in the sense that apart from some lectures that were common to all engineers in the first year, the specialist topics were taught to groups of no more than half a dozen. The lectures on aerodynamics itself were given by N. A. V. Piercy and L. G. Whitehead; other courses included topics such as stresses in solid materials, structures, theory of machines, and thermodynamics. All were given by the lecturers concerned in a manner that made the material easy and even exciting. In his final examinations John was awarded a degree with first-class honours, and the David Allan Low Prize for engineering.

These three years as an undergraduate proved to be life-changing in more ways than one. For a time he lived in student accommodation on Cheyne Walk in Chelsea. Through a mutual friend he met Jean Gentle (see figure 2), a trainee nurse in the Nightingale School at St Thomas's Hospital, which had a nurse's home close to Cheyne Walk. She would eventually become his wife.

After John gained his first degree, the question of what to do next had to be addressed. Piercy was keen on the idea of a PhD, as was John. There were those who, for various reasons,

Figure 2. Jean in 1951.

counselled against such an indulgence. However, John's intentions won the day and he started life as a postgraduate student, along with Colin Plane, who had been a fellow undergraduate, in October 1952. His maintenance grant from the Department of Scientific and Industrial Research amounted to £300 a year. Jean, by now a qualified nurse, gave up nursing for a more lucrative job as a Hoover washing machine demonstrator. John and Jean were married in December 1953.

At that time the Aeronautical Engineering Department was shortly to commission a small intermittent-operation wind tunnel designed to run at speeds of up to Mach 2. Piercy was anxious for experimental work on unsteady high-speed flow to be conducted in this facility, and he allocated to Colin Plane 'wings', and to John Clarke 'bodies'. It was usual by that time to mount models consisting of a conical nose attached to a cylindrical body on a forward-facing 'sting' that penetrated the hollow cylinder and was fixed to it close to the conical nose and carried strain gauges that responded to the forces and moments generated by the airflow over the body. For unsteady flow it was first necessary to modify the system so that an electric motor, via suitable linkages, could make the model pitch about any chosen axis on its centreline. Measurement of forces and moments were again to be made by strain-gauge bridges, but now supplied with alternating current of a frequency exactly equal to the frequency of the model's motion. The complete assembly of the model, and associated measurement facilities, was quite complicated but worked well in practice. Sadly, Piercy died, in post, early in 1953 and did not see the results of this investigation. His students temporarily became the responsibility of Whitehead until Alec Young (FRS 1973) took up his professorial appointment in 1954. Theoretical work complemented the experiments in the derivation of a second-order approximate theory of the compressible flow past oscillating bodies. Engineering students did not receive much in the way of mathematics teaching in those days; this work represents the first phase of John's becoming a self-taught mathematician of considerable ability. His thesis entitled 'An investigation of the forces on a body of revolution in non-steady motion at moderate Mach numbers' was submitted in 1957. An account of the experimental work was subsequently published by the Aeronautical Research Council (3)*.

ENGLISH ELECTRIC COMPANY, 1955–57

After his period as a research student, John secured offers of employment from the Royal Aircraft Establishment at Farnborough and the English Electric Company's Guided Weapons Division at Luton. He opted for a position in the aerodynamics section of the latter. At that time the emphasis was on the ballistic missile re-entry problem of flow around a hypersonic vehicle. The combined effects of mass, momentum and energy transfer in the context of chemically active, multi-species, mixtures of gases was something new in vehicle aerodynamics. The structural integrity of the vehicle itself was of concern, because under the intense heat most usable surface materials would either sublime or liquefy. John made a contribution to the understanding of how quickly surface liquid would blow away. But it was perhaps his work on dissociating gases (1) that foreshadowed what would later become the main thrust of his subsequent research. However, in 1957 a government White Paper predicted (incorrectly) the demise of the military aeroplane, and its replacement by guided missiles. This led to redundancy for several members of the aircraft aerodynamics group at the end of the year. As it happens, John's attention had been drawn to a vacant lectureship at the College of Aeronautics, Cranfield, for which he applied successfully.

CRANFIELD, 1958–91

In January 1958 John left the English Electric Guided Weapons Division to take up the lectureship in the Aerodynamics Department at the College of Aeronautics. The family, augmented during the previous two years by daughters Jenny and Julie, moved to rented accommodation on the campus. They moved to their own home in a neighbouring village a decade or so later. From the outset, as a teacher at this level, John maintained that the material taught should be informed by research. His research, now determined by personal choice, ranged widely, often returning to earlier topics. As a consequence we have chosen to discuss his work thematically, rather than strictly chronologically.

Shock waves

It was well known that, in a high-speed flow, convective steepening of a pressure wave is resisted by the naturally occurring dissipative phenomena associated with heat conduction and viscous actions, which results in the very thin waves of compression known as shock waves. Any chemical reactions in the gas also have the capacity to create irreversible increases in local entropy. At the time it was natural to ask whether reaction-resisted shock waves can

---

* Numbers in this form refer to the bibliography at the end of the text.

exist in the absence of any other dissipative phenomena. The answer was positive for a pure dissociating diatomic gas such as oxygen or nitrogen (6). The character of the velocity and chemical composition profiles through a typical weak shock wave were determined.

The academic year 1961–62 was spent as a Fulbright Scholar at Stanford University hosted by Walter Vincenti. At that time Vincenti and his students were producing a series of papers on the interactions between acoustic waves and thermal radiation in the atmosphere through which they propagated. In view of John's previous work (6) it was natural to investigate the interactions between shock waves and radiation. A consequence was a paper (7) in which it was shown that radiation-resisted shock waves could exist, in the absence of any other dissipative mechanisms. The structure of such shock waves is determined solely from the competing effects of energy transfer by radiation and convective steepening. The work on 'real gas effects' represented by his previous papers (1, 6) and the flow of chemically reacting gases (2) led to a collaboration with Malcolm McChesney and the publication of the first edition of their book on this topic (10) (a revised version was subsequently published (30)).

Although at this time the influence of dissipative phenomena on shock formation was well understood, the influences of energy transfers to and from the internal structures of molecules, so-called 'relaxation' processes, were less well understood. M. J. (later Sir James) Lighthill FRS demonstrated that there were two basic classes of such shock waves (Lighthill 1956). The first were very weak fully dispersed shocks in which the whole structure is supplied by a relaxing process competing with nonlinear wave steepening. The second, partly dispersed waves, have a conventional discontinuous shock at their head, followed by a zone in which relaxation plays a major part. Together with Rodgers, a master's degree student, John analysed the structure of plane steady shock waves in a gas with several internal energy modes (11), which relax in parallel, in the absence of transport effects and chemical reactions, so that the number of relaxing modes remains constant. Both fully and partly dispersed waves were treated. It was shown, in particular, that internal-mode energy contents may overshoot their local equilibrium values.

During the 1960s there was considerable interest in the use of shock tubes to determine the thermal conductivity of hot gases and gas mixtures. One experimental design to provide the necessary information was the use of shock waves reflected from the closed end of a simple shock tube. The transient heat-transfer process in the tube could be analysed theoretically to extract appropriate information. John analysed such reflections from a heat-conducting wall (13). The technique employed was an early use of matched asymptotic expansions popularized by Van Dyke (1964). In this way he was able to incorporate the displacement effects that arise from the existence of a thermal boundary layer on the end wall of the tube and, in addition, the so-called 'accommodation effects' in the restoration of new states of equilibrium in the gas. Satisfactory agreement with the published experimental results of Sturtevant & Slachmuylders (1964) was obtained. Subsequently, with John Busing (14), experimental work on this configuration was taken further at Cranfield. In this work, among others, measured values of accommodation coefficients for air molecules on thin platinum films were lower than expected. A successful modification to take account of heat transfer into a platinum film of finite thickness was performed by Ron Hanson (Hanson 1971), a visiting postdoctoral researcher from Stanford.

Shock wave reflections were pursued some years later; in this case the configuration was that of a plane shock wave impinging on a plane boundary, obliquely at a prescribed angle of incidence. For a solid surface, regular reflection takes place; however, interest was now focusing on the situation in which the solid surface is covered by a porous medium. The modelling of the influence of the irregular porous structure is crucial. John invoked Darcy's law (44), in which the motion is governed by a balance between the pressure gradient and viscous forces alone. However, this was later augmented by the introduction of a linearized inertia term (50). The principal result is that the reflected wave system in the ambient atmosphere consists of an expansion fan centred at the point of intersection of the incident shock with the porous surface, with a reflected shock developing on the last characteristic of the fan, which gradually acquires a strength equal to that of a regularly reflected wave from a solid surface, thus overwhelming the expansion fan. Furthermore, John showed that there is a one-to-one correspondence, in the limit as the angle of incidence of the impinging shock wave approaches zero, between the two-dimensional steady configuration and the one-dimensional unsteady situation. This limiting case was investigated further (51) as a shock wave travelling in a shock tube reflects from a porous plug.

The foregoing discussion of shock waves has been concerned with their behaviour. Subsequently two papers (47, 48) discussed their initiation by thermal rather than mechanical means. With his collaborators, John considered the behaviour of an inert compressible gas confined between planar, parallel walls in an initial equilibrium state. Heat flux at the wall induces a gas motion arising from thermal expansion. In the first of these papers the timescale of the added energy is larger than the mean time between molecular collisions; but in the second it is on a timescale comparable with the mean time. In the first case, weak shocks eventually develop. However, the latter case is of greater interest: there the thermomechanical response of the gas near the boundary is described by the complete Navier–Stokes equations in a layer with the thickness of a few molecular mean free paths. Numerical solutions show how a spatial pressure variation is generated adjacent to the boundary, which then propagates away as an almost steady shock wave. If heat addition is continued, a high-temperature expanding layer develops in which the pressure remains uniform. This in turn acts like a contact surface in a shock tube. The investigation showed in particular the importance of power as a crucial factor in the determination of shock strength.

Although most of John's work on shock waves, as outlined above, involved propagation through a gaseous medium, a paper with Alec Melvin of the Gas Council (64) introduces the shock wave as a seismic source, for hydrocarbon exploration. The main aim of the paper was to examine the gasdynamic principles of the shock-wave source. It also illustrated the behaviour of compressional and shear waves generated by the source in both sedimentary rock and granite.

Gas dynamics and physics

As we have already seen, the mutual interactions between gas flows and chemical reactions were central to much of John's research work. One application for studies of this kind was provided by the strong interest in very-high-speed flight and hypersonic flows, which began in the 1950s and 1960s. This involved, for example, the problem of an object entering the Earth's atmosphere at a sufficiently high speed to cause significant dissociation of air molecules in the layer between the object and its bow shock wave. The British Aerospace HOTOL (Horizontal take-off and landing) project some 30 years later briefly revisited this question, and John, with co-authors Mughal, Poll, Roe and Stollery, contributed an analysis (59, 60) of the resulting forces and moments on the proposed aircraft.

Vehicles for use at hypersonic speeds invariably have blunt noses, to combat effects of aerodynamic heating, but small-disturbance slender-body analysis is applicable to the flow downstream of the nose, and this enabled John to develop purely analytical solutions to several hypersonic reacting flow problems: a dissociating gas flow (4), relaxation effects (5), an application of a Green's function analysis with Cleaver (8), and a review with Cleaver and Lilley (9). A much later review article (19) provided an extensive overview of the small-disturbance approach to reacting flows, which included discussions of the use of bulk viscosities in models of relaxing and reacting gases, and an examination of energy-transfer problems and diffusion flames. He went on to analyse the wave system attached to a slender body in a supersonic relaxing gas stream (31, 33). The use of heat release to modify external flows was briefly fashionable in the late 1960s, and this led him to analyse the supersonic flow past a wedge with a flame sheet at its apex with Foster (16), and the supersonic flow associated with a conical flame sheet with Petty (24).

Subsequently, in an important series of papers (32, 34, 35, 43), John explored the amplification of propagating disturbances as a result of chemical reactions. He derived a remarkable nonlinear differential equation,

$$\frac{\partial}{\partial t}\left(\frac{\partial^2}{\partial t^2} - \frac{\partial^2}{\partial x^2}\right)T = \left(\gamma\frac{\partial^2}{\partial t^2} - \frac{\partial^2}{\partial x^2}\right)e^T,$$

in which T is a dimensionless temperature variable and γ is the ratio of specific heats for the gas at constant pressure and constant volume. This equation, which has become known as Clarke's equation, captures both adiabatic and isothermal sound speeds and properly describes both constant-volume and constant-pressure explosion phenomena. It has subsequently been widely used by many other researchers.

A related one-dimensional unsteady flow problem, the propagation of a shock wave into a reactive gas mixture, was studied with Cant (52), first in a linearized analysis, and then an essentially nonlinear differential equation was derived and solved numerically. If the shock wave of the earlier analysis is replaced by an initial compression of the gas in a small region (36), creating a planar pulse, a complex sequence of events is initiated and is found to be strongly dependent on the activation energy of the combustion reaction.

John also wrote another very valuable pair of papers (38, 40). The first explored the propagation of disturbances in an initially uniform cold reactive medium subject to a simple Arrhenius form of one-way reaction in a planar, cylindrical or spherical geometry. Nonlinear convective effects arising with wavelets that travel at adiabatic speeds of sound relative to local convection velocities were considered in the second paper, which derives a single governing equation, a modified version of the nonlinear Burgers equation, containing an algebraic term to account for interaction between the propagating wave and the reacting atmosphere. The significance of chemically frozen adiabatic and isothermal sound speeds is illustrated. Waves travelling at chemically frozen adiabatic speeds of sound are associated with local exponential growth of disturbances, and secondary isothermal waves are governed by a diffusion equation with a known negative diffusion coefficient, and so have a finite time to 'blow up'. The analysis envisages a piston at the left-hand side of a computational domain, set impulsively in motion at time zero. To the right of the piston there is a region of hot chemically inert gas that has been created by the passage of the flame through a mixture that has itself been heated by a shock wave driven by the piston–flame combination. The propagation speed of the flame is sensitive to the local temperature. If the chemical reaction becomes too intense, the Burgers equation, which deals with wave propagation in only one direction, breaks down. Numerical analysis is then required. Computations by Wang (57), during a three-month stay at Cranfield after his doctoral studies at Southampton, predict the presence of an ignition event immediately ahead of the flame. This can be an important step in the sequence of events leading to transition from deflagration to detonation.

John also worked extensively on problems of internal ballistics, often in collaboration with Dr E. F. Toro, who had escaped from Pinochet's Chile. A central feature of their cooperation was the development of numerical methods for the solution of the set of partial differential equations for the propellant gases created by the burning of solid propellant material (53–55). The continuation of this line of enquiry led to papers with Caroline Lowe (65, 68, 69), who was initially a PhD student at Cranfield and stayed on there after submitting her thesis. John went on to propose a theoretical model of condensed phase combustion via a Sabelnikov-type reaction process (70), whose solutions were found to include the possibilities of hang-fire and misfire under plausible circumstances.

Flame theory

Diffusion flames

From the mid 1960s John's research on chemical reactions and associated flow problems continued, but with the general direction switched from endothermic or dissociation activities to exothermic, namely combustion, actions. This change was largely at the suggestion of D. Küchemann FRS of the former Royal Aircraft Establishment. His first foray into combustion theory was the area of diffusion flames. The distinguishing feature of a diffusion flame is that the cold reactants are not mixed until they meet and simultaneously react, or burn, within the structure of the flame itself. The fact that mixing relies on interdiffusion of the different chemical reactant species is responsible for the name of the combustion process, which generally lies close to a streamline of any steady-state flow configuration.

In his first investigation (12), two uniform parallel gas streams, oxidant and fuel, interact at the trailing edge of a semi-infinite thin diaphragm. The fuel and oxidant concentrations in these streams were in stoichiometric ratio and the reaction between them was assumed to be one-step and irreversible. Oseen flow (in which convective terms are linearized) was assumed and the Burke–Schumann flame sheet, a planar extension of the diaphragm, was examined.

Inadequacies of this configuration were recognized and, subsequently, the diaphragm separating the fuel and oxidant streams was replaced by a parabolic cylinder with downstream-pointing vertex (15). The one-step reaction was retained, but off-stoichiometric mixtures were allowed. A parabolic cylinder coordinate system was adopted, the advantages of which were apparent when it was shown that the resulting streamwise Burke–Schumann flame sheet, originating at the boundary, is itself a parabola. Treating the flame sheet as an outer solution the method of matched asymptotics was adopted in which the inner solution provided information on the flame structure.

The same technique was also used to discuss the Emmons problem, in which a semi-infinite flat plate is placed parallel to an oxidizing stream (20). Gaseous fuel sublimes or vaporizes from the plate to react with the oxidizer in the assumed boundary layer. John replaced the plate with a parabolic cylinder, vertex pointing upstream, and again adopted the Oseen approximation. The Burke–Schumann flame sheet was again parabolic, and the solution close to the leading edge was more realistic for a nose region than the singular behaviour predicted by boundary-layer theory. Together with one of the present authors (N.R.) the Emmons problem was revisited, but in the absence of a free stream (29). The fuel that evaporates from the surface burns in the oxidizing atmosphere where, again, a flame-sheet model was adopted. The heat generated internally within the boundary layer induces a pressure gradient, and concomitant flow, along the boundary. A simple experiment confirmed the results obtained.

The above investigations are all based on the assumption that the chemical kinetics can be represented by the simple irreversible reaction 'fuel plus oxidant yields product'. To proceed further, with hydrogen as fuel and oxygen as oxidant, a scheme of four reversible chemical reactions was chosen, including the influence of the hydroxyl radical, to represent the kinetics of the hydrogen–oxygen flame (18). The physical problem adopted is again that in which the flowing streams of hydrogen and oxygen are separated by a parabola with a downstream-pointing vertex. The chemical behaviour is dominated by the size of the equilibrium constant for the dissociation–recombination reaction of hydrogen. When the reciprocal of this is small, the flame sheet again emerges as the dominant outer solution uninfluenced, at leading order, by the more complex chemical kinetics. The structure of the diffusion flame, or inner region, depends on the detailed kinetics of the combustion processes that are assumed. These lead (18) to the so-called equilibrium-broadening of the flame sheet. Subsequently (21) the same problem was addressed except that the hydrogen dissociation reaction was assumed to be so slow that it could be neglected. The analysis led to the so-called reaction-broadening of the flame sheet. Later, with his student Moss, there was a return to the equilibrium-broadened flame (22), at large values of the hydrogen dissociation activation energy, to obtain more accurate asymptotic estimates of the flow structure. After these investigations of the hydrogen–oxygen flame there was a collaboration with scientists at the British Gas Research Laboratories on an experimental investigation of the structure of flat diffusion flames on a Parker–Wolfhard burner (26). Measurements of the hydroxyl radical concentrations showed that the flames are reaction-broadened at sufficiently low temperatures but equilibrium-broadened at higher temperatures. In addition, the variations of this radical concentration with maximum flame temperature are strikingly similar to those predicted theoretically.

Attempts to understand more about the experimental results described above are set out in two papers (23, 27). In the first of these, John, with Moss, examined the structure of a spherical diffusion flame. The combustion process was now presumed to be sustained by five reactions and was created by the radial injection of hydrogen through a 'fuel sphere' into a pure oxygen atmosphere. There was now a single, radial, velocity component for which there was no need for approximation. In addition, the several diffusion coefficients were allowed to vary realistically with temperature. Within the diffusion flame the reaction of the hydroxyl radical with a hydrogen atom may produce either an oxygen atom and hydrogen molecule, or a water molecule that acts as a chain-breaking step. In the second paper John looked at the interaction between a reaction-broadened diffusion flame and a planar acoustic wave, orthogonal to the flame itself, with the direction of propagation parallel to the plane of the flame sheet. When the flame temperature is sufficiently low, the acoustic disturbance is amplified and an expansive disturbance can reduce the flame temperature further, leading to extinction.

Somewhat later, with his student Allison, John returned to the hydrogen–oxygen chemical kinetic scheme, but now incorporating six reactions (39). The flame forms downstream of a plane partition, and for the flow a boundary-layer model was chosen in preference to the Oseen approximation, allowing variable diffusion coefficients to be included in the analysis. In addition, unlike the previous analyses, the asymptotic model was based on the large energy-activation limit. The resulting flame is of the near-equilibrium reaction-broadened type.

The investigations of diffusion flames, described above, were all for steady-flow conditions. With a visitor, Gil Stegen, John undertook a study of some unsteady motions of a diffusion flame sheet (17). The flame sheet forms, again, downstream from a plane partition and for the unsteady conditions a boundary-layer model linearized about the free stream velocity was adopted. Several examples are given. To mention one: suppose that at the initial point, where the partition ends, the oxidant and fuel mass fractions are time-dependent. It was found that, downstream, the flame-sheet position at any point is that which it would occupy in a flow whose free-stream composition was that of the instantaneous local value. In a much later unsteady configuration (56), analysed with his student Dold, fuel is released into an unconfined oxidant environment. A single one-step exothermic reaction was taken to occur. A criterion was identified for any diffusion flame to exist after the passage of a deflagration flame.

As we have seen above, it was during the late 1960s that John was developing diffusion-flame-structure theories that resulted in equilibrium-broadened or reaction-broadened flames. In one paper (25), which may be seen as expository, he sets out clearly the conservation equations for the chemical species, revealing the two small parameters that give rise to the singular perturbation problems, and their role in the flame-sheet structure. General results are derived for arbitrary flame geometry and a criterion for the retention in a solution of both parameters is established.

Premixed flames

Interest, in general, was moving from diffusion flames to premixed flames by the mid 1970s. John considered (28) the case of a steady plane flame propagating through a mixture of fuel, oxidant, diluent and product species, which burns according to a one-step reversible reaction. The leading terms of asymptotic series were obtained on the basis of the assumed high activation energy of the burning reaction. Mixture strengths, from fuel-lean to fuel-rich situations, were encompassed. It was also found that acoustic disturbances do not suffer the reaction-induced amplification which is found possible in the presence of a diffusion flame (27).

There followed a series of papers with his student McIntosh. The first (37) gives a detailed account of the case in which the premixed flame is adjacent to a porous plug flameholder as used in the laboratory by, for example, Botha & Spalding (1954). An irreversible one-step reaction was assumed and, again, a theory was developed based on high-activation-energy asymptotics. The flameholder passes fresh reactants into the space to its right, where a flame sheet of intense chemical activity exists. The flameholder receives energy from the hot gas at a rate proportional to the temperature across it with a constant of proportionality known as the conductance of the flameholder. It was shown, in particular, that this conductance has a strong influence on the details of the flame behaviour, and in particular the stand-off distance between the flame and holder. Domains of static stability and instability are identified, which help to explain observations of flame behaviour on a coplanar holder. In another paper (46), various theories that had been put forward to model burner-anchored flames are reviewed and compared. They show, among other things, that for most practical burners the conductance is large and that the flame stand-off distance increases logarithmically with activation energy. The review briefly summarizes the theories and compares them with empirically derived relationships of stand-off distance, flame speed and flame temperature.

Although the above papers relate to steady-state situations, they go on to consider time-dependent cases. John, with McIntosh, considered (41) the response of a plane flame-front to known inputs, in particular to oscillatory inputs in composition and inlet mass flux. It is shown in certain circumstances that there may be a resonant frequency close to which the flame position and temperature oscillations are large. A comprehensive theory of unsteady burner-anchored flames followed (45). Again an asymptotic theory based on high activation energy is developed, but now to second order. The aim of the investigation is to examine the stability of burner flames. It is shown in particular that heat losses to the burner can be destabilizing.

The above discussion of premixed flames relates to low-speed flames for which diffusion, chemical actions and convection are all necessary for any description of their structure. Changes in the structure of a premixed flame as its speed increases were also examined (42, 49). With the flame anchored to a burner, it is shown, using high-activation-energy asymptotics, that there is a continuous spectrum of inflow speeds. As the speed increases, the flame moves further downstream from the burner, and diffusion processes become less significant. These combustion waves, now travelling rapidly, exhibit explicit effects of compressibility and are described as deflagrations. The results of these investigations are useful in the discussion of the evolution of detonation waves.

Detonations

The generation of shock waves, by thermal rather than mechanical means, has been discussed above. The work described there was extended by John and his co-workers to include wave generation, again by the addition of heat power through a plane boundary, into a combustible gas mixture (58, 61). As in the comparable cases for an inert gas (47, 48), numerical solutions of the Navier–Stokes equations were obtained, including now a simple one-step Arrhenius model of the chemical kinetics. With rapid transference of energy to the gas from the plane boundary a shock wave is generated, as for an inert gas. Behind this precursor shock there lies an unsteady induction domain and an initially quasi-steady fast flame. All of these processes interlock in a continuously accelerated sequence that progresses towards a steady state in the shape of a plane Zel'dovich–von Neumann–Doring (ZND) detonation. These numerical solutions of the Navier–Stokes equations required some augmentation of the various coefficients of diffusion. However, it was clear that, once formed, the triplet combination of shock wave, unsteady induction domain and fast flame continued to propagate without assistance from diffusion of any kind. This prompted the investigation, with his student Singh, of an Euler model that was analysed numerically by adoption of the Random Choice Method (RCM) (62). In the absence of diffusion, the whole process was 'switched on' by a strong plane shock wave created by the input of mechanical power from a piston. Unsurprisingly the 'triplet' preceding the ZND detonation was essentially as in the preceding studies. At about the same time, John was participating in investigations of the propagation of unsteady detonation waves in high-energy solids, in other words chemical explosives (63). For one-dimensional situations the RCM method proved to be adequate.

The investigations outlined above all relate to one-dimensional situations with the formation of planar waves. However, the notion of a one-dimensional detonation wave had already been rendered out of date by experimental studies. One approach to a further understanding had been to examine the stability of planar ZND detonations. However, John, together with his former student N. Nikiforakis, chose to simulate the evolution of other than planar configurations. Retaining the inviscid model, the flow is again governed by the reactive Euler equations. In this case the evolution of the flow was followed from the time that an incident shock reflects from the end wall of a shock tube. A small hot-spot is assumed to exist in one of the corners between the end wall and the walls of the shock tube. The RCM method used to capture the discontinuities in one-dimensional flows was no longer appropriate and was replaced by the

Figure 3. Jenny in 1964. (Online version in colour.)

so-called Weighted Average Flux method. The method was validated in one paper (66) and used in a subsequent one (67) for an in-depth study of this shock-reflected problem. The complicated sequence of events leads to the appearance of curved ZND waves.

FAMILY

A decade or so after John started working at Cranfield, he and Jean lived near Milton Keynes with their daughters. The large and lovely garden was Jean's domain. Julie succinctly describes her father's enthusiasms outside his work as 'fast cars (Lotus, F1), music (female voice, opera, jazz), humour (Goons, puns), books, art, rugby, ice cream, social democracy and education.'

His interest in art was not only as an admirer of other people's work: he was also a talented and prolific painter. Indeed, his artistic ability, already noted, was recognized while he was still at school, and his report from Warwick School for the summer of 1941 includes the prophetic statement 'Art: Very good, he has unusual ability.' He specialized in portraits, and his paintings of Jenny and Julie, completed in the mid 1960s when they were still small, illustrate the remarkable quality of his work (see figures 3 and 4).

French friends describe how, the first time they met him, he seemed to them to be the typical English gentleman, dressed immaculately, and arriving in the Alps in his sports car after enjoying the drive over mountain roads. Ask other people who knew John what they remember of him, and they, too, mention the fast cars, but they also describe an exceptionally warm, friendly and approachable man, who was always generous with help and encouragement for students or colleagues.

Figure 4. Julie in 1964. (Online version in colour.)

Figure 5. John at his desk in 2007.

Retirement from Cranfield came in 1991, although fruitful research activity continued for more than a decade beyond that (see figure 5). In 1992 he spent the Lent Term at Gonville and Caius College, University of Cambridge, as the first G. C. Stewart Visiting Fellow. In the same year he was elected to an Honorary Fellowship at Queen Mary and Westfield College, University of London. In the following year he spent a term at Bristol University as the Benjamin Meaker Visiting Professor.

AWARDS AND HONOURS

1961   Fulbright Scholar at Stanford University
1965   FIMA
1969   FRAeS
1987   FRS
1992   Honorary Fellowship of Queen Mary and Westfield College, London University
        First G C Steward Visiting Fellow at Gonville and Caius College, Cambridge
1993   Benjamin Meaker Visiting Professor at Bristol University
1999   FInstP

ACKNOWLEDGEMENTS

The authors would like to thank Jean, Jenny and Julie Clarke for their assistance in the compilation of this memoir. The frontispiece photograph was taken by Godfrey Argent and is reproduced with permission.

REFERENCES TO OTHER AUTHORS

Botha, J. P. & Spalding, D. B. 1954 The laminar flame speed of propane/air mixtures with heat extraction from the flame. *Proc. R. Soc. Lond.* A **225**, 71–96.

Hanson, R. K. 1971 The influence of film thickness on the calibration of thin-film-gauge backing materials. *AIAA J.* **9**, 975–977.

Lighthill, M. J. 1956 Viscosity effects in sound waves of finite amplitude. In *Surveys in mechanics* (ed. G. K. Batchelor & R. M. Davies), pp. 250–351. Cambridge University Press.

Sturtevant, B. & Slachmuylders, E. 1964 End-wall heat-transfer effects on the trajectory of a reflected shock wave. *Phys. Fluids* **7**, 1201–1207.

Van Dyke, M. D. 1964 *Perturbation methods in fluid mechanics*. New York: Academic Press.

BIBLIOGRAPHY

The following publications are those referred to directly in the text. A full bibliography is available as electronic supplementary material at http://dx.doi.org/10.1098/rsbm.2014.0012 or via http://rsbm.royalsocietypublishing.org.

(1)   1958   Energy transfer through a dissociated diatomic gas in Couette flow. *J. Fluid Mech.* **25**, 441–465.

(2)   *The flow of chemically reacting gas mixtures*. College of Aeronautics, Cranfield, report no. 117.

(3)   1960   *The measurement of unsteady forces and moments on slender bodies oscillating in a wind tunnel.* Aeronautical Research Council Reports and Memoranda no. 3170. London: HMSO.

(4)   The linearised flow of a dissociating gas. *J. Fluid Mech.* **7**, 577–595.

(5)   1961   Relaxation effects on the flow over slender bodies. *J. Fluid Mech.* **11**, 577–603.

(6)   *Reaction-resisted shock waves.* College of Aeronautics, Cranfield, report no. 150.

(7)   1962   Radiation-resisted shock waves. *Phys. Fluids* **5**, 1347–1361.

(8)   1963   (With J. W. Cleaver) *Green's functions and the non-equilibrium equation with applications to non-equilibrium free streams.* College of Aeronautics, Cranfield, report no. 163.

(9)   1964   (With J. W. Cleaver & G. M. Lilley) A review of analytical studies of reacting or relaxing gas flows. *Proc. Inst. Mech. Engrs* **178**, 3–28.

(10)   (With M. McChesney) *The dynamics of real gases.* London: Butterworths.

(11)   1965   (With J. B. Rodgers) Shock waves in a gas which has several relaxing internal energy modes. *J. Fluid Mech.* **21**, 591–610.

(12)   1967   The laminar diffusion flame in Oseen flow: the stoichiometric Burke–Schumann flame and frozen flow. *Proc. R. Soc. Lond.* A **296**, 519–545.

(13)   The reflexion of a plane shock wave from a heat conducting wall. *Proc. R. Soc. Lond.* A **299**, 221–237.

(14)   (With J. R. Busing) Shock reflection and surface effects in the shock tube. In *AGARD Conference Proceedings* no. 12, part 1, pp. 165–190. London: NATO.

(15)   The laminar diffusion flame behind a blunt body: a constant pressure Oseen-flow model. *J. Inst. Maths Applics* **3**, 347–361.

(16)   1968   (With R. Foster) Supersonic flow past a wedge with a flame at its apex. *Aeronaut. Q.* **19**, 80–90.

(17)   (With G. R. Stegen) Some unsteady motions of a diffusion-flame sheet. *J. Fluid Mech.* **34**, 343–358.

(18)   On the structure of a hydrogen–oxygen diffusion flame. *Proc. R. Soc. Lond.* A **307**, 283–302.

(19)   1969   Small disturbance theories. In *Gasdynamics; non-equilibrium flows*, vol. 1 (ed. P. P. Wegener), ch. 1. New York: Marcel Dekker Inc.

(20)   Emmons' problem according to the Oseen approximation. *Phys Fluids* **12**, 241–242.

(21)   Reaction-broadening in a hydrogen–oxygen diffusion flame. *Proc. R. Soc. Lond.* A **312**, 65–83.

(22)   (With J. B. Moss) The effect of the large hydrogen dissociation activation energy on an equilibrium-broadened hydrogen–oxygen diffusion flame. *Proc. R. Soc. Lond.* A **313**, 433–443.

(23)   1970   (With J. B. Moss) On the structure of a spherical H_2O_2 diffusion flame. *Combust. Sci. Technol.* **2**, 115–129.

(24)   (With D. G. Petty) The supersonic flow field associated with a conical flame sheet. *Aeronaut. Q.* **21**, 368–378.

(25)   1971   The diffusion flame as a singular perturbation problem. *J. Engng Maths* **5**, 179–185.

(26)   (With A. Melvin and J. B. Moss) The structure of a reaction-broadened diffusion flame. *Combust. Sci. Technol.* **4**, 17–30.

(27)   1974   Behaviour at acoustic wave fronts in a laminar diffusion flame. *Q. J. Mech. Appl. Math.* **27**, 161–173.

(28)   1975   The pre-mixed flame with large activation energy and variable mixture strength: elementary asymptotic analysis. *Combust. Sci. Technol.* **10**, 189–194.

(29)   1976   (With N. Riley) Free convection and the burning of a horizontal fuel surface. *J. Fluid Mech.* **74**, 415–431.

(30)   (With M. McChesney) *Dynamics of relaxing gases.* London: Butterworths.

(31)   1977   (With Y. L. Sinai) The wave system attached to a slender body in a supersonic relaxing gas stream: basic results: the cone. *J. Fluid Mech.* **79**, 499–524.

(32)   Chemical amplification at the wave-head of a finite amplitude gasdynamic disturbance. *J. Fluid Mech.* **81**, 257–264.

(33)   1978   (With Y. L. Sinai) The wave system attached to a finite slender body in a supersonic relaxing gas stream. *J. Fluid Mech.* **84**, 717–741.

(34)   Amplification at a disturbance wave-head in a homogeneous explosion. *Acta Astronaut.* **5**, 543–556.

(35)   Small-amplitude gas dynamic disturbances in an exploding atmosphere. *J. Fluid Mech.* **89**, 343–355.

(36) 1979 On the evolution of compression pulses in an exploding atmosphere: initial behaviour. *J. Fluid Mech.* **94**, 195–208.

(37) 1980 (With A. C. McIntosh) The influence of a flameholder on a plane flame, including its static stability. *Proc. R. Soc. Lond.* A **372**, 367–392.

(38) 1981 On the propagation of gas dynamic disturbances in an explosive atmosphere. *Prog. Astronaut. Aeronaut.* **76**, 383–402.

(39) (With R. A. Allison) Theory of a hydrogen-oxygen diffusion flame. II. Large activation energy asymptotics. *Combust. Sci. Technol.* **25**, 97–108.

(40) A generalised Burgers equation for plane waves in a combustible atmosphere. In *Proc. 27th Conf. Army Math., West Point, NY, USA, 10–12 June.*

(41) 1983 (With A. C. McIntosh) The resonant response of a flat flame near a flame holder. *Prog. Astronaut. Aeronaut.* **88**, 3–37.

(42) On changes in the structure of steady plane flames as their speed increases. *Combust. Flame* **50**, 125–138.

(43) Combustion in plane steady compressible flow. General considerations and gas-dynamical adjustment regions. *J. Fluid Mech.* **136**, 139–166.

(44) 1984 Regular reflection of a weak shock wave from a rigid porous wall. *Q. J. Mech. Appl. Math.* **37**, 87–111.

(45) (With A. C. McIntosh) Second-order theory of unsteady burner-anchored flames with arbitrary Lewis number. *Combust. Sci. Technol.* **38**, 161–196.

(46) (With A. C. McIntosh) A review of theories currently being used to model steady plane flames on flame-holders. *Combust. Sci. Technol.* **37**, 201–219.

(47) (With D. R. Kassoy & N. Riley) Shocks generated in a confined gas due to rapid heat addition at the boundary. I. Weak shock waves. *Proc. R. Soc. Lond.* A **393**, 309–329.

(48) (With D. R. Kassoy & N. Riley) Shocks generated in a confined gas due to rapid heat addition at the boundary. II. Strong shock waves. *Proc. R. Soc. Lond.* A **393**, 331–351.

(49) Fast flames. In *Combustion and nonlinear phenomena* (ed. P. Clavin, B. Larrouturou & P. Pelce), pp. 101–122. Paris: Les Éditions de Physique.

(50) The reflection of weak shock waves from absorbent surfaces. *Proc. R. Soc. Lond.* A **386**, 365–382.

(51) Reflection of a weak shock wave from a perforated plug. *J. Engng Maths* **18**, 335–349.

(52) 1985 (With R. S. Cant) Non-steady gas dynamic effects in the induction domain behind a strong shock. *Prog. Astronaut. Aeronaut.* **95**, 142–163.

(53) (With E. F. Toro) Gas flows generated by solid-propellant burning. *Lecture Notes in Physics* **241**, 192–205.

(54) (With E. F. Toro) *Notes on the random choice method.* College of Aeronautics, Cranfield, report no. NFP 85/6.

(55) (With E. F. Toro) *Application of the random-choice method to computing problems of solid-propellant combustion in a closed vessel.* College of Aeronautics, Cranfield, report no. NFP 85/16.

(56) (With J. W. Dold) Combustion of a finite quantity of gas released in the atmosphere. In *Proc. Twenty-first (International) Symposium on Combustion*, pp. 1349–1356. Pittsburgh, PA: The Combustion Institute.

(57) 1986 (With Z. W. Wang) *Dynamic behaviour of combustible gases between a shock wave and a following flame.* College of Aeronautics, Cranfield, report no. 8616.

(58) (With D. R. Kassoy & N. Riley) On the direct initiation of a plane detonation wave. *Proc. R. Soc. Lond.* A **408**, 129–148.

(59) (With S. Mughal, D. I. A. Poll, P. L. Roe & J. L. Stollery) *Forces and moments on HOTOL at Mach 25 at an altitude of 75km.* College of Aeronautics, Cranfield, report no. NFP 86/19.

(60) 1989 Physico-chemical gas dynamics and its relationship to hypersonic flow. In *Hypersonic flow* vol. 1 (Defining the hypersonic environment) (ed. J. J. Bertin, R. Glowinski & J. Periaux), pp. 263–301. Boston, MA: Birkhauser.

(61) 1990 (With D. R. Kassoy, N. E. Meharzi, N. Riley & R. Vasantha) On the evolution of plane detonations. *Proc. R. Soc. Lond.* A **429**, 259–283.

(62) 1992 (With G. Singh) Transient phenomena in the initiation of a mechanically-driven plane detonation. *Proc. R. Soc. Lond.* A **438**, 23–46.

(63) 1993 (With S. Karni, J. J. Quirk, P. L. Roe, L. G. Simmonds & E. F. Toro) Numerical computation of two-dimensional unsteady detonation waves in high-energy solids. *J. Comput. Phys.* **106**, 215–233.

(64) 1995 (With A. Melvin) The free shock wave as a seismic source. *Proc. R. Soc. Lond.* A **450**, 351–370.

(65) 1996 (With C. A. Lowe) Combustion with source flows. *Math. Comput. Mod.* **24**, 95–104.

(66)   (With N. Nikiforakis) Numerical studies of the evolution of detonations. *Math. Comput. Modell.* **24**, 149–164.

(67)   (With N. Nikiforakis) Quasi-steady structures in the two-dimensional initiation of detonations. *Proc. R. Soc. Lond.* A **452**, 2023–2042.

(68)   A reactor model for ignition and burning of a gasifying solid. *J. Chem. Soc. Faraday Trans.* **92**, 2951–2958.

(69) 1999 (With C. A. Lowe) Aspects of solid-propellant combustion. *Phil. Trans R. Soc. Lond.* A **357**, 3639–3653.

(70) 2002 (With C. A. Lowe) Gas flows generated by propellant burning. In *Godunov methods: theory and applications* (ed. E. F. Toro), pp. 1–14. New York: Kluwer Academic/Plenum Publishers.

MALCOLM ROY CLARKE

24 October 1930 — 10 May 2013

Malcolm R Blake

MALCOLM ROY CLARKE

24 October 1930 — 10 May 2013

Elected FRS 1981

BY PETER J. HERRING

Little Hanger, Petworth Road, Wormley, Surrey GU8 5TR, UK

Malcolm Clarke was a leading authority on cephalopods and their significance in the world oceans. Much of his knowledge of their abundance was gained through a study of their beaks from the stomachs of predators, particularly sperm whales. He had a lifelong enthusiasm for sperm whales (and for other cetaceans), leading him to reappraise their buoyancy control. Postgraduate experience as a whaling inspector in the Antarctic led to his joining the National Institute of Oceanography in 1958 to work on oceanic squids. In 1972 he moved to the Marine Biological Association's Plymouth laboratory, where he was elected FRS in 1981 and was awarded a Special Merit promotion. He remained there until retirement in 1987, during which time he set up the Cephalopod International Advisory Council (CIAC). After retirement he travelled widely and continued his research on whales and squids, based first at home in Plymouth and later at his house in Pico, in the Azores.

EARLY LIFE, EDUCATION AND CAREER

Malcolm was born at Coldbath Farm, his maternal grandmother's family home on the outskirts of Birmingham. His grandfather had died in World War I, and their children (his mother, Ellen or 'Poppy' Woodward, was one of five) supported his grandmother there. Malcolm's father, Cecil ('C.D.'), had numerous jobs, including clerical work at Erdington Hall Infirmary and then as a Relieving Officer, taking small weekly benefits to Birmingham families who had hit hard times. Malcolm was an only child, as was his older cousin, David, who was brought up with him like a brother. The farm buildings were let to different small businesses, and part was used as a storage site for steamrollers. It was a great environment for the two boys.

The family moved several times following his father's employment, and Malcolm went to ten different schools. The family moved to Ross-on-Wye when his father became Registrar of Births, Marriages and Deaths in the area. A later move took them to a small ferryman's

http://dx.doi.org/10.1098/rsbm.2014.0011

cottage at Shillingford and Malcolm to Wallingford Grammar School. He spent a happy summer swimming in and boating on the Thames in a family punt with attached outboard motor, an early indication of a lifelong enthusiasm for small boats. Indeed, his memories of boyhood were largely of an unfettered outdoor life, roaming freely over the countryside.

He left school in 1948 with three Certificates of Higher Education and subsidiary Art (he was later to enjoy painting as a relaxation), and applied to several medical schools. His lack of mathematics and physics held him back, and instead he did National Service in the Royal Army Medical Corps. He was based near Aldershot and one day, when in sole charge, he granted an apparently healthy patient leave to visit the town. The patient was there because he might have contracted smallpox (he had not), and a great hue and cry ensued when he was identified as missing. Malcolm's medical training came in handy later: on an early research cruise, the netman fell down a companionway and almost severed his ear. Malcolm was deputed to sew it back on, which he did, very successfully.

After demobilization in 1952 Malcolm applied to the University College of Hull, which participated in the external degree programme of London University. His parents had taken over a smallholding at Burton Stather on Humberside, where they grew Christmas trees and had kennels and a cattery. Vacation work involved cutting the trees and selling them in Scunthorpe market. The college soon became the independent University of Hull and he was among the first of its graduates, gaining an upper second class BSc in Zoology in 1955, specializing in parasitology in his final year. He continued as a PhD student in the Zoology Department of Professor P. G. 'Espinasse under the supervision of Professor J. N. R. Grainger. In August 1955 Malcolm answered an advertisement for a Whaling Inspector on one of the Antarctic factory ships and then took off on holiday, hitch-hiking with a friend around France. He came back to find that he had got the job and was due to sail in six days' time.

In a short memoir to Jose Xavier, for the February 2011 Newsletter of the Association of Polar Early Career Scientists, Malcolm wrote:

> My first experience with the Antarctic and the deep sea came in 1955 when my Professor generously agreed that I could sail on an eight month cruise of a whale factory ship [Salversen's *Southern Harvester*] as a Government Whaling Inspector as part of my Ph.D. The position was offered by the National Institute of Oceanography (NIO) with the condition that I should collect information and whale samples for staff of the Institute.

Detailed formal instructions came with a long list of the equipment with which he would be supplied. In the event this included not just alcohol for preservation of samples but also several cases of whisky to facilitate the cooperation of the whalers with the sampling. NIO staff advised him on how best to collect material, which included whole squids and their beaks, from sperm whale stomachs. To his surprise, virtually nothing was known about the alimentary tract of the sperm and fin whales that he was likely to encounter. Surely all he needed to do to advance knowledge (and his PhD) was to collect tissues in preservative and section them when he got home?

> What could go wrong? Why had it not been done before? The one thing my NIO tutors could not really teach me was the bulk of the animals with which I must deal. My first day's sperm whales were over 16 m (53–54 ft) long and each weighed over an estimated 50 tons. As these were cut and pulled apart by 10 ft steam saws and winches, I began to realise how big they were. It took me two days even to find the pancreas which was 2 m long! … Now I knew why scientists had been unable to study the anatomy of the whale guts. The one whale I collected from was 14.5 m (49 ft) long and had an alimentary tract of 214.7 m (706 ft) i.e. almost 15 times its length.

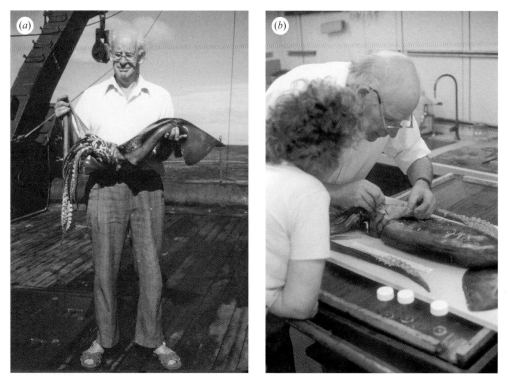

Figure 1. Malcolm's study of oceanic squids began with the family Ommastrephidae. (*a*) A freshly caught ommastrephid squid in 1986 on RRS *Challenger*. (*b*) Dissection, with Helen Martins, in the ship's laboratory. (Photographs by P. L. Pascoe.)

On return home:

> My failures in studies on the gut led me back to my third year specialisation in parasitology. I found some long tapeworms in the liver of sperm whales [3 specimens, max length 21 m] which proved to be from a genus new to science and, with other parasites, I completed a rather dull Ph.D.

It was during this PhD work that he met his future wife, Dorothy (Dot) Knight, who was completing her Postgraduate Certificate in Education before starting on a career as a biology teacher.

On leaving Hull in October 1958 he took up a post at the NIO in Wormley, Surrey, to work on oceanic squids. This new topic was initiated on the advice of Sir Alister Hardy FRS, Professor C. M. (later Sir Maurice) Yonge FRS and Professor J. Z. Young FRS. Malcolm began with the Atlantic near-surface ommastrephid squids, frequently seen at night in ship's lights (figure 1). For this he spent two months in Madeira, where there was a summer fishery for them. While in Madeira his host, Dr G. E. Maul, took him and Dot to visit the whaling station at Caniçal, where they were able to collect all the squids in a sperm whale's stomach, as well as several thousand loose beaks. This was a seminal event. On return to the NIO he refocused on the squid material he had brought back from the Antarctic, including some new species, and instigated the collection of beaks from sperm whales from around the world, either from whaling stations or from strandings. However, he had first to recognize and describe the beaks of different species of squid, with almost no previous work to go on. Then he could determine how important squid were in the diet of a variety of predators, including other cetaceans, seals, fish and birds. Further, if he could establish where, and at what depth, oceanic squid lived, and their abundance, he could assess their importance in the ecology of the world ocean.

As the nets he employed at the NIO now enabled him to capture live (or at least undigested) midwater squids, he became interested in their physiology and behaviour and encouraged other researchers to work on them at sea. Among these was Eric (later Sir Eric) Denton FRS, with whom he collaborated on studies of squid buoyancy. Some species, such as the omma-strephids, are fast muscular animals, whereas others, such as the cranchiids and histioteuthids, have gelatinous bodies and achieve neutral buoyancy by using ammonium ions. The giant squid *Architeuthis* also uses ammonium ions, something Malcolm first realized when served a piece of a specimen cooked by Chung-Cheng Lu after the latter's PhD viva. The taste was bitter and he took a sample back to Plymouth, where he and Eric Denton confirmed that the cause was the ammonium ions. Another of Malcolm's interests was the study of statoliths, small stony structures in the statocysts that control the animal's balance and orientation. He first found statoliths in freshly caught ommastrephids in Madeira, but they dissolved in the formalin used for the long-term preservation of most squids.

In 1970 his extensive knowledge of sperm whale anatomy and behaviour, combined with his interest in squid buoyancy, led to him formulating a new hypothesis on how the sperm whale could adjust its buoyancy (and thus conserve energy during its dives), by controlling the density of the huge store of spermaceti oil in its head (4)*.

The multidisciplinary nature of the NIO gave him a broad view of the deep sea, which he offered to a wider audience in 1971 by co-editing and contributing to a popular volume, *Deep oceans*, illustrated with photos and technical drawings by many of his colleagues (5).

Soon after this, Eric Denton was influential in persuading him to transfer from the NIO (by now renamed the Institute of Oceanographic Sciences, and part of the portfolio of the Natural Environment Research Council (NERC)) to the Marine Biological Association's laboratory at Plymouth (the MBA, itself grant-aided by NERC). At first J. E. (later Sir Eric) Smith FRS, the director, was somewhat reluctant to 'poach' Malcolm from a sister establishment, but he was persuaded, and Malcolm, Dot and their three sons moved to a large old vicarage at Morval in Cornwall (said to be haunted), where daughter Zoe was born. The West Country and immediate access to the sea must have been a potent part of the attraction of the MBA, alongside the physiological interests of its distinguished visitors and scientific staff.

The vicarage was large enough for him to create two flats to accommodate his and Dot's parents and still have room for visitors. An early project was the construction of a swimming pool, which he and the family dug with a mechanical digger and finished off with spades. The walls were lined with linoleum sheets and the water was warmed by a unique form of solar heating: the circulating hosepipe was fed through a line of glass milk bottles with their bottoms cut off, focusing the sun's rays. Malcolm's enthusiasm for small boats was rekindled by Eric Denton's lending him a mould for a double canoe, which he constructed from fibreglass with the help of Robert Moore, a family friend.

Their next house was Ridge Court, overlooking the harbour at Newton Ferrers. It was no ordinary property: one part had previously housed two wallabies! They had been presented

---

* Numbers in this form refer to the bibliography at the end of the text.

to Queen Victoria, who had given them to her equerry, the house owner. Malcolm again converted it to provide a flat for visitors and later divided it into two. The house had a large flat roof, which leaked. With the expertise he had gained earlier with fibreglass, Malcolm solved the leak by fibreglassing the entire roof area, enlisting the help of a squad of family and friends. He had acquired a fine Drascombe lugger and enjoyed taking friends out sailing in it. Professor Clyde Roper remembers a wonderful sail during which they chatted so much that they failed to recognize a falling tide and ended up on the mudflats—and were very late for dinner!

It was at Newton Ferrers that Malcolm felt the first intimation of heart disease, while he was helping to carry the corpse of a stranded dolphin up the beach. In hospital for the necessary angioplasty he was renowned as the patient 'who had a heart attack carrying a dead dolphin'.

He and Dot moved from there to Ancarva, a house at Millbrook, Plymouth, so close to the sea that the tide sometimes lapped over the lawn and his boat was only yards from the front door. The unusual purchase agreement involved the sale price of one half of Ridge Court plus Malcolm's help in sailing the owner's yacht back from the Caribbean.

Malcolm published the detail of his sperm whale buoyancy hypothesis in 1978 and continued to study the cephalopods in the stomach contents of a wide range of predators, allowing him to calculate the probable biomass of cephalopods in the oceans (15). He received his DSc in marine zoology from the University of Hull in 1979 (the first awarded). He was an inspiring and enthusiastic personal tutor and relished sharing his experience with many youthful workers on cephalopods, establishing lifelong friendships in the process. Passionate, ingenious, enthusiastic, eccentric, generous and energetic are just a few of their descriptions, 'fun' being a common thread. Professor Lu worked with him in the early 1970s, and Professor Paul Rodhouse spent six months with him studying beaks and squids when he joined the British Antarctic Survey, initially working on albatross regurgitations in collaboration with Professor John Croxall (FRS 2005) and colleagues. Malcolm's interest in statoliths continued, and Dr Marek Lipinski joined him at the MBA for a year to study these structures, as did Dr Tsunemi Kubodera, who brought his own collection from Tokyo.

Malcolm continued his quest to improve the net catches of midwater squids, and in the 1980s he discovered that putting a light on the trawl could significantly improve the cephalopod catch. He published extensively, and contributed to the three volumes of *The Mollusca* of which he was joint editor, summarizing his interpretation of the general evolution of Recent cephalopods as well as the detail shown by statoliths, beaks, buoyancy and locomotion (17). In 1981 he was elected FRS for 'wide-ranging and major studies of the physiology, distribution and systematics of squid.'

Dr Eric Corner FRS remembers that during an inspection of the MBA Malcolm had an interview with Lord Shackleton in which he put forward the idea of setting up a European North Atlantic biological laboratory with easy access to deep water, suggesting Madeira as a possible location. Despite a full proposal to the NATO Scientific Affairs Division, the finance was not forthcoming. Work on the physiology of deep-sea animals remained limited to the opportunities (and by the conditions) on research ships.

He initiated a major review of the role of cephalopods in the world oceans (19) and in 1981 proposed an organization for regular meetings of cephalopod workers, which two years later became the Cephalopod International Advisory Council (CIAC). He retired from the MBA in 1987 but continued working from Ancarva, where he kept his personal collections of beaks

Figure 2. Malcolm and Dot Clarke in Pico, on the occasion of their golden wedding anniversary in 2008.
(Photograph by P. J. Herring.)

and other material. His enthusiasm for the stomach contents of sperm whales led to his being described as 'a modern-day Jonah' in the Channel 4 series *Inside Nature's Giants*.

The Azores were one of the last outposts of sperm whaling in the Atlantic, ending officially there in 1984. Malcolm had worked in a permanent collaboration with the Department of Oceanography and Fisheries, University of the Azores, from 1981 onwards, particularly with the marine biologist Dr Helen Martins, and was a Visiting Scholar from 1990 to 2011. He loved the island of Pico, where he and Dot bought a house, initially for use during the summer but it later became their main residence (figure 2). From his house and garden high on the southern slope he could watch sperm whales and dolphins way below him. Not that he spent much time just watching, because he remained as energetic as ever and wanted to provide an insight into the life of the sperm whale and its squid prey for the general public. A museum of whaling methods already existed on Pico and seemed the ideal site for this project, but, despite great efforts to attract investment from the European Union, the funds, though promised, never materialized. Undaunted, he set up his own public museum in his garage and garden, greatly helped by Dot, who fashioned very accurate fabric models of squid to hang from the ceiling. Her *pièce de résistance* was a model of a giant squid, made during a return to the UK in 2000 for the Aberdeen CIAC meeting. He and Dot visited the family of a friend from Hull zoology days and astonished them by producing the 12 m 'Architeuthis' from the car and stretching it across two rooms!

From Plymouth and Pico he travelled extensively, despite a triple bypass operation in 1997. On one occasion he and Dot were caught in a devastating hurricane on the Hawaiian island of Kauai. He was at various times Visiting Professor at the Universities of Liverpool and the National Chung Hsing University in Taichung, Taiwan, and the National Institute of

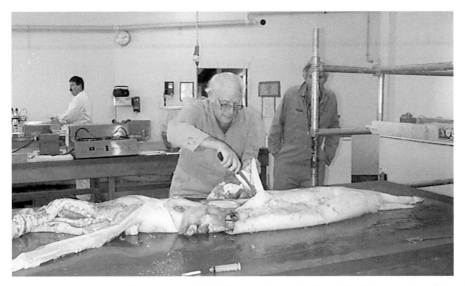

Figure 3. Dissecting a giant squid (*Architeuthis*) in Wellington, New Zealand, in 2002. (Photograph by C. C. Lu.)

Atmospheric and Water Research, New Zealand. He was much in demand as a consultant for film companies seeking to film sperm whales in combat with giant squid. Clyde Roper writes (in Rodhouse *et al*. 2014):

> I had support from National Geographic Television (NGTV) to conduct an expedition in search of a living giant squid, *Architeuthis* (1996). We were to employ the very clever Critter Cam™, a video camera system that quite successfully had been attached to live dolphins and sea turtles. We felt that the critter cam could be attached to a sperm whale's head (carefully!) with a large, non-invasive, suction cup. When asked by NGTV where the best place to go would be, I immediately selected the Azores as a most promising spot because of the long history and tradition of sperm whaling there ... sperm whales and giant squid. It was a clear and obvious choice to invite Malcolm to join in the expedition. While we were unsuccessful in getting images of giant squid being pursued and captured, we did get first-time video footage of sperm whales swimming at depth and audio recordings of them vocalizing and communicating.

Subsequently, during a 2001 expedition funded by the Discovery Channel, Malcolm and his colleagues did capture the first recognized larvae of the giant squid. Later (in 2011) he was the Azores consultant for the making of the National Geographic TV film *Hunt for the Giant Squid*.

Clyde Roper continues:

> Following our work in the Azores, we decided to go to the next obvious location for relatively easy, near-shore access to sperm whales and their giant squid prey, Kaikoura Canyon, South Island, New Zealand. While we were ashore in New Zealand awaiting completion of work on the chartered ship, we learned of the stranding of three sperm whales up on North Island. Malcolm and I could 'smell' adventure, so we flew up to the remote stranding site to examine the whales, knowing they would have at least thousands of squid beaks in their stomachs, even if not whole *Architeuthis*. ... A similar stranding situation happened later, and we were supplied with a huge collection of over 40,000 beaks, which a delighted Malcolm thoroughly identified during the expedition [figure 3].

This was not the first occasion on which Malcolm had attached instruments to sperm whales. A decade earlier he had collaborated with Tony Martin of the Sea Mammal Research Unit and Bob Forster of the MBA to try to attach satellite tags to the whales. At the same time Malcolm wanted to pioneer a suction device (involving several drain plunger cups!) to attach depth monitors to sperm whales. Trials were carried out in Plymouth Sound, in which the top of an old Morris Minor was put on floats and towed behind a small boat while Malcolm attempted from another boat to get close enough to the 'whale' to attach the suction system. The whole procedure was filmed by the BBC, to the great surprise of some family friends when it was shown publicly. They had some limited success in the Azores when the method was transferred (dangerously) to real whales. To get near enough to attach the satellite dart or suction cups, Tony or Malcolm had to be strapped to the mast of an inflatable catamaran, which Bob then took up to the whale.

In 1993 Malcolm was awarded a Leverhulme Fellowship for studies of cetacean anatomy and physiology, particularly in dwarf and pygmy sperm whales. He was indefatigable in the pursuit of locally stranded whales, for exhibits in his museum as well as for anatomical information and stomach contents. Colleagues in the Azores arranged to bury several specimens found on the beaches of other islands so that he could exhume the skeletons later.

Malcolm's enthusiasm remained undiminished by health problems and he had several ongoing projects in 2013, including an illustrated book on Atlantic squids and an almost complete autobiographical manuscript, 'Whale Fever'. The World Congress on Malacology was held in July in the Azores, and one session was dedicated to 'The role of cephalopods in the world's oceans: a symposium in honor of Malcolm Clarke'. He was greatly looking forward to the occasion and to meeting all his friends on home territory, but it was not to be. Malcolm died on 10 May 2013, and the symposium became his memorial.

Net developments to catch more squids

While at sea, ommastrephids could sometimes be caught by hand on a squid jig at night and Malcolm tried many other methods, including cast nets, explosives and electrocution. An early attempt to use a diver's harpoon gun resulted in the gun and harpoon disappearing separately over the side! A powerful crossbow was purchased and special squid bolts were made in the NIO workshop but this, too, was unsuccessful and was finally donated to the crew of a weather ship.

The focus of the biology group at the NIO had shifted from the Antarctic to the North Atlantic and from the zooplankton to larger animals including squids and fishes. The conical nets used had bridles in front of their mouths and were small. Capture of fish, squids and larger crustaceans required a better net system (a trawl), and Malcolm was encouraged by Ron Currie (later Director of the Oban Marine Laboratory) to develop larger nets. Malcolm used the Isaacs–Kidd midwater trawl in the early 1960s, and much larger commercial trawls, operated from fisheries research vessels and from RRS *Discovery*, in the Atlantic and in the Indian Ocean. The ambitious NIO programme was aimed at quantifying the vertical distribution and migrations of zooplankton and micronekton (which included squids) and required nets that could be opened and closed on command. The large trawls caught more squids than conical nets did, but were fished open and so gave no information about the animals' depth distribution. To overcome some of these difficulties, Malcolm and his NIO colleague Arthur

Figure 4. Malcolm (centre) deploying an open RMT8 from RRS *Discovery* in 1967. (Photograph by P. J. Herring.)

Baker designed a rectangular midwater trawl (RMT) with an 8 m² mouth (RMT8) (figure 4). It was not obscured by its towing bridles, and it could be opened and closed by acoustic signals from the ship (3, 7). The first three models of the net (to 1 m²) were made by Dot on her sewing machine. The system became the standard NIO biological sampling tool but it was still not very good at catching squids, the species and size range captured being greatly inferior to those from the stomachs of large predators (10). Nevertheless, in 1974 and 1975 he and Professor Lu described the vertical distribution of cephalopods obtained with these nets from 11° N to 60° N at 20° W, the most detailed survey ever achieved (8).

Malcolm tried scaling the trawls up to 25 m² and 90 m², but the largest ones were difficult to handle. He also developed conical 'pop-up' nets that sank to a defined depth at which a weight was jettisoned and the net fished slowly back to the surface under its own buoyancy. The largest of these was 10 m in diameter but was lost on its first deployment (figure 5). He counted himself a scientific fisherman, and for the remainder of his seagoing career he concentrated on using RMTs for catching squids and other animals for studies of their physiology and anatomy, using a variety of net sizes and conformations, including RMT1s, RMT7s, RMT10s, RMT50s and RMT60s, depending on which research vessel was to deploy them (22). Then in the 1980s, with his MBA assistant Phil Pascoe, he put a diver's underwater light on the head of the RMT50 and discovered that it markedly increased the catch of both squids and fishes (20). He also experimented with longlines and bottom trawls to target different cephalopods, and with dredges and grabs to look for their beaks, which had been found in abundance on the floor of the Indian Ocean.

Figure 5. Pop-up net 10 m in diameter being assembled from RRS *Discovery* by Malcolm (right) and Arthur Baker (left), in November 1966. (Photograph by P. J. Herring.)

CEPHALOPOD BEAKS, WHALES, AND DIETS

Cephalopods are soft-bodied animals with few tissues resistant to digestion. Their beaks are important exceptions, being made of a horny material and persisting in the stomachs of predators. Sperm whales may contain more than 10 000 beaks, even though they vomit them up every few days. While in the Antarctic, Malcolm collected beaks from sperm whales for others, but without a personal interest. It was only after joining the NIO to work on squids, and particularly on his 1959 visit to Madeira, that squid beaks became a core part of his research. There had been one previous Russian paper identifying beaks from a sperm whale (Beteshava & Akimushkin 1955), but the methods had not been described. Malcolm started all over again, using museum material in association with the 4000 beaks from the Madeira whale, which had also provided specimens of the very rare scaled squid *Lepidoteuthis*, a small male of the giant squid *Architeuthis* and the second specimen of *Taningia danae*. He could distinguish lower beaks better than upper ones, and focused on these. Comparison with beaks from identified squids of all sizes, both from stomachs and from nets, was necessary for the identification of individual species from isolated beaks. The description of their complex three-dimensional shape was essential to enable others to use the parameters for their own identifications. He began by looking at a very wide taxonomic range of preserved specimens of oceanic squids (Oegopsida), neritic squids and cuttlefish (Myopsida), and Octopoda. He could soon differentiate between families, but not species, and demonstrated a clear relationship between the dimensions of the beak and the body weight of the cephalopod (1).

Malcolm moved on from the one Madeiran whale to the Southern Hemisphere sperm whales. He enlisted the help of Dr Peter Best in South Africa and Dr John Bannister in Australia. To get the best idea of what the whales were eating, he needed entire stomach contents rather than samples. Neil McCleod was a whaling friend on the *Southern Harvester*. When medical issues forced him ashore he joined the NIO and became Malcolm's stalwart assistant, expert in the collection, handling and identification of squid beaks. Dr Ray Gambell arranged for him to collect material in Durban in 1964 and he returned to the NIO with material from 124 sperm whales, including the entire contents of 92 stomachs. In 1976 he was seconded to the MBA for a year to assist with the squid beak work.

In all, Malcolm (and Neil) examined 461 samples, comprising 338 identifiable cephalopod remains and 129 000 lower beaks, of which 61 000 were measured (14). He found considerable variation in the diet of whales from different regions: numerically 50% of beaks in the Antarctic and New Zealand were from the Onychoteuthidae, whereas in other regions the Histioteuthidae dominated. When considered by mass of squids, the variation was even greater: *Mesonychoteuthis* (a cranchiid) comprised 76% of stomach contents in the Antarctic, whereas *Taningia* (an octopoteuthid) was the main component at Durban, South Africa, and at Albany, Australia (21% and 36%, respectively). The presence of squids from areas other than where the whale was captured provided evidence of its recent migration from other waters (6).

This monumental work provided many insights into squid biology, including growth, spawning and distribution, as well as sperm whale feeding. However, as Malcolm noted, 'Descriptive work on lower beaks is still in its infancy … less than 100 species have been described in detail' (14). He was aware of the numerous other squid predators, particularly seals and birds in the Antarctic, which could potentially provide information on squid abundance and distribution. There was virtually no overlap between the size of squids sampled by sperm whales and those taken in nets, despite Malcolm's best attempts to improve the latter's efficiency. He concluded, 'It would seem inescapable that [comparison between nets and predators] must raise serious doubts of the value of nets to assess relative or absolute numbers of any midwater animals, including fish, in the deep sea' (14). These misgivings notwithstanding, he estimated the annual consumption of squids by sperm whales to be around 100 million tons.

This was but a start to using the predators of squids as windows to their biology. His skill in identifying beaks caused many biologists to send him their collections from other predators. He canvassed his colleagues to collect beaks for him from almost any source, and was keen to do so himself whenever possible. Although 'collecting the stomach contents of whales is a very distasteful operation' (14), it never inhibited him. A rotting sperm whale was stranded in Cornwall; Malcolm was anxious to collect from it but, by the time he, daughter Zoe, and Phil Pascoe arrived, the whale had been broken up with a digger and dumped in pieces on a local farmer's muckheap. Nothing daunted, Malcolm in oilskins dived in to try to find the stomach. He succeeded, got the beaks out and published the results.

He identified beaks from a range of cetaceans, as well as four species of seals. His expertise was in demand for birds, including albatrosses, penguins, shearwaters and petrels. When he and Tony Martin were staying in the Azores they regularly ate in a restaurant to the sound of Cory's shearwaters flying in at dusk to feed their chicks. At the end of the meal Tony would hurry out to the burrows close by, grab a chick and persuade it to regurgitate its recent meal into a plastic bag. He would return to the restaurant and tip the bag into an empty ashtray, whereupon Malcolm would pick out and identify the squid beaks. Over a few days of this routine they acquired a fascinated following!

Malcolm was acutely aware of the importance of training others to identify squid beaks, not just to relieve him of the work but in the knowledge that the more that the capability was spread, the better it would be for a broader understanding of the role of cephalopods in the ocean economy. As he wrote in 'Whale Fever':

> As the number working on diets has escalated one of my nightmares has been 'Are they correct in their identification?' Anyone can put names on beaks but how many can put correct names and do they know the implications of being wrong?

His answer was to organize three workshops for beak identification, at which he and other experts passed on their experience. He also taught several individuals on a personal basis, among them Professor Lu and Professor Rodhouse. The 1981 workshop at Plymouth was published in 1986 with full descriptions, and stereo photographs, of the beaks of 113 genera from almost every family and geographical area. It gave methods for their preservation and keys to their identification (16). Thousands of beaks were brought to that workshop for examination, and there are now reference collections of beaks available worldwide. The techniques were reviewed by Malcolm at a subsequent workshop on the estimation of cephalopod biomass. Malcolm believed that the details of beak shape might give clues both to the evolution of cephalopods and to their adaptations to different types of prey, although at the time little was known about cephalopod diets.

By the late 1990s Malcolm felt that enough was known about the diets of predators for a start to be made on assessing their role in the world's oceans, particularly now that squid fisheries were increasing in economic importance. He organized a review relating the numbers of squids and their consumption by predators to their populations and dynamics, to their energetics, and to their importance as a globally exploited resource. Their impact on the populations of other oceanic animals is indicated by an estimate of their annual prey consumption at 2–4 Gt. Malcolm contributed substantially to knowledge concerning the cephalopod diets of sperm whales, Weddell and elephant seals, penguins and albatrosses, and played a major part in quantifying the role of cephalopods in the Antarctic. The review (19) provided a very comprehensive compendium of the existing data and again emphasized the inadequacy of the sampling systems available.

Malcolm compared the distribution of his whole collection of eastern North Atlantic net-caught cephalopods with those from the stomach contents of 241 sperm whales taken from the same area (24). In more than 700 hauls of various sizes of nets he identified more than 7700 specimens and almost four times as many from sperm whale stomachs. The two sets gave completely different pictures. For example, the nets caught only six *Histioteuthis bonellii*, whereas there were 20 243 in the stomach collections. He concluded, 'Can we ever obtain a correct measure of what is in the sea or the relative numbers or mass of different organisms without drying it out and seeing what is left? The answer is clearly no!' (24) and he advocated using predators' stomach contents as monitors of the variety and abundance of oceanic squids. As he noted, without an accepted baseline it will be impossible to judge the impact of any changes in the cephalopod populations, whether from fisheries or from other ecological influences.

STATOLITHS

Despite much work on the otoliths of fishes, no one had described anything similar in squids when Malcolm was in Madeira studying ommastrephids. While dissecting the heads he noticed a pair of tiny chalky inclusions, or statoliths. These structures had not been reported since 1845 but were visible in a subsequent photograph of an octopus statocyst (Young 1960). Malcolm found they had regular growth rings and saw their potential significance for cephalopod studies (2). In 1978 he published a detailed account of statolith form in representatives of the Teuthoidea, Sepioidea and Octopoda, noting that in the last of these the shape was very different. He showed the aragonite crystal structure and provided a template for future descriptions and measurements by which the complex shape of statoliths from different species could usefully be compared (11). He noted that because statoliths are hard, inflexible structures (in contrast to beaks, cartilages and gladii), accurate and repeatable measurements are much easier. The shape of statoliths changes considerably during development and there are large differences between those of different taxa. He was unsure of the frequency of the growth rings in statoliths but they now seem to be daily increments and are widely used to give an indication of growth rate, ageing and life history, provided that the lines can be validated by data from animals of known age. Indeed, statoliths have been described as cephalopod 'black boxes or life recorders'. A chance meeting with John Fitch, an expert on otoliths from fossil strata, led to their identifying statoliths in shallow-water Cainozoic deposits in North America and the UK, and in Jurassic deposits in southern England (9, 13). Malcolm hoped that, with so few other fossil remains of Recent cephalopods, statoliths might provide a clue to the evolution of cephalopod taxa (21), extending back to the Jurassic fossil specimens.

The statocyst (and statolith) of cephalopods is concerned with the animals' orientation and balance and its sensitivity to low-frequency sound. Malcolm believed that a relationship would be discernible between the statolith form and the animals' locomotion, habitat and lifestyle (on the basis of different buoyancy strategies, from gelatinous ammonium-storing taxa to muscular swimmers such as the ommastrephids). Such relationships might also be extended to the fossil taxa. In practice he found relatively few clear correlations between statolith form and lifestyle, despite wide variation in statolith shape. In principle the numbers of statoliths present in marine sedimentary deposits, compared with those of fish otoliths, might also give an indication of the relative importance of the two groups at the time of deposition. Fitch's sorted Cainozoic samples averaged 351 otoliths to each statolith, but the otolith screening mesh size of 0.5 mm would not have retained many of the smaller statoliths. However, in Jurassic English deposits statoliths outnumbered otoliths by 8:1.

BUOYANCY AND SPERM WHALES

The sperm whale has a proportionally much larger head than any other whale, and much of the head is filled with spermaceti oil (2–3 tons in a 40-ton whale). Malcolm's familiarity with the animals, and his 1960s experience of working with Eric Denton on the buoyancy of squids, led him to reconsider the function of the spermaceti, hitherto regarded largely as a means of focusing the sounds produced by the whale (Norris 1975). The spermaceti is liquid in a freshly captured whale but quickly solidifies when cooled below about 30 °C, a change of state that affects its density. Sperm whales are the deepest-diving large whales, regularly reaching 1000 m and staying down for 50 minutes or more, and when dead they float at the surface, unlike most baleen whales. Malcolm realized that if they were buoyant at the surface the animals must experience a significant upthrust when in deeper, colder (and therefore denser) water, against which they would have to expend energy to stay down. He came to the conclusion that the whale might be able to adjust its buoyancy during its dives by warming or cooling the huge store of oil. If, at the start of its dive, the spermaceti could be cooled to the point at which it froze, its density would increase and the whale's buoyancy would decrease, assisting it in its deep dive. Conversely, if the spermaceti could be rewarmed to liquid while at depth, the additional buoyancy would help the whale return to the surface. In principle, if the whale could control the temperature of the oil throughout the dive it could also achieve neutral buoyancy, regardless of the ambient water temperature and pressure (in other words, at any depth and latitude). A key element was the remarkable difference between the left and right nares, the latter being much larger, more complex and traversing the centre of the spermaceti. If cold water could be drawn into it, the oil might cool rapidly.

Although the hypothesis seemed attractive (and remained compatible with sound focusing), Malcolm needed to demonstrate that the characteristics of the oil were appropriate, that the whale's anatomy provided both a system for cooling the oil and a means of dissipating the latent heat generated both by freezing the oil and the activity of the dive, and that there was a mechanism for rewarming the oil. The timescale for these changes needed to be appropriate for the dive. Quantification of all these factors required a detailed knowledge of the anatomy of the head and the relative quantity of the oil, its physical properties and the behaviour and distribution of the whale. Malcolm had some of these data already from his whaling days and from the study of some stranded specimens, but more were essential. With the help of Dr Ray Gambell and Dr Peter Best he spent two months in 1968 at the whaling station in Durban, making detailed anatomical measurements (even sectioning one whole whale's head at 20 cm intervals), experimenting with cold water in the right naris, measuring the oil temperature in freshly killed whales and observing the dive patterns from a spotter plane. On return he elicited the help of Dr D. Ambrose from the National Physical Laboratory in measuring how the density of the oil changed under different conditions of temperature and pressure.

Armed with all this information he published an outline of the theory in 1970 (4) and followed it up with the details of the data and observations on which his calculations were based (12), having made many observations of the relevant anatomy on commercial whales, during which he noted, 'Scrambling about on one's hands and knees among the entrails removes all pretentiousness' ('Whale Fever').

He was aware that 'final proof of the hypothesis must await measurement of the temperature or density of the oil within the spermaceti organ in the course of a deep dive. This is a difficult and costly task but not an impossible one' (12). Engineers built a successful robot diver based on the same system (Mcfarland *et al.* 2003), and deep ocean gliders are designed round a similar system, but the *in vivo* proof is still outstanding.

One critic noted that the smaller dwarf and pygmy sperm whales also had spermaceti but not enough to be useful in buoyancy control. Malcolm's calculations confirmed this, but after retirement he was able to examine several stranded specimens and establish that their nose structure and spermaceti were related to sound production (23). As he put it, 'This small nose, often less than 30 cm in length, contains a bagpipe, a sound producer, a set of vocal chords, a loudspeaker and a focusing device' ('Whale Fever').

Figure 6. At the first CIAC meeting in Banyuls-sur-mer 1983. From left to right: John Wormuth, Nancy Voss, Sigurd Boletzky, Malcolm Clarke, Gill Voss, Clyde Roper and Katharina Mangold. (Photograph by C. F. E. Roper.)

CIAC

When Malcolm began his research on cephalopods he soon recognized the shortage of cephalopod specialists and the lack of any forum in which new researchers could learn at first hand from the experience and expertise of others. In March 1981, at a workshop in Australia, 'Biology and Resource Potential of Cephalopods', stimulated by increasing commercial interest in their populations, he suggested the setting up of an international body of cephalopod specialists. Later that year, at a workshop on the identification of beaks, which he hosted in Plymouth, a Charter committee was formed to develop the organization. As Professor Lu notes, 'Naturally Malcolm carried the bulk of the work load' (Rodhouse *et al.* 2014). This committee reconvened at the Laboratoire Arago in Banyuls-sur-mer in 1983 and set up a General Council for CIAC (figure 6). As its instigator, Malcolm was elected its first Executive Secretary, serving two three-year terms, from 1983 to 1988. Three years later he was elected president (1992–94), and in 1997 was awarded Honorary Life Membership. Sadly he had recently had a triple bypass operation and was unable to travel to Cape Town to receive the accolade in person. CIAC's remit is to convene workshops and/or symposia every two or three years and to publish the results, to co-sponsor joint meetings, and to endorse relevant events organized by others. The emphasis is very much on sharing information, and on the training and encouragement of junior researchers. The memories and publications from the subsequent triennial meetings are some of the many legacies that Malcolm has left (18, 21). He always regarded the creation of CIAC as one of his most important scientific accomplishments. The 2013 World Congress on Malacology meeting in the Azores was endorsed by CIAC and was to have been in his honour. It was indeed, and poignantly so, following his death two months earlier.

ACKNOWLEDGEMENTS

I am most grateful to Mrs Dorothy 'Dot' Clarke, who encouraged me to undertake this memoir and provided me with much personal material. Mrs Pauline Simpson helped immensely with the compilation and formatting of the bibliography. Many of Malcolm's friends, colleagues and relatives responded most generously with their memories and tributes, and I am particularly grateful to Quentin Bone FRS, Eric Corner FRS, Bob Forster, Peter Foxton, Marek Lipinski, Chung-Cheng Lu, Nigel Merrett, Robert Moore, Phil Pascoe, Paul Rodhouse, Clyde Roper, Rui Prieto, Howard Roe, Joyce Woodward and Jose Xavier.

The frontispiece photograph was taken by Godfrey Argent and is reproduced with permission.

REFERENCES TO OTHER AUTHORS

Beteshava, E. I. & Akimushkin, I. I. 1955 Food of the sperm whale (*Physeter catodon*) in the Kurile islands region. *Trudy Inst. Okeanol.* **18**, 86–94.

McFarland, D., Gilhespy, I. & Honary, E. 2003 DIVEBOT: a diving robot with a whale-like buoyancy mechanism. *Robotica* **21**, 385–398.

Norris, K. S. 1975 Cetacean biosonar. I. Anatomical and behavioural studies. In *Biochemical and biophysical perspectives in marine biology* (ed. D. C. Malins & J. R. Sargent), vol. 2, pp. 215–236. London: Academic Press.

Rodhouse, P. G. K, Lu, C.-C. & Roper, C. F. E. 2014 Malcolm Roy Clarke FRS. *J. Mar. Biol. Assoc. UK.* (In the press.)

Young, J. Z. 1960 The statocysts of *Octopus vulgaris*. *Proc. R. Soc. Lond.* B **152**, 3–29.

BIBLIOGRAPHY

The following publications are those referred to directly in the text. A full bibliography is available as electronic supplementary material at http://dx.doi.org/10.1098/rsbm.2014.0011 or via http://rsbm.royalsocietypublishing.org.

(1) 1962 The identification of cephalopod 'beaks' and the relationship between beak size and total body weight. *Bull. Br. Mus. Nat. Hist. Zool.* **8**, 419–480.

(2) 1966 A review of the systematics and ecology of oceanic squids. In *Advances in marine biology* (ed. F. S. Russell), vol. 4, pp. 91–300. London: Academic Press.

(3) 1969 A new midwater trawl for sampling discrete depth horizons. *J. Mar. Biol. Assoc. UK.* **49**, 945–960.

(4) 1970 The function of the spermaceti organ of the sperm whale. *Nature* **228**, 873–874.

(5) 1971 (Ed., with P. J. Herring) *Deep oceans*. London: Arthur Barker Ltd.

(6) 1972 New technique for the study of sperm whale migration. *Nature* **238**, 405–406.

(7) 1973 (With A. de C. Baker & M. J. Harris) The N. I. O. combination net (RMT 1+8) and further developments of rectangular midwater trawls. *J. Mar. Biol. Assoc. UK.* **53**, 167–184.

(8) 1975 (With C.-C. Lu) Vertical distribution of cephalopods at 11° N, 20° W in the North Atlantic. *J. Mar. Biol. Assoc. UK.* **55**, 369–389.

(9)   (With J. E. Fitch) First fossil records of cephalopod statoliths. *Nature* **257**, 380–381.

(10) 1977   Beaks, nets and numbers. In *The biology of cephalopods* (Symposia of the Zoological Society of London, no. 38) (ed. J. D. Messenger & M. Nixon), pp. 89–126. London. Zoological Society.

(11) 1978   The cephalopod statolith—an introduction to its form. *J. Mar. Biol. Assoc. UK* **58**, 701–712.

(12)   Buoyancy control as a function of the spermaceti organ in the sperm whale. *J. Mar. Biol. Assoc. UK* **58**, 27–71.

(13) 1980   (With L. Maddock & E. Steurbaut) The first fossil cephalopod statoliths to be described from Europe. *Nature* **287**, 628–630.

(14)   Cephalopoda in the diet of sperm whales of the Southern Hemisphere and their bearing on sperm whale biology. *Discovery Rep.* **37**, 1–324.

(15) 1983   Cephalopod biomass—estimation from predation. *Mem. Nat. Mus. Victoria* **44**, 95–107.

(16) 1986   (Ed.) *Handbook for the identification of cephalopod beaks*. Oxford: Clarendon Press.

(17) 1988   (Ed., with E. R. Trueman) *The Mollusca*, vol. 12 (*Paleontology and neontology of cephalopods*). London: Academic Press

(18) 1992   (Ed., with M. J. Sweeney, C. F. E. Roper, K. M. Mangold & S. V. Boletzky) *'Larval' and juvenile cephalopods: a manual for their identification* (Smithsonian Contributions to Zoology, no. 513.) Washington DC: Smithsonian Institution Press.

(19) 1996   (Ed.) The role of cephalopods in the World Ocean: a theme. (Discussion Meeting.) *Phil. Trans. R. Soc. Lond.* B **351**, 979–1112.

(20) 1998   (With P. L. Pascoe) The influence of an electric light on the capture of oceanic cephalopods by a mid-water trawl. *J. Mar. Biol. Assoc. UK*. **78**, 561–575.

(21)   (Ed., with A. I. L. Payne, M. R. Lipinski & M. A. C. Roeleveld) Cephalopod diversity, ecology, and evolution. *S. Afr. J. Mar. Sci.* **20**, 1–469.

(22) 2003   Searching for deep sea squids. In *Proceedings of the International Symposium on Coleoid Cephalopods through Time, Berlin, 17–19 September 2002* (Berliner paläobiologische Abhandlungen, Band 3) (ed. K. Warnke, H. Keupp & S. V. von Boletzky), pp. 49–59. Berlin: Weinert GmbH.

(23)   Production and control of sound by the small sperm whales, *Kogia breviceps* and *K. sima* and their implications for other Cetacea. *J. Mar. Biol. Assoc. UK* **83**, 241–263.

(24) 2006   Oceanic cephalopod distribution and species diversity in the eastern North Atlantic. *Arquipelago, Ciencias Biologicas e Marinhas* **23A**, 27–46.

PAUL MORITZ COHN

8 January 1924 — 20 April 2006

Biogr. Mems Fell. R. Soc. **60**, 127–150 (2014)

PAUL MORITZ COHN

8 January 1924 — 20 April 2006

Elected FRS 1980

BY GEORGE BERGMAN[1] AND TREVOR STUART[2] FRS

[1]*Department of Mathematics, University of California, Berkeley,*
CA 94720-3840, USA

[2]*Department of Mathematics, Imperial College London, London SW7 2AZ, UK*

Paul Cohn was born in Hamburg, where he lived until he was 15 years of age. However, in 1939, after the rise of the Nazis and the growing persecution of the Jews, his parents, James and Julia Cohn, sent him to England by Kindertransport. They remained behind and Paul never saw them again; they perished in concentration camps. In England, being only 15 years old, he was directed to work first on a chicken farm but later as a fitter in a London factory. His academic talents became clear and he was encouraged by the refugee committee in Dorking and by others to continue his education by studying for the English School Certificate Examinations to sit the Cambridge Entrance Examination. He was awarded an Exhibition to study mathematics at Trinity College. After receiving his PhD in 1951, Paul Cohn went from strength to strength in algebra and not only became a world leader in non-commutative ring theory but also made important contributions to group theory, Lie rings and semigroups. He was much admired, and he travelled widely to collaborate with other algebraists. Moreover, he was a great supporter of the London Mathematical Society, serving as its President from 1982 to 1984.

PART A. PERSONAL AND FAMILY, BY TREVOR STUART

1. INTRODUCTION

Paul Cohn wrote at least two interesting accounts of his early life. One (28)*, which focused on his years in Germany, was published in German but an English translation is available as electronic supplementary material at http://rsbm.royalsocietypublishing.org/content/suppl/2014/08/14/rsbm.2014.0016.DC1/rsbm20140016supp2.pdf. The other (22), which is concerned with his early years in England, is in English.

* Numbers in this form refer to the bibliography at the end of the text.

http://dx.doi.org/10.1098/rsbm.2014.0016

2. Early life and career

It may be helpful to start by summarizing parts of Paul's own accounts. Moreover, Juliet (Aaronson) Cohn, after discussions with her mother, Deirdre, and sister, Yael, has written some additional details of her father's life and these also are used throughout this section but without precise quotations.

Paul Cohn's parents were born in Hamburg, as were three of his grandparents. Earlier generations came from Hamburg, Leipzig, Berlin and Greiffenberg but, so far as he was able to trace, always from Germany. They considered themselves German (at least until 1933). His father was Jacob Cohn (1883–1942), but he was always known as James, and his mother was Julia Mathilde Cohn, *née* Cohen (1888–1941). His father joined the cigar-importing business belonging to his father-in-law in 1921. His mother had been a teacher since the age of 20 years. Paul was born on 8 January 1924 in Hamburg and was an only child. Initially his parents lived with his maternal grandmother but, when she died in 1925, they moved to a rented flat in a new building in the district of Winterhude. The front of the building overlooked the elevated railway, which Paul frequently observed, but the rear of their home overlooked a laundry yard with a small adjacent chicken run. The cock crowed in the morning like an illustration in Paul's favourite book, *Max and Moritz*, by Wilhelm Busch. In 1928 Paul developed scarlet fever and was taken to hospital by horse and carriage. (Scarlet fever was a serious complaint for children in the 1920s and 1930s in the UK as well as Germany; I had a similar experience in England.) In April 1930 Paul entered school (Alsterdorfer Strasse School); he enjoyed the lessons but was often teased in breaks, although anti-Semitism seemed to play no part. Later he was in a class with a teacher who continually picked on him and punished him without cause. His parents learned from the school head that his teacher was a National Socialist; they moved him to Meerweinstrasse School, which was where his mother taught. It was progressive and coeducational. Paul recalled that in 1932 there was a small sensation when one or two boys came to school in Nazi uniforms, but without repercussions.

His father's cigar-importing business declined in the years during Germany's Depression in the 1930s and was wound up in 1933, as people were discouraged from trading with Jews. Thus Paul's parents intended him to train as an optometrist or something similar. In 1933 Paul's mother was dismissed from her teaching position after the introduction of new legislation that removed Jews from the civil service. Paul's parents decided to send him to a Jewish school in Hamburg in the Grindel quarter, the Talmud-Tora-Schule. However, his mother was advised that he needed to improve his knowledge of mathematics so he worked flat out (just as he did much later in studying in England). The German lessons by Dr Ernst Loewenberg, the son of the poet Jacob Loewenberg, gave Paul a knowledge of and predilection for his native language that he never lost.

After Kristallnacht in 1938 his father was arrested along with many other Jewish men in Germany. Later his war record enabled his mother to have him released from the Sachsenhausen concentration camp; even so his parents were deported in 1941 to a concentration camp in Riga. (Paul's father had been awarded the Iron Cross in World War I after he rescued wounded comrades while under fire. A consequence was that Paul played without toy guns or other military toys as his father's experiences led to a hatred of war and all things associated with it.) After Julia's unsuccessful attempts to find any country to which they could all migrate, James and Julia Cohn found a place in 1939 for Paul on a Kindertransport to England, as he satisfied the requirement of being under 17 years old. However, they themselves had to remain in Germany and never saw their son again, perishing in concentration camps.

On arrival in England in May 1939 by Kindertransport, Paul was greeted at Liverpool Street Station in London by Mrs Lisbet Mueller-Hartmann, whom he remembered well as a distant relation from Hamburg. From there she escorted him by Underground to Victoria Station and arranged for him to take the train to Dorking, Surrey; there he was met by a lady from the refugee committee, who drove him to a farm at Newdigate, where Mr and Mrs Panning kept about 5000 chickens. Being over the school age of 14 years, Paul was required to work on the farm (unpaid, as this was a requirement of being accepted for Kindertransport). As he later recalled, before he left Germany he had told his father that he was fine with that, so long as he did not have to kill any chickens. Needless to say within a week he was doing so. This was a sort of introduction to British ways! His cousin, Peter, who worked on another farm, likewise unpaid, told him of being given a small amount of pocket money each week. This would probably have been one or two shillings and some pence (with 12 pence in one shilling and 20 shillings in £1), something else of British ways that Paul would have learned. Therefore Paul asked Mr and Mrs Panning for a similar amount, which was granted at the rate of 2 shillings and 6 pence (known as half a crown; in decimal currency 12½ pence) per week, this amount being increased gradually. Paul worked for 70 hours per week, with three half days off every two weeks. He would spend his pocket money at the local cinema, for which the charge was 6 pence, watching the same film many times to improve his use of English. Paul corresponded regularly with his parents during the summer of 1939, pursuing the possibility of their being accepted as immigrants to the UK if they gained employment as housekeeper and gardener (his father was an enthusiastic allotment gardener in Hamburg). His efforts were unsuccessful, and when war broke out all possibility of emigration ended. From this point onwards he received only a short letter once a month from his parents through the Red Cross. The letters became less frequent and stopped in late 1941. In fact they were deported to concentration camps in Riga on 6 December 1941.

However, the government intended that Paul should work for the duration of the war, but would then send him to Canada or Australia when the Atlantic Ocean was free of the dangers of U-boats. This transfer never happened and he stayed in England. It is an interesting reflection that had his future been determined otherwise, we might have been celebrating a Canadian or Australian mathematician!

It seems that because of his being on the young side (less than 16 years old), Paul was not sent as an alien to the Isle of Man, as were three musicians who later formed three-quarters of the Amadeus String Quartet! As the result of a shortage of feedstuff the small farm was eventually not viable, and Paul was saddened by the auction that followed closure. However, he was given a work permit and moved to London, where he worked as a fitter in a factory. He was still in touch with the refugee committee in Dorking, which, recognizing his intelligence and love of learning, and his special interest in mathematics, encouraged him to study for the Cambridge Entrance Examination and the School Certificate and Higher School Certificate Examinations, all of which he did by correspondence course. At that time Latin was still a requirement to enter the University of Cambridge, so he studied Latin from scratch. During his studies in his unheated room and before he started work, Paul needed to heat up his pen because the ink in it would freeze during the winter. (I am reminded of similar conditions in the 1940s due to coal shortages.) Thus his experience was not atypical.

Paul gained an Exhibition to study mathematics at Trinity College. He was released from the factory in 1944 and went up to Cambridge, but was asked to return to the factory after one

Figure 1. Paul Cohn in Cambridge in about 1950. (Copyright © Ramsey & Muspratt; reproduced with permission.)

term because he had been released in error. In spite of having had only one term of full-time study he passed the first-year examinations. He was finally released from the factory after one more year and resumed his studies in Cambridge.

Paul graduated with a BA in 1948 and then undertook research in algebra with financial support from a Department of Scientific and Industrial Research award. He was supervised by Philip Hall FRS and studied rings and free groups, obtaining his PhD in 1951 (figure 1). For the following academic year he was a Chargé de Recherche at the Université de Nancy. He became a lecturer at the University of Manchester in 1952. In 1962 he joined the University of London, initially at Queen Mary College until 1967, but after a year's sabbatical in Princeton, NJ, he moved in 1968 to Bedford College in its idyllic setting in Regent's Park. In 1984 he transferred to University College London, together with several other staff from Bedford College. He succeeded Professor Ambrose Rogers FRS as Astor Professor of Mathematics in 1986 and became Emeritus Professor in 1989. During his career in the field of algebra, in which he became a popular and influential figure, he visited many universities abroad, including Chicago (6 months in 1964), Novosibirsk, Rutgers, Princeton, Berkeley, Paris, Tulane, the Indian Institute of Technology in Delhi, Alberta, Carleton in Ottawa, the Technion, Iowa State University, Bielefeld in the country of his birth, and Bar Ilan University.

Paul's time in Manchester had two distinct benefits (in no particular order): (i) his research work and his reputation as an algebraist developed greatly; (ii) he had the pleasure of meeting Deirdre Sharon, who was a psychology undergraduate and who was to become his wife. They were married in 1958 and had two daughters, Juliet and Yael, each of whom read mathematics at university, Juliet at Trinity College, Cambridge, and Yael at Somerville College, Oxford

(Mary Somerville, after whom the college was named, was a mathematician in the nineteenth century). Paul had five grandchildren: James, Olivia and Hugo Aaronson, and Malke and Rusi Rappaport. It would have given him great pleasure had he known the interest his grandchildren take in mathematics. The eldest, James, following in his grandfather's footsteps, is currently studying mathematics at Trinity College, University of Cambridge.

Paul was fascinated by the study of language and its origins and was enthusiastic to learn something of the languages of the countries he visited; for example, he learned some Hindi when flying to Delhi. As to reading he enjoyed German philosophers and German literature, and Mozart was a favourite composer of his. He enjoyed also watching the Marx Brothers. In spite of having few relations to consult, Paul Cohn was very interested in his family ancestry and visited institutions of record—libraries, cemeteries, tombstones, and not least in Hamburg—so as to learn more of his heritage. He found that over the years many ancestors had a love of learning and scholarship; his genealogical research enabled him to trace his ancestors back to 1450.

Science in the UK benefited enormously from refugees such as Paul Cohn, who came to our shores as a safe haven, for which Paul was always grateful. In addition he felt gratitude to the refugee committee in Dorking, and to the composer Ralph Vaughan Williams, for encouraging and helping him to find his passion in mathematics. It was Vaughan Williams who particularly encouraged him to study mathematics at Trinity College in Cambridge. This passion for mathematics took him to many far-flung places, where people would have a different way of looking at a particular mathematical problem. He was always very excited to meet and talk to others who shared his passion for algebra, and indeed any branch of mathematics.

Paul did not feel completely English, but was always grateful to the country that had saved his life and given him a home in England. Another refugee, Harry Reuter, had views, as expressed in conversation to me, which in some ways were not unlike those of Paul Cohn. (For Harry Reuter's background, see https://de.wikipedia.org/wiki/Harry_Reuter.)

3. Research students, colleagues and research visits

According to the Mathematics Genealogy Project (http://www.genealogy.math.ndsu.nodak. edu/id.php?id=27131), Paul Cohn had 17 students and at the time of writing has more than 40 mathematical descendants with the number growing (students, students of students, and so on). His students were wholly within the University of London. Although Paul Cohn was not the official supervisor of George Bergman, the co-author of this memoir, he was a member of his dissertation committee and provided enormous help. For example, Bergman would mail him the draft of his thesis in instalments of about 25 pages and Paul would typically send a five-page letter of suggestions and corrections. In addition, Cohn arranged for him to visit Bedford College in 1969–70, where Bergman had a very productive year. They continued to correspond well into the twenty-first century.

We describe below some recollections received from Paul's students. Aidan Schofield was the author of an obituary notice in *The Independent* of 8 August 2006 in which he wrote:

> He was devoted to research which was profound, original and lonely, choosing to work on what he felt to be important rather than to follow fashionable trends in mathematics. In the early sixties he set himself a particular task and, 20 years later, he had completed it. In doing so he uncovered

mathematical structures whose importance is beginning to be recognized in areas apparently far removed from the algebras and skew fields with which he worked.

On a more personal note, Schofield wrote:

> In 1980 I became Paul Cohn's graduate student at Bedford College in Regent's Park. His books had been an inspiration and delight for me and he himself fulfilled all I had been led to expect from them. His books reflected a scholarly and gentle approach. He was always willing to take time to talk about mathematics and he had a desire to explain what he had seen to those that had not. He also wanted to hear what others had to say and took pleasure in the successes of those around him.

Another of his students, Muhammad Zafrullah, has written to us with interesting anecdotes about Paul, of whom he writes affectionately as 'my Mathematical Old Man'! He started working with Paul in 1971. He comments on the important contribution that Paul made to mathematics through education and training: 'He was very strict over those he accepted as students and then trained them to think and work independently, giving pointers from time to time on how to proceed in certain situations.' At one point in his research, Muhammad sensed that Paul was uncomfortable with his working on commutative topics independently, with Paul working on non-commutative algebra. Paul Cohn therefore arranged for Masayoshi Nagata to visit the college. 'The meeting with Nagata did wonders for me', writes Zafrullah, saying further, 'Paul did so much to help his students.' When Paul died, Muhammad felt his loss greatly.

A student from Paul's early days at Queen Mary College was Bill Stephenson, who comments, 'Paul was an assiduous/meticulous supervisor.' Sometimes during his regular supervision sessions with Paul, Bill would raise topics in Algebra that were not necessarily relevant for his thesis, but 'Paul could straightaway go into this area I had asked about. He really was Mr Algebra.' After gaining his PhD in 1966, Bill spent a year in Russia before joining the staff in 1967 at Bedford College, to which Paul had moved. However, Bill became involved in trade unions in the late 1960s, during which time Paul teased him with good humour about this interest and commented that he himself had actually been a union member in the 1940s when he worked in a factory. Bill also writes that he was 'genuinely pleased when he heard that Paul had become an FRS.' He finishes by saying, 'I owe so much to Paul for supervising me, appointing me and standing by me in difficult times.'

Some recollections from other university colleagues and from research associates in the USA and Russia are now described. Another member of staff at Bedford College was Wilfrid Hodges, who was Reader in Mathematical Logic until in 1987 he moved with the same title to Queen Mary College, becoming later Professor of Mathematics and Dean of Mathematical Sciences there. He writes:

> When I first came to Bedford College in 1968, it was to join the Philosophy Department in the first instance. But the Head of Philosophy, David Wiggins, knew of my interest in mathematics and approached Paul Cohn about the possibility of my being a joint lecturer in Philosophy and Mathematics. Paul took a big gamble on this since, at that stage, I had no mathematical qualifications beyond A level. But it worked out, and in 1974 I joined the Mathematics Department full time. I am hugely in debt to Paul for allowing all this.

He also says, 'Paul always treated me as a fellow researcher like himself' and 'from early days he quoted remarks of mine in his papers and books, which certainly helped to get my name known in the algebraic community. He also strongly encouraged me to set up a model-theory

Figure 2. Paul Cohn at a blackboard in 1989.

research group.' At one of the regular meetings for morning coffee, Wilfrid Hodges recollects 'Paul announcing that his books had sold 100,000 copies!' With reference to the move from Bedford College upon its closure and merger with Royal Holloway College, he says 'Paul took his Bedford team to University College London to form part of the algebra unit there.' Wilfrid Hodges in logic moved to Queen Mary College. George Bergman recalls that at the same time Paul arranged for the Departmental Secretary, Eileen Simpson, to move to a staff position at the London Mathematical Society (LMS).

In relation to Bedford College and his colleagues (25), Cohn writes:

> Reflecting on my seventeen years with the College, I found the atmosphere, both physical, in one of London's finest parks, and mental, surrounded by colleagues who were both stimulating and sympathetic, very conducive to productive research and rewarding teaching.

A photograph of Paul Cohn at the blackboard is shown in figure 2.

I have mentioned earlier the pleasure that Paul Cohn gained from visits to other universities and from colleagues whom he met and with whom he discussed mathematics, and whose friendship he gained. One such colleague was George Bergman; another was Professor Carl Faith, who has commented on the pleasure that Paul gained from the copious open spaces of Princeton and his remark that they seemed 'wasted, that is, uncultivated.' 'The open spaces are still there', writes Carl, with the 'Institute for Advanced Study holding over 100 acres of woods for members to trample through', together with the Veblen Arboretum and another patch of woodland under the aegis of the Audubon Society. Princeton University and the Institute are contiguous with Lake Carnegie. Carl Faith writes that when 'Paul arrived in Princeton with his wife, Deirdre, his two daughters and two students, he enriched our lives immeasurably.'

Carl Faith wrote a 'long appreciative review in *Mathematical Reviews* about Cohn's solution of Artin's problem'. Paul told Carl of the happiness that this gave him. Faith writes, 'Many had previously tried to solve Artin's problem but no-one had done so before!' See Cohn's paper (4) and the review by Faith (1963).

Paul Cohn had a long association with Leonid A. Bokut, who writes (in a letter translated by George Bergman), 'at Moscow State University my academic advisor A. I. Shirshov drew my attention to the work of Cohn', which, 'together with the work of Shirshov, became the starting point for my future doctoral dissertation which I defended in Novosibirsk.' His first meeting with Cohn occurred in 1966 at the Moscow Congress, where Bokut heard him and S. A. Amitsur speak of work by their students, Andrew Bowtell and Avraham Klein, which was rather closely related to that of Bokut, who had followed a different approach. 'The Congress was the start of my friendship with Cohn', he says, one that lasted for the remainder of his life. He continues that 'in March–April of 1970 I visited Cohn at Bedford College for two months. P. M. Cohn showed great attention and concern for me' and 'organised a colloquium which many attended at which I spoke of my results and on a very new solution by Matiyasevich of Hilbert's 10th problem (George Bergman translated my talk). Cohn held a big reception for me at his home, where I chatted with the recent Fields Medalist, Paul Cohen.' Later 'I went with Cohn in his car to York, where I met Abraham Robinson and was introduced to Serre by Cohn. In general I was charmed by Cohn, his attention to me, his quality as a person, his mathematical breadth. I became a lifelong admirer of Cohn, his mathematics and his personality'. Finally he writes, 'I often mention Cohn in my seminars and lectures in Russia and China as an exceptional scholar and person, the intellectual father of mathematical constructions used by leading world mathematicians.'

4. The London Mathematical Society and other mathematical
activities

Paul Cohn was dedicated to the LMS, and indeed it may be said to be part of his union with England and the UK. J. J. O'Connor and E. F. Robertson have written, in their biography of Paul (http://www-history.mcs.st-andrews.ac.uk/Biographies/Cohn.html), that 'Cohn was an enthusiastic member of the LMS, and he has served as its secretary during 1965–67, as a Council member in 1968–71, 1972–75 and 1979–84, being President of the Society during 1982–84. He also acted as editor of the LMS Monographs during 1968–77 and again 1980–93.'

Indeed, Paul may be said to have been the backbone of the Monograph series, because he was one of the Editors (with Harry Reuter) who started the series; Paul acted as Editor for two periods totalling 22 years.

Anthony Watkinson, who was at Academic Press from 1971 and then at Oxford University Press, was always associated with the LMS publishing. When Paul 'retired reluctantly' from his first stint as Editor, Watkinson also was reluctant to see him leave; but leave he did, although he returned some three years later. Watkinson says, 'the reason why I wanted to continue with Paul was that he was one of the best series editors in any field that I have ever worked with.' He continues:

> We built up a close understanding and I tried myself to be active in mathematics too. I therefore
> offered authors to the series and Paul showed huge tact in making clear to me whether or not such

and such a mathematician should be encouraged and another should not be encouraged, without ever saying that the person concerned was a poor mathematician.

On the positive side, Watkinson says 'a fair number of mathematicians will have had cause to thank him. I would like to say that I brought John Conway to the series with "On Numbers and Games", but I think that Conway came to the series because of Paul.' On another but related matter he says, 'Paul helped in delicate matters and coached me in the task of bearding a journal Editor in his room, getting him to turn out his drawers and hand over manuscripts that he had been sitting on for years in some cases.' Watkinson continues: 'I remember him as a very private person though we did discuss occasionally some personal matters. I think of him as a gentleman of the old school.'

Paul served as a member of the LMS Council from 1968 to 1982; David A. Brannan recalls that as Council secretary from 1973 to 1981 he came to know Paul Cohn as 'an exceptionally nice chap'.

Alan Pears has written that when he became Meetings and Membership Secretary in 1983, Paul helped him to 'settle into this post with great kindness and courtesy'.

A few years later, Alan became secretary of the Board of Studies in Mathematics of the University of London while Paul was its chairman; Alan writes that 'shortly after my appointment both my parents died and Paul's kindness and understanding helped me through a difficult time.' This illustrates Paul's understanding from having lost his own parents at an early age, albeit in very different circumstances. Moreover, his association with the Board of Studies is indicative of the breadth of responsibilities that Paul undertook in the wider mathematical scene, including not only the University of London but also the Mathematics Committee of the Science Research Council and the Council and Committees of the Royal Society.

PART B. RESEARCH AND PUBLICATIONS, BY GEORGE BERGMAN

5. FOR THE NON-SPECIALIST: WHAT ARE NON-COMMUTATIVE RINGS?

The main area of Cohn's research was non-commutative rings, and §§6–11 below, written for the reader with some knowledge of that subject, discuss his work. The present section is aimed at giving readers far from that area some idea of what the field he worked in is about.

'Ring' is a term used by mathematicians for any system of entities that can be *added*, *subtracted* and *multiplied*, and in which these operations satisfy certain laws. The most familiar example is the set of integers (whole numbers; positive and negative). The set of all real numbers, and the set of all polynomials with real coefficients, are two more examples of rings.

Let us now consider two less elementary examples, one of which will be familiar to readers who have taken a basic course in linear algebra, while the other will be described for those who have had a semester of calculus.

The first is the ring of $n \times n$ matrices over the real numbers, for a fixed $n > 1$. Note that concepts of adding, subtracting and multiplying $n \times n$ matrices are indeed defined, and again yield $n \times n$ matrices; note also that these satisfy most of the familiar laws satisfied by the similarly named concepts for numbers, for example $A(B + C) = AB + AC$. But there is one law that holds for numbers but not for matrices: commutativity of multiplication, $ab = ba$. For two $n \times n$ matrices A and B, one typically has $AB \neq BA$.

As our other example, let us consider certain *operations* on polynomials $f(x)$, namely *multiplication by x*, which, as an operation, we will call X, and *differentiation with respect to x*, generally written d/dx, which we shall here write D. We can define the 'product' of two operations as the result of applying first one and then the other. So, for example, DX is the operation that takes any polynomial $f(x)$ to $D(X(f(x)))$; that is, d/dx $(xf(x))$, and XD takes $f(x)$ to $X(D(f(x))) = x(\mathrm{d}/\mathrm{d}x\, f(x))$. Addition and subtraction are defined more mundanely; for instance, $D + X$ takes each $f(x)$ to $D(f(x)) + X(f(x))$. If we now allow ourselves to form all the operations that can be obtained from these two operations X and D, and the real numbers (where each real number r is regarded as the operation of multiplying polynomials by r), using repeated applications of addition, subtraction and multiplication, we get what is called the 'ring of differential operators generated by X and D'. Like the ring of $n \times n$ matrices, this ring fails to satisfy the commutative law of multiplication. Indeed, using the product law for differentiation from calculus, the reader can check that $DX - XD = 1$. (Incidentally, in the magical realm of quantum mechanics, it is this instance of non-commutativity of differential operators that yields the Heisenberg uncertainty principle, saying that one cannot exactly measure both the position and the velocity of a particle simultaneously.)

This is not the place to give the full list of conditions defining a ring. Suffice it to say that the most studied class of these objects, called *commutative rings*, satisfy a list of laws that includes commutativity of multiplication, $ab = ba$, whereas the main area of Cohn's research was *non-commutative rings*, rings for which the other main conditions are assumed, but not that one; and which thus include the two examples just noted.

Going back to the commutative ring we began with: at some time in our childhood, we learn the structure of the ring of integers; not long afterwards, we learn about rational numbers (fractions). But in learning about the latter, we do not start from scratch: we learn that each fraction is obtained by dividing one integer by another. Much later, we learn that by dividing one polynomial by another, we similarly get things called *rational functions*. Commutative rings such as the ring of the rational numbers, and the ring of rational functions in x and y, in which one can *divide* any element by any nonzero element, are called *fields*. Based on the way in which rational numbers are constructed from integers, the field of rational numbers is called the *field of quotients* of the ring of integers; and the field of rational functions is likewise the field of quotients of the polynomial ring.

Not every commutative ring has a field of quotients. For instance, if one starts with polynomial functions on the plane (polynomials in two variables) and then restricts the set on which one considers them from the whole plane to the union of the x axis and the y axis, one finds that, for these restricted polynomial functions, the function x and the function y, though neither is the zero function, have for product the zero function, and this throws a monkey-wrench into any attempt to form a field of quotients in which both x and y can occur as denominators.

But the answers to the questions of *which* rings have fields of quotients, and how to compute with these, have long been understood, and are second nature to any algebraist.

Not so for non-commutative rings! But—as described for the specialist in the next few sections—a major part (although far from all) of Paul's work was to advance enormously our understanding of that subject.

(We remark that although the term 'non-commutative rings' is used, as above, when contrasting the subject with that of commutative rings, the subject does not exclude rings that are commutative, but merely includes them along with those that are not; workers in the field often call the objects of their study 'associative rings', alluding to the identity $a(bc) = (ab)c$, which *is* still assumed. Both terms are used in the sections below, depending on the point being made.)

6. THE PROBLEM: MAPPING RINGS INTO DIVISION RINGS

In surveying Paul's research, we will begin with his stunning achievement, the classification of homomorphisms from a fixed associative ring R into division rings* D, then move backwards and forwards from there. To see what he gave us, we need to review some background.

For a commutative ring R, the classification of homomorphisms into fields is well understood. The image of R under a homomorphism into a field F is an integral domain, hence isomorphic to R/P for some prime ideal $P \subseteq R$. The subfield of F generated by the image of R can thus be identified with the field of quotients $Q(R/P)$. Hence, given R, the isomorphism classes of pairs (F, f), where F is a field and $f : R \rightarrow F$ a ring homomorphism such that $f(R)$ generates F as a field, correspond bijectively to the prime ideals of R.

In this classical situation, if we take for R a polynomial ring $k[X_1, \ldots, X_n]$ over a field k, and take for P the zero ideal, we get the rational function field $k(X_1, \ldots, X_n)$. We would like to say that this is an extension of k as a field by a 'universal' n-tuple of elements, but what universal property can these elements have? Given $a_1, \ldots, a_n$ in an arbitrary field extension F of k, there will not, in general, exist a homomorphism $k(X_1, \ldots, X_n) \rightarrow F$ carrying each X_i to a_i, since field homomorphisms are one-to-one.

Yet every element of $k(a_1, \ldots, a_n)$ can clearly be obtained by substituting $a_1, \ldots, a_n$ for $X_1, \ldots, X_n$ in some element of $k(X_1, \ldots, X_n)$. If we analyse this fact, we discover that $k(a_1, \ldots, a_n)$ is a homomorphic image of a *local subring* of $k(X_1, \ldots, X_n)$, consisting of those rational functions that can be written with denominators that do not vanish under the indicated substitution. A homomorphism φ from a local subring of a field E to another field F is called a *specialization* from E to F. These are trickier to study than homomorphisms from E to F, because E alone does not determine the domain of the map φ; but once one sets up the right definitions, one finds that $k(X_1, \ldots, X_n)$ is indeed generated over k by an n-tuple $X_1, \ldots, X_n$ universal with respect to specializations.

None of the above elegant theory appears to be applicable to non-commutative rings. A non-commutative ring R without zero divisors need not be embeddable in a division ring; and if it is embeddable, the structure of the division ring generated by its image is not in general unique. The first fact means that the possible kernels of homomorphisms f from a fixed ring R into division rings D form some non-obvious subclass of the completely prime ideals (the ideals P such that R/P has no zero divisors); the second means that when D is a division ring generated by the image of a homomorphism f on R, the kernel of f may not be enough to determine the pair (D, f) up to isomorphism. For an explicit example of this

---

* Paul used the term 'field' in the context of non-commutative ring theory to mean 'division ring'. Terms used by others have included 'skew field' and its abbreviation 'sfield'. Below we will use the term 'division ring', reserving 'field' for the commutative concept.

    We will also, for brevity, be loose about questions of which conditions have distinct right and left forms; e.g., we will not mention, when we introduce the properties of being a fir and a semifir in §§8 and 9, that for the former there are distinct 'left fir' and 'right fir' conditions, while the latter is right–left symmetric.

second fact, let us recall that the free monoid $\langle X, Y \rangle$ on two generators has many embeddings in groups, and let us compare two of these: (i) its canonical embedding in the free group on X and Y, and (ii) the map into the group of invertible affine transformations of the real line, $\{a_{m,b} : t \mapsto mt + b \mid m \neq 0\}$, given by $X \mapsto x = a_{1/2,\,0}$, $Y \mapsto y = a_{1/2,\,1/2}$. (Key to showing that this map is an embedding: examine the relation between a monoid word $w(X, Y)$ and the interval $w(x, y)([0,1]) \subseteq [0,1]$.) These monoid embeddings induce embeddings of the monoid algebra $k\langle X, Y \rangle$ over any field k, that is, the free associative algebra on X and Y, into the group algebras of these two groups. As a consequence of the orderability of these groups, their group algebras can each be embedded in a Mal'cev–Neumann division ring of formal power series (see Mal'cev (1948) and Neumann (1949)). Now the elements x and y used in (ii) have the property that xy^{-1} and $y^{-1}x$ commute (since they are both translations), while in the free group on X and Y used in (i), XY^{-1} and $Y^{-1}X$ do not commute; so the two pairs (D, f) are not isomorphic, although both maps f are injective.

What about the question of finding a 'universal' division algebra over k on an n-tuple of elements $X_1, \ldots, X_n$? That is, among embeddings of the free associative algebra $k\langle X_1, \ldots, X_n \rangle$ in division algebras, is there one that is universal with respect to specialization? S. A. Amitsur in fact proved (Amitsur 1966) that there exists a division ring having the desired universal property, which he constructed by using an ultraproduct of division rings generated by generic matrices of unbounded integer sizes over commutative rings. But is there any natural way to obtain this division ring from $k\langle X_1, \ldots, X_n \rangle$? I had played with that question, but concluded that it was a hopeless dream—a dream so beautiful that it was worth trying one's hand at from time to time, but not something one should expect to achieve.

And then Paul astonished us all by solving the problem of classifying homomorphisms of a ring R into division rings, and did this in a way that showed in particular which division ring was universal for $R = k\langle X_1, \ldots, X_n \rangle$.

7. PRIME MATRIX IDEALS

The key insight of his approach (which he says in the notes to Chapter 7 of (14) was inspired by work of Schützenberger and Nivat on rational non-commuting formal power series) is that to study a homomorphism $f : R \mapsto D$, one should look not merely at the set of elements of R that go to zero under f, but also at the set of square matrices over R that become singular under f, which he named the *singular kernel* of f.

He showed that the singular kernel of f precisely determines the rational relations satisfied by the images of the elements of R in D; he found necessary and sufficient conditions for a set P of square matrices over an arbitrary associative ring R to be such a singular kernel, calling a set with these properties a 'prime matrix ideal' of R; and he obtained an explicit construction for the division subring of D generated by $f(R)$ in terms of that singular kernel.

He showed, moreover, that *inclusions* of prime matrix ideals correspond to *specializations* over R between the corresponding division rings; and for an important class of rings R, the *free ideal rings* (whose definition we shall recall in the next section), which include the free associative algebras $k\langle X_i \mid i \in I \rangle$, he showed that the class of prime matrix ideals has a smallest member, the set of all square matrices A that can be factored $A = BC$ where B is $d \times (d - 1)$ and C is $(d - 1) \times d$. Thus, the division ring corresponding to that prime matrix ideal has the desired universal property.

For another class of examples to which these results were immediately applicable, consider any two rings R_1 and R_2 with a common subring R_0. One can form their coproduct $R_1 *_{R_0} R_2$ with amalgamation of R_0, and Paul had previously shown that if R_0 was a division ring D_0, and R_1 and R_2 were free ideal rings, then this coproduct was again a free ideal ring. Hence this is true, *a fortiori*, when all three objects are division rings, D_0, D_1 and D_2; and the universal division ring associated with the least prime matrix ideal of the free ideal ring $D_1 *_{D_0} D_2$ gives a 'coproduct of D_1 and D_2 over D_0 as division rings', $D_1 \circ_{D_0} D_2$, again characterized as universal with respect to specialization.

Paul obtained the above results in about 1970, announced them in 1971 in (12), and gave the detailed proofs in (13) and (15).

8. FREE IDEAL RINGS ...

We stated, above, an elegant description of the least prime matrix ideal of R in the case where R is a free ideal ring.

What is a 'free ideal ring'?

That concept had developed out of Paul's earlier work on free associative algebras $k\langle X_i \mid i \in I \rangle$ (k a field). When $|I| = 1$, this algebra $k\langle X \rangle$ is also the free commutative associative algebra; that is, the polynomial algebra $k[X]$, which by the division algorithm for polynomials is a principal ideal domain. As soon as $|I| = 2$, however, both the polynomial ring $k[X, Y]$ and the free associative algebra $k\langle X, Y \rangle$ lose the property that ideals, respectively left ideals, are principal; it is easy to see that neither the ideal of the first nor the left ideal of the second generated by X and Y can be generated by a single element. In the case of $k\langle X, Y \rangle$, those generators are in fact left linearly independent over the base ring, which makes the ring particularly bad from the classical point of view. Rings without zero divisors in which any two nonzero elements have a nonzero common left multiple are the *left Ore* rings, the rings for which the classical construction of division rings of fractions is possible; so the existence of elements without such a left common multiple puts free associative algebras 'beyond the pale'. Yet looking at things another way, the fact that X and Y are left linearly independent means that the left ideal that they generate is a *free* left module, and in that respect, it resembles ideals of $k[X]$ better than the ideal of $k[X, Y]$ generated by X and Y.

Of course, not every pair of nonzero elements of $k\langle X, Y \rangle$ is left linearly independent. Obvious counterexamples are pairs of elements $f(u)$ and $g(u)$, where u is any element of that ring, and f and g are polynomials in one indeterminate over k, since they satisfy $f(u)g(u) = g(u)f(u)$. A less obvious example is given by the elements $YX + 1$ and X, which have the common left multiple $XYX + X$. But in both these cases, one finds that the left ideal generated by our two elements is free on *one* generator. (For the $f(u), g(u)$ case, one can deduce this by applying the division algorithm to the polynomials $f(t), g(t) \in k[t]$; in the other case, we see that $1 \cdot (YX + 1) - Y \cdot X = 1$, so that $YX + 1$ and X generate $R \cdot 1$ as a left ideal.)

And, to make a long story short, every left ideal of $k\langle X, Y \rangle$ (and more generally, of the free associative algebra on any set, finite or infinite, over a field) is free on some set of generators.

Over a non-commutative ring, even the classification of free modules can be messy, since such a module may have free bases of various cardinalities; but this does not happen over our free associative algebras. (It is automatically excluded over any ring admitting a homomorphism to a field.) Paul gave rings with this combination of properties—that all left ideals are free, and all free modules have invariant basis number—the name *free ideal rings*, or *firs* (6).

(L. A. Skornjakov of Moscow wrote a paper (1965) in which he renamed firs *konovskije kol'ca* ['Cohn rings']. Paul was upset: 'But then what will I call them?' Fortunately for him, his term 'fir' prevailed.)

How does one prove a ring to be a fir? One sufficient condition that Paul established is an elegant generalization of the division algorithm for polynomials. Recall that that algorithm says that given two elements $a, b \in k[X]$ with $b \neq 0$, we can, by subtracting a left multiple of b from a, reduce its degree to less than that of b. The modified condition, for two elements a and b of a ring with a degree function v, says roughly that one can do the same *if* the elements a and b are left linearly dependent. More precisely, rather than restricting to the case where a and b have an actual left linear dependence relation, one merely assumes that the sum of some left multiple of a and some left multiple of b has less than the expected degree (that they are 'left v-dependent'), and concludes that the greater of the degrees of a and b can be reduced by subtracting from the element of that degree an appropriate left multiple of the other element. This property is actually a statement about elements-modulo-elements-of-lower-degree (technically: elements of the associated graded ring). Rather than just assuming that condition for pairs of elements, Paul's condition assumes the corresponding statement for arbitrary finite families, so that one can handle left ideals generated by more than two elements.

Because of the added v-dependence hypothesis, Paul named his condition 'the weak algorithm' (5). In retrospect, the term is excessively self-effacing. Although the condition can be looked at as a weakening of the classical division algorithm by the addition of an extra hypothesis, that extra hypothesis is vacuous in the commutative case, while in the non-commutative case it is what we need if the algorithm is not to force our rings to be Ore rings; that is, next-door to commutative. So the 'weak algorithm' is not really weak. But the name (like 'imaginary number') has become standard.

Workers in commutative ring theory, and its partners algebraic geometry and number theory, far outnumber those in non-commutative rings, and tend to regard the latter area as excessively 'far out'. ('If we don't know our rings are commutative, how can we trust anything we know?') Among non-commutative ring theorists there is a tension between the tendencies to hug close to the border with the more popular commutative theory, judging results as 'good' to the extent that they look like standard results from the commutative case, and to venture far from the commutative and discover what results are natural to the rings one finds there. Paul was one who strode into the wilds of the non-commutative, and uncovered great beauty.

The above dichotomy between mimicking the commutative world and leaving it behind is, of course, an oversimplification. Indeed, the way the above discussion introduced the concepts of fir and weak algorithm shows that what happens deep in the world of the non-commutative may be describable by a creative extension of what is known in the commutative case.

Another such creative generalization concerns the concept of torsion module. Over a commutative principal ideal domain R, one knows exactly what the finitely generated torsion modules look like: they are direct sums of modules R/Rq, where q is a power of a nonzero irreducible element of R. When R is a non-commutative fir, the first question we must decide is what class of modules to focus on. Given a nonzero element $a \in R$, there will typically be elements $b \in R$ that are left linearly independent of a, in which case the image of b in R/Ra will not be a torsion element. So: should we look at some class of modules typified by the modules R/Ra $(a \neq 0)$, or at a class of modules all of whose elements are torsion? Paul discovered that one obtains a beautiful theory if one makes the former choice and studies finitely generated left modules in which the number of relators equals the number of generators, in a robust way;

precisely, modules $M = R^d/R^dA$, where A is a $d \times d$ matrix that *cannot* be factored $A = BC$, where B is $d \times (d-1)$ and C is $(d-1) \times d$. Over a commutative principal ideal domain, the modules with such presentations are the finitely generated torsion modules. Paul called such left modules M over a fir *left torsion modules* (10), and the analogous class of right modules the *right torsion modules*; he showed that each of these classes forms an abelian category, and that there is a duality (contravariant equivalence) between the two categories. The existence, within torsion modules, of non-torsion submodules, noted above, turns out to be immaterial: one cannot 'see' such a submodule from within the category because it is never the kernel or image of a homomorphism of torsion modules.

We do not yet have the understanding of torsion modules over general firs that we do for commutative principal ideals domains. In the latter case, the minimal building blocks are the modules R/Rp for p an irreducible element of R, and these fit together in easily understood ways. In the general case, more exploration is needed.

The module theory of firs turned out to be providential as background for Paul's construction of universal maps into division rings, and it is tempting to conjecture that this work in the years preceding 1970 was aimed at providing that background—tempting, but unlikely. It is hard to imagine that, before discovering the relevant properties of free algebras, one could predict what use they could be put to. And in working with Paul on firs, free algebras, and so on, from 1966 onwards, I heard no foreshadowing of this idea.

Still, the preface of the first edition of (14) begins with the quotation from *A Midsummer Night's Dream*,

> I have had a dream,—
>> past the wit of man to say what dream it was:
> man is but an ass,
>> if he go about to expound his dreams.

So who knows what dream he may have been keeping to himself?

9. ... AND THEIR RELATIVES

Paul brought together in his 1971 book (14) the main results that had been obtained so far in this area. Its title, *Free rings and their relations*, is a multiple play on words.

A free object is, by definition, presented by generators subject to *no relations*; so that title is, on the face of it, an oxymoron. However, elements other than the free generators can satisfy non-trivial relations—we noted, for instance, the relation $X \cdot (YX + 1) = (XY + 1) \cdot X$—and the study of such relations is, in one form or another, what much of the theory of free algebras is about.

'Relations' also means 'relatives', and it would be a pity to prove results for free rings alone, without looking at larger classes of rings to which the same or similar methods apply. We have already seen that free algebras fall within the class of rings with weak algorithm, and these within the class of firs. Other examples of firs include group algebras of free groups, and, as we have mentioned, ring-coproducts of division rings.

Recall that whereas the classical division algorithm concerns pairs of elements, the statement of the weak algorithm refers to arbitrary finite families. If we only assume the condition of that algorithm for families of $\leq n$ elements, for a given n, we have what Paul named the 'n-term weak algorithm', yielding rings in which every left ideal generated by $\leq n$ elements is free of unique rank; these he named *n-firs*. He showed in particular that, for various sorts of rings arising from *universal matrix constructions*, if those constructions are such that, whenever a matrix with r columns is multiplied by a matrix with r rows in one of the imposed relations, we have $r > n$, then the resulting ring will satisfy the *n*-term weak algorithm (8).

There are also rings that are *n*-firs for every positive integer *n*, and are thus called *semifirs*, but which are not firs. Such examples cannot be established directly by the weak algorithm, because if a degree function v satisfies the relevant condition for all finite *n*, the ring is a fir. But one can get examples as direct limits of firs (for example, $k[X, X^{1/2}, \ldots, X^{2^{-n}}, \ldots]$ is a direct limit of polynomial rings $k[t]$) or by ultraproduct constructions.

It is a general principle of module theory that whatever free modules are good for, *projective* modules are likely to be equally good for; so important relatives of firs and semifirs are rings all of whose left ideals (respectively finitely generated left ideals) are projective as modules. These are the left (*semi*)*hereditary* rings. To make these conditions comparable to those of being a (semi)fir, one needs some analogue of the condition that free modules have unique rank. One such condition is the existence of a 'rank' function from isomorphism classes of finitely generated projective modules to natural numbers (or non-negative rationals, or reals) under which the rank of a direct sum is the sum of the ranks of the summands, and Paul also studied rings of these sorts.

Finally, although rings like $k[X, Y]$ are homologically 'worse' than rings like $k[X]$ and $k\langle X, Y \rangle$, they still have good qualities. Paul investigated a class of non-commutative rings that are as well-behaved as $k[X, Y]$ and better than $k[X, Y, Z]$, namely the rings over which Sylvester's law of nullity holds, a matrix-theoretic property that has a key role in the construction of the universal division rings of firs. He named these *Sylvester domains*. They include all free associative algebras over commutative principal ideal domains; for example $\mathbb{Z}\langle X, Y \rangle$.

A different sort of 'relatives' of free algebras are non-commuting formal power-series algebras. To say that the relation between a free associative algebra $k\langle X_i \mid i \in I \rangle$ and the formal power-series algebra $k\langle\langle X_i \mid i \in I \rangle\rangle$ is that the latter is a completion of the former is correct, but it is not the most relevant fact for the point at hand. Recall that in studying a free associative algebra, one uses the highest-degree terms of elements to define one's degree function, and uses finite induction to take advantage of the weak algorithm. Elements of a power-series algebra have no highest-degree term, so one looks instead at *lowest*-degree terms. In the non-commutative formal power-series case, an analogue of the weak algorithm allows one to take left linearly dependent elements, and to use left linear maps to strip off more and more low-degree terms from one of them, and finally use completeness to conclude that it is a linear combination of the others. The graded algebras associated with the highest-degree-term filtration in the free algebra case, and with the lowest-degree-term filtration in the formal power-series case, are the same; and the property of those graded algebras that gives the former algebras the weak algorithm, gives the latter the analogous construction sketched above, which Paul named the *inverse weak algorithm*. He showed that a complete filtered ring with inverse weak algorithm is a semifir and is a 'topological fir', in the sense that every one-sided ideal has a linearly independent topological generating set.

10. EARLIER WORK

Paul's 1951 doctoral thesis (1), written under the supervision of Philip Hall, concerned the relation between free groups, free associative algebras and free Lie algebras, and his first two published papers were based on that thesis.

Although the subject of free associative algebras points towards his later work, his next few papers moved in various directions with no common theme. Four of them answered some unrelated questions, two posed by B. H. Neumann and two by I. Kaplansky (three counter-examples and a proof all together). There were also two papers on special and semispecial Jordan algebras, two on pseudovaluations on commutative rings, two on rings where all (or almost all) equations $a\xi - \xi b = c$ ($a, b \neq 0$) have solutions, two on embeddings of semigroups, and two expository volumes, one on Lie groups and one on linear equations, as well as single papers on several other topics.

Amid these, in 1959 and 1960, came two papers on *free products* of associative rings, the name that Paul used for coproducts of rings over a common subring when they have the properties that the given rings embed faithfully in the coproduct, and are disjoint except for the common subring. The first of these papers concerned conditions for such free products to exist (that is, for the coproduct to have these properties) in terms of module-theoretic properties of the given system of rings; the second showed that the coproduct of two division rings over a common division subring is (in the language he would later use, noted in the preceding section) a 2-fir. Neither of these results was needed as such in his later work: the free products that he considered later were almost always over division rings, so that the delicate module-theoretic considerations of the 1959 paper were not needed, while the 2-fir result of the 1960 paper was to be subsumed in the statement that such a free product is a fir. But these were steps towards that body of work. The year 1961 saw the first major result in that work, the statement of the weak algorithm (not yet so named) and its consequences, in (2).

Two other 1961 papers of Paul's are also worth mentioning:

On the one hand, in (4) he studied extensions K/k of division rings such that K is 2-dimensional as a *right* k-vector-space. That topic is much less trivial than in the commutative case. In particular, he obtained an example in which the left dimension was not the same as the right dimension, answering a long-standing open question of E. Artin.

In (3), on the other hand, he proved the embeddability of a large class of rings into division rings, not by a construction anything like his later universal one, but under the assumption that the ring has a filtration 'modulo which' it behaves approximately like a right Ore ring. This applies in particular to the universal enveloping algebra of any Lie algebra over a field, because by the Poincaré–Birkhoff–Witt theorem, such a ring has a filtration whose associated graded ring is a commutative polynomial ring. Thus, as he observed, the result is applicable to free associative algebras, regarded as universal enveloping algebras of free Lie algebras. It is striking how dissimilar this filtration is from the one used in his later results, the standard filtration on a free associative algebra.

That free associative algebras could be embedded in division algebras was not new (it had been proved by Moufang (1937), Mal'cev (1948) and Neumann (1949)). But this paper suggests that ways of getting such embeddings, and perhaps the question of whether there were 'canonical' embeddings to be found, may already have been on Paul's mind.

Incidentally, a few years after Paul obtained his universal embedding of $k\langle X_1, \ldots, X_n \rangle$ in a division algebra, Lewin (1974) showed that, in any Mal'cev–Neumann division algebra on the free group on $X_1, \ldots, X_n$, the division subalgebra generated by $X_1, \ldots, X_n$ is isomorphic to Paul's universal division algebra.

11. LATER WORK

Paul's study of universal fields of fractions did not end with the proof of their existence. Just as an element u of the field of fractions of a commutative ring has various expressions ab^{-1}, and one studies the relation between such expressions (finding, for instance, that if the ring is a unique factorization domain, there is an essentially unique expression for u 'in lowest terms'), so, likewise, given an element u of a division ring D generated by an image of a non-commutative ring R, one may look at various expressions for u in terms of inverses of square matrices over R (say as products $x^{\mathrm{T}}A^{-1}y$, where A is an $n \times n$ matrix and x and y are height-n vectors over R—this is one of several closely related forms that Paul studied) and seek 'lowest terms' expressions and other invariants of u. One such invariant, which always has the value 1 in the commutative case but is unbounded in general, is the least n for which one can get such an expression $u = x^{\mathrm{T}}A^{-1}y$, which Paul named the 'depth' of u. He obtained striking results on these topics in (18–20).

If S is a generating set for the above ring R as an algebra over a field k (for instance, if R is the free associative algebra on S), and if one has an expression for an element $u \in D$ using the inverse of a matrix over R as above, then one can construct another such expression for u, in which all the matrix entries are k-linear combinations of 1 and elements of S, at the price of using larger matrices. Properties of such expressions are developed in (24).

Incidentally, ring extensions obtained by inverting matrices are a powerful tool even when the result is not used to construct a skew field, and these are now often known as 'Cohn localizations'; see, for example, Ranicki (2006).

The papers on miscellaneous questions in algebra noted in the preceding section did not come to a halt when Paul began obtaining his central results. If, in his early years, they suggested someone who had not yet found his direction, their continuation indicates that the edifice he was creating did not extinguish his interest in the rest of algebra. Several papers on radical rings, and on general linear groups of commutative rings, are in this category. Of course, one cannot always draw a sharp line separating these from papers in his main area. For example, in (9) he studied the groups GL_2 for many sorts of rings, ranging from classical commutative rings of algebraic integers to free associative algebras. Others of his papers concern properties of division rings obtained by Ore's construction, and so could be considered either as cases of his general theory of division rings or as a visit to a classical topic.

Another important thread in his work, beginning early on and continuing throughout his career, is the factorization of ring elements. His early paper (11) on *commutative* rings with various factorization properties is still regularly cited. The equation $X \cdot (YX + 1) = (XY + 1) \cdot X$ in the free associative algebra $k\langle X, Y \rangle$ (mentioned twice already) might seem to indicate that that ring satisfies nothing like unique factorization. But after one has absorbed Chapter 4 of (29), one can view the theory of commutative UFDs as a degenerate case of the much more diverse theory of not-necessarily-commutative rings with *distributive divisor lattices*, which include the free associative algebras.

Although we suggested that the quote from *A Midsummer Night's Dream* that introduced the first edition of (14) might refer to the dream that was achieved in that book, it could have referred to a grander dream. Some of Paul's later expository articles, such as (16) and (21), look towards the possibility of a full-blown non-commutative algebraic geometry. An important tool in algebraic geometry is the theory of valuations on fields. Valuations on division rings were the topic of the doctoral thesis of one of Paul's students; the two wrote jointly on that topic in (17), and Paul wrote three further papers on the subject.

The question of whether a non-commutative algebraic geometry based on homomorphisms into division rings can in fact be achieved—whether, indeed, it is what we should be looking for—remains to be answered.

12. TEXTBOOKS, TRANSLATIONS, ETC.

If one searches MathSciNet for *books* by Paul, one obtains 25 results. If one cuts this down as far as possible, by treating multivolume works as single items, and by treating as extensions of a work its translations into other languages and its subsequent editions (even if the latter have been considerably revised, and even if they appeared, at the wish of the publisher, under changed titles), one can bring the number down to about 10, to which a web search adds three books not shown on MathSciNet. (He also wrote some mathematical articles for *Encyclopaedia Britannica*, although that work does not show authors' names, so that these articles do not appear in the online bibliography associated with this memoir.)

Two of Paul's books—(14) (revised as (29)) and (23)—are presentations of the central areas of his work: free algebras, free ideal rings, and constructions of division algebras.

Another advanced monograph (7) (which, with its second edition and Russian translation, constitutes three of the MathSciNet listings) is not specific to his area of research, but treats some basic material underlying most of algebra, and the name P. M. Cohn is probably most widely known among mathematicians outside ring theory for that book.

Other advanced monographs include the book on Lie groups mentioned in §10, the one on GL_2 of rings mentioned in §11, a volume on Morita equivalence, and one on algebraic numbers and algebraic functions. At a more elementary level are the notes on linear equations mentioned in §10, a text on linear algebra, one on solid geometry, and a basic graduate text in ring theory.

Finally, Paul was the author of a multi-volume textbook on algebra, which begins with the material of an undergraduate 'abstract algebra' course, covers the graduate 'groups, rings and fields' course, and goes on to more advanced topics. At the wishes of the publishers, the successive revisions of this work several times changed title and number of volumes (it constitutes $7 = 2 + 3 + 2$ MathSciNet citations, and there was a retitled version of one volume not shown by MathSciNet). Its final form comprises two volumes (26, 27).

Paul was comfortable enough with French and German to publish seven papers in the former language and three in the latter, and sufficiently proficient in mathematical Russian to translate two lengthy articles from Russian for the *Encyclopaedia of Mathematical Sciences* in the mid 1990s. He also co-translated from the French, with J. Howie, a volume by Bourbaki.

(He did at least one piece of non-mathematical translation work, mentioned to me in an email of September 1999, in the course of describing the things he was busy with: 'Rather foolishly I took on the job of translating a book on genealogy from … German to English, but that is also finished now. It was extremely interesting, at least from the linguistic point of view, and not always easy.' But I have not been able to find any reference to a book on genealogy listing him as translator.)

Figure 3. Paul Cohn on a walk near to the Weisshorn in Switzerland, March 1994 or 1996.
(Online version in colour.)

13. 'It is not your duty to complete the work'

When one opens the second edition of (14), one finds that the *I have had a dream* quotation has been replaced by one from Rabbi Tarphon (first century CE):

> It is not your duty to complete the work,—
> But neither are you free to desist from it.

This was used again in (29), the final version of (14), on which Paul worked from 1999 to 2004, and which came out shortly after his death.

He is at last free to desist from his work. Let us hope others will carry it further.

Part C. Conclusion, by George Bergman and Trevor Stuart

14. Summary and appreciation

Paul Cohn's achievements in non-commutative ring theory are ones of which he could feel justifiably proud. Moreover his books contributed greatly to algebraic knowledge in the mathematical community, both at the research level and in undergraduate texts. He was greatly revered for these reasons.

His quiet personality, coupled with the ability to listen and respond, was appreciated by students and other researchers alike. He was respected and admired the world over for these qualities. Paul Cohn gave great support to the LMS and was its President from 1982 to 1984.

Paul Cohn was a loving family man who never forgot his background in Germany and who always remembered his parents' sacrifice and devotion in sending him by Kindertransport to England. He cherished his UK citizenship, and England was his home. He had a great love of all activity, including walking in the Alps (figure 3). Moreover he loved mathematics, to which he contributed greatly.

HONOURS AND AWARDS

1972   Lester R. Ford Award, Mathematical Association of America
1974   Senior Berwick Prize, London Mathematical Society
1980   Fellow of the Royal Society
1982–84   President of the London Mathematical Society
1986   Astor Professor of Mathematics at University College London

ACKNOWLEDGEMENTS

We wish to thank especially Juliet Aaronson (Cohn), her mother Deirdre and sister Yael Rappaport, but also Leonid Bokut, David Brannan, the late Carl Faith, Wilfrid Hodges, Alan Pears, Aidan Schofield, Lance Small, Bill Stephenson, Anthony Watkinson and Muhammad Zafrullah for their advice and help.

The frontispiece photograph was taken in 1982 by Godfrey Argent and is reproduced with permission.

REFERENCES TO OTHER AUTHORS

Amitsur, S. A. 1966 Rational identities and applications to algebra and geometry. *J. Algebra* **3**, 304–359.
Faith, C. 1963 Review of (4) below, at http://www.ams.org/mathscinet-getitem?mr=0136633&return=doc.
Lewin, J. 1974 Fields of fractions for group algebras of free groups. *Trans. Am. Math. Soc.* **192**, 339–346.
Mal'cev, A. I. 1948 On the embedding of group algebras in division algebras (Russian). *Doklady Akad. Nauk SSSR* N.S. **60**, 1499–1501.
Moufang, R. 1937 Einige Untersuchungen über geordnete Schiefkörper. *J. Reine Angew. Math.* **176**, 203–223.
Neumann, B. H. 1949 On ordered division rings. *Trans. Am. Math. Soc.* **66**, 202–252.
Ranicki, A. 2006 Noncommutative localization in topology. In *Noncommutative localization in algebra and topology* (London Mathematical Society Lecture Note Series, no. 330) (ed. A. Ranicki), pp. 81–102. London: London Mathematical Society.
Skornjakov, L. A. 1965 On Cohn rings. [In Russian.] *Algebra i Logika Sem.* **4**, 5–30.

BIBLIOGRAPHY

The following publications are those referred to directly in the text. A full bibliography is available as electronic supplementary material at http://dx.doi.org/10.1098/rsbm.2014.0016 or via http://rsbm.royalsocietypublishing.org.

(1)   1951   *Integral modules, Lie-rings and free groups.* PhD thesis, Trinity College, Cambridge.
(2)   1961   On a generalization of the Euclidean algorithm. *Proc. Camb. Phil. Soc.* **57**, 18–30.
(3)   On the embedding of rings in skew fields. *Proc. Lond. Math. Soc.* (3) **11**, 511–530.
(4)   Quadratic extensions of skew fields. *Proc. Lond. Math. Soc.* (3) **11**, 531–556.
(5)   1963   Rings with a weak algorithm. *Trans. Am. Math. Soc.* **109**, 332–356.

(6)   1964   Free ideal rings. *J. Algebra* **1**, 47–69.

(7)   1965   *Universal algebra.* New York: Harper & Row.

(8)   1966   Some remarks on the invariant basis property. *Topology* **5**, 215–228.

(9)   On the structure of the GL_2 of a ring. *Inst. Hautes Études Sci. Publ. Math.* no. 30, pp. 5–53.

(10)   1967   Torsion modules over free ideal rings. *Proc. Lond. Math. Soc.* (3) **17**, 577–599.

(11)   1968   Bezout rings and their subrings. *Proc. Camb. Phil. Soc.* **64**, 251–264.

(12)   1971   Un critère d'immersibilité d'un anneau dans un corps gauche. *C. R. Acad. Sci. Paris* A/B **272**, A1442–A1444.

(13)   The embedding of firs in skew fields. *Proc. Lond. Math. Soc.* (3) **23**, 193–213.

(14)   *Free rings and their relations* (London Mathematical Society Monographs, no. 2). London: London Mathematical Society. (2nd edn, London Mathematical Society Monographs, no. 19; 1985.)

(15)   1972   Universal skew fields of fractions. *Symp. Math.* **8**, 135–148.

(16)   1979   The affine scheme of a general ring. In *Applications of sheaves* (Lecture Notes in Mathematics, no. 753) (ed. M. P. Fourman, C. J. Mulvey & D. S. Scott), pp. 197–211. Berlin: Springer.

(17)   1980   (With M. Mahdavi-Hezavehi) Extensions of valuations on skew fields. In *Ring theory, Antwerp* (*Proceedings of a Conference at the University of Antwerp, Antwerp, 1980*) (Lecture Notes in Mathematics, no. 825) (ed. F. van Oystaeyen), pp. 28–41. Berlin: Springer.

(18)   1982   The universal field of fractions of a semifir. I. Numerators and denominators. *Proc. Lond. Math. Soc.* (3) **44**, 1–32.

(19)   1985   The universal field of fractions of a semifir. II. The depth. *Proc. Lond. Math. Soc.* (3) **50**, 69–94.

(20)   The universal field of fractions of a semifir. III. Centralizers and normalizers. *Proc. Lond. Math. Soc.* (3) **50**, 95–113.

(21)   Principles of noncommutative algebraic geometry. In *Rings and geometry* (*Proceedings of the NATO Advanced Study Institute, Istanbul, Turkey, 2–14 September 1984*) (NATO Advanced Science Institutes Series C (Mathematical and Physical Sciences), no. 160) (ed. R. Kaya, P. Plaumann & K. Strambach), pp. 3–37. Dordrecht: Reidel.

(22)   1990   [Untitled account.] In *I came alone: the stories of the Kindertransports* (ed. B. Leverton & S. Lowensohn), pp. 56–59. Lewes: The Book Guild Ltd.

(23)   1995   Skew fields. Theory of general division rings. In *Encyclopedia of mathematics and its applications*, p. 57. Cambridge University Press.

(24)   1999   (With C. Reutenauer) On the construction of the free field. *Int. J. Algebra Comput.* **9**, 307–323.

(25)   2001   Mathematics. In *Bedford College, Memories of 150 Years* (ed. J. Mordaunt Crook), ch. 12. London: Royal Holloway and Bedford New College.

(26)   2003   *Basic algebra. Groups, rings and fields.* London: Springer.

(27)   *Further algebra and applications.* London: Springer.

(28)   2006   Kindheit in Hamburg. In *Eine verschwundene Welt. Jüdisches Leben am Grindel* (ed. U. Wamser & W. Weinke), pp. 316–319. Springe: zu Klampen Verlag. (Expanded and revised from *Ehemals in Hamburg zu Hause: Jüdisches Leben am Grindel*; VSA-Verlag, Hamburg, 1991). An English translation of Cohn's narrative in this book is given at http://rsbm.royalsocietypublishing.org/content/suppl/2014/08/14/rsbm.2014.0016.DC1/rsbm20140016supp2.pdf.

(29)   *Free ideal rings and localization in general rings* (New Mathematical Monographs, no. 3). Cambridge University Press.

JAMES FRANKLIN CROW

18 January 1916 — 4 January 2012

James F. Crow

JAMES FRANKLIN CROW

18 January 1916 — 4 January 2012

Elected ForMemRS 2001

By Daniel L. Hartl[1] and Rayla Greenberg Temin[2]

[1]*Department of Organismic and Evolutionary Biology, Harvard University, Cambridge, MA 02138, USA*

[2]*Laboratory of Genetics, University of Wisconsin, Madison, WI 53706, USA*

James Crow enjoyed relating how he and the first issue of the journal *Genetics* were scheduled to arrive on the same day—18 January 1916—and how he was delivered on time, whereas the journal was delivered several weeks late (22)*. The coincidence was altogether fitting, as Crow became one of the leading geneticists of the twentieth century. Renowned as scholar, teacher, mentor, author and historian, he had a career in science that spanned 70 years, primarily at the University of Wisconsin–Madison. Professor Crow's research was in theoretical and experimental population genetics, focusing on *Drosophila* as his model organism and extending his results to human genetics. He had further influence on the field of genetics as a writer and speaker and as a synthesizer and disseminator of knowledge, and he performed service to his colleagues in many different capacities.

Early life, 1916–37

James Crow was born in Phoenixville, Pennsylvania. At the time, his father taught biology at Ursinus College in nearby Collegeville. In 1918 the family moved to Wichita, Kansas, where his father, who was able to obtain a position teaching biology at Friends University, could care for his own ageing parents.

Crow's mother and father had both studied at Friends; his father later attended the University of Kansas and earned a masters degree with Clarence E. McClung, the famous

* Numbers in this form refer to the bibliography at the end of the text.

This memoir originally appeared in *Biographical Memoirs of the US National Academy of Sciences* and is reprinted, with slight modifications, with permission.

grasshopper geneticist who discovered the X chromosome. The family's return to Wichita took place while the 1918 influenza pandemic was in full force, and the two-year-old baby Crow became infected and barely survived (Harper 2005).

The family was poor, but not destitute, and as devout Quakers, Crow's parents practised a life of modesty and simplicity. Intellectual pursuits were encouraged, and the young Crow had reading and music lessons as a child. His parents thought he had deep sensitivity to music because whenever they played a recording of Edward MacDowell's 'To a wild rose' on their wind-up Victrola—a selection that Crow later called 'pretty corny music'—the boy would go off into a corner and sob (25). Actually, the song reminded him of the leaping flames that had frightened him when a neighbouring house had burned down (25). But his reaction inspired his parents to start him on piano lessons at the age of six, and at eight years of age he switched to violin.

As a first-grader, James was enrolled in a rural two-room school, but a few years later he moved to the urban Wichita system (22). He went on to the newly built Wichita North High School on the banks of the Little Arkansas River, where his favourite subjects were music, mathematics, chemistry and physics. At first he planned to be a professional musician and he studied violin and viola diligently, but soon Crow realized that although he loved music and was good at it, his talent was not that of a professional. Nevertheless, music became a lifetime avocation (25).

He polished his social skills working nights operating the soda fountain in a drugstore frequented by high-school and college students. In his senior year of high school he took a job at the Wichita Public Library, working five hours every afternoon and all day Saturday as a reference librarian, looking up whatever people asked to know. In this activity, he said, 'I think I learned a comparable amount to what I was learning in school' (25).

For college, Crow attended Friends University, and with characteristic energy he was a full-time student while continuing to work as a reference librarian. He also played viola in dance orchestras, in a string quartet broadcast weekly on the radio, and in what eventually became the Wichita Symphony Orchestra. Having decided against a career in music, he successively considered physics, chemistry and biology. His interest in biology was piqued by a genetics course in his junior year (26), and he graduated with high honours in 1937 with majors in biology and chemistry.

THE TEXAS YEARS, 1937–41

For graduate school in biology or genetics, Crow had several options, but he chose the first school that accepted his application, the University of Texas at Austin (25). Turned down by Harvard and California Institute of Technology, he did receive an offer from the University of Wisconsin–Madison in biochemistry. He later reflected, 'The Texas offer came first, and I was so insecure [it was 1937, the depths of the Great Depression] that I accepted it almost immediately. I expect that if I'd been offered … a good … fellowship at Wisconsin, I'd have accepted that … and been a biochemist.'

Crow began graduate studies at the University of Texas in the fall of 1937. He had initially hoped to work with Hermann J. Muller (ForMemRS 1953), *Drosophila* geneticist nonpareil, who 10 years earlier had discovered that X-rays cause mutations, for which he was awarded the 1946 Nobel Prize in Physiology or Medicine. However, Muller, who had

Figure 1. J. F. Crow, his wife Ann, and their family in 1957. Son Franklin is behind the couch, Laura (with pearls) is to Ann's left, and Catherine (with braids) is between Jim and Ann. The dog's name is Socks.

communist sympathies at the time and was involved in leftist political activities, had gone on leave, first to Germany in 1932 and then to Russia, and he never did return to Austin (21).

Crow decided to work with John T. Patterson and Wilson S. Stone. Patterson, already well known for his work on polyembryony in the armadillo, which usually gives birth to four genetically identical offspring, had become increasingly interested in genetics. 'Dr. Pat', as he was known, was a gruff and portly man with a dark complexion, who introduced himself to his new graduate student by saying, 'You are blonder and skinnier than I thought you would be', whereupon he talked about his collection of Indian arrowheads (24). Crow later described Patterson as 'my crusty and earthy major professor' (14).

The Patterson and Stone laboratory at the University of Texas was to evolutionary genetics of the fruitfly *Drosophila* what the Thomas Hunt Morgan laboratory at Columbia University was to the formal genetics of *Drosophila*. Thanks to these two groups, *Drosophila* was developed as a classic model organism for the study of evolution and genetics.

The Texas laboratory provided a lively intellectual environment, and Crow had a happy experience as a student and as a teaching assistant in the cytology and embryology laboratories. In his first year he helped Stone solve a problem in mathematics, whereupon Stone encouraged him to read the papers of Sewall Wright (ForMemRS 1963) and Ronald A. (later Sir Ronald) Fisher FRS, the famous founders (along with J. B. S. Haldane FRS) of modern population genetics. Crow found this work fascinating and decided to specialize in population genetics himself. Assigned to study species in the *Drosophila mulleri* group, he discovered a mutation that caused lethality between, but not within, species. This mutation formed the basis of the thesis for his PhD, which he received in 1941.

While a graduate student, Crow played viola in the University Orchestra, where he met Ann Crockett, who played clarinet. They married in 1941 after his graduation (25) and were together for 60 years; Ann Crockett Crow passed away in 2001. They had three children: Franklin, Laura and Catherine (figure 1).

A memorable incident from Crow's days in the University Orchestra melded his musical and scientific activities. One day he left his viola in the laboratory, so that he could pick it up later on his way to a concert. One of his laboratory mates took the opportunity to stealthily place thousands of anaesthetized fruitflies inside the viola, timing it so that as Crow began to play at the performance, the flies gradually awakened and fluttered up out of the F-holes. He often recounted this as 'one of the diabolically cleverest jokes that anyone ever perpetrated' (25).

DARTMOUTH, 1941–47

Crow had hoped to do postdoctoral studies with Sewall Wright at the University of Chicago, but by then it was clear that the USA would become involved in World War II, and plans changed. Crow accepted a one-year teaching position at Dartmouth College substituting for James V. Neel, who had taken leave to try a year in medical school. Neel never came back and went on to establish a brilliant career in human genetics. Crow stayed on at Dartmouth.

'When I was in graduate school,' he recalled, 'I really expected to be a teacher. I wasn't sure that I was cut out for research' (22). His Dartmouth years gave him ample opportunity to teach. He was hired to teach genetics and general zoology, but, following his own desire, he added embryology and comparative anatomy to his teaching load. Once the war was on, he took a course in navigation, in case he might be drafted, and he found the subject quite easy. He passed the exam with a score high enough to qualify him as an instructor, and so he taught navigation, too. But he was the only one around who had ever studied parasitology, and his arm was twisted to teach that course also, which he did by staying only a day or two ahead of his students. Part of his study of tropical diseases and parasitology was in a month-long course in Guatemala and Costa Rica, which he very much enjoyed (25). The medical school decided soon afterwards that they needed a course in statistics, and Crow was the logical instructor. All this transpired while he was teaching mathematics to undergraduates. As a member of the biology department, he could teach whatever mathematics he wanted, and so he included analytical geometry and three semesters of calculus. Of this dizzying schedule, he later reflected: 'At least one student and possibly half a dozen had six or seven courses all taught by me—so I was totally responsible for whatever these students knew. … Much of the time, need I say, I was barely ahead of the class, but I never regretted the broadening experience' (26).

Until the war, Crow had been a pacifist, and as a graduate student he was active in peace groups that later proved to be fronts for the Communist Party. This caused him anxiety during the McCarthy years (1950–56), but nothing ever came of it. At Dartmouth he informed his draft board that he was willing to serve in the armed forces if called, but evidently his teaching led to his continued deferment (26).[1]

Amidst the heavy teaching, the turmoil of war, and a new baby (Franklin was born in 1943), Crow managed to carry out and publish original research. Always interested in mathematics, he found a mathematical series that made the significance level of a χ^2 test essentially a linear function of the χ^2 value. He set out to produce a set of graphs of significance level against χ^2 for various degrees of freedom, which he did by expanding the series, which proved to converge very slowly. 'And it took me all afternoon with [an] old-fashioned kind of chunk, chunk, chunk calculator … [and] I finally finished this graph and published it in the *Journal of the*

American Statistical Association [(1)]. ... [It is] far and away the most popular thing I've ever done in the sense of the number of copies and reprints requested' (25).

During this period, he also pondered the phenomenon of heterosis, in which hybrids of inbred lines usually show improved performance over the parental inbreds. He suggested two hypotheses: (i) 'nicking', which means that inbred lines are inferior because each is homozygous for many recessive deleterious mutant alleles of small effect, and (ii) 'overdominance', which means that hybrids are superior because, on a gene-by-gene basis, heterozygous genotypes are better than homozygous genotypes (2). The distinction set off decades of research, and although more than a handful of individual genes showing overdominance have been discovered, the overwhelming evidence favours nicking.

Among the most sociable people that either of us has ever met, Crow kept up his professional contacts even while under pressure of work at Dartmouth. For example, H. J. Muller was at Amherst College in Massachusetts, and Crow drove to meet him on several occasions. After the war, when Muller moved to Indiana University in Bloomington, Crow took a semester of leave and spent some of the time in Bloomington, interacting on a daily basis with Muller, for whom he had enormous respect.

WISCONSIN, 1948–2012

It was the University of Wisconsin–Madison that opened Crow's door to the broad sunlit uplands of his career. It all started in the summer of 1947 when he attended a Cold Spring Harbor Symposium and met Joshua Lederberg (ForMemRS 1979). Lederberg had given a talk on recombination in bacteria, and Crow asked a question about crossover interference. Lederberg was impressed that anyone in the audience knew enough about crossover interference to ask an intelligent question, and the two men had a lengthy conversation afterwards. Lederberg was just about to start a position at the University of Wisconsin, and in the next year Crow received a job offer from 'out of the blue', though presumably at Lederberg's behest (22). Lederberg became one of Crow's closest personal friends and a valued scientific colleague. They talked almost every day.

It was a great disappointment when Lederberg left Wisconsin for Stanford in 1958, shortly after being awarded the Nobel Prize in Physiology or Medicine. Lederberg had hoped to entice Crow to join him at Stanford, but Crow decided to stay in Wisconsin. This seems to have been the only time that Crow seriously considered leaving the University of Wisconsin (22).

TEACHER AND MENTOR

From the beginning, Crow regarded his teaching career as at least as important as his research. He was a popular and successful teacher and won several teaching awards. Almost every year from 1948 until his retirement in 1986, he taught a large-enrolment undergraduate genetics course, General Genetics 560. The course was legendary. He obviously loved to teach, and came so well prepared that his lectures seemed extemporaneous. Relying mainly on blackboards and chalk, he could explain a complex concept so lucidly that a student could seemingly understand it clearly during the lecture, but then realize after class that the concept was not so simple after all.

Figure 2. J. F. Crow lecturing on population genetics in 1979.

His lectures (figure 2) were enlivened with humorous anecdotes and historical asides. And, to spare students the chore of taking notes while listening, he published his lecture notes as a book, *Genetics notes*, referred to by everyone as 'Crow's Notes'. Eventually it went into eight editions (12) and was translated into several languages. *Crow's notes* included interesting and challenging problems, which were educational in their own right. The early editions had a spiral wire binding and were printed only on the left-hand pages, leaving the right side pages blank for students to take additional notes. By the sixth edition (1966), there had been so many advances in genetics that *Crow's notes* had to be printed on both sides of the page. Crow often joked that genetics was such a fast-moving field that he could ask the same exam questions every year and merely change the answers.

In addition to General Genetics, Crow taught courses in population genetics, human genetics, segments of other courses, and various graduate seminars. The content of his population genetics course formed the framework of his influential book with Motoo Kimura (ForMemRS 1993), *An introduction to population genetics theory* (8).

Crow also spent time in Hollywood consulting on a 53-minute 1960 Warner Brothers film, 'The Thread of Life', which dealt with genetics and heredity in humans, showing various traits and the methods used to study their inheritance.[2]

Although undergraduate teaching was a pleasure for him and he did it most willingly, Crow excelled at mentoring graduate students. He later commented, 'Part of my legacy is students …. I've been conspicuously successful with graduate students' (Hartl 2011). And so he was. Many of his former graduate and postdoctoral students went on to make distinguished careers of their own.[3] He often singled out two of these students for special mention: Newton Morton, a pioneer in human genetics and genetic epidemiology, and Motoo Kimura, a major figure in theoretical population genetics. Both were students in the mid 1950s, when Lederberg was on the faculty. Crow spoke of these years with such fondness that it is hard to

Figure 3. J. F. Crow on a bicycle with parasol in Mishima, Japan, in 1957.

escape the suspicion that these were some of the happiest years in the life of a generally happy man (22, 25, 26) (Harper 2005).

His mentoring of Kimura led to a long-lasting collaboration, with Crow travelling to Japan (figure 3) and Kimura to Wisconsin on many occasions. (Ann Crow often accompanied him; she was fluent in Japanese and admired Japanese culture.) It also led to Crow's mentoring a series of Japanese students, with each successive student recommending the next in line. In 1985 Crow was made an honorary member of the Japan Academy, and at his induction the Emperor cited his contributions to training Japanese geneticists.

Colleague

Crow was a geneticist who played on the international stage. In his early years, his self-assertiveness got him acquainted with many famous geneticists, including Muller and Lederberg, with whom he quickly made friends. While at Dartmouth, Crow attended a summer statistics course in Raleigh, North Carolina, at which the famous statistician and population geneticist R. A. Fisher lectured. One evening Fisher spoke about his new three-locus model for the genetic determination of rhesus blood groups, after which Crow asked a question, and then approached Fisher as the audience began to disperse. Fisher asked whether he'd like a glass of beer, and they adjourned to a nearby bar. Alas, the pub had no beer, nor any wine. What it did have was a bottle of champagne, which they were not allowed to drink owing to a North Carolina blue law. So they took the champagne to Crow's dorm room and forged a friendship that lasted the rest of Fisher's life (17).

Crow similarly cultivated a friendship with Sewall Wright. He often drove from Madison to Chicago to visit Wright, who was teaching at the University of Chicago. In 1954, when Wright turned 65 years of age, he was forced to retire from Chicago, and Crow arranged an appointment for him at the University of Wisconsin. Wright was a professor at Wisconsin until his retirement at age 70, and then he remained active for another 25 years. Crow called Wright 'the best bargain Wisconsin ever had' (15). To Wright, he was a good friend and showed his characteristic generosity. Crow got the department to buy Wright one of the first electronic calculators; Wright was at first rather suspicious of the contraption, until he discovered that it could calculate exact factorials up to 69! In Wright's later years, when he suffered from macular degeneration, Crow bought him a special magnifying machine so that he could continue to read.

Crow was a joyful and beloved friend of his colleagues at the University of Wisconsin. One example: in December 1960, Crow and Seymour Abrahamson, who had been a student of Muller's, set off to New York to help celebrate Muller's 70th birthday. During the dinner, which was at Columbia University, Muller collapsed and was rushed to a hospital, where he fortunately recovered. But during the commotion, Crow was heard to remark, *sotto voce*, that when he celebrated his own 70th birthday, he hoped he would be young enough to enjoy it. Upon returning to Madison, Seymour, his colleague Larry Sandler, and others in the laboratory began to plan a surprise mock '70th birthday party' for Crow on 18 January 1961, when he would actually turn 45. It was carefully and elaborately planned—kept secret even from Ann, his wife—and it came off perfectly with songs and skits and numerous (fabricated) messages from geneticists living and dead (including Gregor Mendel). Crow kept all of his '70th birthday' Western Union telegrams, delivered by messenger, among his mementos (Abrahamson 2012). One such telegram read: 'Roses are red, violets are blue, I say balanced, you say *mu*. Th. Dobzhansky.' This reflected the ongoing debate about genetic variation in populations: whether this was attributable mainly to hidden, mostly recessive mutations, or more largely to balancing selection for genes at loci where the heterozygote is superior in fitness to either homozygote.

In 1986 there was a real 70th birthday celebration, an International Genetics Symposium, the 'Crowfest', presented by Crow's large and illustrious cohort of students, postdoctoral students and colleagues, and he was indeed still healthy enough in mind and body to fully enjoy it.

RESEARCH

Most of Crow's research was in experimental and theoretical population genetics, making use of mathematical and statistical methods. After Dartmouth, much of his work was collaborative.

Crow's experimental research focused on the model organism *Drosophila melanogaster*, and it included studies of the evolution of resistance to DDT as an example of natural selection in action. A recurring theme in Crow's experimental work was hidden genetic variation—variation with no great or visible manifestation. How much of this hidden variation, for example, in natural populations at equilibrium between mutation and selection, is due to genes that, when made homozygous, have large or drastic effect (such as lethals), and how much to genes with individually very small effect ('detrimentals')? Crow was especially interested in the total impact of the latter, those minor-viability mutations, which in the long run, acting cumulatively, may even have as much overall effect as the lethals (11). An associated issue was whether the 'recessive' mutations that affect viability are fully recessive, or whether they have mildly deleterious effects even in heterozygous carriers. His research with Rayla

Figure 4. J. F. Crow and Rayla Greenberg Temin, 2006. (Courtesy of Hilde Adler, Madison, Wisconsin.)
(Online version in colour.)

Greenberg Temin (figure 4) showed that such 'partial dominance' is, in fact, usually the rule (4, 6, 9) (Temin 1978).

Crow's group similarly investigated new mutations, spontaneous or induced by radiation or chemicals, and estimated their rates and effects both when homozygous and when heterozygous, including effects on fertility and other facets of total fitness (9, 10). Crow also considered how principles of *Drosophila* fitness might extend to humans. He made major contributions, both by mathematical modelling and experimental measurement, to the concept of 'genetic load', which estimates the amount by which average population fitness is reduced by mutation, selection or other evolutionary processes.

Crow was fascinated by genes that violate Mendel's rules by giving themselves an advantage in genetic transmission from one generation to the next. A remarkable case in *Drosophila*, known as segregation distortion, was first discovered in his laboratory in the course of the fitness studies (5). Segregation distortion works by interrupting the development of sperm carrying the normal gene. A diagram of the spiralling approach to equilibrium of three genotypes involved in segregation distortion in nature graces the cover of Crow's book, *Basic concepts on population, quantitative, and evolutionary genetics* (13). Another important exception to Mendelism was elucidated in Crow's laboratory: the *P* factor, a transposable element responsible for hybrid dysgenesis, a set of genetic instabilities observed in hybrids from particular crosses between males of one *Drosophila* population and females from another (16) (Engels 1988).

Crow had an abiding interest in human genetics, especially in aspects related to population genetics. He made estimates of the genetic load of deleterious mutations in the human genome, often using insightful indirect methods that made use of inbreeding data (3). One contribution he especially enjoyed was related to isonymy, the analysis of surname frequencies in a population and among mates to estimate the extent of inbreeding and make inferences

Figure 5. J. F. Crow with Ronald Aylmer Fisher (centre) and Motoo Kimura in Madison, Wisconsin, in 1961.

about population structure (7). In studies of mutation rates of human genes, he found much greater rates in males than in females, and during his retirement he wrote frequently on the paternal age effect (18, 20, 23, 27).

One thread running through all of Crow's research is that of population genetics theory. Undoubtedly his great interest in theory reflected his lifelong love of mathematics. He extended the concept of effective population number to distinguish inbreeding (inbreeding effective size) from random drift effects (variance effective size). He studied the consequences of small population size, inbreeding and non-random mating, and he developed the infinite-alleles model of mutation, in which each new mutation yields a new type of allele not already present in the population. He studied the conditions under which a subdivided population can lead to the evolution of altruism. He worked on the theory regarding the evolutionary benefits of sexual reproduction maintained by two different sexes. Fascinated by the theoretical foundations of Fisher's 'fundamental theorem of natural selection', which deals with the rate of increase in average fitness under natural selection, Crow also studied the conditions under which the theorem holds and the limits to its applicability.

Crow's interest in theory was also sustained by his long-term collaboration with Kimura (figure 5), who began as a graduate student working out the mathematics of fixation of neutral alleles. This early work eventually culminated in Kimura's neutral theory of molecular evolution, with its many applications in modern studies of genomic DNA sequences, such as estimating rates and times of species divergence and serving as the null hypothesis in tests for natural selection. Through the years, the two remained close friends and collaborators, and Kimura rarely published anything he thought important without first seeking Crow's opinion.

Consistently of the highest quality, Crow's research was characterized by the breadth and diversity of topics on which it touched. In a self-appraisal of his research (22) he explained:

I don't regard any particular discoveries as being outstanding … I would say that the most important thing really is not any one experiment but a more or less persistent study of the variability in natural populations and how it is maintained with partial dominance, and the other things that grew out of this. I also think that I've made some substantial contribution to theoretical population genetics, but mostly these have been in collaboration … My life has been characterized more by diversity than by systematic concentration on one or two subjects. It's been richer for that reason and enjoyable, but I'm not sure what that means from the standpoint of contributions.

Of contributions there were many: his full publication list includes almost four hundred citations and can be accessed at http://www.genetics.wisc.edu/documents/CrowCV2010_1.pdf.

To honour Crow's significant contributions to evolutionary theory, the J. F. Crow Institute for the Study of Evolution was established at the University of Wisconsin, comprising an affiliation of more than 70 faculty members throughout the campus.[4] When it was named in his honour in 2010, Crow noted with characteristic humour: 'I am honored. Usually these things are named after a person who has died. But I am not going to take the hint.'

Service

Much of Crow's time was spent in university, national and community service. He was highly personable and able to get along with nearly anyone, which made him a superb leader, committee member and chair. At the University of Wisconsin he chaired the Department of Medical Genetics from 1958 until 1963, was acting dean of the Medical School from 1963 until 1965, and served as chairman of the Departments of Genetics and Medical Genetics from 1965 until 1972 and from 1975 until 1977. Throughout his long career, he was an active member of the Genetics Society of America (serving as vice president in 1959 and president in 1960) and the American Society for Human Genetics (serving as president in 1962).

Crow was elected to the National Academy of Sciences in 1961. He was active in the Academy and on numerous committees of the National Research Council, often as chair. With his research in population genetics, including that on the impact of new mutations, Crow was able to bring his expertise and knowledge to bear on public policy. The committees included those set up to measure the effects of radiation on human health after the atomic bombing of Hiroshima and Nagasaki in World War II, and those on related public health issues,[5] namely the following:

- Committee on Biological Effects of Atomic Radiation (BEAR, Genetics section 1955–63, chair from 1960);
- Committee on Biological Effects of Ionizing Radiation (BEIR, Genetics Section 1969–72), chair;
- Committee on Nuclear and Alternative Energy Systems (1977–82), Risk/Impact Panel chair;
- Committee on Chemical Environmental Mutagens (1979–83), chair;
- Scientific Advisory Committee of the Radiation Effects Research Foundation (RERF) in Hiroshima (1975–83);
- Committee for Scholarly Communication with the People's Republic of China, Science and Engineering Committee, chair (1983–85);
- Committee on DNA Technology in Forensic Science (1994–95), chair.

The committees dealing with radiation took up questions of mutational damage, of how to get estimates of genetic risk from exposure to low doses of radiation, and of the impact of radioactive fallout from atomic weapons testing. The work extended to general health risks from radiation, in particular carcinogenicity, and thus the effects of radiation exposure on current and future generations. Concerns arising from the work helped to ban the above-ground testing of nuclear weapons. Further, the work directed attention to chemical and environmental mutagens, and the essential need to focus on those. Crow's committee on forensic DNA tests and his skills in explaining the underlying genetic theory to those in the justice systems helped lead to the widespread use of such tests in the courts (Abrahamson 2012).

Consider just one example of Crow as conciliator: Warren Weaver, whose work as director of the Division of Natural Sciences at the Rockefeller Foundation was instrumental in supporting the early years of research in molecular biology, chaired the first meetings of the BEAR committee. He was soon caught between two factions, one led by Muller and the other by Wright. The Muller faction argued that considerations of genetic load were relevant to evaluating the biological effects of radiation, whereas the Wright faction felt that the theory of genetic load was too simplistic for practical application. The two leaders, each a giant of genetics in his own right, squared off and each stuck stubbornly to his position. A potential fiasco was in the making until Crow, a masterful manager of strong personalities and a friend of both protagonists, got them to a reasonable compromise. The final report introduced the concept of 'doubling dose' of radiation—the dose expected to double the spontaneous mutation rate—which is still used today in the evaluation of human genetic risk (19) (Abrahamson 2012).

Crow was also active with the National Institutes of Health. He served on the Advisory Committee to the Director from 1971 to 1973; on the Genetics Study Section from 1959 to 1963 and as chair of the section from 1965 to 1968; on the Genetics Training Grant Committee from 1980 to 1983; and on the Mammalian Genetics Study Section from 1984 to 1988, serving as chair from 1986 to 1988. Of his work on review panels, he remarked (22):

> I had one nice privilege for comparative purposes. I was Chairman of the Genetics Study Section when it was quite young [1965–68] and then again just a few years ago [1986–88], and there's a big contrast. … In the early days when there was enough money to go around and almost every good project got funded, it was fun being on the study section; but now, when you know that a lot of good work is not going to be supported, it is very discouraging, at least for me.

Crow was, as noted, a lifetime musician, and gave generously of his time to share his musicianship with his local community. He played viola (figure 6) in the Madison Symphony Orchestra for about 45 years and continued playing in chamber groups throughout the city for the rest of his life. He was president of the Madison Civic Music Association (1973–74) and president of the Madison Symphony Orchestra (1984–86).

LATER YEARS

Although he officially retired in 1986 at the age of 70 years, Crow remained very active in his profession. He no longer taught his own courses, but gave guest lectures and seminars, travelled, and served on committees. When home in Madison he was in his office nearly every day. Fittingly, he was the recipient of numerous honours, many awarded before his retirement, including, at the University of Wisconsin: the Bascom Professorship Award for Distinguished

Figure 6. J. F. Crow and viola, 1995. (Courtesy of Wolfgang Hoffman, College of Agricultural and Life Sciences, University of Wisconsin–Madison.) (Online version in colour.)

Service and Teaching (1965), the College of Agricultural and Life Sciences Teaching Award (1972), the Senior Distinguished Research Professorship (1984), the Distinguished Teaching Award (1985) and the Distinguished Service Award from the University of Wisconsin College of Agricultural and Life Sciences (1995).

More widely, too, the recognition and awards continued to roll in: election as honorary member of the Japan Academy (1985), the Thomas Hunt Morgan Medal of the Genetics Society of America (1987), an honorary doctorate from the University of Chicago (1991); election to the Royal Society of London (2000), and the University of California San Diego Merck Life Sciences Achievement Award (2009).

Much of Crow's time in retirement was spent writing short general and historical essays on genetics and geneticists. In 1987 Jan Drake, the editor of the journal *Genetics*, asked him to take on the editorship of a new monthly column to be called Perspectives. Crow explained that he had been asked because Drake knew 'I was a person who knew how to meet a deadline' (22). Crow accepted the assignment, and with a Wisconsin colleague, William Dove, he over-saw a valuable and popular new feature of this venerable publication. Most of the Perspectives were written by others, either by invitation or direct submission, but Crow wrote more than 50 of these essays himself, often on a short deadline after a promised piece never materialized. This was his métier. He was perfect for the job, preadapted to it by his friendly and direct style of writing, his seemingly inexhaustible store of anecdotes, his encyclopaedic knowledge of genetics, and personal ties and connections with geneticists extending back to his youth.

James F. Crow passed away peacefully in Madison on 4 January 2012, two weeks before his 96th birthday. We are quite sure that if he could, he would share a fitting anecdote or witty remark to help us bear his passing. We remember him as a man of uncommon energy, superior intellect, joyful disposition, friendly manner, quick wit and high culture. He had an unusual ability to make others feel at ease, to understand and respect their opinions, to foresee and avert potential conflict, and to help people with divergent views find consensus. No longer will we be able to get an answer to almost any question about the history of genetics by saying, 'Let's ask Jim', although we will have his writings and his extraordinary legacy to treasure.

ACKNOWLEDGEMENT

We thank Millard Susman for his many years of friendship, for his careful reading of the manuscript, and for his astute comments.

The frontispiece photograph was taken in 2001 by Prudence Cumming Associates and is copyright © The Royal Society.

NOTES

1   Much of his teaching between 1943 and 1946 was in connection with the V-12 Navy College Training Program, designed to increase the number of commissioned officers in the Navy and Marine Corps during World War II. Dartmouth was one of 131 colleges and universities in the United States that participated in this programme.
2   This film is available online at http://archive.org/details/thread_of_life.
3   Table 1 in Hartl (2011) includes what is believed to be a complete list of 52 scientists who studied with him, including undergraduates, graduate students, postdoctoral students and visiting senior scientists who carried out research in his laboratory.
4   For more information on the J. F. Crow Institute for the Study of Evolution, see http://www.evolution.wisc.edu.
5   Crow also served on the United Nations Scientific Committee on the Effects of Atomic Radiation, Genetics section, in 1957; the Department of Energy Health and Environmental Research Advisory Committee, from 1985 to 1988; and the Board of Scientific Overseers for the Jackson Laboratory, in Bar Harbor, Maine, from 1961 until 1988.

REFERENCES TO OTHER AUTHORS

Abrahamson, S. 2012 James F. Crow: his life in public service. *Genetics* **190**, 1–4.
Engels, W. R. 1988 *P* elements in *Drosophila melanogaster*. In *Mobile DNA* (ed. D. E. Berg & M. Howe), pp. 437–484. Washington DC: American Society for Microbiology.
Harper, P. 2005 Interview with James F. Crow, 24 October 2005. In Interviews with Human and Medical Geneticists series, Special Collections and Archives, Cardiff University, Cardiff, UK (http://www.genmedhist.info/interviews/Crow).
Hartl, D. L. 2011 James F. Crow and the art of teaching and mentoring. *Genetics* **189**, 1129–1133.
Temin, R. G. 1978 Partial dominance of EMS-induced mutations affecting viability in *Drosophila melanogaster*. *Genetics* **89**, 315–340.

BIBLIOGRAPHY

The following publications are those referred to directly in the text. A full bibliography is available as electronic supplementary material at http://dx.doi.org/10.1098/rsbm.2014.0004 or via http://rsbm.royalsocietypublishing.org.

(1)   1945   A chart of the χ^2 and *t* distributions. *J. Am. Statist. Assoc.* **40**, 376.
(2)   1948   Alternative hypotheses of hybrid vigor. *Genetics* **33**, 477–487.

(3) 1956 (With N. E. Morton & H. J. Muller) An estimate of the mutational damage in man from data on consanguineous marriages. *Proc. Natl Acad. Sci. USA* **42**, 855–863.

(4) 1960 (With Y. Hiraizumi) Heterozygous effects on viability, fertility, rate of development, and longevity of *Drosophila* chromosomes that are lethal when homozygous. *Genetics* **45**, 1071–1083.

(5) (With Y. Hiraizumi & L. Sandler) Meiotic drive in natural populations of *Drosophila melanogaster*. III. Populational implications of the Segregation-Distorter locus. *Evolution* **14**, 433–444.

(6) 1964 (With R. G. Temin) Evidence for the partial dominance of recessive lethal genes in natural populations of *Drosophila*. *Am. Nat.* **98**, 21–33.

(7) 1965 (With A. P. Mange) Measurement of inbreeding from the frequency of marriages between persons of the same surname. *Eugenics Q.* **12**, 199–203.

(8) 1970 (With M. Kimura) *An introduction to population genetics theory*. New York: Harper & Row.

(9) 1972 (With T. Mukai, S. I. Chigusa & L. E. Mettler) Mutation rate and dominance of genes affecting viability in *Drosophila melanogaster*. *Genetics* **72**, 335–355.

(10) 1977 (With M. J. Simmons) Mutations affecting fitness in *Drosophila* populations. *Annu. Rev. Genet.* **11**, 49–78.

(11) 1979 Minor viability mutations in *Drosophila*. *Genetics* **92**, s165–s172.

(12) 1983 *Genetics notes: an introduction to genetics*, 8th edn. Minneapolis, MN: Burgess.

(13) 1986 *Basic concepts in population, evolutionary, and quantitative genetics*. New York: W. H. Freeman.

(14) 1988 A diamond anniversary: the first chromosomal map. *Genetics* **118**, 1–3.

(15) Sewall Wright (1889–1988). *Genetics* **119**, 1–4.

(16) The genesis of dysgenesis. *Genetics* **120**, 315–318.

(17) 1990 R. A. Fisher: a centennial view. *Genetics* **124**, 207–211.

(18) 1993 How much do we know about spontaneous human mutation rates? *Environ. Mol. Mutagen.* **21**, 122–129. (Erratum: *Environ. Mol. Mutagen.* **21**, 389.)

(19) 1995 Quarreling geneticists and a diplomat. *Genetics* **140**, 421–426.

(20) 1997 The high spontaneous mutation rate: is it a health risk? *Proc. Natl Acad. Sci. USA* **94**, 8380–8386.

(21) (With S. Abrahamson) Seventy years ago: mutation becomes experimental. *Genetics* **147**, 1491–1496.

(22) 2000 *Conversations in genetics: an oral history of our intellectual heritage in genetics*, vol. 2, no. 2: James F. Crow, interviewed by Daniel Hartl. Executive producer, Rochelle Easton Esposito; video production, Aaron Stadler. Bethesda, MD: The Genetics Society of America.

(23) The origins, patterns and implications of human spontaneous mutation. *Nature Rev. Genet.* **1**, 40–47.

(24) 2001 (With R. P. Wagner) The other fly room: J. T. Patterson and Texas genetics. *Genetics* **157**, 1–5.

(25) 2005 UCLA Oral History of Human Genetics Project: James F. Crow, interviewed by Andrea Maestrejuan (http://ohhgp.pendari.com/Interview.aspx?id=9#).

(26) 2006 Interview with Professor Crow. *BioEssays* **27**, 660–678.

(27) Age and sex effects on human mutation rates: an old problem with new complexities. *J. Radiat. Res.* **47** (Suppl. B), B75–B82.

QUENTIN HOWIESON GIBSON
9 December 1918 — 16 March 2011

Quentin H. Gibson

QUENTIN HOWIESON GIBSON

9 December 1918 — 16 March 2011

Elected FRS 1969

BY JOHN S. OLSON[1] AND H. GUTFREUND FRS[2]

[1]*Department of Biochemistry and Cell Biology, Rice University, 6100 Main Street, Houston, TX 77005-1892, USA*

[2]*Somerset House, Chilton Road, Upton, Oxfordshire OX11 9JL, UK*

Quentin Howieson Gibson was born in Aberdeen, obtained his MD (1944) and PhD (1946) from Queen's University in Belfast and subsequently took a faculty position at the University of Sheffield (1947), where he was appointed Professor of Biochemistry in 1957. In 1963 he moved to the USA, where he held a faculty position at the University of Pennsylvania before he became the Greater Philadelphia Professor in the Section of Biochemistry and Molecular Biology at Cornell University in 1966. After retiring from Cornell, he became a Distinguished Faculty Fellow at Rice University and an Adjunct Professor at the University of Massachusetts Medical School at Worcester. While at Cornell, Quentin was elected a Fellow of the Royal Society (1969), a member of the American Academy of Arts and Sciences (1970), and a member of the National Academy of Sciences, USA (1982), served as an associate editor of *Journal of Biological Chemistry* (1975–94) and received the Keilin Memorial Medallist Award and Lectureship (1990). Quentin's major scientific accomplishments include the discovery of the biochemical cause of familial methaemoglobinaemia, construction of the first practical stopped-flow rapid-mixing spectrometer, adaptation of flash photolysis methods to haem proteins, identification of the first semi-stable intermediates in the O_2 reactions of flavoenzymes, the first direct kinetic measurement of intermediates for the reaction of O_2 with cytochrome c oxidase, quantitative kinetic evaluations of cooperative O_2 binding to haemoglobins, determinations of how iron reactivity and ligand diffusion govern rates of ligand binding, and experimental mapping of the pathways for O_2 entry into the active sites of globins.

Quentin Gibson was a remarkable scientist with a publishing career that spanned 66 years and was characterized by both the construction of innovative rapid-mixing and flash photolysis instruments and their use in clever and definitive kinetics experiments on enzymes and globins. His basic stopped-flow spectrometer design has stood the test of time and is used in

http://dx.doi.org/10.1098/rsbm.2013.0018

almost all modern instruments, and his discoveries and conclusions about how haemoglobin functions are now textbook material for biochemistry, biophysics and haematology classes. This memoir is divided into four parts. The first section describes his early life and education (1918–42), and the second section provides a summary of his work in Belfast and Sheffield and then his accomplishments in Philadelphia (1943–69). The third section describes his reflections on family and career in 1971, and the fourth covers the last 40 years of his life (1971–2011), which were devoted almost exclusively to ultrafast kinetic studies of globins.

Quentin's biography best begins with his own words from a handwritten personal record that he deposited in the Royal Society Library in 1971 (24)*.

I have just finished writing about my old friend and colleague FJW Roughton for Biographical Memoirs of the RS. He had not left any material on deposit, and this made it difficult to write about his early life, although fortunately I had known him for more than 20 years and was able to fill in some of the gaps with the help of his wife and former colleagues at Cambridge where he lived continuously for more than 50 years. I, on the other hand, have moved often and this will scarcely be possible for the man who draws the short straw on me. I am therefore setting out rather a full account of things I remember and thought important. A bibliography will be available, which, if wanted, will be available from a retrieval service.

There was nothing very special about my family, except perhaps that the members I know about were geographically widely scattered. My great-grandparents included a Scot, Agnes Macintosh, a Suffolk builder of slums in Ipswich, Pooley, a Welsh farm manager who moved to East Anglia, and small farmers from the Monymusk district of Aberdeenshire, some of whom called Troop, were reputed to have left Holland in discreditable circumstances (maritime robbery) some time earlier, as well as the Gibsons who have moved from Northumberland to Edinburgh, where my great-grandfather and grandfather were watch and clockmakers. The business effectively ended in the 1860's with the rise of the Swiss industry, and my grandfather moved to London where he became a clerk for the St Pancras Town Council and inspector of weights and measures for the London County Council on its formation. My father went to school in Rochester and later to University College School, then to University College, where he was a student of Sir William Ramsay (rare gases). He worked on explosive manufacture during World War I and at the end moved to Northern Ireland, first as Chemist and factotum to the York Street Spinning Company and then Director of the Linen Industry Research Association, a mixed Government and Industry Research Institute at Lambeg. He returned to the Armament Research Division of the Ministry of Supply on the outbreak of WWII and stayed on there until retiring age and indeed a couple of years beyond it.

My maternal grandfather started life as a plumber and was very proud of his status. In addition he took evening courses at Aberdeen in engineering and mechanical subjects and invented an improvement to the hydraulic ram, which he patented. He then set up shop to manufacture his rams, which sold well and my earliest memories include seeing the casting of components in gunmetal and bronze, and their finishing in a machine shop full of noise and people. His business was already in decline before I was born, chiefly because of enforced manufacture of munitions under uneconomic conditions during WWI and as I grew up it became clear that my future lay elsewhere.

An only child, I was born on 9 December 1918 at Aberdeen and moved to Bangor, a small coastal town on Belfast Lough about a year later. My father commuted to his job in Belfast and gardened and played tennis on a grass court in our yard on weekends. I was taught to read at an early age by my mother and a Miss Jones, who was called a governess, but in a misuse of the word, since she did not live in. Soon my father bought me a chemistry set and I can remember

---

* Numbers in this form refer to the bibliography at the end of the text.

Figure 1. W. H. Gibson, Director of the Linen Industry Research Association, with Prime Minister Stanley Baldwin, outside Glenmore House, 1933. (Reproduced with permission of Lisburn Historical Society.)

making ink, adding acids and alkalies to phenolphthalein, making gunpowder (fizzy stuff this) and carrying on with other experiments from what I remember as an excellent instruction book, which was even arranged with some regard for the periodic tables.

EARLY LIFE AND EDUCATION, 1926–42

In 1926 Quentin's father was appointed Director of the Linen Industry Research Association. The family was living in Bangor, Northern Ireland, which was quite a formidable commute to the research laboratory in Lambeg. However, the Director was required to live at the Institute, and an early order of business was to move to Lambeg and decide where in the 42-room pile of Glenmore House the family would actually live (figure 1).

As Quentin wrote for the Lisburn.com website ('Memories of Glenmore House'; http://lisburn.com/books/historical_society/volume10/volume10-4.html):

It was a wonderful place for a small child. There was always something going on, with thirteen acres of estate and two acres of kitchen garden. In the early years oats were grown to feed the donkey that pulled a small cart. These were harvested by men with scythes, and at least one shotgun for the rabbits expected to be trapped in the diminishing island of oats. After threshing, they were dried in a special building behind the yard with a perforated iron floor to allow warm air from a stove to percolate through them. In summer, corncrakes lived among the crops and their harsh calls competed with drummers trying out their Lambegs for the Glorious Twelfth.

After attending a day school at Lisburn, where Quentin claimed to have learned very little, he was sent to a boarding school near Kilkeel, where, in contrast, he was driven very hard. The curriculum was purely linguistic and classical. He expressed doubts whether the ability to form plurals correctly of words derived from Latin and Greek was worth the time and labour invested. Quentin disliked team sports and rugby more than soccer. On that basis Repton was chosen as one of only six decent soccer schools. He won a scholarship and announced firmly that he was through with dead languages.

Science teaching at Repton was quite good and Quentin was particularly fortunate to have a bright young mathematics master, P. S. Newell, who helped him to make rapid progress from a very low base in that subject. There is a curious contrast between his comments that 'school staff were generally dissatisfied with my progress' and 'I got all the form prizes each year'(24). After Quentin had been at Repton for three years his father decided that he should go to medical school, and Quentin started at Queen's University in 1936, living at home and commuting to Belfast.

Quentin had a great deal of respect for and intellectual empathy with his father, but his relationship with his mother was not always a very happy one, so he soon moved to a university hostel to complete his studies (24). Quentin's own description of life as a medical student is amusing, but not exceptional. After qualifying, he obtained a position in the Department of Physiology at Queen's University in Belfast, which determined his career for a time and led to his first publications in 1943.

Establishing a career and becoming a Fellow of the Royal Society, 1943–70

Methaemoglobinaemia, the slow move to Sheffield, and introduction to kinetics

Quentin moved officially from Belfast to Sheffield in 1947 to take up an appointment as a university lecturer in physiology. However, he had some difficulties with his new head of department, David Smyth (FRS 1967), because he was still publishing with some Belfast colleagues and using the Belfast address on these papers, even after he was on staff at Sheffield. It is of interest to note that Smyth, 10 years Quentin's senior, was also a graduate of the Belfast Queen's University Medical School and familiar with the local Physiology Department.

During Quentin's last years one of us (H.G.) corresponded with him about the serendipity that governed both their careers at every turn. Among other events, he described his exit from physiology and entry into the biochemistry of haem proteins (24). This came through some ideas of a Northern Ireland medical practitioner, Dr James Deeny. Deeny had got it into his head that ascorbic acid had a powerful beneficial effect on chronic cardiac failure, but had some difficulty in convincing his colleagues in the Belfast hospitals of his ideas (61). He was looking for relevant patients. One day, during office hours, he saw a cyanotic man walk down the street. Cyanosis or 'blue jaundice' is often associated with poor oxygenation of red cells and greater amounts of deoxygenated haemoglobin, which give venous blood a bluish colour. This condition is often associated with compromised heart or lung function, which is what got Deeney's attention. Afterwards he went to the police station and asked whether they could tell him who the blue man was; at that time the population of Bainbridge was only 5000. They produced the address of two cyanotic brothers and he made contact with them. Fully conscious of the scientific method, he succeeded in turning one of them pink within three weeks of treatment with Pauling-size doses (of the order of 1 g per day) of ascorbic acid, leaving the other as control (Deeny *et al.* 1943). The only disappointment for Deeny was that when he showed the brothers off in the Belfast Hospital it turned out that they had perfectly sound hearts. This observation was the first published report of familial methaemoglobinaemia in the British Isles. News about this case reached Quentin when he was just starting his research career in Belfast, and he set out to determine how methaemoglobin was reduced in normal cells and what was wrong with the cells of the patients, which he did successfully in a series of six remarkable papers (for example (1) and (61)) between 1943 and 1951. This work involved a programme of research on different aspects of familial methaemoglobinaemia in collaboration with D. C. Harrison of the Queen's University Department of Biochemistry, and much of the later work was done while Quentin was officially employed in Sheffield. No doubt through the influence of Quentin's previous chief in the Belfast Physiology Department, Henry Barcroft (FRS 1953), this effort resulted in the invitation to contribute to the Joseph Barcroft Memorial Symposium on all aspects of research on haemoglobin, which took place in Cambridge in June 1948.

Some of Quentin's earliest experiments performed in the Sheffield Physiology Department stimulated his interest in biochemical kinetics. He wrote: 'Late in 1948 Sidney Elsden came to Sheffield and had a good deal of influence on me—first by initiating work on amino-acid absorption, which led to the demonstration that there was an active mechanism rather than passive diffusion across the gut' (24).

After making some ^{14}C-labelled amino acids, Quentin studied their rate of uptake by the gut. From the more rapid specific uptake of the L-isomers of amino acids, he concluded that there was only active transport of these stereoisomers. In July 1950 he submitted the paper 'Selective absorption of stereo-isomers of amino-acids from loops of the small intestine of the rat' for publication in *Biochemical Journal* (3). These results received the attention and respect of Hans (later Sir Hans) Krebs FRS, at that time head of the Sheffield Biochemistry Department. It was the start of Quentin's lifelong interest in the use of kinetic analysis to examine molecular mechanisms of key biological processes. However, these amino acid transport studies were also the start of the most important research programme in David Smyth's career; as a result, Quentin chose to move to other areas of research and construct a rapid-mixing device (24).

The first stopped-flow apparatus; success and happiness

The Barcroft meeting on haemoglobins in Cambridge in June 1948 had several important consequences for Quentin's career. The gathering was small enough for participants to meet many of the leading figures as well as more junior ones such as Quentin and one of the present authors (H.G.) for informal discussions. The easy preparation of large quantities of relatively pure haemoglobin from different species made it a very useful material for the development of many biophysical techniques. The gathering in Cambridge provided the opportunities for wide-ranging informal discussions of many topics in biophysical chemistry, apart from the specific physiological functions of haem proteins. These first contacts did not lead to immediate collaborations but made it easier for Quentin to approach Roughton and Rossi-Fanelli's group when his own interests on the interaction of ligands with haem proteins developed into a molecular kinetics programme in Sheffield.

A particularly important event for Quentin at that meeting was the demonstration of the reaction of oxyhaemoglobin and dithionite with the use of the rapid-flow apparatus designed by Britton Chance (ForMemRS 1981). The equipment had been left in Cambridge after Chance had done some work with Keilin and Hartree at the Molteno Institute. After inspection of the operation of Chance's equipment and perusal of his papers, Quentin came to the conclusion that, although it was clearly a technical *tour de force*, there was no possibility for him to reproduce it. As it happened, neither did anybody else, unlike the stopped-flow machine developed by Quentin four years later that was easily portable to other laboratories.

Although temporarily discouraged by the complexity of Chance's equipment, a year or two later Quentin decided to venture into rapid-mixing experiments, starting with some simpler equipment. He purchased RCA 931 photomultipliers (about £3 each) and got the laboratory glassblower to make mixers. High-voltage batteries were used to power the multiplier, and car batteries and bulbs with a filter served as light source for a simple instrument. Quentin wrote further (24): 'I soon found out what was wrong with Chance's records: the deceleration in his method is too gradual. The mixture at the final point of observation is often at sub-turbulent velocity, resulting in inadequate mixing.'

It was a revelation that the apparatus had to be constructed to result in a really sudden stop, and his simple apparatus produced the first correct reaction records with a time resolution of about 1 ms. Quentin claimed this to be one of his very, very few original ideas—be that as it may, it was a very important one—his Eureka moment. Quentin recognized that Hartridge and Roughton's continuous-flow method (Hartridge & Roughton 1923) might improve on the time resolution of the stopped-flow apparatus. However, its great expense of reactants (litres of reagents) made it unsuitable for studies on systems with limited supplies of proteins. The further development of the Gibson stopped-flow apparatus included improved reactant economy, greater spectral resolution with the use of grating monochromators, and adaptation to fluorescence measurements; it resulted also in ever-wider applications to biochemical problems.

The year 1951 was Quentin's '*annus mirabilis*'. He had cut his personal (a troubled engagement) and scientific ties with Belfast and was beginning to be remarkably productive in the Sheffield laboratory as a result of his successful stopped-flow apparatus. Probably most important for this change to a more pleasant lifestyle was that he met Jane Pinsent (figure 2), who had joined Sidney Elsden's microbiology group in Sheffield. As he described it, the final permanent move to Sheffield had a very happy ending (24):

> This general life (between Belfast and Sheffield) went on for three years until my engagement was finally broken off in the fall of 1950, and I returned to Sheffield, accepting for the first time that my future, if any, did not lie in the North of Ireland. Soon after, I met Jane Pinsent, who had just come to Sheffield after a year at Van Neil's laboratory in Pacific Grove, California, to work with Sidney Elsden, then lecturer in charge of Microbiology. … This time things went very differently and we had decided on marriage in 1951.

Jane and Quentin's marriage resulted in a happy union that lasted until Jane's death in 2008. Their life can be characterized by enormous mutual respect and several important joint interests in life. Their scientific activities, family life, music and the enjoyment of mountain holidays, which were stimulated by Jane's knowledge of Switzerland, made for a full life.

Collaborations with F. J. W. Roughton and the beginnings of a lifelong study of ligand binding to haemoglobins and myoglobins

Encouraged by having met Roughton at the 1948 Barcroft meeting, Quentin wrote to him on 19 January 1951 (2):

Figure 2. Jane (Pinsent) Gibson hiking at Justiztal, Switzerland, in the 1950s.
(Photograph taken by Quentin Gibson and sent to J.S.O. after Jane's death in 2008.)

Dear Professor Roughton,

In the last few months I have been engaged in building a stopped-flow rapid reaction apparatus and naturally looked to the blood pigments as a means of testing it out. In this process one or two results have turned up which may be of possible interest to you, although, of course, the data were not collected in a systematic manner.

I thought it would be interesting to repeat the experiment of Legge & Roughton (1950)…

Quentin had been remeasuring CO binding to deoxyhaemoglobin and the reaction of oxyhaemoglobin with sodium dithionite, and his results did not quite agree with some of Roughton's old results (Legge & Roughton 1950). To try to resolve the discrepancies, Roughton invited Quentin to Cambridge for discussions. This visit was the start of a very fruitful collaboration and friendship that lasted until Roughton's death in 1972, and Quentin's own interest in globins continued for another 55 years. Between 1954 and 2009 he published about 200 papers on various aspects of the interactions of ligands with haemoglobins and myoglobins from all kingdoms of life. Most of the work on haemoglobin is reviewed in the fourth part of this memoir. In the remainder of this section, the focus is on Quentin's contributions to the general application of rapid-mixing techniques and flash photolysis methodologies for measurements of biochemical kinetics.

Commercialization and widespread use of the Gibson stopped-flow
spectrometer in enzymology

Notwithstanding Chance's 'Whig interpretation of history' (Chance 2004), the simple Gibson stopped-flow machine was really the first instrument to deserve that name. The initial published record of the Gibson stopped-flow apparatus appeared as a short note in the Faraday Society

Discussion 'The Study of Rapid Reactions' (4). The details of the apparatus and its method of use for the measurement of the rate of displacement of oxygen from haemoglobin by carbon monoxide are described in a classic paper with Roughton (5). A footnote on the front page of the paper stated: 'The experimental part of this work is due to Gibson and the theoretical part, in the main, to Roughton.' Perhaps even more importantly, their rationale and algebraic analysis for deducing the rate of dissociation of a ligand from a binding site by displacement with another substrate have had wide applications in studies on biological systems.

The Gibson stopped-flow spectrometer was easily reproduced in Cambridge by one of us (H.G.) for the first application to enzymes (Gutfreund 1955). In addition, Quentin and Milnes built a number of machines that were given to colleagues both in Sheffield and at other universities around the world (10). In a message sent in 2004, Quentin thanked H.G. for referring to him in a paper on the contributions of rapid-flow techniques to enzymology (Gutfreund 1999). He remarked that his and Roughton's names are slowly disappearing from reference lists in papers on rapid-mixing experiments and on haemoglobin. From personal experience we can testify to Quentin's always generous reference to any work relevant to his own activities, particularly older papers that younger scientists had either forgotten or never read.

Quentin wrote in his personal recollections (24) that he tried to get Unicam, a Cambridge firm of instrument makers, interested in the fully engineered machine (10, 20). They did not think that there would be enough demand (the same argument as that used by British and US automobile manufacturers when they declined the gift of Volkswagen at the end of World War II). The first commercial stopped-flow apparatus was produced by a US company (Durrum, Inc., of Palo Alto, CA; later Dionex), which sold over 500 Gibson–Durrum instruments between 1965 and 1985. At the time of writing, two British (Hi-Tech Scientific and Applied PhotoPhysics), at least three US (Update Instruments, KinTek Corporation and On-line Instrument Systems, Inc.) and one French company (Bio-Logic Scientific Instruments) are manufacturing, with commercial success, stopped-flow instruments of essentially the basic Gibson design, albeit with elaborate accessories. The continued introduction of the commercial form of Quentin's stopped-flow machine into most well-equipped laboratories all over the world, together with the related quenched-flow machine (Barman *et al.* 2006), has resulted in major contributions to enzymology, molecular biology and many areas of chemistry; probably more so than some developments that have been rewarded with a Nobel prize.

Quentin's own meticulous attention to the detailed interpretation of data resulting from the use of stopped-flow equipment made him aware of pitfalls in published work. Difficulties often arose with the application of transient (rapid reaction) kinetics by groups more familiar with the interpretation of steady-state enzyme kinetics. Examples are found even among contributions from distinguished laboratories as a result of neglect of the response time of instruments and proper distinction between the orders of reactions. For example, Geraci and Gibson (15) carefully re-examined the reaction of liver alcohol dehydrogenase with NADH, and found, contrary to reports by Theorell, Ehrenberg and de Zalenski (Theorell *et al.* 1967), that the fluorescence change follows a single, simple second-order reaction. The data published by Theorell *et al.* were perturbed by the response time of their instrument, which introduced a lag phase at the beginning of the reaction, so that the remainder of the time course was misinterpreted as a second step in the reaction. It is interesting that other authors have attempted to report two steps for the association of NADH with lactate dehydrogenase but again, after careful examination with the Gibson stopped-flow apparatus, one simple bimolecular step seems to occur (Holbrook *et al.* 1977).

Renowned for having a lathe and drill press in or next to his office, Quentin continued to refine and develop the stopped-flow machine and in due course to combine it with flash photolysis for the study of key kinetic intermediates as they were being generated. Quentin was always attracted to biochemical problems that needed new technical developments. As described in the first section, two of his great-grandfathers were in occupations involving mechanical skills, and he was following in their footsteps. His workshop activities tended to be problem oriented, and he made the comment in his reminiscences that one should not have to adapt the experiment to an existing instrument; instead, the instrument should be built or adapted to the experiment (24, 62).

Increased commercial production of a wide range of solid-state devices in the 1960s made it easier to work with complicated electronic circuits and, more importantly, analogue and digital computers. In May 1960, Quentin visited the Gutfreund home in Berkshire, UK, to discuss some overlapping results on reactions of reduced flavins and xanthine oxidase with oxygen. This occasion also included a visit to Solatron to discuss components for analogue computers to model kinetic systems. (His letter of thanks for H.G.'s hospitality included a comparison of their respective five-month-old daughters. He was very much a family man.) Quentin had begun to build up quite an extensive array of analogue devices for data analyses so that by 1965, when he moved from the University of Pennsylvania to Cornell, he regarded it as a priority that larger new modules should precede him to Ithaca, NY. However, when H.G. visited him three years later, Quentin proudly demonstrated the linking of the output of a stopped-flow machine to a PDP-8S digital computer with suitable data reduction for storage. H.G. soon copied this system in his Bristol laboratory, and the rapid increase in the capacity of digital computers had already started to take over data analysis and the modelling of kinetic systems by the early 1970s (Gutfreund 2010).

Application of flash photolysis techniques to haem proteins

Next to the stopped-flow spectrometer, Quentin's other major equipment developments were in the area of flash photolysis and its combination with rapid-mixing techniques. *The Three Princes of Serendip* came to his aid again. First, a paper by Keilin and Hartree (Keilin & Hartree 1955) that came to him for editorial review drew his attention to the photosensitivity of CO–haem compounds. Second, the arrival in Sheffield of George (later Lord) Porter (FRS 1960), who was the world expert on flash photolysis, provided him with significant technical advice. Third, Quentin quickly demonstrated how the high-intensity flash lamps available at that time could be used to study the rate of binding CO to haemoglobin after photodissociation of the bound ligand (6). These experiments fulfilled the desire that Hartridge & Roughton had expressed in 1923 to use the photochemical sensitivity of haem protein complexes for kinetic experiments (Hartridge & Roughton 1923). Quentin was also gratified to have an independent method to verify the data for the reaction of haemoglobin with CO obtained in his stopped-flow, rapid-mixing experiments.

Quentin used improved flash circuits, observation geometry and synchronized shutters for protection of the photomultipliers recording the reaction to obtain a time resolution on the order of 100 µs. Detailed analysis of the new results showed that immediately after dissociation of CO, the free haemoglobin is transiently in a form that rebinds the ligand more rapidly (8). These results had to be considered together with the findings of Gibson and Roughton (7), who had shown that the last of the four CO molecules binds 50-fold faster to haemoglobin than the other three, and were later incorporated in models for cooperative ligand binding to haemoglobin by using both Perutz's crystallographic structures and various mathematical models for allostery as described in the fourth section. However, in 1959 the interest in the photochemistry of haem proteins soon shifted to the development of the flash-flow method in conjunction with major investigations of cytochrome *c* oxidase, particularly when Quentin moved to the University of Pennsylvania.

The Rome group, a long-lasting set of friendships

Quentin and Eraldo Antonini from the University of Rome established a close friendship during Quentin's last few years at the University of Sheffield, even though their backgrounds and views on life were quite different. Both were very smart, intelligent, full of humour, and passionate about kinetic experiments and their analysis. This friendship extended to Eraldo's students, particularly Maurizio Brunori, who continued collaborations for the remainder of Quentin's life, many of which are discussed in succeeding sections. In response to our request, Maurizio wrote the following description of Quentin's early work with the Rome group:

> Their working connection started in 1958 when they met at the International Biochemistry Congress in Vienna. Quentin invited Eraldo to Sheffield to carry out stopped-flow experiments on the combination of haem with apo-haemoglobin. Eraldo had succeeded in preparing native apoprotein from human haemoglobin that was reconstituted into a fully functional tetramer by addition of stoichiometric haem. The collaborative work involved a study on the kinetics of combination with gases and haem binding using several modified porphyrins (meso-, deutero-, …). At that time Gibson was already famous because he had constructed a very efficient and reliable stopped-flow apparatus that was built in the workshop of the Sheffield Institute.
>
> Eventually Gibson decided to come to the Biochemistry Institute in Rome to tackle the project, and he drove his car bringing the stopped-flow apparatus and his family. The kinetic data were published in two papers that appeared in 1960 in *Biochemical Journal*. The experiments proved for the first time that reconstitution of fully functional haemoglobin by combination of stoichiometric globin and haem was a very rapid process, completed in a few milliseconds and was consistent with a mechanism involving a bimolecular (almost diffusion-controlled) complex formation followed by a monomolecular event, attributed to a conformational change. Their contacts continued in the 1960s and indeed Quentin came again to Rome to visit Eraldo, once Jeffries Wyman had settled at the Regina Elena Institute. It was an interesting experience to follow these 'giants' discussing all aspects of haemoglobin's function, at the time when Quentin was actively collaborating with Professor Roughton to measure the rate constants for the combination of deoxyhaemoglobin with CO and other gases.

The bond between Quentin and the Rome group was sealed on his first visit when Quentin presented Antonini's group with a Gibson–Milnes stopped-flow instrument that had been built in Sheffield and transported by hand to Rome. This gift serves as a great example of Quentin's generosity to his colleagues.

Chair of Biochemistry at the University of Sheffield, 1957–63

Hans Krebs, the Professor of Biochemistry in Sheffield, received the 1953 Nobel Prize in Physiology or Medicine and moved to Oxford in 1955. Quentin was appointed to succeed Krebs (figure 3), and his move to the Chair of Biochemistry diverted him to some extent from his previous singular attention to projects connected with collaborations on haemoglobin with Roughton in Cambridge and Antonini in Rome. More freedom to administer departmental funds, direct access to grant facilities, and contacts with new staff and students gradually broadened his field of action. Of particular interest and pleasure to Quentin was his increased

Figure 3. Group picture of the Department of Biochemistry, University of Sheffield, in 1960 with Quentin and Hans Krebs in the centre of the first row and some of Quentin's research colleagues labelled in the third row. (Photograph donated by Graham Palmer, who was Vincent Massey's graduate student and is the fourth person from the right in the third row.)

contact with Gregorio Weber, a member of staff in the Biochemistry Department, who was one of the most distinguished contributors to the application of fluorescence and thermodynamics to biochemistry. Quentin always appreciated Weber's advice, friendship, and contributions to the success of the physical biochemistry programme in Sheffield. Curiously enough, they never published together. In a similar way one of us (H.G.) valued 50 years of friendship and advice from Quentin without ever having our two names heading a publication together.

Weber knew Vincent Massey (FRS 1977) from their graduate school days at Cambridge University, and in 1957 he persuaded Quentin to hire Massey as a lecturer in biochemistry at Sheffield. Massey brought considerable expertise on several enzyme systems from his recent travels in the USA and his PhD work with Malcolm Dixon FRS. In addition, students and foreign visitors added productive green fingers and new systems to Weber's, Massey's and Gibson's laboratories (figure 3). These interactions provided a unique opportunity to establish highly productive collaborations between those experienced with technical facilities in Quentin's laboratory and the production of pure and well-characterized biochemical preparations. Sheffield had become a Mecca for transient kinetic studies of proteins and enzymes in the late 1950s and early 1960s. On the basis of these collaborations, which survived the move to the USA, Quentin, Massey and Woody Hastings published several groundbreaking papers on flavin cofactors, flavoenzymes and bioluminescence that are now considered 'classics' (9, 11–13, 17).

However, Quentin found it difficult to handle relations with the administration of the university when attempting to advance the careers of his successful colleagues, particularly Weber and Massey, whose achievements were not recognized by the Sheffield administration. Any scientific correspondence during 1961–62 always contained comments about difficulties in keeping his department in Sheffield intact. These problems eventually led to exodus of much of the talent from the Biochemistry Department (Weber, Massey and Gibson to the USA, and Hoffman to Canada). As always, there were possible faults on both sides. As described above, Quentin's early days in the Physiology Department were accompanied by friction over the amino acid transport projects. There is an interesting contrast between the fact that he had many close friends in long-term, very successful collaborations, but he disliked team sports and larger social events. This inclination applied to leisure as well as to work. His favoured forms of exercise were walking and sailing. His major achievements can be traced to work on his own or with one collaborator at a time. For relaxation he liked one-on-one company, preferably Jane and/or his children. He was also fiercely independent in that he wanted to do things in his own way, when and how he felt it was best to do them. He was known to decide to make use of an unexpectedly nice afternoon and go for a country walk with Jane—forgetting on one occasion that someone was coming from Oxford for an interview. He had been known to depart a day or two before the end of a meeting, of which he was one of the organizers, because he wanted to get back to his experiments.

These comments may serve as a partial explanation for the contrast between his administrative problems at Sheffield University and the considerable success of his local contemporary George Porter. Porter established a fine reputation for Sheffield physical chemistry between 1955 and 1963, and he left the university with the whole Chemistry Department in much better shape than it had been on his arrival. As hands-on scientists and keen sailors they had much in common, but George was also a very sociable person, enjoying a party as well as a team spirit at work. Quentin had some contact with George in connection with the latter's expertise with photochemical equipment. It is, however, an indication of the difference in personality that there is no record of any personal contact or joint effort for the benefit of local science. Quentin also claims that the Vice-Chancellor (J. M. Whittaker FRS) did not appreciate some of his frivolous jokes during his inaugural lecture for his Biochemistry chair and may never have taken him seriously thereafter (24). However, unbeknownst to Quentin, Whitaker did add his signature to the certificate of proposal for his election to the Royal Society—as did George Porter and Hans Krebs.

Move to the USA

Although personnel and personality problems may have contributed to the break-up of the Biochemistry Department at the University of Sheffield, the major cause was lack of research funding in the UK compared to that in the USA in the early 1960s. The Soviet Union's launching of Sputnik 1 into low Earth orbit in 1957 caused the US Congress to start massive funding of basic research at universities and medical schools throughout the USA. This federal support led to aggressive recruiting of talented scientists from Europe for newly created faculty positions with generous start-up funding and laboratory space. The initial recruiting of the Sheffield faculty started at the University of Illinois, where Woody Hastings held a faculty position in the early 1960s. In his memoir for Quentin, which will be published by the US National Academy of Sciences, Hastings has written:

> I first came to know Quentin Gibson when, in late January 1961, he came on sabbatical leave to the Biochemistry Division of the Chemistry Department at the University of Illinois in Urbana. This was on the invitation of the Chair, Irwin C. Gunsalus (Gunny) who, in his relentless search for talent, had earlier enticed two members of Sheffield University's Biochemistry Department,

Gregorio Weber and Vincent Massey, to come to Urbana as visiting Professors. Some time later Gibson told me that the invitation to him was in response to his complaint, asking Gunny why he himself, the chairman of the Department, had not been invited.

I volunteered to meet the Gibsons at O'Hare airport in Chicago and drive them down. They arrived with four young children, the youngest only a few months old, and I not knowing that my own fourth child would be born that afternoon. The skies were brilliantly red over the prairie that late afternoon, and the very cold temperature was an appropriate introduction for them.

In his wisdom, I dare say, Gunny gave Quentin a laboratory having an inner door connecting with mine. Wandering in to chat, I saw that he was unpacking and assembling a piece of equipment unfamiliar to me. It was, of course, his now-famous stopped-flow apparatus, constructed in the Sheffield machine shop to his exacting specifications.

Without much knowledge of my research, I imagine, Quentin asked if there was a reaction I would like to study using stopped-flow. Without hesitation I proposed that a study of the rapid autoxidation of reduced flavin would be of interest. I had found that I could produce a single turnover in the bacterial luciferase reaction by rapidly mixing excess reduced FMN [flavin mononucleotide] with the luciferase, evidently because any reduced flavin not captured by the enzyme in the first milliseconds was rapidly oxidized chemically, so that each enzyme molecule experienced only a single turnover. It was not known how fast the autoxidation actually was, and the nature of the reaction pathway. This was the beginning of our intense research collaboration.

The lure of readily available faculty positions and research funding in the USA resulted in the unfortunate collapse of one of the best research and teaching groups in enzymology and physical biochemistry in England. Weber took a position in Hastings and Gunsalus's department at the University of Illinois at Urbana-Champaign, and Vincent Massey went to the University of Michigan in Ann Arbor.

Quentin himself accepted a tempting offer from Britton Chance to join the Johnson Foundation in Philadelphia on 1 July 1963 and shortly thereafter obtained a three-year grant of US$186000 from the US National Institutes of Health (NIH). This move seemed quite logical, particularly because Quentin had begun to work on cytochrome c oxidase from beef heart mitochondria with Colin Greenwood at Sheffield and then took this project and his collaborative studies with Hastings on flavins and bioluminescence to the University of Pennsylvania. Chance had previously worked on both systems, the first with intact mitochondria and the second with bioluminescent bacterial cells. Thus, the Johnson Foundation seemed to be a very promising environment for Quentin's programme of developing optical measurements for rapid-mixing and photolysis experiments. However, that conclusion turned out to be illusory.

Cytochrome c *oxidase and dioxygen reactions*

Greenwood joined Quentin as a graduate student in 1959 and then moved with him to the University of Pennsylvania in 1963 as a postdoctoral colleague. Their highly productive collaboration on cytochrome oxidase is described in a series of papers published between 1963 and 1967. It remained one of Quentin's major interests for some time, and he and Greenwood published their last paper together in 1991 with Richard Blackmore (50). This enzyme, by which living things convert oxygen to water, contains both iron and copper, giving it a beautiful green colour. These colours change as the enzyme conducts various reactions with substrates and inhibitors, and it thus presented an ideal system for study by the rapid-mixing and flash photolysis techniques already available in Sheffield.

Greenwood and Gibson worked to combine photochemical methods with rapid mixing, and the techniques they developed to examine the oxygen reactions of reduced cytochrome c oxidase became the standard for examining ultrafast biochemical reactions with transient intermediates (16). In effect, Gibson and Greenwood were the first to 'see' the initial O_2 complex with reduced haem a_3 in cytochrome c oxidase under physiological conditions and then to describe the pathway for electron transfer in the purified enzyme from the reducing substrate, cytochrome c, to haem a and then haem a_3, which seemed to react directly with O_2, the oxidizing substrate (14, 16). Their trick was to mix the CO complex of fully reduced cytochrome c oxidase with O_2, quickly flash off the CO, and then follow the initial O_2 reactions while measuring traces at multiple wavelengths, an approach that is still used when examining oxidases today. This work continued with David Wharton, who helped discover the role of copper in cytochrome c oxidase (18) and also moved to Cornell in the late 1960s. Quentin's early work on cytochrome c oxidase was considered 'pioneering' in the field and served as inspiration for others to follow (see Wikstrom *et al*. 1981; Babcock *et al*. 1985).

Cornell, Fellow of the Royal Society, and on-line data collection

Judging from the number of papers published, the two and half years spent in Philadelphia were very productive. However, the Chance–Gibson association was not a happy one. At a meeting with H.G. in the summer of 1965 Quentin remarked that the former had not warned him adequately of Chance's way of working and running the Johnson Foundation. An example of the type of problem encountered in Philadelphia is described below in a letter to J.S.O. from Larry Parkhurst, who joined Quentin's laboratory at the Johnson Foundation in the summer of 1966 and is currently a professor in chemistry at the University of Nebraska. This story also describes how Quentin purchased the major components of his machine shop, which became a mainstay in his laboratory at Cornell:

> Quentin had been promised by Chance that when he came to the JF [Johnson Foundation] he would have virtually free machinist time. He was subsequently outraged when he was billed some exorbitant amount for a small rectangular block of stainless steel with a hole in it. He ordered a Maximat, unknown to B.C., and it arrived in pieces. It was a magnificent device … , a complete lathe, milling machine, drill-press, and universal head with indexing, etc. made in Austria. I certainly learned machining on it and subsequently used those skills to build most of a stopped flow here at Nebraska.

In his personal recollections Quentin further commented (24): 'We soon came to the conclusion that the JF and Philadelphia would not do. The city was unsafe, it was difficult to arrange for our children's education, and the suburbs were too far away for comfortable commuting.'

After spending only one year in Philadelphia, Quentin began to look for other opportunities at well-known US research universities in smaller cities with less urban problems. He narrowed the search to the University of California, Davis, and Cornell University. He chose the latter, in part because he and Jane received a package deal, with both being hired as faculty members and without the requirement that Quentin be a professor.

Quentin moved his family to Ithaca, NY, in 1966, and in 1969 his scientific work was recognized by election as a Fellow of the Royal Society (figure 4). His accomplishments during the first 25 years of his academic career were truly outstanding and included (i) discovery of the major biochemical cause of familial methaemoglobinaemia; (ii) design and development of a stopped-flow rapid-mixing device that was rugged, easy to use and readily adopted by chemists, enzymologists and physiologists; (iii) determination of the origin of kinetic cooperativity for the reaction of CO with deoxyhaemoglobin; (iv) adaptation of flash photolysis techniques to haem protein kinetics; (v) identification of some of the first transient charge-transfer

Figure 4. Quentin Gibson in front of one of his analogue computer modules in his office at Cornell University. This publicity picture was taken when Quentin was elected to the Royal Society of London. (Picture reproduced from p. 54 of H. Franklin Bunn and Bernard G. Forget, *Hemoglobin: molecular, genetic, and clinical aspects* (1986), W. B. Saunders Company, Philadelphia, PA, with permission from Elsevier.)

complexes and semiquinone intermediates in flavoprotein enzymes with Massey; (vi) definition of the kinetics of luciferases and O_2 reactions with reduced flavins, with Hastings; and (vii) the first direct measurement of intermediates for the reaction of reduced cytochrome c oxidase with O_2 under physiological conditions.

Quentin's first major technical achievement after moving to Ithaca was to modernize data collection methods for both rapid-mixing and eventually flash photolysis experiments. Previously the data points had been obtained by photographing the traces observed on oscilloscope screens with illuminated graticules. The negatives were then projected on to graph paper and points read off from the time courses by hand, which was both laborious and potentially fraught with errors when tracing the curves. This problem was solved by close collaboration between Quentin and his ingenious postdoctoral fellow Richard DeSa, who received his PhD from the University of Illinois under the guidance of Hastings. When asked to provide a history of on-line data collection at Cornell, DeSa wrote the following:

> I joined Quentin in the early fall of 1964 at the Johnson Foundation, soon after meeting him when he gave a seminar at Urbana and spent a little time in Woody Hastings' lab, where I was doing my graduate research. For the next 15 months, we worked on stopped-flow related issues including developing a dual-wavelength stopped-flow. (We were at the JF, after all!) I also continued to learn about electronics, something I started at Illinois, inspired by Gregorio Weber's group's use of the oscilloscope and other novel tools for data acquisition. Quentin seemed appreciative of my curiosity about new tools as well as biochemistry, and he gave me plenty of opportunities to tinker with hardware and, soon, software.

When Quentin accepted a position at Cornell University in late 1965, I uprooted my young family again to remain under his brilliant and engaging tutelage. For the next three years, we enjoyed exciting, challenging, and (for me) formative work in the laboratory, not so much on wet chemistry but on developing data acquisition and analysis tools. Relatively early in our time at Cornell, Quentin purchased a new powerful (and to us, beautiful) analog computer which we were soon using for the study of kinetic mechanisms. The computer was set up in Quentin's office. My experience at Illinois with electronics and my time in Philadelphia working on kinetic issues led him to invite me to share the office with him and the computer. How many hours the three of us were together! … He and I stumbled alone in that room with the analog computer and then, in the spring of 1967, a digital version. The digital computer was a PDP-8S from Digital Equipment Corporation. It had a 12 bit processor with 4K memory and came with numerous switches and lights on the front panel. After the excitement of unpacking this shiny new PDP-8S, we two stood looking down on this computer, Quentin looked at me, and then the computer, and then back at me again. I looked at him and then the computer. Next was that marvellous moment that I have recounted tens if not hundreds of times. With this shiny new toy sitting between us, Quentin spoke the classic words 'What do we do now?'

The answer to that was hundreds of hours learning how to write software code that did something useful for us. Within a year, we had developed data acquisition software for the stopped-flow that led to the first publication of what would eventually occupy me and hundreds of labs worldwide, and was entitled *A practical automatic data acquisition system for stopped-flow spectrophotometry* [(19)].

Nearly twenty years after I left Quentin's laboratory for my own, I was in Ithaca on business and made my way onto Cornell campus and then Wing Hall on a lovely Saturday afternoon. The building was open and I headed to my old space to reminiscence. Imagine my surprise and absolute delight to find Quentin in his 'workshop,' busy at the small lathe he had installed during my tenure there. We enjoyed a mutually heartfelt reunion and then I asked him what he was making. I had machined many a little part on that lathe and knew it was capable of quite nice work. 'A muffler for my car' was his answer! How perfect: this notoriously frugal man was making rather than purchasing a muffler! But, more than his frugality, this scene also addresses his inspiration, his ability to imagine his inspiration in 3D, his skill at making things, and—critically—his subsequent use of his creations.

He always maintained that if an experiment was being prevented or delayed for want of a component—perhaps a mount for a photomultiplier tube or a housing for a flash lamp—it was better to make it, so as to get on with the experiment. In his world, it was easier to make the required component himself than to think of it, draw it, submit a request for it, wait for it, etc. 'Get on with the experiment' was always his way. To this day, I admit a similar impatience inspired by his.

Like his stopped-flow apparatus, the DeSa–Gibson on-line software was easily portable to other laboratories and readily commercialized, which DeSa did when he moved to Georgia and set up On-Line Instruments, Inc., which is now marketing stopped-flow devices, spectrophotometers, and global data analysis packages. In effect, the Gibson stopped-flow device had entered the digital age and again an enormous output of kinetic data was generated from workers around the world using his basic designs.

A PAUSE TO REFLECT ON FAMILY AND CAREER BEFORE THE NEXT 40 YEARS

After completing the biographical memoir for Roughton in 1971 (31), Quentin paused to write some personal thoughts, some of which are quoted at the beginning of this memoir. Toward the end of these recollections, Quentin's spirits were low as a result of poor health, and he made the following comments (24):

Work in the lab was pretty hectic between 1968–1971—lots of things took off. This time saw the end of the dimer hypothesis and work on the α-β chain difference, on probes of R-T transformations, and on a variety of chemically altered and mutant haemoglobins. There were too many people in the lab, and as I had always insisted on doing the kinetic experiments with my own hands, the load became too much. Without warnings that I heeded, I had a pyloro-duodenal perforation and when that was followed by some radiologically visible stenosis, I went to England for a pyloroplasty and secretomotor-vagotomy. As I write, the time has come to consider the rather dismal future. It is unlikely that my energy will ever return to that of 10 years ago or that I will be assailed by a stream of good ideas. So at last I must think of myself of middle aged. Though, of course, I do not feel any differently than I ever did. Looking back at this point in time my predominant feeling is that I was exceptionally lucky all along the line. I seem to have squeezed into things ....

During his extended visit to England in May 1971 for the stomach operation, he included a few days in Cambridge for discussions with Roughton and Perutz. He accepted the suggestion to come to Bristol and stay with one of us (H.G.) for a few days' rest. When visiting the laboratory he delighted some of H.G.'s young colleagues with his expert recognition of the meaning of oscilloscope traces, even if the experiments were on systems unknown to him. Another recollection is of his medical self-treatment. When offered a glass of milk as a soothing nightcap for his ailing stomach, he expressed a preference for some gin!

Quentin's tone in the quote above seems to reflect the end of a career, but happily that did not occur. Between 1944 and 1970 Quentin published 104 papers. As described in the previous section, this work alone was sufficient to establish his reputation and election as a Fellow in the Royal Society in 1969. However, he was not finished by any means. Between the ages of 52 and 91 years, he published another 146 refereed papers, the last involving co-authorship on a paper containing molecular dynamics simulations, laser photolysis experiments and time-resolved X-ray crystallography with a library of recombinant invertebrate haemoglobins (63). Quentin was also selected to serve as an Associate Editor of *Journal of Biological Chemistry* from 1975 to 1994, was elected a member of the US National Academy of Sciences in 1982 and received the Keilin Memorial Medallist Award and Lectureship in 1990.

At the same time, Quentin's children grew up, left home and became, as he predicted, successful. William was valedictorian of his class at Williams College, earned an MD from Duke University and worked for the World Health Organization in Fiji before his untimely death in 1981. Katharine received a PhD in 1982 from the University of Illinois, worked in industry as a biochemist and, like her mother, served as an editor for *Applied and Environmental Microbiology*. Ursula earned degrees in physics from Dartmouth College and Cornell University, pursued an academic career at Dartmouth College, married Ulf Osterberg and raised three children. Emma earned a BS in natural resources from Cornell University and an MS in technical writing from Rensselaer Polytechnic Institute and is now a freelance technical author. She and her husband Michael Dvorak also have three children.

Jane's career flourished at Cornell during this period. Her initial academic career was probably more stellar than Quentin's. She earned a double first at Cambridge and a PhD from the Lister Institute in London, where she was the first person to associate a requirement for selenium with the expression of a specific enzyme, formate dehydrogenase. On the basis of that work she won a Commonwealth Fellowship to study with C. B. van Niel at the Hopkins Marine Station (Stanford University) in Pacific Grove, CA, where she became interested in photosynthetic bacteria. As described above, Jane and Quentin met when she returned to England to work with Sidney Elsden at the University of Sheffield. After they emigrated to the USA, Jane held faculty positions at the University of Pennsylvania and then at Cornell University, where she rose through the ranks to become a full professor. In the summers she also taught at the Marine Biological Laboratory in Woods Hole in Massachusetts, while Quentin worked with Frank Carey on fish haemoglobins, and they both went sailing in his beloved boats, *Flamingo* and *Monymusk*.

Jane became a well-recognized authority on the transport and utilization of ammonia in the major groups of phototrophs and later investigated the anaerobic degradation of benzoic acid in *Rhodopseudomonas palustris*. At Cornell, Jane's commitment to teaching was legendary. Among other courses, from 1975 to 1996 she initiated, taught, and constantly re-created the very popular Laboratory in Cell Biology, which provided students with updated experiments every year, using the very latest methods and technology. In honour of this effort she was awarded the prestigious Edith Edgerton Career Teaching Award in 1994. After her official retirement Jane continued to work as a visiting scientist in Carrie Harwood's laboratory at Cornell, Heidi Kaplan's laboratory at the University of Texas Medical School at Houston, and finally in Deborah Hogan's laboratory at Dartmouth during the last seven years of her life.

For the most part, life worked out much better than Quentin thought it would in 1971. Over the next 40 years, Quentin helped to determine, in quantitative detail, the structural factors that govern ligand binding in haemoglobins and myoglobins. The next sections discuss his key experiments, some of the stories behind them, and the colleagues and adversaries who were involved in the discoveries. We are fortunate that Quentin wrote his own account of haemoglobin kinetics after he retired more permanently in Hanover, NH (62). Quentin's essay is from his viewpoint and is a personal reflection. The remaining sections reflect our view of Quentin's contributions to the biochemistry and biophysics community as a whole. It is interesting to compare the two views, both of which are valid in their own ways.

A LIFE'S WORK ON HAEMOGLOBINS AND MYOGLOBINS, 1971–2009

*The haemoglobin battles: rapidly reacting Hb**

Quentin was correct: the period from 1966 to 1972 was unusually hectic and his laboratory was overflowing. There were multiple postdoctoral fellows, including Richard DeSa, Larry Parkhurst, Mike Cusanovich, Robert Gray, Keith Moffat, Ronald MacQuarrie, Francis Cole and Francis Knowles, and almost all of them took faculty positions in leading universities in the USA. A variety of visiting scientists, both young and well established, came for shorter periods for collaborative kinetic studies, including Giuseppe Geraci, Robert Noble, Robert Cassoly, Maurizio Brunori, Ron Nagel, Frank Bunn, Austen Riggs and Henry Kamin. During this period, Quentin also managed to direct the PhD thesis research of two graduate students, one of us (J.S.O.) and Melvin Andersen. It is little wonder that he made the conscious decision to slow down and reduce his laboratory to a more manageable size and to spend his next 15 summers at Woods Hole working with Frank Carey on fish haemoglobins and sailing on his boats, all at a more leisurely pace.

However, the number of important discoveries that he made during this period is remarkable, particularly with regard to how adult human haemoglobin functions in solution. The kinetic results far outpaced structural interpretations based on Max Perutz's first high-resolution crystallographic structures (Bolton & Perutz 1970; Perutz 1970), which in turn led to controversies that persisted in the literature for many years to come. In retrospect, Quentin's work from the early 1970s actually addressed and resolved many of these later controversies, but often neither he nor the antagonists realized the importance of the results until much later. In addition, the first ideas for looking at motions of CO in haemoglobin crystals were conceived by Quentin and Keith Moffat, when Keith was a newly hired assistant professor at Cornell. Keith subsequently moved to the University of Chicago and succeeded in obtaining the first 'snapshots' of ligand movement in myoglobin by time-resolved X-ray crystallography in the late 1990s (Srajer *et al.* 2001).

One source of controversy in the late 1960s was the nature of 'rapidly reacting' haemoglobin (Hb*), which binds CO roughly 50 times more rapidly than deoxyhaemoglobin in simple rapid-mixing experiments. In the late 1950s Quentin had applied flash photolysis techniques to try to measure the bimolecular rate of CO binding to the last intermediate in the Adair scheme for ligand binding to tetrameric haemoglobin; that is, $Hb_4X_3 + X \rightarrow Hb_4X_4$. He observed that, after not more than 10% photolysis of $Hb_4(CO)_4$, he could observe this last step in ligand binding directly, and the bimolecular rate constant was roughly $5.0 \ \mu M^{-1} \ s^{-1}$. In contrast, the rate for the first step in CO binding, $Hb_4 + X \rightarrow Hb_4X$, was 50-fold slower, about $0.1 \ \mu M^{-1} \ s^{-1}$ (7, 8). This observation fitted with the idea that successive additions of ligand to tetrameric haemoglobin caused conformational changes that increased the kinetic reactivity and ligand affinity of the remaining unliganded subunits.

These kinetic observations were put on a firmer theoretical and structural foundation in the 1960s. The Monod–Wyman–Changeux (MWC) two-state allosteric model showed that preferential ligand binding to a high-affinity R or 'relaxed' quaternary state can provide algebraic expressions for the successive kinetic and equilibrium Adair constants (Monod *et al.* 1965). These expressions successfully simulate the measured parameters if the original low-affinity, unliganded T or 'tense' quaternary state is much more stable than the R state in the absence of ligands. This simple but powerful model was put on a firmer structural basis by Perutz, who assigned the low-affinity T state to the deoxyhaemoglobin structure and the high-affinity, rapidly reacting, R state to the fully liganded structure (Perutz 1970).

Dimers versus tetramers, the Rome group, and quaternary enhancement

Even with the MWC model and Perutz's crystal structures there were several controversial and unresolved problems. Rapidly reacting Hb* was observed after complete flash photolysis of CO–haemoglobin at low concentrations and in simple mixing experiments of deoxyhaemoglobin with CO at very high pH. In addition, the Rome group worked out methods to separate and isolate free α and β subunits from tetrameric human haemoglobin, and the resultant monomers showed rapidly reacting, high-affinity R-state-like behaviour. Antonini and his colleagues then suggested that perhaps haemoglobin cooperativity resided primarily in αβ dimers that worked relatively independently within a tetrameric structure.

Between 1966 and 1970 Quentin and his colleagues resolved these dimer issues. First, with Larry Parkhurst and Giuseppe Geraci, Quentin confirmed the Rome group's result that isolated haemoglobin subunits have R-state or Hb* reactivity. Then Quentin and Stewart Edelstein, who had just moved to Cornell in 1968, showed that low concentrations of liganded haemoglobin dissociate into dimers and that deoxyhaemoglobin dimers generated by complete photolysis show R-state or Hb*-like rate constants, affinities and spectral properties. In this work, Quentin measured bimolecular CO recombination time courses after full photolysis of dilute CO–haemoglobin by using a roughly 1 ms excitation pulse. Stewart and his students then measured sedimentation coefficients on the same dilute samples. They obtained a 1:1 correlation between the fraction of rapidly reacting haemoglobin and the fraction of dimers (22). Then Keith Moffat, Mel Anderson and Quentin showed that when deoxyhaemoglobin dimers generated at high pH were 'jumped' to neutral pH, they also reacted rapidly with CO (26); similar experiments were done by Kellett & Gutfreund (1970) in which deoxyhaemoglobin dimers were generated from low concentrations of oxyhaemoglobin by rapid reaction with high concentrations of sodium dithionite. Thus, by about 1970, Quentin's group had shown that cooperative O_2 binding and formation of the low-affinity T state requires tetramer formation. As Quentin put it, 'the dimer hypothesis was dead', and only tetramers show cooperativity (62).

During much of this time there was an intense but friendly competition with the Rome group headed by Eraldo Antonini, Quentin's colleague from the early 1960s, and Antonini's younger protégé Maurizio Brunori. The Rome group supported the idea that cooperativity occurred primarily through haemoglobin dimers, whereas Quentin was convinced that only the tetramer showed cooperativity. Although Quentin won the debate, the relationship with Rome was pretty equal in terms of productivity and discoveries and remained friendly for the rest of Quentin's life, even after the premature death of Antonini in March 1983. Maurizio Brunori was always a welcome visitor in Ithaca, Woods Hole, and then later in Houston when Quentin moved his laboratory to Rice University in the late 1990s. Most of Maurizio's visits resulted in seminal research publications on subjects ranging from cytochrome *c* oxidases to ultrafast laser photolysis experiments and molecular dynamics simulations of ligand pathways.

Perhaps more importantly, Antonini and Brunori rekindled Quentin's interest in sailing during his early visits to Rome. Years later, Quentin sailed on the Mediterranean in Maurizio's boat, which was coincidentally designed by Britton Chance's son. However, according to Maurizio, the best times they had were sailing off Woods Hole in Quentin's *Tartan 30* with Colin Greenwood, including a trip around Martha's Vineyard. Maurizio still takes pride in knowing that he was partly responsible for Quentin's renewed enthusiasm for sailing in the late 1970s, and without a doubt this activity contributed greatly to Quentin's peace of mind and productivity during the latter stages of his career.

In the 1980s Gary Ackers's group challenged Gibson's conclusion that haemoglobin monomers, dimers and R-state tetramers all have the same high affinity for ligands. Instead Ackers suggested that the last step in oxygen binding to tetramers ($Hb_4(O_2)_3 + O_2 \rightarrow Hb_4(O_2)_4$) shows a higher oxygen affinity than that for subunits and dimers. Ackers termed this phenomenon 'quaternary enhancement' (Mills & Ackers 1979). This phenomenon was an integral part of his 'cooperon' model. Ackers's proposal stimulated Stewart Edelstein and Quentin Gibson to work together one more time in 1987 to again demonstrate experimentally that the affinity of Hb_4X_3 for ligands is the same as that for dimers and monomers (46), a result that has been verified many times over the past 25 years. Quentin's 1987 paper with Edelstein reinforces some wisdom that he imparted to one of us (J.S.O.) during a visit to Ithaca in the 1980s. He argued that if you stay in a field long enough, you do not have to keep doing new things. After about 15 years people stop looking at your old work and begin reporting discoveries and analyses that you know are incorrect. As a result, you get to do the old experiments over again to prove them wrong and still often learn something new and novel. He was definitely right about the 15-year rule in the dimer case and in many others concerning haemoglobin and fights over the allosteric mechanism for cooperative O_2 binding.

MWC versus induced-fit models

Several workers in the haemoglobin field have suggested that the two-state model for cooperative O_2 binding is incorrect and that more complex models are required in which ligand binding induces progressive quaternary conformational changes that alter the strengths of the various subunit interfaces. These models predict intermediate reactivities when one, two or three ligands are bound. This view was initially proposed by Linus Pauling (ForMemRS 1948) in the 1930s (Pauling 1935), and reinvented in a more rigorous form by Daniel Koshland and others in the 1960s (Koshland *et al.* 1966). This induced-fit progressive model was revitalized, albeit in a more rigorous thermodynamic manner, by Gary Ackers in the 1980s and 1990s (Ackers *et al.* 1992), leading to several interesting clashes in the literature that persisted until the early 2000s.

However, despite more than 40 years of wrangling and literally hundreds of papers, it is clear that the simple two-state allosteric model is a reasonable first approximation for explaining the key features of cooperative O_2 binding to haemoglobin, particularly if changes in the properties of the T or low-affinity state with pH, effector binding, chemical modification, and mutation are accepted. Quentin showed the applicability of this modified MWC model with several ingenious kinetic experiments in the early 1970s, which were made possible by computerized data collection systems developed with Richard DeSa and by Quentin's ability to do rigorous mathematical analysis of complex kinetic schemes, using both exponential fitting and numerical integration of networks of differential equations.

By 1971 the physiological role of organic phosphates (such as 2,3-bisphosphoglycerate (humans), ATP (some fishes) or inositol pentaphosphate or hexaphosphate (birds)) in regulating O_2 affinity in vertebrate haemoglobins had been discovered. The stoichiometry of binding was one organic phosphate per tetramer; in all cases these effectors bound more strongly to the T or deoxy quaternary conformation, causing a rightward shift in the O_2 equilibrium curve (lower affinity for oxygen, or higher P_{50} (partial pressure of oxygen in the blood for 50% saturation of haemoglobin)). To examine when these anions are released by haemoglobin during ligand binding, Quentin and Ron MacQuarrie (27) developed a fluorescent bis-2,3-phosphoglycerate (BPG) analogue, 8-hydroxy-1,3,6-pyrenetrisulphonate (HPT), which bound to the positively charged cleft between β subunits in T-state deoxyhaemoglobin and could be displaced by BPG. The fluorescence of this anionic dye was almost completely quenched by the haem groups when bound to deoxyhaemoglobin tetramers, its affinity for the fully liganded state was very small, and its release during ligand binding could be followed by a marked increase in fluorescence. When deoxyhaemoglobin containing bound HPT was mixed with CO, there was a marked lag in the increase in fluorescence in comparison with the changes in absorbance associated with CO binding, indicating that the anion was not released until roughly three ligands had been bound and the switch to the R quaternary state had occurred, as predicted by the two-state MWC model.

Two years later Quentin looked at the change in reactivity of β Cys 93 with *p*-hydroxymercuribenzoate (pMB) during the binding of CO to deoxyhaemoglobin in similar rapid-mixing experiments (34). In this case, pMB reacts about 100-fold more slowly with the β Cys 93 thiol side chain in the T or deoxyhaemoglobin conformation. By adjusting the CO and pMB concentrations, Quentin was able to set up the experiment so that no pMB would react with the β Cys 93 in the deoxygenated T state on the experimental time scales but would immediately react once the high-affinity R state formed. The thiol reaction could be followed specifically by changes at 250 nm, where the thiol–mercuribenzoate complex has an absorbance band.

Again, when deoxyhaemoglobin was mixed with pMB and CO, there was a lag in the spectral change for the pMB reaction with β Cys 93. The marked 100-fold increase in reactivity with the mercurial compound did not start to occur until roughly three ligands had bound, just as with organic anion release. These results showed clearly in 1973 that it takes the binding of several ligands before major changes in ligand reactivity, organic phosphate binding and β Cys 93 thiol reactivity occur in human haemoglobin. Thus, the major conformational change in haemoglobin tetramers is concerted and can be approximated by invoking just two states, R and T, and not intermediate ones, as predicted in the Koshland induced-fit and Ackers cooperon models. It is true that some effectors can alter the intrinsic ligand-binding properties of these two states, but the overall process is highly concerted.

Differences between the α and β subunits of human haemoglobin

In 1970 Perutz suggested strongly that O_2 cannot bind to β subunits in the T quaternary state, on the basis of the position of the β Val 67 (E11 helical position) side chain, which seems to sterically hinder access to the iron atom in the high-resolution crystal structure of human deoxyhaemoglobin. Perutz therefore suggested an ordered addition of ligands, in which O_2 first bound to α subunits then to β subunits after the switch to the high-affinity R state when β Val 67 moves away from the haem iron. Again, Quentin had already been working on this problem with his students in Ithaca.

In 1968 Quentin, Parkhurst and Geraci (21) showed unambiguously that large triatomic ferric ligands bind more rapidly to β subunits than to α subunits, implying that the β active site is more sterically accessible. Quentin and one of us (J.S.O.) (29) extended this approach to ferrous ligands with the use of alkyl isocyanides as larger ligands to exaggerate any differences in steric hindrance between the active sites of the haemoglobin subunits. The association and dissociation rate constants for n-butyl isocyanide binding to the β subunits are between five-fold and tenfold greater than those for binding to α subunits, in both isolated monomers and in tetramers in either quaternary state. However, the ratios of these rate constants are roughly the same in both subunits, indicating equal affinities. For O_2 binding, Quentin's group also showed that the association and dissociation rate constants for β subunits are roughly double those of α subunits, but again the affinities are identical. Thus, Perutz's initial interpretation of the crystal structure was wrong: the active site in β chains is more accessible kinetically and there is little or no affinity difference between the subunits under normal conditions.

Quentin pointed out these kinetic results to Max Perutz in person at a meeting in 1971 and suggested that there was no ordered addition of O_2. Unfortunately, Perutz's response was that there must be something wrong with the experiments and that Quentin 'didn't understand the power of modern stereochemistry' (62). The latter remark made Quentin so furious that he refused to look carefully at any crystal structures for the next 15 years, despite the fact that Keith Moffat had got Quentin's students to build a wire model of the deoxyhaemoglobin dimer. This structural model sat on a bench in a prominent place in the Gibson laboratory for about a year until Keith was given a faculty position and his own space in 1972. Again, the results published on chain differences in the early 1970s have stood the test of time, been verified many times over in experiments with recombinant mutant haemoglobin libraries and various metal haemoglobin hybrid molecules, and were finally accepted by Perutz in the early 1990s.

Thus, despite Quentin's negative statements in his personal recollections (24), he was coming up with some of his best ideas, making key and definitive observations about how human haemoglobin works and, most importantly, performing remarkably clever and novel kinetic experiments that only he could have designed. The papers from this period have served as guides for almost all subsequent functional studies of haemoglobin, even if sometimes the new authors fail to recognize the origins of the methods and approaches.

Haemoglobinopathies, fish haemoglobins, plant and invertebrate haemoglobins, metal hybrids and model compounds, and other collaboration

One of the hallmarks of Quentin's research career was the large number of highly successful collaborations. As Tony Wilkinson, a collaborator from York University, remarked in an email to J.S.O. after Quentin's death, 'he had a great generosity of spirit', which is rare among more modern highly competitive scientists. Visitors were normally treated to dinners with Jane at his home, which in Ithaca included a large farmhouse with barns on Slaterville Road and then later a smaller home closer to Cornell on Game Farm Road. The drive to the latter house was idyllic and involved one traffic light and two stop signs; it ended along a narrow English-like blacktop lane surrounded by pheasant runs where foxes could often be seen trying to penetrate the highly meshed fences. These dinners were filled with science, politics and hilarious anecdotes. Lunch in the laboratory often involved meeting with David Wilson, Peter Hinkle and Leon Heppel, biochemistry professors in Quentin's department, and then going for vigorous walks around the beautiful Cornell campus, listening to more stories, often about past and present university administrators.

Some of the first collaborations in Ithaca involved studies of haemoglobinopathies (for example haemoglobins Hiroshima, Bethesda, Chesapeake, Kansas and Kempsey) where single point mutations cause changes in the allosteric behaviour of haemoglobin, leading to either abnormally high or low O_2 affinities. Three key colleagues were Ronald Nagel and H. Frank Bunn, who were world-renowned haematologists at Albert Einstein College of Medicine and Harvard Medical School, respectively, and Austen Riggs from the Department of Zoology at the University of Texas (28, 33, 36). Nagel and Quentin also carefully examined the kinetics of haptoglobin binding to haemoglobin by following quenching of the tryptophan fluorescence of haptoglobin by the haem groups in the complex (23). Quentin also helped characterize some of the haemoglobin derivatives prepared by John Kilmartin's group at the MRC in Cambridge, which were designed to look at the origin of Bohr-effect protons (32).

Work with fish haemoglobins had also begun at this time, in part because of connections with both Frank Carey at Woods Hole (35) and Robert Noble at SUNY at Buffalo (30) and because Mel Andersen's major PhD thesis project involved characterizing the ligand-binding properties and dimeric structure of lamprey haemoglobin (25). The latter work was often quite exciting when Andersen showed up with a garbage can full of three-foot-long lampreys and then recruited other laboratory members for the bloodletting process. These studies continued for the next 10–15 years when Quentin spent his summers in Woods Hole, often bringing back various samples of teleost and elasmobranch red blood cells. Wilma Saffran did her PhD work on studies of pH and salt effects on ligand binding to carp and menhaden haemoglobins (43). Quentin and Frank Carey also looked at the effects of hydrostatic pressure on ligand binding to haemoglobins in general and in some of the proteins from deeper-diving fish (39).

In the 1980s Quentin collaborated with Jonathan and Beatrice Wittenberg and Cyril Appleby on studies of plant leghaemoglobins and with Serge Vinogradov, Luc Moens, Maurizio Brunori and Andrea Bellelli on experiments with a wide variety of invertebrate haemoglobins, including a haemoglobin from the intestinal parasite *Ascaris suum*, which has a higher affinity for O_2 than for CO, and the myoglobin from the sea slug *Aplysia limacina*, which lacks a distal histidine (47, 49, 51, 57, 58, 60). He also began a long and interesting examination of ligand binding to the homodimeric haemoglobin from the red clam *Scapharca inaequivalvis*. These studies were initiated with Emilia Chiancone from the Rome group and then expanded with William Royer from the University of Massachusetts Medical School at Worcester. Royer solved the crystal structure of this protein in the mid 1990s and, with Gibson and Chiancone, showed that the structural mechanism of cooperative O_2 binding involves direct haem–haem interactions at an unusual hydrophilic subunit interface (52, 56).

From the late 1970s to the early 1990s, Quentin also collaborated with Robert Cassoly, Brian Hoffman, Takashi Yonetani, Masao Ikeda-Saito and Naoya Shibayama on mixed-valence haemoglobin hybrids, model haems and metal-substituted haemoglobins (37, 40, 53, 55). In the work with hybrid haemoglobins, one set of subunits was either oxidized or replaced with a metal other than iron to allow more direct measurements of ligand binding to the remaining 'normal' Fe^{2+} α or β subunit. In most cases, these studies confirmed the earlier 1970–74 work: the α and β subunits of human haemoglobin A have very similar O_2 affinities in either the R or T quaternary state, and the two-state allosteric model is a reasonable approximation if both the unliganded R to T isomerization equilibrium constant, L, and the T state parameters are allowed to vary with differing starting conditions. Some of the work with metal-substituted haemoglobins combined with picosecond and nanosecond laser photolysis experiments also provided new and detailed structural insights into what governs iron reactivity in globins.

The meaning of quantum yields, iron reactivity, and geminate recombination

The deoxyHb* (rapidly reacting) → deoxyHb (slowly reacting) spectral transition can also be seen after the complete photolysis of CO–haemoglobin at low ligand concentrations, where bimolecular rebinding cannot compete with the R → T conformational transition, which is very rapid (about 5000 s^{-1}) and hard to measure with simple xenon-flash lamps. In the early 1970s Quentin concluded that laser technology was required to improve time resolution and photolysis efficiency to permit the more direct measurement of the speed of the R → T (Hb* → Hb) spectral transition and its dependence on the number of ligands bound.

As a result, Quentin began to construct a flashlamp-driven, dye laser photolysis instrument with Robert Gray, Charles Sawicki and others. The initial goal was to increase the photolysis time resolution to about 0.5 μs and was achieved in a fairly straightforward manner. Sawicki and Gibson (41) used this instrument to measure the rates of the R → T transition after various levels of photolysis and confirmed that the speed of the transition is roughly 5000 s^{-1} at room temperature and decreases as more ligands bind, in a manner consistent with the two-state allosteric model. The greater time resolution and higher-intensity excitation also allowed measurements with oxyhaemoglobin samples, for which the initial rates of O_2 dissociation are on the order of 1000–5000 s^{-1}, precluding measurements by rapid mixing. Again, analyses of bimolecular O_2 recombination kinetics and R → T spectral changes could be well approximated by two-state MWC models.

As Quentin moved towards the use of even shorter laser excitation pulses, both he and his competitors had to come to grips with how to correlate internal geminate rebinding of ligands with overall association and dissociation rate constants measured in conventional mixing experiments and the overall quantum yields for photodissociation of the ligand into solvent. In effect, they had to try to work out experimentally what determines the absolute values of these overall rate parameters and then use this framework to interpret the reactivity differences between the physiological ligands O_2, CO and NO and between various haemoglobins and the R and T conformational states in terms of specific structural features.

Hans Frauenfelder's group at the University of Illinois developed the initial framework for these correlations in the late 1970s (Austin *et al*. 1975). His group initially started with analyses of low-temperature high-viscosity photolysis experiments, in which CO was trapped inside myoglobin by the glass-like structure of the surrounding medium, and then extrapolated the results to more physiological conditions under which the ligand could escape. The internal rebinding processes are called geminate rebinding because the same pairs of Fe and CO atoms (twins) recombine without the ligand escaping from the protein and mixing with gas molecules in the solvent. Study of these internal reactions allows direct measurements of iron reactivity and the effects of the constraints on in-plane movement of the iron-proximal histidine complex without the complications of ligand diffusion into and capture within the haem pocket of the globin.

At about the same time, several workers looked at the initial, ultrafast first-order absorbance phases that occurred when oxymyoglobin (MbO_2) or HbO_2 were photodissociated under physiological conditions with nanosecond yttrium aluminium garnet (YAG) lasers. Morris, Duddell and Richards at the University of Salford, UK (Duddell *et al*. 1980) were among the first to suggest that these changes represented ligand rebinding from within the protein and were analogous to the traces seen in the low-temperature experiments of Frauenfelder and co-workers. Similar ideas and conclusions were reported by Hochstrasser's, Eaton's, Magde's and Friedman's groups at the University of Pennsylvania, the NIH, the University of California, San Diego, and Bell Laboratories, respectively, using even faster solid-state lasers.

When Roger Morris came to Ithaca in 1980 to work with Quentin and help him construct a nanosecond laser system, many of the key issues associated with geminate rebinding and its interpretation were controversial. However, even before the nanosecond apparatus was built, Quentin and Morris quickly came to several important—although at the time tentative—conclusions based on empirical comparisons of quantum yields for the complete photodissociation of NO, O_2 and CO complexes of haemoglobins. In a prescient paper published in 1980 (42), they suggested that the very low overall quantum yield for the complete photodissociation of HbNO is due to an extremely high rate of internal bond reformation as a result of the radical nature of NO. This high rate of internal bond formation means that the overall bimolecular rate constant for NO binding measured in mixing experiments is limited exclusively by the speed of movement into the protein and not by the reactivity of the iron atom. Once the NO reaches the active site it rapidly forms a bond with the iron atom before it has time to escape. This conclusion explained Gibson and Cassoly's 1975 observation (37) that the bimolecular association rate constant for NO binding to haemoglobin, k'_{NO}, is very high, about 50 μM^{-1} s^{-1}, and is independent of whether the protein is in the R or the T state. The quaternary conformational state only affects the ease of in-plane movement of the iron atom and its reactivity within the active site, not the rate of ligand entry into the distal pocket. NO binding is still cooperative but the change in reactivity of the iron atom is only manifested kinetically by large 100-fold increases in the rate of NO dissociation during the R $\rightarrow$ T transition, which had been reported earlier by Quentin and his graduate student Edwin Moore in the mid 1970s (38).

The other key conclusion in Morris and Gibson's initial 1980 paper (42) was that CO binding is limited by iron reactivity and not the rate of entry into the protein. For this ligand, the rate of internal bond formation is very small compared with the rate of escape of ligand from the active site. As a result the overall association constant is determined by the equilibrium constant for partitioning into the active site multiplied by the rate of internal bond formation, which depends markedly on iron reactivity and quaternary state. The low rate of internal bond formation also explains the high quantum yield of HbCO complexes, because almost all photodissociated ligands escape before any internal rebinding can occur. Frauenfelder and his group had come to similar conclusions on the basis of their low-temperature studies with CO–myoglobin, using more general and complex analyses (Doster *et al.* 1982).

At the same time there remained many issues and controversies regarding the interpretation of ultrafast, internal rebinding time courses, including the photo-physical yield of true geminate states; the number and location of the internal, dissociated ligand positions; and the pathways for ligand entry and escape. Many of the big names in experimental and theoretical biophysics became interested in these problems, which were now amenable to molecular dynamics simulations and various time-resolved methodologies, including Fourier-transform infrared spectroscopy, resonance Raman spectroscopy, more conventional ultraviolet–visible spectral measurements, and both low-temperature and time-resolved X-ray crystallography. Part of the attraction was that the laser technology allowed the visualization of true transition states (namely photodissociated ligands in the haem pocket) that had previously only been implied in the theories of Eyring, Debye, Smoluchowski and others, and connections could be made with high-resolution globin structures.

Undaunted by the competition, Quentin proceeded to build nanosecond and picosecond photolysis instruments in his own style, which was to design a rugged instrument that would allow the examination of large numbers of protein samples quickly and avoid signal averaging over long periods. In effect, he wanted to retain the style of his stopped-flow, rapid-mixing apparatus. With the help of Roger Morris he modified a Phaser-R 2100B flashlamp-driven laser to operate in cavity dump mode using a Pockels cell. The initial flashlamp light was used to trigger a krytron device, which in turn sent a pulse to rapidly switch and then return the plane of polarization of the Pockels cell. This switch created a 17 ns square-wave excitation pulse in which the decay of the trailing edge was 1.0 ns or less, which, in effect, was the time resolution of the instrument.

To obtain better signal-to-noise traces for the high-speed photomultiplier, the observing xenon arc lamp was pulsed (about 0.2–0.5 ms) to 20-fold higher energy just before the laser excitation pulse was triggered. This feature was unique to Quentin's instruments and allowed the accumulation of three to five relatively noise-free traces for unstable HbO_2 and MbO_2 complexes within 10–15 min after sample preparation. Most other instruments used conventional xenon lamps for absorbance monitoring and required the averaging of 500–5000 traces over long periods, which almost always leads to degradation of oxygenated globin complexes in solution at room temperature. Perhaps more importantly, many different samples could be screened for interesting results in a relatively short period. A similar pulsed observing beam was used in his later nanosecond instruments, which employed frequency-doubled solid-state YAG lasers with excitation pulses of about 7 ns.

In the late 1980s Richard Blackmore and Quentin built a 35 ps laser photolysis apparatus using a Nd active–passive mode-locked laser, which was frequency doubled to 532 nm (48). To obtain data in the picosecond time regime, a probe-pulse data collection system was used. The Nd–YAG pulse was split, with one beam used for photolysis and the other passed through a Raman shifter. The first anti-Stokes line at 436 nm of the weaker laser beam was used to probe the transmittance of the sample cuvette. An automated optical delay line was constructed to obtain absorbance readings with time delays from −0.1 to 1.5 ns with about 1 ps time resolution.

As with the stopped-flow apparatus and early photolysis devices, Quentin was himself involved at every step in the construction, maintenance and repair of all these laser photolysis devices, and he was involved in writing both the data collection and analysis software. Postdoctoral fellows and technicians came and went, but Quentin kept everything working, often by himself. In fact, he was most happy tinkering with and perfecting the instruments. Most importantly, he always participated in the data collection, to the delight and sometimes consternation of all involved. As Tony Wilkinson recalled from a visit in the early 1990s, 'I particularly remember him turning to me after firing his laser and recording a rather baffling looking trace. When I asked him what it all meant, he replied, "Well, I don't know; it's your sample, Dr Wilkinson!"' Many people had already heard that same response in years past, including us.

Rates of internal O$_2$ versus CO binding

One of the key controversies in the mid 1980s was how to interpret overall and geminate O$_2$ rebinding to HbO$_2$ and MbO$_2$ samples. Most people avoided experiments at room temperature because of autooxidation that was accelerated by repeated photoexcitation when signal averaging was required. Frauenfelder and co-workers had suggested that the 30-fold higher bimolecular rate for O$_2$ binding to myoglobin compared with that of CO was due primarily to a 10-fold greater equilibrium partitioning constant for non-covalent O$_2$ movement in the distal portion pocket of the haem pocket and not a markedly higher rate of internal bond formation (Doster *et al*. 1982). However, this conclusion did not make sense chemically because in the absence of coordination to the iron atom both diatomic gases have similar sizes, apolar character, and solubility in water and organic solvents.

In part to resolve this problem, Gibson had started working with J.S.O. and his students from Rice University in Houston to explore the physical nature of the geminate states and the pathways for binding by altering both the size and chemistry of the ligand and the structure of the globin active site. In an initial study with sperm whale myoglobin, they conducted detailed nanosecond geminate recombination studies with O$_2$, NO, CO and a series of five alkyl isocyanides, varying the laser light intensity to analyse absorbance changes both during and after laser excitation (44). In their analysis they assumed that the photo-physical quantum yield for the first geminate state was roughly 1.0 for all ligands, and in their analyses of the geminate rebinding time courses the fitted value of the rate constant for internal O$_2$ bond formation with the iron atom was always much greater than that for internal CO recombination, unlike the Frauenfelder result. They argued that the Frauenfelder analysis was incorrect and all the differences between the three diatomic ligands were due to changes in the rate of internal bond formation (that is, ligand reactivity with iron) and that there were no differences in the partitioning constant for gas movement into the protein. The resulting paper led to heated discussions with Frauenfelder's group, who often suggested that Quentin's apparatus was too primitive or that the analysis of only room-temperature data was inadequate. These comments led in turn to disparaging remarks at the Gibson dinner table about the relevance of studies in frozen glasses. On one particular night, Jane had had enough and told Quentin, J.S.O. and Ron Rohlfs (a graduate student of J.S.O.'s) that they were a very 'obstreperous and truculent lot' who ought to do something positive instead of always complaining. Two of the three obstreperous participants went home that night with their tail between their legs to find a dictionary.

As fate would have it, shortly thereafter Doug Madge's group (Jongeward *et al.* 1988) at the University of California, San Diego, showed that the picosecond quantum yields for both O_2 and NO geminate states are only 0.2–0.3 and not 1.0, and that all the published analyses of MbO_2, MbCO and MbNO geminate rebinding needed revision. As Rohlfs recalled in an email after Quentin's death, 'Quentin told Dr. Olson and myself, "Gentleman, I see a crow out there. Shall we have it baked or boiled before we have to eat it?"' As with many such disputes, both sides were a little bit right and a little bit wrong. This situation reminded J.S.O. of a rebuke by Quentin in 1979 after the former had complained about the unfairness of a review in *Journal of Biological Chemistry*. In his capacity as Associate Editor, Quentin wrote to him and said, 'John, you should know that authors are not often the best judges of the merits of their own work.'

Battle with cancer and new work on site-directed mutants

In the spring of 1987 Quentin was diagnosed with a large solid lymphoma in his abdomen. He had been having trouble eating but, as is typical of physicians, had avoided seeing doctors, which was a trait he continued for most of his life. As might be expected, he researched the problem carefully and then decided he could be treated in Ithaca as well as anywhere else and began a regime of chemotherapy for roughly six months, which was fairly debilitating and, from his point of view, had an uncertain outcome. It was a fairly depressing time and Quentin began to talk of giving up the laboratory and willing its facilities to some of his collaborators. One of us (J.S.O.) kept in fairly close contact with him over the treatment period because of both concern and joint publication efforts. J.S.O. remembers calling up Quentin in late November 1987, after the treatment regime had been completed and after a last visit with his oncologist. Quentin sounded depressed and in low spirits and had to be coaxed into providing the details of the doctor's report, which was the best of all possible outcomes. The tumour had disappeared, no metastasis had been detected, and he was given a clean bill of health. J.S.O. then asked why he sounded so depressed; and Quentin's response was, 'Oh, now I have to write another NIH grant to keep going.' He did indeed write two more successful NIH R01 grants in 1988 and 1993 and remained fully active for another 20 years, a remarkable outcome for a 70-year-old cancer patient.

During this time, Quentin's laboratory kept running fairly smoothly and publications continued through the efforts of Michael Marden and Starr Hazard, who published several very interesting papers on simple haem–CO and haem–CO/albumin complexes as well as seminal studies on the R $\rightarrow$ T transition of human haemoglobin A and its effects on geminate recombination (45). Marden received his PhD with Hans Frauenfelder and brought a physics perspective to the group. Richard Blackmore arrived shortly thereafter to help with the construction of the 35 ps laser apparatus, which led to many studies on NO geminate rebinding.

The collaborations with J.S.O. and his students at Rice University expanded greatly in 1988 when J.S.O. began working with Steven Sligar at the University of Illinois, Anthony Wilkinson at York University, Masao Ikeda-Saito at Case Western Reserve University, and Kiyoshi Nagai at Cambridge University on site-directed mutagenesis studies with recombinant sperm whale myoglobin, pig myoglobin, human myoglobin and human haemoglobin A. The resultant libraries of mutants allowed a direct connection to be made between rate parameters derived from kinetic mechanisms and specific features in the three-dimensional structure of the globin being studied. In many cases, the crystal structures of key mutants were determined either at Rice University, often in collaboration with George N. Phillips Jr, or at York University

Figure 5. Small group picture from the 1988 Asilomar Meeting on O_2 Binding Proteins. Second row, left to right: Quentin Gibson (Cornell), John Olson (Rice), Kiyoshi Nagai (Medical Research Council (MRC), Cambridge), Jeremy Tame (MRC, Cambridge), Nai-Teng Yu (Georgia Tech), Steven Sligar (University of Illinois). First row, left to right: David Shih (Oregon Health & Science University), Jean-Paul Renaud (MRC, Cambridge), Barry Springer (University of Illinois), Karen Egeberg (University of Illinois), Shun-Hua Lin (Georgia Tech). (Photograph sent to J.S.O. by Kiyoshi Nagai (MRC, Cambridge), after learning of Quentin's passing in March 2011.)

by Tony Wilkinson and his students. Quentin had to reverse his position on crystallography, which was based on his pique at Perutz's 1970 comment that he didn't understand 'modern stereochemistry', and became immersed in looking at Protein Data Bank (PDB) files on his various computers.

Internal ligand movements and reactivities

Quentin's renewed enthusiasm for science can be seen in figure 5, which was taken at the Asilomar Conference on O_2 Binding Proteins in the autumn of 1988 and shows many of the collaborators on the initial recombinant haemoglobin and myoglobin studies. The collaborative site-directed mutagenesis and metal substitution work provided structural mechanisms for how the rate of internal iron–ligand bond formation was regulated. From the work in the 1980s it was clear that values for the different diatomic ligands were in the order $NO \gg O_2 > CO$. However, ease of in-plane movement of the iron atom could markedly affect the measured value of internal bond formation for all three ligands. In definitive work with Naoya Shibayama using Ni/Fe hybrid haemoglobins that are 'stuck' in the T state (55), Quentin was able to confirm unambiguously that rates of geminate rebinding of all ligands are markedly decreased in T-state haemoglobin A, causing increases in quantum yields and dissociation rate constants, conclusions that been reached by more indirect experiments with Charles Sawicki in the late 1970s and Mike Marden in the late 1980s. In effect, Perutz's original 1970 ideas were correct; the decrease in O_2 affinity in the T state is caused by a marked decrease in iron reactivity due to proximal constraints of in-plane iron movement.

Perhaps more interesting were the collaborative observations at Cornell and Rice that the rate of internal rebinding also depends on both the steric accessibility of the iron atom and the size of the cavities available to photodissociated ligands on the distal side of the haem group. Insertion of large aromatic amino acids in the back of the distal pocket of either myoglobin or haemoglobin sequesters the dissociated ligands near the iron atom, facilitating the rate and extent of internal rebinding. In contrast, putting large amino acids very near the active site, which hinder both the bound ligand and its return to the iron atom, greatly decrease the rate and extent of geminate rebinding.

These marked distal effects on geminate rebinding led Quentin and many others in the field to conclude that simple kinetic schemes do not really provide an adequate interpretation of the internal ligand rebinding processes, which involve chemical barriers to bond formation, diffusive processes for ligand movement, rotations of amino acid side chains, and tertiary structure expansions. Quentin was struck by the molecular dynamics simulation that Ron Elber and Martin Karplus had done, to try to determine the pathways for ligand movement into and out of myoglobin, at the 1988 Asilomar Meeting (Elber & Karplus 1990). When Elber moved to the University of Illinois, Chicago, he began to work with Quentin and J.S.O. on ligand movements in the various myoglobin mutants that markedly alter the time courses for geminate recombination. Quentin was so intrigued with these molecular dynamics simulations that he asked Elber to help him set up software and computation equipment in Ithaca so that some of the work could be done at Cornell. Elber was more than willing to help and established a friendship and collaboration that lasted until Quentin's final paper in 2009 (63). Thus in 1993, at 75 years of age, when most older scientists try to avoid learning anything new, Quentin embraced molecular dynamics for the analysis and interpretation of kinetic data and used these simulations with his own staff (Richard Blackmore, Rebecca Regan and Mark Carlson) and with Ron Elber, John Olson, George Phillips, William Royer and their colleagues in successfully interpreting NO, O_2 and CO geminate rebinding to large libraries of recombinant myoglobins and haemoglobins (54, 63).

A five-year hiatus in Houston

By 1996 most of Quentin's colleagues at Cornell had retired, and the lunchtime walks had been mostly curtailed by attrition. He and Jane had also recently purchased a house on Woods End Road in Etna, NH, near Dartmouth College. The house had a magnificent view of the Connecticut River valley and mountains in the distance, and Quentin's second daughter, Ursula, and her husband lived just up the road with their three children. Although the winters were cold and snowy, the summers were mild, and the attraction of living near family was very strong. However, Quentin still wanted to keep working in the laboratory, so he came up with a clever plan. In the summer of 1996 he gave J.S.O. a call and asked whether he could move all his equipment to Rice University so he could spend the winters in Houston doing experiments in the Olson laboratory and then spend the summers in New Hampshire doing molecular dynamics simulations and analyses. He also said he was tired of writing grants and papers and hoped that J.S.O. could help take over those efforts. Rice University was very enthusiastic about helping to facilitate Quentin's move because they would get a Distinguished Faculty Fellow who was both a Fellow of the Royal Society of London and a member of the US National Academy of Sciences, and do so at no cost. Plus, there were still two years left

Figure 6. Quentin performing some of the last geminate recombination experiments in Houston at Rice University for the myoglobin pathway mapping work. (Photograph taken by Jeff Nichols for J.S.O. in January 2001.)

on Quentin's NIH R01 grant, which moved with him. Thereafter, his salary was included on J.S.O.'s grant from the National Institute of General Medical Sciences, which added significant psychological pressure to its renewal.

Literally everything in Quentin's laboratory was moved to Houston, including his machine shop, the lasers and tables, computers, freezer samples dating back to the late 1970s, chemicals, glassware and even half-empty gas tanks. Jeff Nichols, who was working for both J.S.O. and the Biochemistry and Cell Biology Department, stepped in to help Quentin to get all the equipment and the machine shop working within less than two months. This interaction led to a long-term working relationship that continued when Nichols took teaching positions in the southern New Hampshire/central Massachusetts area and Quentin moved back to New Hampshire in 2001.

Mapping pathways for ligand movement into globins

By the winter of 1996, Quentin had got his nanosecond YAG laser system operational at Rice (figure 6) and had begun working with one of J.S.O.'s graduate students, Emily Scott, on the pathways for ligand movement into and out of mammalian myoglobin as a simple model system. In effect they were trying to determine what amino acids and regions in the protein regulate the rate of ligand entry and escape. At the time, many workers in the field were proposing that photodissociated ligands initially migrate into the myoglobin interior and occupy positions in what are called the xenon cavities, which are the spaces that can bind xenon atoms when crystals are exposed to 2–15 atm of this large apolar gas. Movement to these positions and others were seen in almost all molecular dynamics simulations, which suggested that ligands leave globins by multiple pathways that radiate out from the active site through 'softer' apolar regions between major helices in the globin tertiary structure.

Both the initial and most recent time-resolved X-ray crystallographic studies with MbCO crystals by Keith Moffat's group at the University of Chicago and Phil Anfinrud at the NIH showed the appearance of ligand electron density in these cavities within 50 ns after photolysis (Srajer *et al.* 2001; Schotte *et al.* 2004). These motions were in the opposite direction to the distal histidine gate pathway, often called the E7 channel because the histidine is located at the seventh position along the globin E helix. When the distal histidine rotates out into solvent, the E7 channel opens and provides the shortest and most direct route out of the protein. Emily Scott and Quentin addressed this issue experimentally by measuring both geminate and bimolecular rebinding to myoglobin variants in which the interior cavities were filled either with xenon atoms by pressurization with the gas or with large aromatic amino acids by site-directed mutagenesis. This approach was classical Gibson: do a lot of measurements on different samples, analyse the results in terms of complex kinetic schemes, and then try to make sense of it all. In this case the results were highly successful at resolving the pathway issue.

When Emily and Quentin filled the interior cavities with xenon gas, all slow internal rebinding processes disappeared and only a single rapid exponential phase was observed; however, remarkably, the total fraction of geminate O_2 recombination and the bimolecular rate constant for overall binding from the solvent phase did not change (66). Similar results occurred when the internal cavities were filled with the large amino acid side chains of phenylalanine and tryptophan. Thus, in the wild-type protein, photodissociated ligands do reach the internal cavities and return more slowly to rebind, but the fraction of escape to solvent is not affected by these internal movements and is governed only by the actual pathway for entry and escape, which involves the distal histidine gate. This approach of increasing or decreasing the size of cavities by mutagenesis was expanded to a more general mapping strategy using the full capabilities of J.S.O. and Phillips's laboratory at Rice University and then examining the results theoretically by molecular dynamics simulations. For the next several years, Quentin continued this line of study at Rice, with J.S.O. and his students using both haemoglobin and myoglobin mutants, with Maurizio Brunori using myoglobin mutants designed to mimic naturally occurring invertebrate haemoglobin variants, and with Bill Royer using *Scapharca* haemoglobin.

Scott, Gibson and Olson (59) completed the work on myoglobin and published a paper in 2001 in which the pathway for ligand binding was mapped experimentally by measuring the rates of ligand entry and escape for a library of more than 90 different myoglobin variants, which had small (alanine, valine) and large (phenylalanine, tryptophan) amino acid replacements along proposed routes for ligand migration into and out of the protein. The effects of large-to-small substitutions on the rates of entry and escape were quantified and then mapped on to the three-dimensional structure with colour codes to indicate large, medium, small or no effects. The results were remarkably clear and supported Gibson and Scott's earlier work with xenon. The only positions that were highlighted by the experimental results were located at or along the distal histidine gate or E7 channel or in the distal cavity directly above the haem group. Ligands move to the xenon cavities but then return the distal pocket to escape or re-enter through the His(E7) gate as proposed by Perutz some 50 years previously. These results for myoglobin have been verified by additional work by others over the past 10 years (Salter *et al.* 2012) and for the subunits of human haemoglobin (Birukou *et al.* 2010, 2011).

'Retirement' in Hanover, NH

In 2001 Quentin at age 82 and Jane at age 76 decided that it was time to retire permanently to their home in New Hampshire. The effort of driving back and forth to Houston and maintaining two households was substantial, and they looked forward to a more relaxed pace and to spend more time with their immediate family. They were sorely missed in Houston and had become an integral part of the J.S.O. family scene, with Friday night fish dinners and often holiday meals. Two other memorable times were Quentin's participating in a highly competitive Easter egg hunt and a remarkable boat trip with Jane through the Aransas Pass Wildlife Preserve to view whooping cranes. However, the most lasting impression of their time in Houston was seeing Jane and Quentin go for their daily lunchtime walks around the Rice University campus.

Quentin also provided many words of wisdom to J.S.O., Phillips and their students at Rice. He placed a sign in front of his laboratory door that said, 'Learn to Complain without Suffering', advice he had given Stewart Edelstein some 40 years earlier when Stewart became the chair of the Biochemistry Section at Cornell. He would also warn J.S.O. about becoming a VIP and insisted that it was very important 'to actually do experiments or you will eventually become obsolete and have to quit.' There is much wisdom in both statements, and Quentin clearly followed his own advice.

Even when he moved back to New Hampshire permanently, Quentin still wanted to keep some of his experimental and theoretical work going with Bill Royer's group in Worcester, MA, which was only a few hours' drive from Hanover. With support from the NIH, J.S.O. was able to transfer Quentin's remaining salary support to the University of Massachusetts Medical School for the purchase of a YAG laser and to ship an older stopped-flow device to Royer's group. Again with Jeff Nichols' help, Quentin was able to set up a kinetics laboratory and continued doing experiments for several more years. Towards the end, the work was done remotely by communicating with Nichols, who was physically running the instruments and then sending the output to Quentin immediately over the Internet by instant messaging and email. Thus, even after officially retiring, Quentin published four more large papers based on original data, maintained his computational activities with Ron Elber, who by then had moved to Cornell University, and kept up remotely with much of the haemoglobin literature.

Quentin's last paper was published in 2009 and contained ultrafast kinetic data that Quentin and Nichols had collected, time-resolved X-ray crystallography by Royer and his students, site-directed mutagenesis studies and molecular dynamics simulations, all of which showed that, as with myoglobin, ligands also enter and leave *Scapharca* haemoglobin through the distal histidine channel, even if it seems partly blocked by the dimer interface (63). This paper was a fitting end to a long and remarkable career, which started long before even some of the most rudimentary aspects of haemoglobin structure were known and ended with a detailed atomic picture of how O_2 physically migrates into a globin molecule and coordinates to the iron atom.

Full circle: an honorary doctorate of science from the University of Sheffield

Semi-retirement was going smoothly for the Gibsons in New Hampshire until April 2008, when Jane was diagnosed with acute myelocytic leukaemia. She had been feeling poorly but was still working and involved in writing what turned out to be her final paper on *Pseudomonas aeruginosa* and its ability to kill adjacent fungi (*Candida albicans*) by biosynthesizing phenazine derivatives (Gibson *et al.* 2009). The next three months were a devastating time. As

Quentin put it in an email message to J.S.O., 'Obviously every long-married pair has to go through something of the sort we are experiencing … but it feels to me that the meaningful part of my life will die with Jane, but I am trying to live day by day and not to look ahead.' He persisted as best he could, looking after Jane until she passed away in June 2008. Over time he adjusted to his new situation but, as he put it later in the summer, 'Recurrent dismal thoughts are associated with being unable to communicate with Jane. I would love to tell her what I am doing in the garden, for example, about the butterfly I have seen, and all the trivia of everyday life.'

Quentin retained his grief but did adjust and remained active, including keeping up with Christmas cards and lots of entertaining emails to his scientific colleagues as well as to his family. However, health problems did arise, and in January 2010 he moved to the Kendal, a senior living facility in Hanover, NH. As might be expected he also took some of his large computers to his new place so he could keep doing molecular dynamics simulations and maintain lively scientific communications with J.S.O., Royer, Nichols and Elber. He enjoyed the company at the Kendal, which consisted of many retired Dartmouth faculty. He suggested to J.S.O. that the loss of short-term memory was not all that bad because when he and his friends gathered in the afternoons, they could tell the same stories, which always seemed new and entertaining.

In 2010 officials from the University of Sheffield contacted Quentin to inform him that they had voted to award him with an honorary Doctorate of Science. They had also set up an eponymous chair to honour his work at Sheffield in the 1950s and 1960s and his accomplishments throughout his career, which reflected well on their institution. With Quentin's approval, Professor Jonathan Waltho was selected to be the first recipient. Quentin had initially contemplated flying back to England but decided that it would probably be unwise due his deteriorating health. Instead, Professor David Hornby from the University of Sheffield travelled to Hanover, NH, in December 2010 and presented Quentin with the award in person, and even brought the appropriate academic regalia. The Kendal set up a room for the presentation of Quentin's honorary degree, which was attended by all three of his daughters and a large audience of staff and friends (figure 7). Thus Quentin's academic career had come full circle, beginning with his appointment in the Physiology Department at Sheffield in 1948, leading to his elevation to Professor of Biochemistry in 1957, and ending with an honorary degree and named chair from the same institution in 2010.

Quentin's scientific accomplishments were manifold and often groundbreaking in increasing the time resolution and complexity of kinetic experiments. Perhaps even more important was the legacy he left his students and colleagues about how to actually do science and not just 'manage' it. He often disparagingly used the phrase 'science managers' to describe senior faculty, who spent most of their careers sitting in offices writing grants and papers, reviewing articles and directing graduate students and postdoctoral fellows without doing any experiments with their own hands. He also believed strongly in doing measurements right away, as each new idea came up, and not spending extra time trying to set up the ultimate, definitive experiment. Richard Blackmore remarked in an email in 2011 that once, when he was working on the picosecond laser apparatus, Quentin said, 'we are making measurements and not discoveries.' Quentin felt that real discoveries came only after collecting and analysing lots of data, and not in one inspirational Watson and Crick moment. He truly believed that experiments should be done every day if progress were to be made, and when visitors came to his laboratory they usually left exhausted with reams of paper containing hundreds of time courses.

Figure 7. Quentin in December 2010, at the age of 92 years, holding his honorary degree from the University of Sheffield at the Kendal in Hanover, NH, with his daughters, from left to right Emma, Ursula and Katharine. (Photograph taken by staff at the Kendal for the Gibson daughters and reproduced with the latter's permission.)

In the concluding remarks of his 2004 essay 'Haemoglobin kinetics—a retrospect' (62), he commented on 'the value of the attempt to define numbers in kinetic schemes', first referring to Roughton and then to himself. He wondered if his constant push to measure and then analyse more complex time courses was worthwhile, when perhaps the key physiological process could be obtained from a qualitative evaluation. Papers describing detailed kinetic analyses of complex experiments are difficult to read and are unlikely to obtain the fame and notoriety of papers in which physiological phenomena are described qualitatively in colourful diagrams and molecular graphics. However, as Quentin concluded in his essay: 'In the end, a model stands or falls by the test of quantitative experiment', an approach that he followed all his life and passed on to his students. His work on the binding of oxygen to haemoglobins and myoglobins began in the early 1950s with the construction of the first stopped-flow apparatus, when no crystal structures were known, only changes in haem absorbance could be measured, and kinetic schemes assumed simple bimolecular association and unimolecular dissociation processes. His last kinetics papers provided quantitative determinations of pathways for ligand movement through three-dimensional structures and evaluations of the biochemical and biophysical factors that regulate O_2 uptake and release by globins.

This progression from empirical rate constants measured on millisecond time scales to the definition of specific structural processes in time regimes from picoseconds to microseconds is truly amazing. These accomplishments are even more remarkable when one considers that Quentin made almost all the measurements physically himself, using instruments that he constructed or modified with his own hands. As Tony Wilkinson remarked in an email in 2011, Quentin was 'a wonderful character, out of a mould that has long since been cast aside.'

Acknowledgements

We thank Katharine Gibson for providing details about the lives of her mother and her siblings and, with Ursula Gibson and Emma Dvorak, for reviewing the final manuscript; Maurizio Brunori for his description of the connections between Quentin, Eraldo Antonini and other members of the Rome group; Robert Poole for providing a detailed history of Quentin's work on cytochrome *c* oxidase; Woody Hastings for sharing part of his text about Quentin's move to the USA; Richard DeSa for writing an account of the first on-line data collection system; Larry Parkhurst for sending stories of his days as a postdoctoral fellow at the Johnson Foundation and at Cornell; Stuart Edelstein for providing anecdotes about the dimer hypothesis and the early days at Cornell; and William Royer for sharing stories about Quentin's work with him at University of Massachusetts, Worcester. We are also grateful to the many friends, colleagues and students who sent emails to us after learning of Quentin's death. Some of their comments are noted directly in the memoir. J.S.O. also thanks Jayashree Soman for proofreading the initial draft.

The frontispiece photograph shows Quentin H. Gibson working with the nanosecond laser photolysis instrument at Cornell University in the early 1990s. (Copyright © The Royal Society.)

References to other authors

Ackers, G. K., Doyle, M. L., Myers, D. & Daugherty, M. A. 1992 Molecular code for cooperativity in haemoglobin. *Science* **255**, 54–63.

Austin, R. H., Beeson, K. W., Eisenstein, L., Frauenfelder, H. & Gunsalus, I. C. 1975 Dynamics of ligand binding to myoglobin. *Biochemistry* **14**, 5355–5373.

Babcock, G. T., Jean, J. M., Johnston, L. N., Woodruff, W. H. & Palmer, G. 1985 Flow-flash, time-resolved resonance Raman spectroscopy of the oxidation of reduced and of mixed valence cytochrome oxidase by dioxygen. *J. Inorg. Biochem.* **23**, 243–251.

Barman, T. E., Bellamy, S. R. W., Gutfreund, H., Halford, S. E. & Lionne, C. 2006 The identification of chemical intermediates in enzyme catalysis by the rapid quench-flow technique. *Cell. Mol. Life Sci.* **63**, 2571–2583.

Birukou, I., Schweers, R. L. & Olson, J. S. 2010 Distal histidine stabilizes bound O_2 and acts as a gate for ligand entry in both subunits of adult human haemoglobin. *J. Biol. Chem.* **285**, 8840–8854.

Birukou, I., Soman, J. & Olson, J. S. 2011 Blocking the gate to ligand entry in human haemoglobin. *J. Biol. Chem.* **286**, 10515–10529.

Bolton, W. & Perutz, M. F. 1970 Three dimensional Fourier synthesis of horse deoxyhaemoglobin at 2.8 Å resolution. *Nature* **228**, 551–552.

Chance, B. 2004 The stopped-flow method and chemical intermediates in enzyme reactions—a personal essay. *Photosynth. Res.* **80**, 387–400.

Deeny, J., Murdock, E. T. & Rogan, J. J. 1943 Familial idiopathic methaemoglobinaemia: treatment with ascorbic acid. *Br. Med. J.* **i**, 721–723.

Doster, W., Beece, D., Bowne, S. F., DiIorio, E. E., Eisenstein, L., Frauenfelder, H., Reinisch, L., Shyamsunder, E., Winterhalter, K. H. & Yue, K. T. 1982 Control and pH dependence of ligand binding to heme proteins. *Biochemistry* **21**, 4831–4839.

Duddell, D. A., Morris, R. J. & Richards, J. T. 1980 Nanosecond laser photolysis of aqueous carbon monoxy- and oxyhaemoglobin. *Biochim. Biophys. Acta* **621**, 1–8.

Elber, R. & Karplus, M. 1990 Enhanced sampling in molecular dynamics—use of the time-dependent Hartree approximation for a simulation of carbon monoxide diffusion through myoglobin. *J. Am. Chem. Soc.* **112**, 9161–9175.

Gibson, J., Sood, A. & Hogan, D. A. 2009 *Pseudomonas aeruginosa–Candida albicans* interactions: localization and fungal toxicity of a phenazine derivative. *Appl. Environ. Microbiol.* **75**, 504–513.

Gutfreund, H. 1955 Steps in the formation and decomposition of some enzyme–substrate complexes. *Discuss. Faraday Soc.*, 167–173.

Gutfreund, H. 1999 Rapid-flow techniques and their contributions to enzymology. *Trends Biochem. Sci.* **24**, 457–460.

Gutfreund, H. F. 2010 Numerical methods and computing in laboratories: from log tables and slide rules to laptop computers during a lifetime. *IUBMB Life* **62**, 916–923.

Hartridge, H. & Roughton, F. J. W. 1923 A method of measuring the velocity of very rapid chemical reactions. *Proc. R. Soc. Lond.* A **104**, 376–394.

Holbrook, J. J., Hardman, M. J., Parker, D. M., Yates, D. W. & Gutfreund, H. 1977 The putative isomerization of the lactate dehydrogenase–NADH complex. *FEBS Lett.* **78**, 46–48.

Jongeward, K. A., Magde, D., Taube, D. J., Marsters, J. C., Traylor, T. G. & Sharma, V. S. 1988 Picosecond and nanosecond geminate recombination of myoglobin with carbon monoxide, oxygen, nitric oxide and isocyanides. *J. Am. Chem. Soc.* **110**, 380–387.

Keilin, D. & Hartree, E. F. 1955 Cyanide compounds of ferroperoxidase and myoglobin and their reversible photo-dissociation. *Biochem. J.* **61**, 153–171.

Kellett, G. L. & Gutfreund, H. 1970 Reactions of haemoglobin dimers after ligand dissociation. *Nature* **227**, 921–926.

Koshland, D. E. Jr, Nemethy, G. & Filmer, D. 1966 Comparison of experimental binding data and theoretical models in proteins containing subunits. *Biochemistry* **5**, 365–385.

Legge, J. W. & Roughton, F. J. 1950 Some observations on the kinetics of haemoglobin in solution and in the red blood corpuscle. *Biochem. J.* **47**, 43–52.

Mills, F. C. & Ackers, G. K. 1979 Quaternary enhancement in binding of oxygen by human haemoglobin. *Proc. Natl Acad. Sci. USA* **76**, 273–277.

Monod, J., Wyman, J. & Changeux, J. P. 1965 On the nature of allosteric transitions: a plausible model. *J. Mol. Biol.* **12**, 88–118.

Pauling, L. 1935 The oxygen equilibrium of hemoglobin and its structural interpretation. *Proc. Natl Acad. Sci. USA* **21**, 186–191.

Perutz, M. F. 1970 Stereochemistry of cooperative effects in haemoglobin. *Nature* **228**, 726–739.

Salter, M. D., Blouin, G. C., Soman, J., Singleton, E. W., Dewilde, S., Moens, L., Pesce, A., Nardini, M., Bolognesi, M. & Olson, J. S. 2012 Determination of ligand pathways in globins: apolar tunnels versus polar gates. *J. Biol. Chem.* **287**, 33163–33178.

Schotte, F., Soman, J., Olson, J. S., Wulff, M. & Anfinrud, P. A. 2004 Picosecond time-resolved X-ray crystallography: probing protein function in real time. *J. Struct. Biol.* **147**, 235–246.

Srajer, V., Ren, Z., Teng, T. Y., Schmidt, M., Ursby, T., Bourgeois, D., Pradervand, C., Schildkamp, W., Wulff, M. & Moffat, K. 2001 Protein conformational relaxation and ligand migration in myoglobin: a nanosecond to millisecond molecular movie from time-resolved Laue X-ray diffraction. *Biochemistry* **40**, 13802–13815.

Theorell, H., Ehrenberg, A. & de Zalenski, C. 1967 The binding of NADH to liver alcohol dehydrogenase: a two step reaction. *Biochem. Biophys. Res. Commun.* **27**, 309–314.

Wikstrom, M., Krab, K. & Saraste, M. 1981 *Cytochrome oxidase. A synthesis.* London: Academic Press.

HONOURS

1969   Elected Fellow of the Royal Society
1970   Elected Member of the American Academy of Arts and Sciences
1975–94 Associate Editor, *Journal of Biological Chemistry*
1982   Elected Member of the US National Academy of Sciences
1990   Keilin Memorial Medallist and Lecturer, Biochemical Society, UK

BIBLIOGRAPHY

The following publications are those referred to directly in the text. A full bibliography is available as electronic supplementary material at http://dx.doi.org/10.1098/rsbm.2013.0018 or via http://rsbm.royalsocietypublishing.org.

(1)   1948   The reduction of methaemoglobin in red blood cells and studies on the cause of idiopathic methaemo-globinaemia. *Biochem. J.* **42**, 13–23.

(2)   1951   Gibson–Roughton Letters. Royal Society Library Archives.

(3)   (With G. Wiseman) Selective absorption of stereo-isomers of amino-acids from loops of the small intestine of the rat. *Biochem. J.* **48**, 426–429.

(4)   1954   Stopped-flow apparatus for the study of rapid reactions. *Discuss. Faraday Soc.*, 137–139.

(5)   1955   (With F. J. Roughton) The kinetics of dissociation of the first oxygen molecule from fully saturated oxyhaemoglobin in sheep blood solutions. *Proc. R. Soc. Lond.* B **143**, 310–334.

(6)   1956   An apparatus for flash photolysis and its application to the reactions of myoglobin with gases. *J. Physiol.* **134**, 112–122.

(7)   (With F. J. Roughton) The determination of the velocity constants of the four successive reactions of carbon monoxide with sheep haemoglobin. *Proc. R. Soc. Lond.* B **146**, 206–224.

(8)   1959   The photochemical formation of a quickly reacting form of haemoglobin. *Biochem. J.* **71**, 293–303.

(9)   1963   (With J. W. Hastings) Intermediates in the bioluminescent oxidation of reduced flavin mononucleotide. *J. Biol. Chem.* **238**, 2537–2554.

(10)   1964   (With L. Milnes) Apparatus for rapid and sensitive spectrophotometry. *Biochem. J.* **91**, 161–171.

(11)   (With B. E. Swoboda & V. Massey) Kinetics and mechanism of action of glucose oxidase. *J. Biol. Chem.* **239**, 3927–3934.

(12)   (With V. Massey) Role of semiquinones in flavoprotein catalysis. *Fed. Proc.* **23**, 18–29.

(13)   1965   (With J. W. Hastings & C. Greenwood) On the molecular mechanism of bioluminescence. II. Light-induced luminescence. *Proc. Natl Acad. Sci. USA* **53**, 187–195.

(14)   (With C. Greenwood) The reaction of cytochrome oxidase with cytochrome C. *J. Biol. Chem.* **240**, 888–894.

(15)   1967   (With G. Geraci) The reaction of liver alcohol dehydrogenase with reduced diphosphopyridine nucleotide. *J. Biol. Chem.* **242**, 4275–4278.

(16)   (With C. Greenwood) The reaction of reduced cytochrome C oxidase with oxygen. *J. Biol. Chem.* **242**, 1782–1787.

(17)   (With J. W. Hastings) The role of oxygen in the photoexcited luminescence of bacterial luciferase. *J. Biol. Chem.* **242**, 720–726.

(18)   1968   (With D. C. Wharton) Studies of the oxygenated compound of cytochrome oxidase. *J. Biol. Chem.* **243**, 702–706.

(19)   1969   (With R. J. DeSa) A practical automatic data acquisition system for stopped-flow spectrophotometry. *Comput. Biomed. Res.* **2**, 494–505.

(20)   Rapid mixing: stopped flow. *Methods Enzymol.* **16**, 187–228.

(21)   (With L. J. Parkhurst & G. Geraci) The reaction of methemoglobin with some ligands. *J. Biol. Chem.* **244**, 4668–4676.

(22)   1970   (With S. J. Edelstein, M. J. Rehmar & J. S. Olson) Functional aspects of the subunit association–dissociation equilibria of hemoglobin. *J. Biol. Chem.* **245**, 4372–4381.

(23)   1971   (With R. L. Nagel) The binding of hemoglobin to haptoglobin and its relation to subunit dissociation of hemoglobin. *J. Biol. Chem.* **246**, 69–73.

(24)   Handwritten Personal Record. Royal Society Library Archives.

(25)   (With M. E. Andersen) A kinetic analysis of the binding of oxygen and carbon monoxide to lamprey hemoglobin. *Petromyzon marinus* and *Petromyzon fluviatilis*. *J. Biol. Chem.* **246**, 4790–4799.

(26)   (With M. E. Andersen & J. K. Moffat) The kinetics of ligand binding and of the association–dissociation reactions of human hemoglobin. Properties of deoxyhemoglobin dimers. *J. Biol. Chem.* **246**, 2796–2807.

(27)   (With R. MacQuarrie) Use of a fluorescent analogue of 2,3-diphosphoglycerate as a probe of human hemoglobin conformation during carbon monoxide binding. *J. Biol. Chem.* **246**, 5832–5835.

(28)   1972   (With J. S. Olson, R. L. Nagel & H. B. Hamilton) The ligand-binding properties of hemoglobin Hiroshima ($\alpha_2\beta_2^{146asp}$). *J. Biol. Chem.* **247**, 7485–7493.

(29)   (With J. S. Olson) The reaction of n-butyl isocyanide with human hemoglobin. II. The ligand-binding properties of the α and β chains within deoxyhemoglobin. *J. Biol. Chem.* **247**, 1713–1726.

(30)   1973   (With A. L. Tan & R. W. Noble) Conditions restricting allosteric transitions in carp hemoglobin. *J. Biol. Chem.* **248**, 2880–2888.

(31)   Francis John Worsley Roughton, 1899–1972. *Biogr. Mems Fell. R. Soc.* **19**, 563–582.

(32)　(With K. Moffat, J. S. Olson & J. V. Kilmartin) The ligand-binding properties of desHis (146β) hemoglobin. *J. Biol. Chem.* **248**, 6387–6393.

(33)　(With A. Riggs) Oxygen equilibrium and kinetics of isolated subunits from hemoglobin Kansas. *Proc. Natl Acad. Sci. USA* **70**, 1718–1720.

(34)　p-Mercuribenzoate as an indicator of conformation change in hemoglobin. *J. Biol. Chem.* **248**, 1281–1284.

(35)　(With M. E. Andersen, J. S. Olson & F. G. Carey) Studies on ligand binding to hemoglobins from teleosts and elasmobranchs. *J. Biol. Chem.* **248**, 331–341.

(36)　1974　(With H. F. Bunn, R. C. Wohl, T. B. Bradley & M. Cooley) Functional properties of hemoglobin Kempsey. *J. Biol. Chem.* **249**, 7402–7409.

(37)　1975　(With R. Cassoly) Conformation, co-operativity and ligand binding in human hemoglobin. *J. Mol. Biol.* **91**, 301–313.

(38)　1976　(With E. G. Moore) Cooperativity in the dissociation of nitric oxide from hemoglobin. *J. Biol. Chem.* **251**, 2788–2794.

(39)　1977　(With F. G. Carey & F. Knowles) Effect of hydrostatic pressure on ligand binding to hemoglobin. *J. Biol. Chem.* **252**, 4102–4107.

(40)　1978　(With B. M. Hoffman) On the photosensitivity of liganded hemoproteins and their metal-substituted analogues. *Proc. Natl Acad. Sci. USA* **75**, 21–25.

(41)　(With C. A. Sawicki) The relation between carbon monoxide binding and the conformational change of hemoglobin. *Biophys. J.* **24**, 21–33.

(42)　1980　(With R. J. Morris) The role of diffusion in limiting the rate of ligand binding to hemoglobin. *J. Biol. Chem.* **255**, 8050–8053.

(43)　1981　(With W. A. Saffran) Asynchronous ligand binding and proton release in a root effect hemoglobin. *J. Biol. Chem.* **256**, 4551–4556.

(44)　1986　(With J. S. Olson, R. E. McKinnie & R. J. Rohlfs) A kinetic description of ligand binding to sperm whale myoglobin. *J. Biol. Chem.* **261**, 10228–10239.

(45)　1987　(With M. C. Marden, E. S. Hazard & C. Kimble) Geminate ligand recombination as a probe of the R, T equilibrium in hemoglobin. *Eur. J. Biochem.* **169**, 611–615.

(46)　(With S. J. Edelstein) Oxygen binding and subunit interaction of hemoglobin in relation to the two-state model. *J. Biol. Chem.* **262**, 516–519.

(47)　1989　(With J. B. Wittenberg, B. A. Wittenberg, D. Bogusz & C. A. Appleby) The kinetics of ligand binding to plant hemoglobins. Structural implications. *J. Biol. Chem.* **264**, 100–107.

(48)　(With T. E. Carver, R. J. Rohlfs, J. S. Olson, R. S. Blackmore, B. A. Springer &, S. G. Sligar) Analysis of the kinetic barriers for ligand binding to sperm whale myoglobin using site-directed mutagenesis and laser photolysis techniques. *J. Biol. Chem.* **265**, 20007–20020.

(49)　(With A. Bellelli & R. S. Blackmore) Ligand binding to a hemoprotein lacking the distal histidine. The myoglobin from *Aplysia limacina* (Val(E7)). *J. Biol. Chem.* **265**, 13595–13600.

(50)　1991　(With R. S. Blackmore & C. Greenwood) Studies of the primary oxygen intermediate in the reaction of fully reduced cytochrome oxidase. *J. Biol. Chem.* **266**, 19245–19249.

(51)　1993　(With R. Regan, J. S. Olson, T. E. Carver, B. Dixon, B. Pohajdak, P. K. Sharma & S. N. Vinogradov) Kinetics of ligand binding to *Pseudoterranova decipiens* and *Ascaris suum* hemoglobins and to Leu-29→Tyr sperm whale myoglobin mutant. *J. Biol. Chem.* **268**, 16993–16998.

(52)　(With E. Chiancone, R. Elber, W. E. Royer Jr & R. Royer) Ligand binding and conformation change in the dimeric hemoglobin of the clam *Scapharca inaequivalvis*. *J. Biol. Chem.* **268**, 5711–5718.

(53)　(With M. Ikeda-Saito, Y. Dou, T. Yonetani, J. S. Olson, T. Li & R. Regan) Ligand diffusion in the distal heme pocket of myoglobin. A primary determinant of geminate rebinding. *J. Biol. Chem.* **268**, 6855–6857.

(54)　1994　(With M. L. Carlson, R. Regan, R. Elber, H. Li, G. N. Phillips Jr & J. S. Olson) Nitric oxide recombination to double mutants of myoglobin: role of ligand diffusion in a fluctuating heme pocket. *Biochemistry* **33**, 10597–10606.

(55)　1995　(With N. Shibayama, T. Yonetani & R. M. Regan) Mechanism of ligand binding to Ni(II)-Fe(II) hybrid hemoglobins. *Biochemistry* **34**, 14658–14667.

(56) 1996 (With W. E. Royer Jr, A. Pardanani, E. S. Peterson & J. M. Friedman) Ordered water molecules as key allosteric mediators in a cooperative dimeric hemoglobin. *Proc. Natl Acad. Sci. USA* **93**, 14526–14531.

(57) 1998 (With L. Kiger, A. K. Rashid, N. Griffon, M. Haque, L. Moens, C. Poyart & M. C. Marden) Trematode hemoglobins show exceptionally high oxygen affinity. *Biophys. J.* **75**, 990–998.

(58) 2001 (With M. Brunori) Cavities and packing defects in the structural dynamics of myoglobin. *EMBO Rep.* **2**, 674–679.

(59)   (With E. E. Scott & J. S. Olson) Mapping the pathways for O_2 entry into and exit from myoglobin. *J. Biol. Chem.* **276**, 5177–5188.

(60) 2002 (With F. Draghi, A. E. Miele, C. Travaglini-Allocatelli, B. Vallone, M. Brunori & J. S. Olson) Controlling ligand binding in myoglobin by mutagenesis. *J. Biol. Chem.* **277**, 7509–7519.

(61)   Introduction: congenital methemoglobinemia revisited. *Blood* **100**, 3445–3446.

(62) 2004 Hemoglobin kinetics—a retrospect. In *Selected topics in the history of biochemistry personal recollections* (ed. G. Semenz & A. J. Turner), pp. 101–197. Amsterdam: Elsevier.

(63) 2009 (With J. E. Knapp, R. Pahl, J. Cohen, J. C. Nichols, K. Schulten, V. Srajer & W. E. Royer Jr) Ligand migration and cavities within *Scapharca* dimeric HbI: studies by time-resolved crystallography, Xe binding, and computational analysis. *Structure* **17**, 1494–1504.

PETER GRAY

25 August 1926 — 7 June 2012

Peter Gray

PETER GRAY

25 August 1926 — 7 June 2012

Elected FRS 1977

By S. K. Scott

School of Chemistry, University of Leeds, Leeds LS2 9JT, UK

Peter Gray was an internationally recognized research leader in the areas of combustion chemistry and chemical instabilities. His undergraduate education and early research career were in Cambridge. He moved to the University of Leeds in 1955, becoming Head of Physical Chemistry there in 1965. In 1988 he returned to Cambridge as Master of Gonville and Caius College. Peter's scientific contributions covered experimental and theoretical studies of chemical and thermal instabilities in combustion systems and in isothermal systems exhibiting autocatalysis, and of flames and chemical waves. His work provided the framework for understanding the thermokinetic origin of cool flames and multiple-stage ignitions and for the onset of ignition and oscillations in chemical systems more generally. He served on a series of important government committees and held major office for the Faraday Society and the Combustion Institute. He published more than 300 research articles and one monograph and was awarded a series of major prizes, including the Marlow Medal, the Bernard Lewis Gold Medal and the Italgas Prize.

EARLY HISTORY

Peter Gray was born on 25 August 1926 in Newport, Wales, the son of Ivor Gray and Rose Gray (*née* Adcock). Peter's father, one of eight children, left school young and was apprenticed to a printer in Newport—Peter would no doubt have enjoyed the similarity of this stage of his father's early life to Michael Faraday's early experience. His mother was a qualified teacher from Birmingham. She and Peter's father met on a postwar trip to visit the battlefields in France and Flanders, where Ivor had served after exaggerating his age to join the army in 1915.

Peter began his formal education at Durham Road Infants' School at the age of five years and one week in 1931. Peter describes his childhood as 'very happy with exceptionally happy and loving parents', with a love of learning cultivated by both parents and his maternal

http://dx.doi.org/10.1098/rsbm.2014.0013

grandfather in particular; books were always available either at home or from Newport public library. His younger brother, Robert, was born in late 1933. Peter remembers many aunts, uncles and cousins as well as all four grandparents in the extended family of that period. Peter remained at Durham Road until the untimely death of his mother at the age of 38 years in September 1935, after which he moved first to Dr Williams School in Caerleon and then to St Woolos primary school, from where he passed his 11-plus examination in 1937. Peter recalls that at the age of ten years he received a present from his aunt Ella of a chemistry set—and describes how over the next three years he and his friends would supplement this with 'potent reagents including strong acids and alkalis' purchased from a well-known chain of chemist shops—a latitudinous approach to stimulating the interests of budding physical scientists not likely to be found on today's high streets. He was awarded an entrance scholarship to Newport High School, which he attended from 1937 to 1943, taking the School Certificate in eight subjects in 1941 and the Higher School Certificate in chemistry, physics and mathematics in 1943. Peter spoke highly of the educational culture in Newport High School and he received particular encouragement and inspiration from his teachers in chemistry (D. J. B. Summers), mathematics (E. P. Glover) and physics (A. E. Hugh). Peter attended the summer scholarships examinations in Cambridge in August 1943 and was awarded a major scholarship to Gonville and Caius College, persuading him to turn down a scholarship offer from St John's College, Oxford. He went up to Cambridge as a 17-year-old taking Natural Sciences, obtaining college prizes in each year and graduating in 1946 with first-class honours. During this period, Peter's father remarried (Daisy Herbert, *neé* Wills) and he acquired a step-sister, Patricia, and step-brother, Peter Herbert.

CAMBRIDGE, 1943–55

Peter attended lectures given by a long list of now famous names in chemistry during his undergraduate period, but was particularly influenced by a first-year course delivered by the physical chemist and future Nobel laureate R. G. W. Norrish FRS, who revealed that Peter's passion for chain reactions, flames and explosions could be set in a rigorous intellectual framework. Other key figures at that time were A. B. Robertson, who introduced Peter to the concept of thermal explosions, and F. S. (later Lord) Dainton (FRS 1957).

Cambridge widened Peter's world well beyond his academic studies. As a 'light tenor' he joined the college choir and so was introduced to classical music—an interest he widened further by regular attendance at many music concert seasons and one-off recitals. His undergraduate studies were conducted in a nation at war, which affected life even in Cambridge. Many of the dons were members of the local Home Guard or Air-Raid Wardens, and Peter and colleagues assisted in their activities, gaining access to roofs and other areas that were normally out of bounds.

At the end of his undergraduate studies Peter was awarded a Dunlop research studentship for the period 1946–48, and despite being interviewed for jobs with ICI and Courtaulds he began studying for a PhD under the formal supervision of Philip Bowden (FRS 1948), famous for his work on frictional heating and who ran the Physics and Chemistry of Solids (PCS) group. Peter's PhD research was concerned with the initiation of explosion in liquids by impact. The first part of this involved the measurement of the development in time of the pressure in liquids under 'impulsive compression' caused by dropping a 'fall hammer' on a piston; the signal from a piezo-electric quartz crystal was amplified and displayed on a cathode-ray tube, which was photographed, and this record was used to determine the 'critical' impact pressure above which a liquid such as nitroglycerine would explode. The second part of his project was a classical study of the thermal explosion of methyl nitrate vapour on admission to an evacuated hot vessel. This work developed the analogies of the explosion of a single substance with those of oxidations of fuels more generally, and initiated a lifelong feature of Peter's research career: the study of 'cool flames' and 'thermal explosions'. This part of his PhD was effectively supervised by Abe Yoffe, of whom Peter has stated 'an abler and kinder person one could not hope to have had'. During this period Peter attended his first combustion conference event in Paris. He was awarded his PhD in 1949 and was elected to both a college research fellowship and the prestigious Ramsey Memorial Fellowship to continue this work (although one of the trustees for the latter did divulge their concern that Peter might 'blow himself up' with his proposed research programme).

Peter competed unsuccessfully for university demonstratorships (the first step on the academic ladder at Cambridge) in physical chemistry, but in 1951 a new opportunity was presented with a five-year demonstratorship in the newly constituted Department of Chemical Engineering, which he 'jumped at', describing how he was 'head hunted' by the Head of Department, Terence Fox (perhaps rather surprisingly, given Peter's research area and Fox's reputed obsession that his new building might burn down). Fox was assembling a department of physical chemists and mechanical engineers alongside the small available pool of chemical engineers to address the lack of high-quality provision in that area in the UK after the war. This was a tremendously broadening experience in Peter's development, working alongside more senior colleagues such as P. V. Danckwerts (FRS 1969) and K. G. Denbigh (FRS 1965) even though—or more likely because—chemical engineering had a certain reputation in the university at that time for being 'not quite respectable'. (Sir James Chadwick FRS, who was Master of Caius College at the time, apparently expressed the view that applied science was not appropriate for Cambridge.) A more detailed account of life in the early department can be found in a recent biography of Danckwerts (Varey 2012). This period laid the foundations for a later emphasis on both experimental and theoretical studies in chemical reactor engineering at Leeds, in which Peter would be a leading UK figure. Peter began the supervision of two PhD students, John Lee in 1951 and Tom Waddington 1952, and through these he began research into flame propagation and the chemistry of azide explosives as well as extending his own research into the properties of nitrogen dioxide (also known as 'dragon's breath').

As a fellow of the college, Peter became involved in several debates within the college with a view to modernizing some procedures, such as the appointment and terms of office of tutors (an issue that would recur when he returned to Caius as Master): like much of the postwar world, students and fellows were questioning formal preconceptions of authority.

Peter was among a group of Caius students who established the informal society that would become known as the 'Yaks and Crows'—the name apparently emerging during a rambling conversation on a walking holiday in North Wales in 1944. This group would meet annually for dinner, maintaining an almost unbroken sequence for more than 60 years and moving from disrespectability to a fixture of the college dining calendar, with silver cups and cutlery. The 24 group members were initially all male (as was the membership of the college), but it pre-empted the college's move to mixed admissions by including wives in the mid 1960s. It served to maintain contact between the members through departures to other institutions and the production of families when other college friendships might have been lost.

Although the demonstratorship was awarded for a period of five years, Fox indicated to Peter that he did not see Peter's long-term career lying in chemical engineering and that it would be appropriate to seek a permanent post in physical chemistry. Peter married Barbara Joan Hume, a biochemistry graduate from Newnham and then postdoctoral fellow, the daughter of John and Marjorie Hume, on 13 December 1952, at St Bartholomew the Less, the church based in St Bartholomew's hospital, where Barbara's father was Senior Surgeon. Peter and Barbara's first child, Christine, was born in Cambridge in 1954, and so this combination of circumstances prompted Peter to begin the search for a move from chemical engineering and from Cambridge.

LEEDS, 1955–88

The opportunity of a lectureship arose in the Department of Physical Chemistry at the University of Leeds, where Dainton had moved to be Head of Department. Peter took up this post in the autumn of 1955, a year in which he published 17 papers—a record of output that he would not match until 1984. Barbara obtained a lectureship in Biochemistry at Leeds and also became a major influence on the Leeds music scene as member and eventually chair of the Leeds Symphony Society. One PhD student, Michael Pratt, moved to Leeds with Peter to complete his studies on alkyl nitrate decomposition. Two further Cambridge students arrived to start their PhDs: Patrick Wright, working on thermal conductivity measurements, and Michael Harper, studying the decomposition of hydrazine. Peter's first 'Leeds PhD student', Alan Williams, extended the studies of spontaneous combustion to methyl nitrite—recalling that the experiments in the group at the time would probably not pass health and safety assessments now, not least because of the various carcinogenic intermediates formed in the reactions, and how the large collection of potentially explosive reagents disappeared almost overnight after a major explosion at the Defence Research Establishment at Waltham Abbey. (Williams subsequently undertook postdoctoral work funded by the Gas Council on flames at Leeds under the supervision of Graham Dixon-Lewis—another 'son of Caerleon, Durham Road School and Newport High School'—in the Department of Gas and Fuel Industries at Leeds. Williams later obtained an independent lectureship and began work on shock tubes; he later became Livesey Professor and Head of the Department of Fuel and Energy, where he still holds a research chair. Dixon-Lewis went on to obtain a personal chair in the department and be elected as a Fellow of the Royal Society in 1995 for his computational studies of flames.)

Peter found the city, university and environment at Leeds a significant contrast to Cambridge—not least the soot and smoke and winter fogs—but was strongly impressed by the lack of 'politics', the friendship across the University and the dynamic leadership of Dainton as Head of Department and of the Vice-Chancellor (Charles Morris—who was reputed to have taken a train to Cambridge specifically to recruit Dainton) and Registrar (John Loach). The concerns that Peter had that he had now 'destroyed two careers'—one in chemistry and one in chemical engineering—by this move were negated by the award of the Meldola Medal for 'the most meritorious and promising original investigations in chemistry' by a British chemist, typically under the age of 32 years, from the (now) Royal Society of Chemistry in 1955 (a prize of £50, which funded the purchase of a carpet for the new home in Leeds). Peter was subsequently awarded the Marlow Medal from the Faraday Society in 1958. He was promoted to Reader in 1959 and awarded a personal chair in 1962. During this period, the Gray family was extended with the births of Andrew, David and Sally in 1956, 1958 and 1961, respectively. All four children benefited from Leeds schools and subsequently attended Cambridge colleges as undergraduates.

In 1965 Peter succeeded Dainton as Head of Department—he claims to have been only the third choice for this, but the outcome could not have been more propitious for Leeds—and in the next decade he went on to build one of the major physical chemistry departments in the UK and an internationally leading group in combustion chemistry. The additions to existing strengths in radiation chemistry (Edgar Collinson and Don Smithies), kinetics (Don Baulch) and thermodynamics (Alex Carson) of Peter Laye (thermochemistry), Terry Boddington (thermal explosion theory and detonations), Anthony Clifford (transport properties), Brian Gray (combustion theory) and John Griffiths (experimental studies of combustion particularly in flow reactors) were particularly significant: many of these were hired from postdoctoral positions in the USA in one single trip, leading one Yorkshire newspaper to brag that the University of Leeds was reversing the 'brain drain'. Leeds was also at this time widely recognized for combustion research through its Centre for Studies in Combustion and Energy led by Physical Chemistry, Fuel and Energy (Dixon-Lewis and Williams) and Mechanical Engineering (Derek Bradley, FRS 1988).

Peter greatly valued opportunities to spend sabbatical or other extended visits to overseas institutions (with the role of Head of Department being covered by Peter Ayscough, an eminent electron spin resonance spectroscopist who also did pioneering work in computer-based learning in chemistry). Visits included the University of British Columbia (1958–59), where working with C. A. McDowell he used simple nuclear magnetic resonance measurements to discover a very large barrier to rotation in methyl nitrite, only to be 'scooped' to publication by a Californian group; the University of Western Ontario in the 1960s; and Göttingen (as Gauss Professor, where he developed links with Jurgen Tröe at the university and Heinz-Georg Wagner at the Max Planck Institute for Fluid Mechanics). Also significant was a visit to Soviet Armenia in 1977: Peter's great respect for, and familiarity with, the contributions from Soviet science to combustion through the works of N. N. Semenov ForMemRS, D. A. Frank-Kamenetskii, Ya. B. Zel'dovich (ForMemRS 1979), I. E. Sal'nikov and A. G. Merzhanov would be a major influence throughout his career and, in particular, on later work from his group on thermal and chemical instabilities. Visitors to Leeds included Sidney Benson, Antoni Oppenheim, Pierre Van Tiggelen, Pier-Giorgio Lignola, Graeme Wake, Ian Walker, Włodzimierz Kordylewski and Philip Bowes (a long-term visiting fellow) from the combustion/thermal explosion community, and Rutherford Aris and Kenneth Showalter from the engineering/chemical instabilities community. Peter would also establish major interdisciplinary work at Leeds with David Crighton (FRS 1993), John Brindley and John Merkin in mathematics, leading to the creation of the Centre for Nonlinear Studies.

Peter had a tremendous commitment to the Faraday Society, the society for British physical chemistry, serving on its council for several decades, including periods as Treasurer (1977–83) and President (1983–85), when he also was a member of the Council of the (then) Chemical Society. A special issue of *Transactions of the Faraday Society* was organized to celebrate Peter's 70th birthday in September 1996. In a similar manner, he contributed throughout his professional life to the UK and international combustion communities through his engagement with the Combustion Institute, as a founder member of the British Section of the Combustion Institute in 1954, as a committee member from 1974 to 82 and again as chairman from 1986 to 1992, and finally as a Life Member. He additionally served on the Ministry of Defence

Committee on Explosives, originally set up by Bowden, and would later chair it. When that committee was dissolved, the various government laboratories that had benefited from its advice set up the Energetic Materials Advisory Committee (EMAC), chaired by John Field (FRS 1994). EMAC was indeed an energetic committee and produced a great number of Working Parties and 'open' meetings. Its scope was widened in 1990 to cover a wider range of science, becoming TEEMAC (Thermal Effects and Energetic Materials Advisory Committee); Peter and John Field remained on this until its closure in 2007, and served with John Clarke (FRS 1986) and Richard Chambers (FRS 1997). Peter also graced the editorial boards of innumerable journals, and also the Advisory Council for the Ramsay Memorial Fellowship (from 1982 to 2002). Peter was elected a Fellow of the Royal Society in 1977 and served on the Society's editorial advisory board and for a period as scientific editor. He was awarded the Bernard Lewis gold medal of the Combustion Institute in 1978 for 'brilliant research in the field of combustion, particularly on theoretical and experimental thermochemistry', the Royal Society of Chemistry prize for Combustion Chemistry (typically awarded to individuals in 'mid career') in 1986, and the Italgas Prize in 1988.

Peter served on or chaired all the significant administrative committees at Leeds but managed to avoid the most distractive of roles such as Pro-Vice-Chancellor or the lure of Vice-Chancellorships elsewhere. As 'one of the big beasts of Senate', Peter always occupied the same prominent front row seat from which he paid unnervingly concentrated attention to the utterances from the 'top table', not least those of successive Vice-Chancellors. His own verbal contributions were brief, succinct and invariably influential.

Return to Cambridge, 1988

In 1988 Peter was elected Master of Gonville and Caius College (figure 1) and returned to Cambridge (to be succeeded at Leeds by Michael Pilling CBE). Peter managed to maintain scientific activity, partly though connections at Leeds or the diaspora of previous PhD students and also through renewed associations in Cambridge and contributions to teaching in chemical engineering. This period also saw the publication of the only full-length book he authored. Inevitably, however, Peter was drawn by the challenges of the college and university and his determination to 'make an impression' on life there.

His priorities as Master were focused on several areas, including a more strategic approach to planning building acquisitions and developments, improving the student experience, freshening the Tutors and strengthening the Tutorial Office, modernizing procedures around the appointment of research fellows and increasing the number of female fellows, including the appointment of the first female Professorial Fellow. His tenure saw the initial work, which would be completed under his successor, to provide additional and excellent library facilities in the Cockerell Building (formerly the Squire Law Library), the conversion of the 'modestly ornate' cycle shed and fellows' garage to the 100-seater Bateman Auditorium and Lecture Room, and the opening of new undergraduate accommodation in the Stephen Hawking Building on West Road. His tenure was not completely without controversy, but many in the college at all levels enjoyed his refreshing style and approach and feel that he made a real and lasting impact both to the financial basis of the college and to communal life.

Peter's wife Barbara died in 1992, leading to a period of great sadness. Peter remarried in May 1996, to Rachel Herzig, just before retiring as Master of the college.

Figure 1. Peter as Master of Gonville and Caius College in his garden, 1996.
(Photograph provided by Mrs Rachel Gray, from the Gray family collection.)

Peter was awarded an honorary DSc from the University of Leeds in 1997 and served as chairman and president of the Cambridge Philosophical Society. In his later years he suffered from, but battled, the effects of diabetes and macular degeneration, which particularly affected his great loves of reading and walking, but his passion for and determination to engage with science and the events organized by the British Section continued.

Science

Peter Gray was the author of more than 300 research articles in journals or conference proceedings, reviews, contributions to edited volumes, editorship of special issues and collected volumes and one monograph. He wrote consistently with a lucid and fluent literary style that made all his work tremendously accessible—although his handwritten drafts were frustratingly illegible to co-authors and secretaries alike. The themes of spontaneous combustion, explosion and chemical instability run consistently throughout his work, and the scope of additional studies and approaches recruited to develop the body of his work is remarkably broad. The account below identifies several major highlights but cannot be comprehensive.

As described briefly in the previous sections, his early work at Cambridge comprised the elucidation of the mechanisms of initiation of explosion by impact (1946–48), the thermal decomposition and spontaneous ignition of alkyl nitrates (molecules of the form $RO\text{-}NO_2$), alkyl nitrites ($RO\text{-}NO$) and nitroalkanes ($R\text{-}NO_2$), including initial studies of 'cool flame' phenomena and the role of alkoxy radicals in these processes, and combustion supported by nitrogen dioxide (1948–51). Peter's first paper (1)*, published in *Nature*, concerned the inflammation of explosive vapours; it was followed rapidly by his first paper in *Proceedings of the Royal Society* (2). An early paper on impact initiation appeared the following year (3).

Between 1951 and 1955 this work was extended and developed to the study of flame propagation and flame spectroscopy over a wider range of chemical fuels, including hydrazine and hydrogen azide, and theoretical aspects of flame and explosion. To understand these systems, Peter's work also extended to include thermodynamic studies such as low-temperature calorimetry for specific heat measurements and studies of internal rotation and dissociation energies for various alcohols and ethers. Work also began on the reactivity, structure and thermochemistry of azides with a wide experimental programme augmented by theoretical calculation of lattice energies. This activity led to 40 papers from the period as PhD and postdoctoral worker at Cambridge before the move to Leeds. Examples of his publications on hydrazine combustion with J. C. Lee are (4, 5) and on azide decomposition with T. C. Waddington are (6, 7).

Early work in Leeds on alkyl nitrates and nitrites is represented by Gray and Williams (8, 10) and work was begun with Williams on flame measurements leading to key papers (15, 17) with R. MacKinven and D. B. Smith.

A major theme in Peter's work, and one that remains recognized as world-leading, was the development of the theory of thermal explosion and the direct experimental tests of that theory. Thermal explosion occurs when a chemical system evolves heat through an exothermic reaction and the increase in temperature leads to a subsequent increase in the reaction rate and hence the rate of heat release. If the operating heat losses, which also depend on the evolving temperature, cannot balance the heat release, then a 'snowballing effect' leads to a runaway in the temperature and typically to ignition. Peter's earliest contributions in this area include considerations of the time to runaway and the temperature evolution in the period before ignition (9), direct observation of thermal runaway development in hydrazine oxidation (12), the effect of reactant consumption and the temperature evolution in endothermic systems (13, 14). This led to a major review article with P. R. Lee (16). The first direct measurements of temperature profiles in gases were made with fine-wire thermocouples (21–23). With Terry Boddington this work developed into an extended series of studies (19, 25) including a paper (24) in which Peter was delighted to combine thermal runaway with his love of Dickens in considering the alleged spontaneous combustion of Mr Krook from *Bleak House*. A particular goal for Peter was to obtain an analytical solution for the critical condition for thermal runaway in a sphere governed by the (dimensionless) steady-state heat evolution equation

---

* Numbers in this form refer to the bibliography at the end of the text.

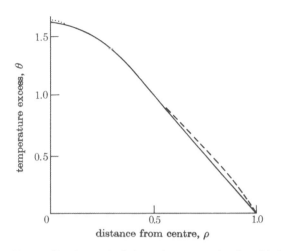

Figure 2. Temperature–position profiles for a spherical reacting mass under the critical conditions for thermal explosion comparing exact numerical results with two approximate routes. (Reproduced from (26).)

$$\frac{\mathrm{d}^2\theta}{\mathrm{d}\rho^2} + \frac{2}{\rho}\frac{\mathrm{d}\theta}{\mathrm{d}\rho} + \delta e^\theta = 0.$$

Here, θ is a scaled temperature rise above the surrounding (ambient) temperature, ρ is the fractional distance from the centre of the sphere, and δ is a measure of the reaction exothermicity and activation energy. Frank-Kamenetskii (1969) had obtained the solutions for slab and cylinder, and numerical solutions building on numerical studies in classical astrophysics by Chandrasekhar & Wares (1949) existed for the sphere, but analytical results for the sphere were (and remain) elusive (Enig 1967). The numerically exact and two approximate analytical solutions for the critical temperature profiles obtained in (26) are shown in figure 2. This series was brought to a culmination in a succession of papers with Feng and other co-workers (32, 33, 35, 36).

An early paper (11) with T. G. Cowling FRS, Professor of Mathematics at Leeds, was followed by a substantial sequence of investigations of transport properties including thermal conductivities and diffusion with Holland, Maczek and Clifford (see, for example, (18, 20, 27)). The extension of these studies to reactive species such as hydrogen atoms led to the unexpected discovery of a chromatographic effect for atoms on surfaces (31).

Peter's early studies of peroxy-alkyl oxidation had already introduced him to 'cool flames' and the interaction of thermal and chemical feedback (thermokinetic or chain-thermal effects). This would become a second major strand during his research at Leeds and was most notably taken forward after the appointments of Brian Gray (no relation), a theoretician who had developed with C. H. Yang a systematic approach to such systems (Yang & Gray 1969*a,b*), and John Griffiths, an experimentalist who led the adoption of flow reactors rather than traditional closed vessels. Work with S. M. Hasko and P. G. Lignola laid bare the fundamentals of cool flame responses in the oxidation of small hydrocarbons (28, 29, 38), their origin in the 'negative temperature coefficient'. Example temperature–time traces for cool flames are shown in figure 3.

In an attempt to find and understand oscillatory combustion in simpler systems, attention was turned to earlier reports of 'oscillatory flames' in carbon monoxide oxidation. Persistent

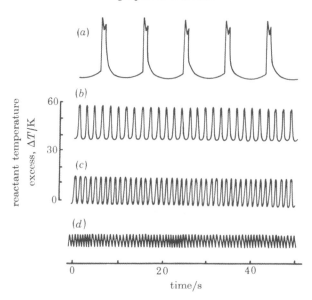

reactant temperature excess, $\Delta T / \text{K}$

time/s

Figure 3. Temperature–time records for sustained cool-flame oscillations of acetaldehyde oxidation under different experimental conditions. (Reproduced from (28).)

studies in classical closed systems with Griffiths and J. R. Bond provided a major step forward in determining reproducible phenomena and indicating the importance of the presence of hydrogen-containing species (30). The adoption of flow reactors with a controlled direct addition of known H_2 (rather than relying on residual H from impurity H_2O and longer or shorter 'drying' of the reactants) eventually provided both the clearest demonstration of this phenomenon and the key to its understanding (40). A further step back to an even simpler system involved using the flow reactors to study the oxidation of H_2 itself (39), again providing oscillatory ignition phenomena that Griffiths would eventually explain through the self-inhibitory production of H_2O and its 'enhanced third body' effect in radical removal, working in conjunction with the self-acceleratory chain branching. These reaction systems would also be used to discover the first examples of 'chaotic combustion' (Johnson & Scott 1990).

The experimental work on CO oxidation suggested the possibility that oscillations might arise in that system even without temperature changes and hence might be driven only by chemical feedback. With the additional stimulus of a challenge thrown down by a long-term adversary and friend, Richard Noyes from Oregon (Noyes 1981), Peter was determined to investigate chemical oscillations driven solely by 'autocatalytic' feedback among the reacting species—and was in possession of a handwritten translation by Terry Boddington of a Russian paper by Zel'dovich (1941) that suggested parallels between thermal feedback based on the Arrhenius law and chemical autocatalysis with a so-called 'cubic' rate law, such that the instantaneous rate would depend on the first power of a reactant species A and the second power of the autocatalyst B. In caricature this might be represented as

$$A + 2B \rightarrow 3B \qquad \text{rate} = k_1 ab^2,$$

where a and b represent the respective instantaneous concentrations of A and B. Coupled with a 'decay' step of the form

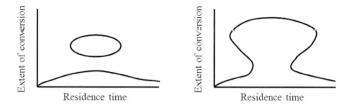

Figure 4. Isola and mushroom patterns of steady-state curves for the cubic autocatalytic model in a CSTR.

$$B \rightarrow C \qquad \text{rate} = k_2 b$$

and studied as if occurring in a continuous-flow stirred-tank reactor (CSTR), this could be thought of as the isothermal analogue of the classic exothermic reaction with Newtonian cooling from chemical engineering. In a CSTR this system shows a surprising array of possible dependence of the steady-state concentrations of A and B as the residence time is varied (the so-called bifurcation diagram), depending on the inflow concentrations a_0 and b_0 of the two species and the ratio of the rate coefficients k_1 and k_2. The steady-state curves can turn back on themselves to create S shapes and Z shapes, join these up to form 'mushrooms' and even squeeze off isolated branches that form 'isolas' (34, 37) (see figure 4). More than this, the steady states can become unstable, and sustained oscillations can arise.

Replacing the constant inflow and outflow of the CSTR with a simple chemical production of A from some precursor species P in a reaction step of the form

$$P \rightarrow A \qquad \text{rate} = k_0 p$$

and treating p as a constant (the so-called 'pool chemical' approximation) provides an even simpler model for an oscillating chemical system (41). Although christened as 'the Autocatalator' by its 'parents', the scheme has become known as the 'Gray–Scott' model and is now widely adopted as an adjunct to the earlier and well-established Brusselator model (Prigogine & Lefever 1968).

Peter's final publication (45) was as co-editor of a themed edition of *Philosophical Transactions of the Royal Society* resulting from a Royal Society Discussion Meeting co-chaired with John Field (who had also become head of the PCS group), which included a broad range of modern work on energetic materials including explosives and propellants and ranging from experimental studies of dislocations and the mechanisms of 'hot spot' initiations to fully developed detonations, and from the organic chemistry of nitration by N_2O_5 to the theoretical basis of differential scanning calorimetry. This was a truly international meeting with 140 delegates from 17 countries, held on 5 November (Guy Fawkes day in the UK); the display from ICI Nobel Explosives was delivered by the courier company TNT.

There are many other surprises and delights in Peter's collected works: the ignition of pyrophoric iron and atomic re-structuring of the catalyst in the platinum-wire-catalysed oxidation of CO with Andrew Galwey from Belfast, for instance, but—like the Giant Rat of Sumatra—those stories must wait for another occasion.*

* This rather odd end to this section is a small act of contrition on the part of the present author, whose timorousness once prevented Peter from ending a research paper with this particular nod to Sherlock Holmes, one of Peter's favourite characters.

Peter Gray the scientist

Looking back on this list of research, Peter's key insights and the major scientific contributions on which he might reflect most proudly would include the systematic unravelling of the thermokinetic basis for ignition and cool flames in the low-temperature oxidation of hydrocarbons, the development of thermal explosion theory and the direct experimental test of that theory, and the study of instabilities in systems governed by autocatalytic feedback. The low-temperature oxidation of hydrocarbons remains important in modern combustion systems, and the key papers (28, 29, 38) have been important in establishing the relationship of cool flames to real physical manifestations such as engine knock. Thermal explosions are routinely assessed for the storage and transport of materials across the world; the relevant review article (16) has been substantially influential on the field, and the lure of finding analytical results for the sphere remains a classic 'unsolved problem' of much attention—see, for instance, the recent paper by Adler (2011) and references therein.

Extensions of the Gray–Scott model, notably by the Showalter group, have provided important insights into chaotic systems and their control. The autocatalytic step also supports travelling-wave solutions, akin to 'isothermal flames', and pattern formation: Showalter, Merkin, Needham and other authors have studied several aspects of these spatiotemporal responses both in collaboration and beyond (see, for example, (43, 44)). By a curious coincidence, one application has been to study the breakdown of simple wavefronts into isothermal 'cellular flames'; the first experimental realization of such 'cellular' structures in real flames was made by Sir Arthur Smithells (Smithells & Ingle 1892), one of Peter's predecessors and the first Head of Physical Chemistry at the University of Leeds in 1902. The range of chemical instabilities, oscillatory solutions and waves formed the basis of the book co-authored by Peter (42).

Peter Gray the person

Alongside all the above achievements in science and senior administration, those of us lucky to have fallen within his orbit will remember an unabashed, lightly mischievous, inspirational and endlessly supportive human being who positively guided and supported the careers and lives of many individuals. Generous in sharing credit and dispensing praise and with strong values rooted in democratic and consensual approaches, Peter possessed rare skills able to inspire individuals and build effective teams, engendering (and showing) loyalty and respect. In an article for *The Caian* magazine (Timms 1988), Peter summarized his philosophy thus:

> I would stress the importance of trying to make opportunities for other people. Attempting to generate an atmosphere in which all members of the department feel they can do what they really want to do and find themselves encouraged for doing it.

Several generations of colleagues and friends can attest to the wisdom of this approach and are thankful to Peter for living it.

Acknowledgements

I was helped in the preparation of this memoir through discussions and advice from many individuals keen to ensure an accurate and sensitive representation: these include Derek Bradley FRS, John Brindley, Christopher Brooke, John Davidson, John Field FRS, Rachel Gray, John Griffiths, Allan Hayhurst, Tony Kirby FRS, Stephen Walley and Alan Williams FRS. Peter was also interviewed for *The Caian* magazine by Edward Timms, a fellow of Caius College, on his accession to the Mastership in 1988, and this memoir has drawn on material from that source at various points, particularly relating to early years in Cambridge.

The frontispiece photograph was taken by Godfrey Argent and is reproduced with permission.

Honours

1949–51   Ramsey Memorial Fellowship
1955   Meldola Medal, Royal Society of Chemistry
1958   Marlow Medal, Royal Society of Chemistry
1977   Elected Fellow of the Royal Society
1978   Bernard Lewis Gold Medal, Combustion Institute
1986   Royal Society of Chemistry Prize for Combustion Chemistry
1988   Italgas Prize
1997   Honorary DSc, University of Leeds

References to other authors

Adler, J. 2011 The spherical Liouville and associated differential equations. *IMA J. Appl. Math.* **76**, 817–833.

Chandrasekhar, S. & Wares, G. W. 1949 The isothermal function. *Astrophys. J.* **109**, 551–555.

Enig, J. W. 1967 Critical parameters in the Poisson–Boltzmann equation of the steady-state thermal explosion theory. *Combust. Flame.* **10**, 197–199.

Frank-Kamenetskii, D. A. 1969 *Diffusion and heat transfer in chemical kinetics*, ch. 7, pp. 374–420. New York: Plenum Press.

Johnson, B. R. & Scott, S. K. 1990 Period doubling and chaos during the oscillatory ignition of the $CO + O_2$ reaction. *J. Chem. Soc. Faraday Trans.* **86**, 3701–3705.

Noyes, R. M. 1981 Restrictions on permissible paths for changing efficiencies of operation of flow reactors. *Proc Natl Acad Sci USA* **78**, 7248–7249.

Prigogine, I. & Lefever, R. 1968 Symmetry breaking instabilities in dissipative systems. *J. Chem. Phys.* **48**, 1695–1700.

Smithells, A. & Ingle, H. 1892 The structure and chemistry of flames. *J. Chem. Soc.* **61**, 204–216.

Timms, E. F. 1988 An interview with Professor Peter Gray: Master of Gonville and Caius College. *The Caian* (November), 19–47.

Varey, P. 2012 *Life on the edge*. Cambridge: PVF Publications.

Yang, C. H. & Gray, B. F. 1969a On the slow oxidation of hydrocarbon and cool flames. *J. Phys. Chem.* **73**, 3395–3406.

Yang, C. H. & Gray, B. F. 1969b Unified theory of explosions, cool flames and two-stage ignitions. *Trans. Faraday Soc.* **65**, 1614–1622.

Zel'dovich, Ya. B. 1941 Towards the theory of combustion intensity. The evolution of an exothermic reaction in a flow. *Zh. Tekh. Fiz.* **11**, 493–500.

BIBLIOGRAPHY

The following publications are those referred to directly in the text. A full bibliography is available as electronic supplementary material at http://dx.doi.org/10.1098/rsbm.2014.0013 or via http://rsbm.royalsocietypublishing.org.

(1) 1949 (With A. D. Yoffe) Inflammation of explosive vapours and the influence of inert diluents. *Nature* **164**, 830–831.

(2) Inflammation of alkyl nitrate vapours and the effect on inert diluents. *Proc. R. Soc. Lond.* A **200**, 114–124.

(3) 1950 Initiation of explosion in liquids: measurement of the transient pressures during impact. *Trans. Faraday Soc.* **46**, 848–852.

(4) 1954 (With J. C. Lee) The combustion of gaseous hydrazine, part 1. *Trans. Faraday Soc.* **50**, 719–728.

(5) 1955 (With J. C. Lee) Explosive decomposition and combustion hydrazine. In *Fifth Symposium (International) on Combustion*, pp. 692–700. New York: Reinhold.

(6) 1956 (With T. C. Waddington) Thermochemistry and reactivity of the azides. Part 1. Thermochemistry of the inorganic azides. *Proc. R. Soc. Lond.* A **235**, 106–119.

(7) (With T. C. Waddington) Thermochemistry and reactivity of the azides. Part 2. Lattice energies of ionic azides, electron affinity and heat of formation of the azide radical and related properties. *Proc. R. Soc. Lond.* A **235**, 481–495.

(8) 1957 (With A. Williams) Chemistry of free alkoxyl radicals. *Spec. Per. Rep. Chem. Soc.* **5**, 97–118.

(9) 1959 (With M. J. Harper) Thermal explosions. Part 1. Induction periods and temperature changes before spontaneous ignition. *Trans. Faraday Soc.* **55**, 581–590.

(10) (With A. Williams)The thermochemistry and reactivity of alkoxyl radicals. *Chem. Rev.* **59**, 239–338.

(11) 1963 (With T. G. Cowling & P. G. Wright) The physical significance of formulae for the thermal conductivity and viscosity of gaseous mixtures. *Proc. R. Soc. Lond.* A **276**, 69–82.

(12) (With M. Spencer) Thermal explosions in the oxidation of hydrazine by nitric oxide and nitrous oxide. *Trans. Faraday Soc.* **59**, 879–885.

(13) 1965 (With P. R. Lee) Thermal explosion and the effect of reactant consumption on critical conditions. *Combust. Flame* **10**, 202–203.

(14) 1967 (With P. R. Lee) Temperature distributions in endothermic reactions. *Combust. Flame* **11**, 86–88.

(15) (With R. MacKinven & D. B. Smith) Combustion of hydrogen with ammonia or nitrous oxide: laminar flame speeds and flammability limits at low pressures for ternary mixtures. *Combust. Flame* **11**, 109–119.

(16) (With P. R. Lee) Thermal explosion theory. *Oxidat. Combust. Rev.* **2**, 1–184.

(17) (With R. MacKinven & D. B. Smith) Combustion of hydrogen and hydrazine with nitrous oxide and nitric oxide: flame speeds and flammability limits of ternary mixtures at sub-atmospheric pressures. *Combust. Flame* **11**, 217–226.

(18) 1969 (With S. Holland & A. O. S. Maczek) Thermal conductivities of binary gaseous mixtures of hydrogen, deuterium, oxygen and nitrous oxide. *Trans Faraday Soc.* **65**, 1032–1043.

(19) 1970 (With T. Boddington) Temperature profiles in endothermic and exothermic reactions and the interpretation of experimental data. *Proc. R. Soc. Lond.* A **320**, 71–100.

(20) (With S. Holland & A. O. S. Maczek) Thermal conductivities of binary mixtures of organic vapours and inert diluents. *Trans Faraday Soc.* **66**, 107–126.

(21) (With D. H. Fine & R. MacKinven) Thermal effects accompanying spontaneous ignition in gases. I. An investigation of the heating effects which accompany the rapid admission of inert gas to an evacuated vessel. *Proc. R. Soc. Lond.* A **316**, 223–240.

(22) (With D. H. Fine & R. MacKinven) Thermal effects accompanying spontaneous ignition in gases. II. The slow exothermic decomposition of diethyl peroxide. *Proc. R. Soc. Lond.* A **316**, 241–254.

(23) (With D. H. Fine & R. MacKinven) Thermal effects accompanying spontaneous ignition in gases. III. The explosive decomposition of diethyl peroxide. *Proc. R. Soc. Lond.* A **316**, 255–268.

(24) 1971 (With T. Boddington & D. I. Harvey) Thermal theory of spontaneous ignition: criticality in bodies of arbitrary shape. *Phil. Trans. R. Soc. Lond.* A **270**, 467–506.

(25) 1977   (With T. Boddington & G. C. Wake) Criteria for thermal explosion with and without reactant consumption. *Proc. R. Soc. Lond.* A **357**, 403–422.

(26) 1981   (With T. Boddington & S. K. Scott) Correction of kinetic data in non isothermal reactions with non uniform temperatures: analytical treatments for spherical reactant masses. *Proc. R. Soc. Lond.* A **378**, 27–60.

(27)   (With A. A. Clifford) Thermal conductivities of argon, nitrogen and hydrogen between 300 and 400 K and up to 25 MPa. *J. Chem. Soc. Faraday Trans. 1* **77**, 2679–2691.

(28)   (With J. F. Griffiths, S. M. Hasko & P. G. Lignola) Oscillatory ignitions and cool flames accompanying the non-isothermal oxidation of acetaldehyde in a well-stirred, flow reactor. *Proc. R. Soc. Lond.* A **374**, 313–339.

(29)   (With J. F. Griffiths, S. M. Hasko & P. G. Lignola) Novel, multiple-stage ignitions in the spontaneous combustion of acetaldehyde. *Combust. Flame* **43**, 175–186.

(30) 1982   (With J. R. Bond, J. F. Griffiths & S. K. Scott) Oscillations, glow and ignition in carbon monoxide oxidation. II. Oscillations in the gas-phase reaction in a closed system. *Proc. R. Soc. Lond.* A **381**, 293–314.

(31)   (With A. A. Clifford, R. S. Mason & J. I. Waddicor) Measurement of the diffusion coefficient of reactive species in dilute gases. *Proc. R. Soc. Lond.* A **380**, 241–258.

(32)   (With T. Boddington & S. K. Scott) Temperature distributions, critical conditions and scaling for exothermic materials under different boundary conditions. Part 1. Semenov and Frank-Kamenetskii extremes. *J. Chem. Soc. Faraday Trans 2* **77**, 801–812.

(33)   (With T. Boddington & S. K. Scott) Unifying approaches to the stationary-state theory of thermal explosion. Part 1. *J. Chem. Soc. Faraday Trans 2* **78**, 1721–1730.

(34) 1983   (With S. K. Scott) Autocatalytic reactions in the isothermal, continuous-flow stirred-tank reactor. Isolas and other forms of multistability. *Chem. Engng Sci.* **38**, 29–43.

(35)   (With T. Boddington & C.-G. Feng) Thermal explosion and times-to-ignition in systems with distributed temperatures. I. Reactant consumption ignored. *Proc. R. Soc. Lond.* A **385**, 289–311.

(36)   (With T. Boddington & C.-G. Feng) Thermal explosions, criticality and transition in systems with variable heat-transfer coefficient. *J. Chem. Soc. Faraday Trans. 2* **79**, 1481–1489.

(37) 1984   (With S. K. Scott) Autocatalytic reactions in the isothermal, continuous-flow stirred-tank reactor. Oscillations and instabilities in the scheme A + 2B → 3B, B → C. *Chem. Engng Sci.* **39**, 1087–1097.

(38)   (With J. F. Griffiths & S. M. Hasko) Ignitions, extinctions and thermokinetic oscillations accompanying the oxidation of ethane in an open system (continuously stirred tank reactor). *Proc. R. Soc. Lond.* A **396**, 227–255.

(39)   (With J. F. Griffiths & S. K. Scott) Branched chain reactions in open systems: theory of the oscillatory ignition limit for the hydrogen + oxygen reaction in a continuous-flow stirred-tank reactor. *Proc. R. Soc. Lond.* A **394**, 243–258.

(40) 1985   (With J. F. Griffiths & S. K. Scott) Oscillations, glow and ignition in carbon monoxide oxidation in an open system. I. Experimental studies of the ignition diagram and the effects of added hydrogen. *Proc. R. Soc. Lond.* A **397**, 21–44.

(41) 1986   (With S. K. Scott) A new model for oscillatory behaviour in closed systems: the autocatalator. *Ber. Dt. Bunsenges. Phys. Chem.* **90**, 985–996.

(42) 1990   (With S. K. Scott) *Chemical oscillations and instabilities*. Oxford: Clarendon Press.

(43)   (With J. H. Merkin, D. J. Needham & S. K. Scott) The development of travelling waves in a simple isothermal chemical system. III. Cubic and mixed autocatalysis. *Proc. R. Soc. Lond.* A **430**, 509–524.

(44) 1991   (With S. K. Scott & K. Showalter) The influence of the form of autocatalysis on the speed of isothermal chemical waves. *Phil. Trans. R. Soc. Lond.* A **337**, 249–260.

(45) 1992   (Editor, with J. E. Field) *Energetic materials*. London: The Royal Society. (Also published as *Phil. Trans. R. Soc. Lond.* A **339**, 265–429 (1992).)

FRIEDRICH ERNST PETER HIRZEBRUCH

17 October 1927 — 27 May 2012

Biogr. Mems Fell. R. Soc. **60**, 229–247 (2014)

FRIEDRICH ERNST PETER HIRZEBRUCH

17 October 1927 — 27 May 2012

Elected ForMemRS 1994

By Sir Michael Atiyah OM FRS

School of Mathematics, University of Edinburgh, Mayfield Road,
Edinburgh EH9 3JZ, UK

Friedrich Hirzebruch was the outstanding mathematician of postwar Germany, who made Bonn a great international mathematical centre.

FAMILY BACKGROUND AND EARLY YEARS

Friedrich Hirzebruch, universally known, like his father and paternal grandfather, as Fritz, was born in Hamm on 17 October 1927. His grandfather had been a master saddler, an important position at a time when horses were the main form of transport. His father had mathematical talent and studied mathematics and natural sciences in Göttingen, Berlin and Münster before becoming a high-school teacher in Minden. In due course he became the headmaster of a large secondary school in Hamm, where he stayed for the remaining 25 years of his career. His wife, Martha (*née* Holtschmit), came from a family that worked in the Westphalian metal industry.

Martha and Fritz had four children. The eldest, Friedrich Ernst Peter, was the future mathematician. The youngest, Ulrich, also became a professor of mathematics. Another son, Ernst Otto, went into business and eventually emigrated to South Africa. The one daughter, Renate, married the physicist Heinz Röttger and moved later to The Netherlands.

The war years were inevitably difficult for the whole family. Hamm was a major railway centre and was being bombed as early as 1940. In 1944 major bombing raids destroyed much of the town including Fritz's school, and killed many of its citizens. The Hirzebruch family split up, with Martha taking the younger children with her to join other relatives at Balve. It was not until August 1945 that the entire family returned to Hamm.

During the last years of the war 'our' Fritz, still under 18 years of age, was attached to an anti-aircraft unit, but his mathematical skills were not put to serious use. When the war ended, Fritz was for a mercifully short time a prisoner of war. However, he was released in July 1945

Figure 1. Fritz in Erlangen, 1952.

and able to begin his studies at the University of Münster that winter. Fritz had been a student at the school where his father was headmaster, and his interest in mathematics was strongly encouraged by his father. In Münster he later met Karl Stein, one of his father's pupils who eventually became a professor in Münster and close associate of the great Heinrich Behnke. It was in this way that Fritz became part of the Behnke school of complex analysts, a school that produced such other prominent figures as Hans Grauert and Reinhold Remmert.

A second important part of Fritz's education came from a two-year stay at the ETH in Zürich, where he was mentored by Heinz Hopf, a leading topologist. This dual immersion in complex analysis and topology was the foundation of Fritz's career and provided him with just the right background to benefit from the new ideas that emerged after 1945. His thesis (1)* on singularities of complex surfaces was an interesting fusion of topology and analysis, an early indication of the elegant and lucid style that was to characterize all his future work.

After Zürich he spent three semesters at Erlangen as an Assistant (figure 1). But he was clearly marked out for greater things, and his chance came a short while later.

---

* Numbers in this form refer to the bibliography at the end of the text.

PRINCETON

In 1952 Hirzebruch was invited for two years to the Institute for Advanced Study (IAS) in Princeton. This marked a turning point in his mathematical development, propelling him within a few years into the first rank of mathematicians worldwide. It was his good fortune to be the right man at the right time. New techniques, originating in Paris, had in the hands of Kodaira and Spencer transformed the classical field of algebraic geometry. Hirzebruch, with his background in both complex variable theory and topology, was able to absorb these new ideas rapidly and, in the virtuoso fashion that was to become his hallmark, he produced elegant machinery that helped to solve many of the outstanding problems of the subject.

The two new ingredients of postwar geometry were sheaf theory and Chern classes. Sheaf theory had been pioneered by Jean Leray (ForMemRS 1983) in a prisoner-of-war camp and then applied with remarkable success to the theory of several complex variables by Henri Cartan (ForMemRS 1971). These were pushed further by Cartan's brilliant student Jean-Pierre Serre (ForMemRS 1974), who also developed a purely algebraic version. Chern Classes, although named after S. S. Chern, who laid down the differential–geometric foundations, trace their roots back to prewar work of J. A. Todd (FRS 1948) and M. Eger. All of this viewed Chern classes in terms of the geometry of cycles on a manifold. The dual point of view of cohomology led to much more tractable algebra. This was carried out systematically by Hirzebruch in collaboration with Armand Borel, who brought with him expertise on Lie groups (5). Their joint papers tamed Chern classes completely and prepared the ground for Fritz's great synthesis of Chern classes and sheaf theory.

The main outcome of Hirzebruch's work in Princeton were the two great theorems that established his reputation: the Hirzebruch Signature Theorem (2) and the Hirzebruch–Riemann–Roch Theorem (3, 4). These deserve separate and detailed descriptions.

HIRZEBRUCH SIGNATURE THEOREM

A non-degenerate real quadratic form can be written as

$$\sum_{i=1}^{p} x_i^2 - \sum_{j=1}^{q} y_j^2 .$$

The number $p - q$ is now called the signature of the form and is independent of the coordinates used. It was Hermann Weyl (ForMemRS 1936) who pointed out in 1923 that a compact oriented 4-dimensional manifold M has a non-degenerate quadratic form on its 2-dimensional cohomology group (dual to the intersection matrix of 2-cycles). Its signature $\mathrm{Sign}(M)$ is then a topological invariant of the manifold. The same is true more generally for a manifold of dimension $4k$ based on $H^{2k}(M;\mathbf{R})$.

Hirzebruch's Signature Theorem asserts that, for all $4k$-manifolds,

$$\mathrm{Sign}(M) = L_k(p)[M],$$

where L_k is a polynomial in the Pontrjagin classes p_i of M of total weight k, and we evaluate L_k on the fundamental cycle of M.

Because the Pontrjagin classes of M can be represented by explicit expressions in the curvature of a fixed Riemannian metric on M, the Hirzebruch Signature Theorem identifies the cohomological invariant Sign(M) as an integral over M of a curvature expression. As such it is analogous to, but much deeper than, the Gauss–Bonnet Theorem for the Euler characteristic of M.

Hirzebruch discovered a simple generating function for the L_k polynomials (whose coefficients are rational numbers closely related to the Bernoulli numbers). Hirzebruch's formalism was to use the Borel–Hirzebruch description of the Pontrjagin classes p_i as the elementary symmetric functions of variables $(x_1^2, x_2^2, \ldots, x_k^2)$, where the x_j have formal dimension 2. For an even formal power series $Q(x)$ in one variable x,

$$Q(x) = 1 + a_2 x^2 + a_4 x^4 + \ldots .$$

Hirzebruch introduced the corresponding polynomials $Q_j(p)$ in the Pontrjagin classes by

$$Q = \Sigma Q_j = \Pi Q(x_i).$$

Evaluating Q on the fundamental cycle of M gives us the invariant $Q(M)$. The key property of such an invariant is that it is multiplicative:

$$Q(M \times N) = Q(M) . Q(N).$$

Hirzebruch called this invariant the Q-genus because of its relation to the genus in algebraic geometry, described below.

The signature is easily seen to be a multiplicative invariant and the Hirzebruch formula arises by taking

$$Q(x) = x/\tanh x.$$

The first few values of the L_k-polynomials are

$$L_1 = \tfrac{1}{3}p_1, \; L_2 = \tfrac{1}{45}(7p_2 - p_1^2), \; L_3 = \tfrac{1}{945}(62p_3 - 13p_1 p_2 + 2p_1^3),$$

clearly exhibiting the complicated coefficients and demonstrating the power of Hirzebruch's formalism.

Hirzebruch had discovered his formula quite quickly but lacked a method of proof. Just at this time Thom's results on cobordism appeared, a quite radical new idea for which Thom was awarded a Fields Medal. Because the signature is easily seen to be a cobordism invariant, the proof that had eluded Hirzebruch was now immediate.

Thom had known that the signature would be given by a polynomial in the Pontrjagin classes, but he did not know how to handle the formulae. This was Hirzebruch's key contribution.

Hirzebruch–Riemann–Roch (HRR) Theorem, 1954

The classical Riemann–Roch Theorem for an algebraic curve (or compact Riemann surface) computes the number of linearly independent meromorphic functions on the surface having a given set of poles D. In modern terminology this is the dimension of the space of holomorphic sections of the line bundle defined by D. The answer depends on the genus of the surface, the number of poles and something called the index of specialty of D.

Generalizing to higher dimensions, the classical Riemann–Roch Theorem for algebraic curves, had been a challenge for the Italian algebraic geometers for a long time. Much formal progress had been made by F. Severi and others but they lacked the tools necessary for the purpose. This was provided by sheaf theory, and with its advent it was soon realized by Serre that the right object to study was the holomorphic Euler characteristic of the sheaf cohomology groups $H^q(X, V)$ of a vector bundle V (over a projective algebraic manifold X of dimension m):

$$\mathcal{X}(X, V) \;=\; \sum_{q=0}^{m} (-1)^q \, \dim H^q(X, V).$$

The hope was that $\mathcal{X}$ was a topological invariant (of the complex structure) and that it should be expressible in terms of the Chern classes of V and of X. For V the trivial line bundle $\mathcal{X}$ becomes (one definition of) the arithmetic genus of X. The Italian geometers believed that it had to be expressible in terms of what we now call Chern classes. Todd had made extensive calculations and laboriously produced the first dozen expressions for what we now call the Todd polynomials, for example

$$T_1 = \tfrac{1}{2}c_1, \; T_2 = \tfrac{1}{12}(c_1^2 + c_2), \; T_3 = \tfrac{1}{24}c_1 c_2,$$
$$T_4 = \tfrac{1}{720}(-c_4 + c_3 c_1 + 3c_2^2 + 4c_2 c_1^2 - c_1^4).$$

Todd was clearly impressed by Hirzebruch's elegant derivation of these Todd classes. He wrote to Hirzebruch, saying, 'Incidentally, I have had to revise a long-held opinion that the Princeton School of Mathematicians despises anything in the nature of algorithmic ingenuity.' Hirzebruch realized at an early stage that these formulae of Todd's were closely related to the L-polynomials occurring in the Signature Theorem. In terms of generating functions, this came from the elementary formula

$$(x/\tanh x) + x = 2x/(1 - e^{-2x}).$$

The generating function $x/(1 - e^{-x})$, which leads to the Bernoulli numbers, led to what Hirzebruch appropriately named the Todd genus. He noted that $f(x) = x/(1 - e^{-x})$ is the only power series in x with the property that the coefficient of x^n in $f(x)^{n+1}$ is equal to 1 (for all n). This follows by a simple application of the Cauchy residue formula and explains why the Todd genus of the complex projective space is equal to 1.

Using his Signature Theorem, the connection between the L-genus and the Todd genus just described and the full power of sheaf cohomology, Hirzebruch was able by a tour de force to prove his Riemann–Roch Theorem, namely

$$\mathcal{X}(X, V) = \{\text{ch } V \,.\, \mathcal{T}(X)\}[X],$$

where

$$\text{ch } V = \sum e^{x_i}, \quad c(V) = \Pi(1 + x_i)$$

defines the Chern classes $c(V)$ (as elementary symmetric functions of formal variables x_i) and

$$\mathcal{T}(X) = 1 + T_1 + T_2 + \dots$$

is the total Todd class of the tangent bundle of X.

This theorem, which has many applications, became the keystone of modern algebraic geometry and has remained a monumental achievement. It also acted as a jumping-off point for two further developments in subsequent years; K-theory and index theory, which are described below.

The appearance of the Bernoulli numbers in the Todd genus and the L-genus led rapidly to their role in algebraic topology through the work of J. Milnor and others. Hirzebruch took a keen interest in these connections between the new topology and classical number theory, a connection that he himself pursued in later years.

BONN

At the end of his two-year stay at the IAS, Hirzebruch returned to Münster for a year before going back to Princeton as an Assistant Professor at the university. This year (1955) was when I myself went to the IAS and made friends not only with Fritz but also with a whole generation of brilliant young mathematicians (such as Serre, Bott and Singer), many of whose careers had been interrupted by the war. To all of us these were 'the golden years'.

Hirzebruch's spectacular achievements clearly pointed to a brilliant future. At one stage it seemed that he would go to the old traditional centre of Göttingen, but in the end, after some difficult negotiations, he accepted a full professorship at the University of Bonn. This turned out to be the perfect position for him, and for Germany: he stayed there for the rest of his life. His youth, his energy and his vision enabled him to transform Bonn into a great mathematical centre, outshining the traditional establishments at Göttingen and Berlin. Postwar Germany had to start anew after the devastation of the war and the exile of much of its intellectual leadership. This renewal was easier in a university not weighed down by an excessively rich past, and Hirzebruch again proved the right man in the right place at the right time.

In returning to Germany, Hirzebruch had a clear mission. He wanted to establish there a centre that would reproduce the exciting interaction of ideas that he had encountered at the IAS. He wanted a centre that would attract mathematicians from all over the world for the advancement of mathematics. He quickly made his first move, which was to establish the 'Arbeitstagung', an annual event, which started modestly but was to grow into a major international conference.

I was fortunate to be one of those invited to the first Arbeitstagung in 1957. The others were Grauert, Grothendieck, Kuiper and Tits, all of whom were rising stars in Europe, but it was Grothendieck who dominated the meeting with his new K-theory and the generalization of the Hirzebruch–Riemann–Roch Theorem. My memory is of Grothendieck almost monopolizing the timetable, lecturing most days for several hours. However, we did not mind because the ideas were so new and so exciting. The fact that the programme was sufficiently generous and flexible to allow this to happen was an early indication of the way in which Hirzebruch wanted the Arbeitstagung to work: no set plan and full steam ahead for novel and exciting mathematics. Nor did Hirzebruch give any indication of resentment that his great achievement, the Hirzebruch–Riemann–Roch Theorem, was being overshadowed. On the contrary, he took pride and pleasure in seeing his ideas being built on and did everything possible to encourage the process. This was typical of his generous spirit and the key to his success in establishing Bonn as a great centre.

Grothendieck's explosive entry on the scene was a hard act to follow, but the Arbeitstagung in those early years saw a succession of new and exciting results, including Milnor's discovery of exotic spheres and their subsequent realization by Brieskorn (a student of Hirzebruch's) via isolated singularities of algebraic varieties (a study initiated by Hirzebruch) (8). In fact, so many new ideas filled the Arbeitstagung air that most of my own work (and probably that of many others) emerged from this background. We learnt many new things from disparate fields, and cross-fertilization became the norm.

Figure 2. Selecting speakers at the Arbeitstagung, 1987.

I went on attending the Arbeitstagung for almost 30 years. It became an obligatory part of the academic calendar at which new results were announced, many famous mathematicians regularly attended, and the whole event was under the careful but loving care of the 'maestro'. Fritz's talents were fully exploited, but not exposed, in these annual gatherings. With their relaxed atmosphere, the Rhine cruises and the skilful selection of speakers by what has been described as 'guided democracy' (figure 2), the Arbeitstagung was unique. Happy family gatherings they may have been, but much serious mathematics was always being presented and fostered. Ideas flowed, collaborations emerged, and successive years reflected the latest movements.

Moreover, as the years passed, Fritz was always keen to attract new talent, and he encouraged me to send promising graduate students to attend. I was happy to respond and, over the years, my students were introduced to the international scene through the Arbeitstagung. Graeme Segal, Nigel Hitchin, Simon Donaldson, Frances Kirwan (all subsequently FRS) and many others came, and became in their turn regular participants.

In the three years 1959–62 Fritz and I wrote eight joint papers, all concerned with topological K-theory and its applications. This had emerged naturally from the early Arbeitstagungs and in particular from Grothendieck's K-theory in algebraic geometry, as expounded in the very first Arbeitstagung. But there were many other ingredients in the background, notably the Bott periodicity theorem.

Topological K-theory was mainly developed by Fritz and myself in 1959, when we both had a sabbatical term at the IAS in Princeton. A preliminary account appeared in 1961 (6), and we planned to write an expanded version in book form. In fact we never had time for this project, but a book (Atiyah 1967) did eventually appear under my name, based on a Harvard course of lectures.

These joint papers are a mixture of general theory and concrete problems. For example, one of them (7) showed that the famous Hodge conjectures were false for integer cohomology

Figure 3. Michael and Fritz in Bonn, 1977.

(still leaving the case of rational cohomology as one of the Clay Institute Millenium Prize problems). Other papers were related to results from Fritz's earlier Princeton period, such as his discovery of a relation between Steenrod squares and the Todd polynomials (2). Some of our joint papers appeared in German (written by Hirzebruch), and others appeared in English (written by either of us), but one appeared in French (written by neither of us!). This gave bounds on the smallest dimension in which various manifolds could be embedded. Although a primitive version was an idea of mine, the final very polished version was an exquisite illustration of Fritz's elegance with algebraic formulae. But my mathematical interaction with Fritz extended far beyond these joint publications and the three years they cover. Much of my work was influenced in one way or another by Fritz, and a later joint publication (9) is one of my favourites. Here we proved that a spin-manifold that admits a non-trivial circle action has vanishing $\hat{A}$-genus. This emerged as a new application of index theory, which first appeared in the Arbeitstagung programme of 1962. Fritz took great interest in the development of index theory, which owed so much to his pioneering work.

Although our later mathematical paths may appear to have diverged, this is only super-ficially true. We met frequently in Bonn and elsewhere (figure 3), and we followed each other's work with great interest. One notable example is Fritz's beautiful results on the resolu-tion of the cusp singularities of Hilbert modular surfaces (as explained below). His key result gave the signature defect of such a cusp singularity as the value of a suitable L-function of the number field. He then conjectured that this result would continue to hold in higher dimensions for arbitrary real number fields. This was one of the main sources of inspiration that eventually led to the index theorem for manifolds with boundary (Atiyah *et al.* 1973) and its application (Atiyah *et al.* 1983) to prove Fritz's conjecture.

INDEX THEORY

While Grothendieck generalized HRR in the context of algebraic geometry and K-theory, a different generalization was to emerge in the context of differential geometry and analysis. This centred on the index of elliptic differential operators (Atiyah & Singer 1963) with topological K-theory embedded in it. The key example was that of the Dirac operator of a spin-manifold. Hirzebruch had already noted that the $\hat{A}$-genus, defined by the power series $x/\sinh x$, was an integer for spin-manifolds. For complex manifolds with $c_1 = 0$ this coincides with the Todd genus, and so Hirzebruch posed the question: is there an interpretation of the $\hat{A}$-genus analogous to the holomorphic Euler characteristic $\mathcal{X}(X, 1)$ of a complex algebraic manifold?

The Dirac operator of theoretical physics soon became the obvious candidate whose index would be the $\hat{A}$-genus. This was first reported on at the 1962 Arbeitstagung. Hirzebruch took a keen interest in this story and its subsequent development, which opened the door to closer interaction with physicists. He organized several meetings of mathematicians and physicists (in Bad Honnef in 1988, and in Schloss Ringberg in 1988, 1989 and 1993). He also extended (13) the work of Witten and others on the elliptic genus, a subject close to his heart.

Although HRR was the natural culmination of a century of development in algebraic geometry, it can now be seen as the key stimulus for new ideas. Connes's theory of non-commutative geometry (Connes 1994) is another offshoot, which, merging functional analysis with topology, can be seen as a sturdy grandchild of HRR.

SINGULARITIES

Hirzebruch had a special interest in isolated singularities of algebraic varieties. His first paper (1) gave the explicit resolution of the quotient of $\mathbf{C}^2$ by a cyclic group showing that it consisted of a chain of rational curves with intersection properties related to the Euclidean algorithm for finding the highest common factor of two integers p, q.

A much deeper case arose in connection with the cusps of Hilbert modular surfaces defined by real quadratic fields $\mathbf{Q}(\sqrt{d})$. These surfaces are the quotient of $\mathbf{H}^2$ (where $\mathbf{H}$ is the upper half plane) by $\mathrm{SL}(2, \mathcal{O})$, where $\mathcal{O}$ is the ring of integers of the quadratic field. This surface can be compactified by adding 'cusps', which are isolated singular points. Hirzebruch showed (10) that these cusp singularities can be resolved by a cycle of rational curves whose intersection properties are determined by the periodic continued fraction expansion of quadratic irrationals. This is a really beautiful result connecting number theory to geometry and was to inspire much further work.

Each isolated singularity leads to a 'signature defect', the local correction that has to be added to the formula for the signature. For quotient singularities it is related to the classical Dedekind sums, whereas for the cusp singularities Hirzebruch was able to use his resolution to identify the signature defect with the value of a certain L-function of the number field at $s = 0$.

Hilbert modular varieties with cusps exist analogously for any totally real number field and Hirzebruch conjectured that the signature defect of the cusps should again be given by the value of an L-function. This was the starting point of my own research with Patodi and Singer on the Signature Theorem for manifolds with boundary (Atiyah *et al.* 1973). The special case associated with cusps was investigated in a paper (Atiyah *et al.* 1983) that led to a proof of Hirzebruch's conjecture on the signature defect and the value of L-functions.

Figure 4. Don Zagier and Fritz Hirzebruch in St Petersburg, 2007. (Online version in colour.)

A special class of singularities is given by the equation

$$z_1^p + z_2^q + z_3^2 + \ldots + z_n^2 = 0.$$

The boundary of a small neighbourhood of the origin in $\mathbf{C}^n$ is a compact manifold M of dimension $2n - 3$, so for $n = 3$ we get a 3-manifold. For $p = 3$, $q = 5$ this is the famous 'fake' Poincaré 3-sphere, namely the quotient of S^3 by the binary icosahedral group. The resolution of this singularity is given by a graph of eight rational curves intersecting according to the Dynkin diagram of the exceptional Lie group E_8.

For higher values of n, M is simply connected and it is the boundary of a plumbing construction again built on the Dynkin diagram but using $(n - 1)$-spheres. Hirzebruch and his students studied such plumbing extensively and showed that for $n = 5$, M is the generator (of order 28) of the Milnor group of exotic 7-spheres. Similar results hold for higher values of n, and these exotic spheres are referred to as Brieskorn spheres.

Brieskorn also studied the deformation theory of the classical case $n = 3$, following ideas due to Grothendieck. This involved the geometry of the complex Lie groups, including E_8.

Hirzebruch's work on Hilbert modular surfaces extended far beyond the cusps and focused on the modular curves on the surface. In a long article (10) that formed the basis of his International Mathematical Union lectures in Japan, he made a very thorough study of the homology of such surfaces and their relation to classical number theory. These were developed even further in two long papers with Zagier (11, 12) (figure 4). The detailed and delicate interaction between geometry and number theory described in all these papers was very close to Hirzebruch's heart, and linked up with his very first papers.

ROLE IN GERMANY

For 50 years Hirzebruch was the outstanding figure in German mathematics. At the research level he embodied the new ideas that emerged after the war. He attracted high-quality colleagues to Bonn, first at the university and later at the Max Planck Institute. He guided the PhD theses of around 50 students and he made Bonn famous as the home of the Arbeitstagung.

His many achievements were only possible because of his multiple skills as researcher, teacher and administrator. Despite his many roles he never seemed to be flustered and had time to talk to younger colleagues and visitors. The secret of all this resided in his methodical efficiency. He kept all his correspondence in well-organized files, always capable of exhibiting old letters on anniversary occasions.

His personal qualities of informal friendliness—unusual in German professors of the old school—led to harmonious relations with staff, faculty and students, and were an important factor in his ability to handle so many problems simultaneously.

His influence was felt well outside Bonn. By a coincidence that seemed willed by fate, Fritz was elected twice to the presidency of the Deutsche Mathematiker-Vereinigung (DMV, the German Mathematical Society) at key moments in the history of postwar Germany and postwar German mathematicians: in 1961, when the Berlin Wall was built, and again in 1989–90 when it fell. The separation of Germany into two blocs fell in the middle of his first term, and he solved the problem of the inability of the East German mathematicians to cross into West Berlin by repeating in its entirety the first DMV meeting that he chaired after the separation. But of course such makeshift measures could not last, and soon the DMV was split into a new East German branch, the Mathematische Gesellschaft der DDR (MGDDR), that for almost three decades was no longer officially connected with the West German one. When the political world changed again and the two halves of Germany were reunited, Hirzebruch was able to preside over the reunification also of the Mathematiker-Vereinigung and to ensure that the transition took place in a spirit of reconstruction rather than of recrimination or retaliation.

For several years after the Wall fell, he travelled almost every week to Berlin, where he had the task of helping the nearly 200 mathematicians of the previous Karl Weierstrass Institute of the East German Academy of Science to find new positions. The individual cases were very dissimilar and the solutions he came up with were varied. The cases where no adequate solution could be found haunted him, and he sometimes spoke to his friends at the Institute of the sorrow he felt. But in the vast majority of cases provisional or permanent positions could be set up, whether in temporary Max Planck Working Groups, in permanent new institutes that he helped establish, in schools, or in universities in Germany or abroad. His contacts with the German Democratic Republic during its years of isolation and the respect in which he was held on both sides of the previous dividing line made him effective in this role in a way that no one else could have been, and his achievements, though little known to outsiders, were received with enormous gratitude by the people involved. Within Bonn, Hirzebruch continued to build the great mathematical centre that he had always envisaged. First it was through the SFB (Sonderforschungsbereiche) that he set up with support from the German Research Council. This in turn led in 1981 to the establishment of a Max Planck Institute for Mathematics under his directorship. This runs an extensive visitor programme, which reproduced the Princeton atmosphere that was its model.

Figure 5. Fritz Hirzebruch with Karl Stein, Reinhold Remmert and Henri Cartan, 1950.

INTERNATIONAL ROLE

From his early visit to Princeton in 1952 Hirzebruch established international contacts, which he continued to foster throughout his life. Contacts with France began immediately after the end of the war in 1945. The aftermath of World War I was a bitter time, when French hostility led to the ostracism of German mathematicians for many years. By contrast, the next generation of French mathematicians led by Henri Cartan was much more enlightened. Cartan's close links with Heinrich Behnke at Münster were re-established amicably and Hirzebruch became part of that rapprochement (figure 5).

The annual Arbeitstagung was fully international, as were the SFB and the Max Planck Institute. Hirzebruch had succeeded in putting Germany, and Bonn in particular, at centre stage, but in four other countries Hirzebruch made a distinctive impact.

The first was Japan, where contacts grew out of Hirzebruch's friendship with Kodaira in Princeton. In the early postwar years it was difficult for Japanese mathematicians to spend time abroad. Invitations to Bonn led to regular visits by young Japanese, and these were stimulated by Hirzebruch's own tour of Japan. A whole generation of students of Kodaira's made their international debut in Bonn. In recognition of Hirzebruch's role he was awarded the very prestigious Order of the Secret Treasure (Gold and Silver Star), and the Mathematical Society of Japan awarded him the Seki Kowa Prize.

Russia was a special case. Because the Russian School of Mathematics was so strong, Hirzebruch regularly invited leading Russians to the Arbeitstagung. Except for one famous year invitations were declined, but even so the international recognition demonstrated by the invitations was a great help to the individuals invited.

Another country where Hirzebruch had a special role was Poland. He was a strong supporter of the Banach Centre, went many times to Warsaw, and was honoured by being awarded the Stefan Banach Medal of the Polish Academy of Sciences.

The fourth country where he played a key role was Israel. In 1988 he was awarded the Wolf Prize in Mathematics. In his acceptance speech in the Knesset he touched on the difficult past:

> As a professor at the University of Bonn, I am one of the successors of the famous mathematicians Felix Hausdorff and Otto Toeplitz. Hausdorff committed suicide in 1942, together with his wife, when deportation to a concentration camp was imminent; Toeplitz emigrated to Israel in 1939 and died there the following year. The memory of these mathematicians is with me always on this trip.

In these sentences he managed to create continuity between the mathematical community in Bonn before and after the Nazis, to establish links between the Jews in Germany and in Israeli society.

After years of lengthy and difficult discussion (in which I was heavily involved), the European Mathematical Society was established in 1990. It was natural that Hirzebruch should be its first President. After the fall of the Berlin Wall, Eastern Europe rejoined the stream of European culture. What had been tentative and delicate links to the West were now allowed to flourish; the timing was therefore perfect for the EMS, and Hirzebruch was again the right man in the right place. In particular the four-yearly European Mathematical Congress was initiated during his presidency.

A PERSONAL ASSESSMENT

Fritz was such a close friend and collaborator of mine that this formal biography has to be supplemented by a more personal assessment. We met in 1954, first in Cambridge, where he had been invited by Hodge and Todd, who were keen to hear about his exciting new results, and then at the International Congress of Mathematicians in Amsterdam. What I remember clearly about these occasions is how friendly and informal Fritz was. Although he was already on his way to becoming an Assistant Professor at Princeton and I was merely a graduate student, there were no barriers between us and we quickly established a friendship that blossomed over the subsequent years.

We spent many terms together at Princeton, first in 1955 (just after my PhD) and again in 1959 when we were both on sabbaticals. On this latter occasion we lived close together and we both had young children who accompanied us on our walks and no doubt interrupted our mathematical discussions. We had earlier spent a month at a conference in Mexico City, been stranded in our car by a flooded road and been photographed on the volcano Popocatépetl (figure 6) in our smartly pressed suits!

Over the subsequent years we met annually in Bonn, and sometimes in Oxford or at international conferences. Our mathematical collaboration and our friendship went hand-in-hand. He was my role model and I learnt from him how to lecture and how to write. His lectures were always crystal clear, a tribute not only to his lucid thinking, but also to the hard work and artistry that he put into his preparation. Referring to the magical surprise that often ended his performance I once said, 'rabbits do not appear out of hats unless they are put there'.

As a person Fritz was calm, cool and collected and I cannot remember seeing him lose his temper. He was kind and helpful, particularly to the young and to foreign visitors. This is graphically captured by Graeme Segal reporting on his stay in Bonn in a letter to me:

Figure 6. Michael and Fritz on Popocatépetl, Mexico, 1956. (Online version in colour.)

The month I spent in Bonn as a second-year graduate student in the autumn of 1964, when I first encountered Fritz Hirzebruch, remains one of my most vivid memories. When I think of all he must have been involved in I am humbled to think of his kindness in spending so much time, not just in talking to me about my work, but in making sure that my wife Desley and I were at home and happy in what was for us a strange new world.

For a young Australian, Germany then was an overwhelmingly formal place. After two years I had just about become accustomed to the increased formality of England, but in Germany it attained another level. In retrospect I see that the country was poised on the brink of a great change in social style, and I think this was essential to Fritz's magic. On one side he was the perfect German professor of the old school: although only 38 he had already served a term as Dean of the Faculty of Sciences, and was a figure of manifest authority. (My status rocketed with the very genteel elderly lady in whose house we were lodging when one day the Herr Professor arrived in person to pick me up.) He gave wonderful lectures, but what I most remember about them was his use of the German language—his long elegant articulated sentences in which every clause clicked faultlessly into place. Mathematicians had long since ceased to lecture like that in English; I wonder whether it still happens in Germany?

Important social events of the Arbeitstagung included the boat trip on the Rhine and the Rector's party (originally held in the Hirzebruch flat). These involved the whole family, so that Inge and the three children all became familiar friends to those who attended regularly. Fritz and Inge (*née* Spitzley) were married in 1952 before the first visit to Princeton, and the elder daughter (Ulrike) was born there; the younger children, Barbara and Michael, were born in Germany (figure 7). Barbara and Ulrike both studied mathematics, encouraged—but not pushed—by Fritz, with Ulrike ending up as a mathematical publisher and Barbara as a mathematics school teacher. Michael diverted from this mathematical tradition, became a doctor and was very helpful to Fritz in his old age.

Inge and Fritz had a long and close marriage, with Inge accompanying Fritz on most of his foreign trips and involving herself fully in all his many activities (figure 8).

Figure 7. The Hirzebruch family, Princeton, 1967.

Figure 8. Inge and Fritz in Bonn, 2007. (Online version in colour.)

Figure 9. Hirzebruch's grave on Poppelsdorfer Friedhof in Bonn. (Online version in colour.)

HONOURS

Because of his mathematical distinction and his key roles both nationally in Germany and internationally, he received many honours, a few of which have already been mentioned. In addition he received medals and prizes from Switzerland, France, the USSR, The Netherlands and many from Germany. He was a foreign member of about 20 academies of science and he was awarded 15 honorary doctorates, including from Oxford in 1984. In Germany he had been a member of the order 'Pour le Mérite', established by Frederick the Great and a model for the British Order of Merit (although the German original was typically more serious, involving annual meetings with scholarly lectures). At his funeral service in Bonn there was an impressive floral display from the Federal President, and Fritz's gravestone (figure 9), with its geometric models, is a fitting tribute.

ACKNOWLEDGEMENTS

I am grateful to Fritz's family, friends and colleagues for much helpful information and for permission to reproduce here some material used in the *Notices of the American Mathematical Society* (which I co-edited with Don Zagier). The American Mathematical Society has been very cooperative. Special thanks are due to Andrew Ranicki, Winfried Scharlau and Don Zagier.

The frontispiece photograph was taken in 1994 and is copyright © The Royal Society.

References to other authors

Atiyah, M. F. 1967 *K-theory*. New York: Benjamin.

Atiyah, M. F. & Singer, I. M. 1963 The index of elliptic operators on compact manifolds. *Bull. Am. Math. Soc.* **69**, 422–433.

Atiyah, M. F., Patodi, V. K. & Singer, I. M. 1973 Spectral asymmetry and Riemannian Geometry. *Bull. Lond. Math. Soc.* **5**, 229–234.

Atiyah, M. F., Donnelly, H. & Singer, I. M. 1983 Eta invariants, signature defects of cusps and values of *L*-functions. *Ann. Math.* **118**, 131–177.

Connes, A. 1994 *Non-commutative geometry*. San Diego: Academic Press.

Bibliography

The following publications are those referred to directly in the text. A full bibliography is available from the Hirzebruch collection at the MPIM (https://hirzebruch.mpim-bonn.mpg.de/) or as electronic supplementary material at http://dx.doi.org/10.1098/rsbm.2014.0010 or via http://rsbm.royalsocietypublishing.org.

(1)   1954   Über vierdimensionale RIEMANNsche Flächen mehrdeutiger analytischer Funktionen von zwei komplexen Veränderlichen. *Math. Annln* **126**, 1–22.

(2)   On Steenrod's reduced powers, the index of inertia, and the Todd genus. *Proc. Natl Acad. Sci. USA* **39**, 951–956.

(3)   Arithmetic genera and the theorem of Riemann–Roch for algebraic varieties. *Proc. Natl Acad. Sci. USA* **40**, 110–114.

(4)   1956   *Neue topologische Methoden in der algebraischen Geometrie* (Ergebnisse der Mathematik und ihrer Grenzgebiete, neue Folge, Heft 9). Heidelberg: Springer. (English translation (1966): *Topological methods in algebraic geometry*. Berlin: Springer.)

(5)   1958   (With A. Borel) Characteristic classes and homogeneous spaces. I. *Am. J. Math.* **80**, 458–538.

(6)   1961   (With M. F. Atiyah) Vector bundles and homogeneous spaces. In *Differential geometry* (*Proc. Symp. Pure Math. 3*), pp. 7–38. Providence, RI: American Mathematical Society.

(7)   1962   (With M. F. Atiyah) Analytic cycles on complex manifolds. *Topology* **1**, 25–46.

(8)   1967   Singularities and exotic spheres. In *Séminaire Bourbaki*, Exp. 314, Textes des conférences, o.S. Paris: Institut Henri Poincaré.

(9)   1970   (With M. F. Atiyah) Spin-manifolds and group actions. In *Memoires dédiés à Georges de Rham* (ed. A. Haefliger & R. Narasimhan), pp. 18–28. Berlin: Springer.

(10) 1973   Hilbert modular surfaces. *Enseign. Math.* **19**, 183–281.

(11) 1976   (With D. Zagier) Intersection numbers of curves on Hilbert modular surfaces and modular forms of Nebentypus. *Invent. Math.* **36**, 57–113.

(12) 1977   (With D. Zagier) Classification of Hilbert modular surfaces. In *Complex analysis and algebraic geometry: a collection of papers dedicated to K. Kodaira* (ed. W. L. Baily Jr & T. Shioda), pp. 43–77. Cambridge University Press.

(13) 1999   Complex cobordism and the elliptic genus. In *Algebraic geometry, Hirzebruch 70: Proceedings of the Algebraic Geometry Conference in Honor of F. Hirzebruch's 70th Birthday, 11–16 May 1998, Stefan Banach International Mathematical Center, Warszawa, Poland* (*Contemporary Mathematics*, vol. 241) (ed. Piotr Pragacz, Michal Szurek & Jarosław Wiśniewski), pp. 9–20. Providence, RI: American Mathematical Society.

SIR DAVID JACK

22 February 1924 — 8 November 2011

Biogr. Mems Fell. R. Soc. **60**, 249–260 (2014)

SIR DAVID JACK

22 February 1924 — 8 November 2011

Elected FRS 1992

By Sir Alasdair Breckenridge CBE FRCP FRSE FMedSci

Cree Cottage, Feather Lane, Heswall, Wirral CH60 4RL, UK

David Jack was the Director of Research and Development of Allen & Hanburys Ltd and then Glaxo Holdings plc from 1961 to 1987. His aim over all these years was to concentrate the companies' research on inventing treatments for common diseases such as those affecting the respiratory, gastrointestinal and cardiovascular systems. Under his research direction, Glaxo became one of the most successful pharmaceutical companies in the world. Medicines that he invented—salbutamol, salmeterol, beclamethasone dipropionate and fluticasone propionate—revolutionized the treatment of bronchial asthma by cutting down the incidence of acute asthma attacks, preventing hospital admissions and reducing the death rate from the disease. He also invented ranitidine for the treatment of peptic ulcer, which became the best-selling pharmaceutical product in the world. He was also responsible for the invention of sumatriptan for the treatment of migraine and ondansetron for the prevention of radiotherapy-induced nausea. David Jack was one of the most successful inventors of new medicines in the twentieth century.

EDUCATION AND EARLY CAREER

David Jack was born at Markinch, Fife, and won a place to Buckhaven High School where, as he later admitted, his performance was not as good as it should have been because he was more interested in golf and the local brass band than in school work. Although advised by his headmaster to apply for a place to study mathematics at Edinburgh University, he knew that he was not a 'natural' mathematician and chose instead in 1941 to join Boots the Chemist in Cupar as an apprentice pharmacist with a view to becoming a Member of the Pharmaceutical Society and, in due course, to work in retail pharmacy. However, having completed his apprenticeship in 1944, he entered a BSc course in the Royal Technical College, Glasgow (now Strathclyde University), and also a course in physiology and pharmacology in Glasgow University. In 1944 he was awarded the Governor's Prize of the college as the best first-year

© 2014 The Author(s)
Published by the Royal Society

student, and in 1945 he won the Physiology Medal of the Faculty of Medicine, a prize normally reserved for medical students. In 1948 he graduated BSc with first-class honours in pharmacy and pharmacology from Glasgow University. He became an assistant lecturer in experimental pharmacology in the Department of Materia Medica in Glasgow Medical School, having turned down two offers to read for a PhD, one with Professor Frank Spring (FRS 1952), whom David was to describe as 'the most inspiring teacher I ever encountered'. Having completed a year's National Service in the Royal Army Medical Corps at the Army College of Health, he returned to the university but decided after a year to stop working with experimental animals; he resigned from his post in 1951. When he explained his reasons for resigning, namely that although he recognized the importance of animal research for human welfare, he felt it was not right for him to pursue this line of work, his head of department introduced David to Dr Tom Macrae, the Research and Development (R&D) Director of Glaxo Laboratories, Greenford, who offered him the post of research pharmacist at Glaxo, which he accepted. This started him on a career in the pharmaceutical industry that culminated in his appointment as Head of Research at Glaxo Holdings plc.

PERSONAL AND FAMILY LIFE

David Jack was born on 22 February 1924, the youngest of six children. His father, Andrew Jack, worked in a local paper mill before becoming a coal miner. Andrew's main hobby was gardening, which became his full-time occupation for 10 years after he had to leave the mines because of ill health. His mother, Mary (*née* Maiden), had wished to become a school teacher but was made to work in a local flax mill by her father, who owned the mill. She and Andrew were married in 1912 and brought up six children in the difficult financial times of the 1920s and 1930s. David met his wife-to-be, Lydia Brown, when they were fellow students of pharmacy in Glasgow, where they graduated on the same day. They were married in 1952 and had two children, Moira (born in 1954) and Norma (born in 1958). Moira later had a career in Human Resources with ICI plc, and Norma's career included working in Operations and Sales at Exxon Chemicals. Moira married in 1981; Norma married in 1992 and had two sons, born in 1993 and 1997.

Lydia, David's wife, graduated in pharmacy and pharmacognosy and taught pharmacognosy for several years before working as a hospital pharmacist. From 1961 onwards she also made a significant contribution to the Girl Guides movement in Hertfordshire, where she was successively District Commissioner, County Commissioner and ultimately President of the Guides.

Moira and Norma have provided the following personal recollection of their father's interests and family life outside his professional work:

> Father had a wide range of interests, outside his work, to which he applied his enquiring mind.
>
> He started playing golf as a boy on the municipal course at Markinch, where cows and sheep had to be encouraged to vacate the greens and he would do odd jobs to raise the small green fees. He was a talented player and ultimately played golf to a high level despite having little time to practice. It was no coincidence that in the 1960s we moved to Gustard Wood to live within 200 metres of the golf course! He and my mother played together and could be a deadly combination in the mixed foursomes. The Mid-Herts Golf Club Honours Boards are testament to his and their success. Although as children we did not share our father's interest in golf, we very much

Figure 1. Sir David Jack in his garden standing beside a *Liquidambar styraciflua* 'Worplesdon'.
(Online version in colour.)

enjoyed sharing the pre-match fried egg sandwiches with lots of ketchup, which were his preferred Sunday morning fare. He was away working a great deal, and mother recalls a day when he was practising and a lady, spotting an unfamiliar face, came to check that he was a member. He was amused when after a short conversation she commented, 'Oh, you're Lydia's husband; well, that's all right then', and he was allowed to continue.

He followed a wide variety of sports, particularly football. Throughout his time living in England he remained faithful to Raith Rovers and often attended Luton Town matches.

Father was musical and as a boy and young man he played the cornet in the Markinch Town Band, winning many prizes. For some years it was part of the Jack family Christmas tradition that he searched out his cornet to check if he could still play! He and mother also enjoyed visits to concerts, opera and ballet.

He inherited his father's love of gardening (figure 1) and created several gardens. He took a great, if restless, interest in his plants, constantly looking to re-site them to better effect.

He was a loving father with high standards, placing great emphasis on education and effective knowledge. One of his regular sayings was 'You think with what you know.' He applied his scientific approach to our development and learning, always encouraging us to think for ourselves and work things out from 'first principles'. When we asked him a question, it was usual to be met with, 'Well, what do you think?' and be encouraged to work it out for ourselves. This could be infuriating when an immediate answer for school homework was required but has stood us in good stead as adults. Life, however, was not always serious and we have happy memories of flying (or trying to fly) homemade brown paper kites, sledging on the golf course, fishing for newts and minnows, and learning to ride bicycles. As we grew up he encouraged us to do what we wanted, to the highest level. He assumed we could do anything, and never treated us as 'girls'. He took an interest in our various activities and took pride in our achievements, even though they were different from his own. In later years he took pleasure in being part of his grandsons' lives, encouraging their learning and appreciating their successes. They in turn valued spending time with him—whether being instructed in the correct way to swing a golf club or discussing their science homework. He cared about all his family and helped to ensure his older sisters were looked after in their old age.

After his retirement he became a member and then Chairman of the Committee of the Local Abbeyfield home. At this time, well-meant legislation requiring retirement homes to be upgraded caused great problems in smaller homes, where this could not be done. This caused great distress to residents, and father helped to ensure that the residents' needs were taken account of whilst the problems were resolved.

He and mother travelled extensively together. They particularly liked Italy and travelled to most parts of the country experiencing the history, culture, food and wine! He put his school Latin to good use, both translating ancient Roman inscriptions and conversing with the locals.

Father was a brilliant man but always modest about his knowledge and achievements. We remember him often saying when asked about something, 'I don't know much about this but …' and then going on to show more knowledge and understanding about the subject than many who considered themselves expert! He was very pleased when his important work was acknowledged with many awards and we know that he particularly valued being elected a Fellow of the Royal Society.

We were delighted when, in his memory and in recognition of his contribution, the Markinch Society chose to mark the house where he was born and brought up with a blue plaque and GlaxoSmithKline named its R&D site at Ware the David Jack Centre for Research & Development.

EARLY CAREER IN THE PHARMACEUTICAL INDUSTRY

The main pharmaceutical products of Glaxo Laboratories at that time were licensed in from other companies and little original research was conducted. David's job was to formulate products of salts of penicillin and supervise their transfer to production. The lessons he learned from this work on relatively insoluble compounds were to prove invaluable in his later work on aerosol suspensions of anti-asthmatic drugs. But the work was tedious and repetitive and in 1953 he decided to seek alternative employment. He became the Senior Development Pharmacist at Menley & James Ltd, a small pharmaceutical company that acted as the British agent for several overseas companies, the largest of which was Smith, Kline & French (SK&F), which took over Menley & James in 1955. David's roles at SK&F were, first, to establish UK expertise for the manufacture of long-acting preparations of Drinamyl, a mixture of amphetamine and amylobarbitone (better known as 'purple hearts') and second, to assess the scientific and medical potential of products identified for in-licensing. This involved regular visits to the US headquarters of SK&F in Philadelphia, where he learned about product development programmes.

He was also asked to devise a new method for the production of one of their products, nitrofurantoin, a urinary antiseptic, because the currently used techniques involved the use of unstable intermediates (1–3)*. David completed this work and it formed the basis for a PhD, which he successfully submitted to the University of London in 1960. It also formed the basis for his election to the Royal Institute of Chemistry.

In 1961 Professor Todd, Head of the School of Pharmacy at the Royal Technical College in Glasgow, retired; David Jack was invited to apply for his position, but his radical views

* Numbers in this form refer to the bibliography at the end of the text.

on what was needed to take the school forward into a new era of drug discovery did not meet with the approval of the selection committee for the post. However, one member of the panel, Cyril Maplethorpe, a director of Allen & Hanburys Ltd and a member of the main board of its parent company, Glaxo Laboratories Ltd, was impressed by David's plans and in due course David was invited to become the Director of R&D at Allen & Hanburys. David laid down certain conditions before accepting, including increasing the size of the research establishment; this was agreed.

Research Director of Allen & Hanburys companies and Glaxo Holdings plc

David Jack was R&D Director of Allen & Hanburys companies from 1961 to 1978 and of Glaxo Holdings from 1978 until 1987. In both these roles he had a determining influence on all research projects and was able to implement strategies of drug development that had been considered unacceptable by the selection committee at the Royal Technical College in 1961. In these roles, one of his constant aims was to concentrate the company's research on treatments for common diseases such as respiratory, gastrointestinal and cardiovascular illnesses. Because he was chairman of all the relevant product development committees, he retained personal responsibility for the selection and conduct of all drug development.

Another aim on assuming his role at Allen & Hanburys was to concentrate on pharmacology-based research that would complement programmes being currently executed at Glaxo Research on steroids, antibiotics, vaccines and veterinary medicines. But he was surprised and disappointed that none of the ongoing projects at Allen & Hanburys was relevant to this plan and, moreover, that there was an absence of expertise in medicine, biochemistry and toxicology, all of which he considered essential disciplines for drug discovery and drug development. So he had to start by appointing a completely new team, although it is significant that he decided to become his own Director of Pharmacology.

David Jack installed unusually productive R&D teams at both Allen & Hanburys and then at Glaxo. He had assembled a staff of 130 at Allen & Hanburys in 1961; when he retired in 1987 there were 800 staff working in R&D at Allen & Hanburys and 3000 at Glaxo. Glaxo became one of the most successful pharmaceutical companies in the world and by 1987 the products from these research activities accounted for 75% of the turnover and profit of the company.

The discovery and development of new medicines

David Jack's major inventions were drugs for treating asthma (salbutamol, salmeterol, beclamethasone dipropionate and fluticasone propionate), a drug for treating peptic ulcer (ranitidine), a drug for treating radiotherapy-induced nausea (ondansetron) and a drug for treating migraine (sumatriptan). Five of these gained the Queen's Award for Technological Achievement.

The success of his research was largely based on a simple approach to project management. A primary objective was always to invent better treatments for relatively common ailments. Accordingly, each project had to contain the possibility of producing such a medicine or be directed at elucidating a physiological or pathological process whose manipulation might lead to one. Short product development times were also a characteristic of the work he undertook.

For example, salbutamol and its longer-acting analogue, salmeterol, were marketed in the UK only three and five years after their first syntheses.

New medicines for asthma

In the early 1960s, isoprenaline was the most efficient product available to treat asthma. Isoprenaline has many pharmacological actions because it activates all β-adrenoceptors. One or two inhalations produce intense bronchodilatation because the drug is actively absorbed from the airways, but its action is of short duration (1–2 hours) because it is rapidly inactivated by catechol-*O*-methyltransferase. Its main side effect is cardiac stimulation. A longer-acting isoprenaline analogue was an obvious research target for David Jack and his team.

β-Adrenoceptor agonists

In 1966, understanding of what was achievable was transformed when AH 3021, the sali-genin analogue of isoprenaline, was found to be at least 200 times more active on bronchial muscle than heart muscle; AH 3365 (salbutamol), its tertiary butyl analogue, was even more selectively active (4–6). This unexpectedly greater selectivity was strong evidence of the subdivision of β-adrenoceptors into β_1- and β_2-adrenoceptors, a classification that was generally accepted from about 1970 onwards (Lands *et al.* 1967). Salbutamol given by inhalation rapidly induces near-maximal bronchodilatation without significant side effects, with a duration of action of 3–4 hours. Oral doses are less effective and cause obvious tremor and tachycardia. Inhaled salbutamol was to become the most prescribed bronchodilator in the world.

However, the duration of action of salbutamol was too short to provide continuous β-agonism in the airways. This problem was solved by the invention of salmeterol. This was based on David's concept of two types of pharmacological agonism. In type 1 agonism, the target cells respond continuously to stimulation, and persistent binding of an agonist to a receptor results in continuing stimulation. Adrenoceptor stimulants and glucocorticosteroids are typical type 1 agonists. In type 2 agonism, the cell, having responded to an effective stimulus, must recover before it can respond to another stimulus. The nicotinic actions of acetylcholine at autonomic ganglia and motor endplates in skeletal muscle are examples of type 2 agonism (7). David initiated a search for a selective β_2-receptor agonist that would bind persistently to its receptor protein because, as a type 1 agonist, it should be long acting (8 10). Even within the Glaxo team this was considered controversial because of the large available literature on desensitization of β-adrenoceptors after continuous stimulation. But the synthesis of analogues of salbutamol with increasingly long flexible non-polar side chains resulted in the eventual synthesis of salmeterol. In large clinical trials in patients with chronic asthma, salmeterol induced near-maximal bronchodilatation lasting 8–12 hours without evidence of tolerance or use-limiting side effects. By inhibiting the release of histamine from mast cells and the histamine-induced contraction of endothelial cells in post-capillary venules, salmeterol also prevents extravasation of the plasma proteins that activate the harmful kinin and complement cascades (16).

Inhaled steroids

Beclomethasone dipropionate was the first potent topical anti-inflammatory steroid shown to have a selective action in the airways when administered by inhalation to patients with asthma (11). This was a major advance in the treatment of asthma because at usual therapeutic doses it is not accompanied by significant glucocorticoid activity elsewhere in the body, and its prolonged duration of action enables twice daily administration to be effective over 24 hours. However, a significant fraction of each dose is swallowed and absorbed from the alimentary tract into the general circulation, and this may cause systemic side effects at higher doses, especially in children. The solution to this problem was found in a drug that had already been made by Glaxo chemists for possible use in dermatology. Fluticasone propionate (FP) has a unique profile of intense anti-inflammatory activity when applied to human skin and a lack of systemic glucocorticoid activity after oral administration in the mouse, a species known to be very sensitive to oral glucocorticoids. Oral FP in both mouse and humans is quantitatively inactivated by first-pass metabolism in the liver, and the anti-inflammatory action of inhaled FP is very selective.

Combination products

Inhalers containing both salmeterol and fluticasone are of great medical importance and are now used to produce effective long-lasting bronchodilatation and control of inflammation in the airways for patients with asthma and chronic obstructive airways disease.

The clinical importance of these products for the prevention and treatment of asthma cannot be overemphasized. They diminish the number of acute asthma attacks, they prevent the need for hospital admissions from asthma and they are an important contributor to reducing the death rate from asthma, that in the UK had been one of the highest in the world.

Histamine H_2-receptor antagonists

In 1972, James Black's team in SK&F published their finding that burimamide, a remote analogue of histamine, inhibited the gastric secretion evoked by the infusion of histamine or pentagastrin as well as that induced by food (Black *et al.* 1972). These results proved that histamine is a physiological mediator of gastric acid secretion and revealed the possibility of a new kind of medicine for treating peptic ulcers. But burimamide was not a useful medicine because it was only weakly active and poorly absorbed from the gut. It was, however, the first step towards the production of cimetidine, which, when marketed in 1976, transformed the treatment of peptic ulcers.

The only important flaw in cimetidine is that its blocking action on histamine H_2 receptors was not entirely selective. Therapeutic doses of cimetidine also inhibited oxidative drug metabolism in the liver by inhibiting cytochrome P450 and therefore could potentiate the effect of commonly used medicines such as theophylline, warfarin and phenytoin if they were administered simultaneously with it. Cimetidine was also a weak androgen antagonist, but this was not usually important at the doses used in treating peptic ulcers.

The search in Glaxo laboratories to invent orally active histamine H_2-receptor antagonists that were not subject to SK&F patents began in 1973. It appeared from work at SK&F that a basic aromatic ring, preferably 5-methylimidazole, was essential for potent histamine H_2 antagonism. But chemists at Glaxo showed that this was not necessarily so and that the required basic centre could be a basic substituent on an aromatic ring. The outcome of this work was the invention of ranitidine, whose general structure was similar to that of cimetidine but which was five times more active (12, 13). It was also qualitatively different from cimetidine in that it did not inhibit hepatic cytochrome P450 or block androgen receptors. Ranitidine was marketed in 1981, and 10 years later it was the best-selling pharmaceutical product in the world.

Figure 2. Sir David Jack with his wife, Lydia, on the occasion of his receiving an honorary DSc at the University of Glasgow in 2000. (Copyright © The Scotsman Publ. Ltd; reproduced with permission.) (Online version in colour.)

Products derived from 5-hydroxytryptamine

After the success of salbutamol and beclamethasone dipropionate, David Jack encouraged work on the identification of subtypes of receptors for extracellular physiological mediators, because selective agonists and antagonists of these might be useful as medicines. The project on 5-hydroxytryptamine (5-HT) was very successful in that two important new kinds of medicines, ondansetron and sumatriptan, were invented.

Ondansetron was a specific antagonist of 5-HT_3 receptors involved in those reflexes which mediate nausea and vomiting. Normally these vomiting reflexes are protective but they become hyperactive during cancer chemotherapy, causing great distress to patients. Ondansetron was an effective antiemetic in such patients and greatly improved their tolerance of chemotherapy. It was marketed in 1990.

Sumatriptan was the first selective 5-HT_{1D} receptor antagonist to treat migraine. It proved to be extremely effective in controlling attacks of migraine, probably by mimicking the constrictive action of 5-HT on cerebral vessels (14, 15).

Conclusion

It is interesting to note that two of the greatest drug discoverers the world has known, David Jack and James Black, were born in the same year (1924) in the same part of West Fife, came from similar family backgrounds and died within a year of each other, in 2011 and 2010 respectively. The contribution that each made to the health of mankind in the fields of respiratory, gastrointestinal and cardiovascular disease is immeasurable.

The enthusiasm that David Jack showed for science has been the catalyst for the work of many others, both in industry and in academia. His logical and systematic approach to drug discovery and development described above has been the inspiration to generations of basic and clinical scientists. Colleagues, both senior and junior, remember him with respect and also affection. The high standards that he expected from others were a reflection of his own.

In all this he was supported by his wife and co-graduand, Lydia (figure 2), and his two daughters.

MEMBERSHIP, AWARDS AND HONOURS

Learned societies

1949 Fellow of the Royal Pharmaceutical Society
1959 Fellow of the Royal Society of Chemistry
1963 Member of the Society for Medicines Research
1965 Fellow of the Institute of Biology
1967 Member of the British Pharmacological Society
1978 Fellow of the Royal Society of Edinburgh
1990 Honorary Member of the British Pharmacological Society
1992 Fellow of the Royal Society
2004 Fellow of the British Pharmacological Society

Awards and honours

1969 Harrison Medal of the Royal Pharmaceutical Society
1980 Medicinal Chemistry Medal of the Royal Chemical Society
1985 The Award for Drug Discovery of the Society for Drug Research
1989 Lilly Medal of the British Pharmacological Society
1992 Mullard Medal of the Royal Society
1993 Knight Bachelor for services to the British pharmaceutical industry
1995 Host–Madsen Medal of the International Pharmaceutical Federation
1996 Galen Medal of the Society of Apothecaries of London
1999 Fellow of King's College, London
2006 Hanbury Memorial Award of the Royal Pharmaceutical Society of Great Britain
      Royal Medal of the Royal Society of Edinburgh

Honorary degrees

1982 DSc, University of Strathclyde
1986 DSc, University of Bath
1987 DSc, Council for Academic Awards
1991 DL, University of Dundee
1996 DSc, University of Liverpool
1999 DSc, University of London
2000 DSc, University of Glasgow

ACKNOWLEDGEMENTS

Many of the recollections above resulted from discussions with David Jack, who provided me with the factual details for this memoir. Five years before he died, he invited me to write this memoir at the appropriate time, and it has been a great honour to do so. I am also grateful to Lydia, his wife, and Moira and Norma for their contributions.

The frontispiece photograph was taken in 1992 on his election to the Fellowship. Copyright © The Royal Society.

REFERENCES TO OTHER AUTHORS

Black, J. W., Duncan, W. A., Durant, C. J., Ganellin, C. R. & Parsons, E. M. 1972 Definition and antagonism of histamine-H$_2$ receptors. *Nature* **236**, 385–390.

Lands, A. M., Arnold, A., McAuliff, J. P., Ludvena, F. P. & Brown, T. G. 1967 Differentiation of receptor systems activated by sympathetic amines. *Nature* **214**, 597–598.

BIBLIOGRAPHY

The following publications are those referred to directly in the text. A full bibliography is available as electronic supplementary material at http://dx.doi.org/10.1098/rsbm.2014.0006 or via http://rsbm.royalsocietypublishing.org.

(1)   1957   (With G. Sutno) British Patent 876,575.

(2)   1959   A new synthesis for 1-aminohydantoin and nitrofurantoin. *J. Pharm. Pharmacol.* **11**, 108T–114T.

(3)   1961   The synthesis and *in vitro* antibacterial activity of some new nitrofuran derivatives. *J. Med. Pharmaceut. Chem.* **3**, 253–263.

(4)   1968   (With D. Hartley, L. H. C. Lunts & A. C. Ritchie) New class of selective stimulants of β-adrenergic receptors. *Nature* **219**, 861–862.

(5)   (With R. T. Brittain, J. B. Farmer, L. E. Martin & W. T. Simpson) α-[(*t*-Butylamino)methyl]-4-hydroxy-*m*-xylene-α^1,α^3-diol (AH.3365): a selective β-adrenergic stimulant. *Nature* **219**, 862–863.

(6)   1969   (With V. A. Cullum, J. B. Farmer & G. P. Levy) Salbutamol: a new, selective β-adrenoceptive receptor stimulant. *Br. J. Pharmacol.* **35**, 141–151.

(7)   1970   (With R. T. Brittain & A. C. Ritchie) Recent β-adrenoceptor stimulants. In *Advances in drug research*, vol. 5 (ed. N. J. Harper & A. B. Simmonds), pp. 197–253. London: Academic Press.

(8)   (With D. T. Collin, D. Hartley, L. H. C. Lunts, J. C. Press, A. C. Ritchie & P. Toon) Saligenin analogs of sympathomimetic catecholamines. *J. Med. Chem.* **13**, 674–680.

(9)   Recent β-adrenoceptor stimulants and the nature of β-adrenoreceptors. *Pharm. J.* **205**, 237–240.

(10)   1973   Selectively acting β-adrenoceptor stimulants in asthma. In *Asthma: physiology, immunopharmacology and treatment* (ed. F. K. Austen & L. M. Lichtenstein), pp. 251–266. New York: Academic Press.

(11)   (With D. M. Harris, L. E. Martin & C. Harrison) The effect of oral and inhaled beclomethasone dipropionate on adrenal function. *Clin. Exp. Allergy* **3**, 243–248.

(12)   1979   (With J. Bradshaw, R. T. Brittain, J. W. Clitherow, M. J. Daly, B. J. Price & R. Stables) Ranitidine (AH 19065): a new potent, selective histamine H$_2$-receptor antagonist. *Br. J. Pharmacol.* **66**, 464P.

(13)   1981   (With R. T. Brittain & B. J. Price) Recent developments in histamine H$_2$-antagonists. *Trends Pharmacol. Sci.* **2**, 310–313.

(14)   1987   (With R. T. Brittain, A. Butler, I. H. Coates, D. H. Fortune, R. Hagan, J. M. Hill, D. C. Humber, P. P. A. Humphrey, S. J. Ireland, C. C. Jordan, A. Oxford, D. W. Straughan & M. B. Tyers) GR38032F, a novel selective 5-HT$_3$ receptor antagonist. *Br. J. Pharmacol.* **90**, 87P.

(15)   (With P. P. A. Humphrey, W. Feniuk, M. J. Perren, A. W. Oxford, I. H. Coates, D. Butina & R. T. Brittain) GR43175, a selective agonist for functional 5-HT$_1$-like receptors in dog saphenous vein. *Br. J. Pharmacol.* **92**, 616P.

(16)   1991   (With D. I. Ball, R. T. Brittain, R. A. Coleman, L. H. Denyer, M. Johnson, L. H. C. Lunts, A. T. Nials, K. E. Sheldrick & I. F. Skidmore) Salmeterol, a novel, long-acting β$_2$-adrenoceptor agonist: characterization of pharmacological activity *in vitro* and *in vivo*. *Br. J. Pharmacol.* **104**, 665–671.

WILLIAM JOHNSON FRENG

20 April 1922 — 13 June 2010

Biogr. Mems Fell. R. Soc. **60**, 261–275 (2014)

Wm Johnson

WILLIAM JOHNSON FRENG

20 April 1922 — 13 June 2010

Elected FRS 1982

BY S. R. REID FRENG FRSE

2 Waters Reach, Poynton, Stockport, Cheshire SK12 1XT, UK

Professor William (Bill) Johnson, engineer, educator and research scientist, died peacefully on 13 June 2010, aged 88 years. His illustrious academic career spanned more than 50 years, during which time he published more than 400 papers and wrote eight books. His primary speciality within applied mechanics was the applications of plasticity theory to manufacturing processes and to impact mechanics, to both of which he contributed well-received text books. However, he also had a long-established passion for the history of science and technology. His research and publications also included engineering aspects of sports, medicine, history and literature. He engaged students with an exciting style of teaching, engendering enthusiasm for the subject at a time when, primarily, only chalk and blackboard were available. He was also an inspirational research collaborator. Many students and colleagues who had their initial training under his guidance have been appointed to chairs throughout the world.

EARLY LIFE

His life is described in his candid autobiography entitled *Record and services, satisfactory* published in 2003 by the Memoir Club (15)*, the title deriving from a War Office letter regarding his military service. A copy of this book is in the library of the Royal Society.

Bill was born in 1922 to James and Elizabeth Johnson in Lower Openshaw, a working-class district of Manchester. James was a labourer and later a foreman in the local wire works. Bill completed his secondary education at Manchester Central Grammar School; it was there that he first met Heather Thornber. She was in the girls' school and he in the segregated boys' school, though both schools were on the same site.

At that time, Central Grammar School was located in Whitworth Street, across the road from the Manchester College of Technology (MCoT), then the Faculty of Technology of the

---

* Numbers in this form refer to the bibliography at the end of the text.

University of Manchester. Later, MCoT was to evolve into the University of Manchester Institute of Science and Technology (UMIST), a separate independent university, and in 2004 to merge into the enhanced University of Manchester. MCoT had its own charter, and Bill enrolled there and graduated in 1943 with a BTech (mechanical engineering) degree; he returned 20 years later as a professor.

After graduating, Bill served in Italy with the Royal Electrical and Mechanical Engineers. It was during this time that he developed his lifelong love for all things Italian, notably opera, ballet, architecture and ice cream! This was a significant formative period in his life.

After his military service, from 1948 to 1950 Bill worked in the Civil Service in an Assistant Principal Administrative Grade; however, his heart remained with engineering and so he combined work with studying as a part-time postgraduate student in the history and philosophy of science at University College London and in 1948 taking an external degree in mathematics at London University. This typifies the breadth of education and interests that formed the foundation to a remarkable career.

Bill married Heather in 1946. She was a part-time writer and poet, Bill's bedrock and partner in every sense of the word; she died on 18 October 2004 in St Austell, Cornwall. Bill is survived by their five children, eleven grandchildren and two great-grandchildren.

ACADEMIC CAREER

Northampton Polytechnic and Sheffield

Feeling a square peg in a round hole at the Civil Service, Bill took up a lectureship at Northampton Polytechnic (now City University, London) in 1950. This was a demanding role involving 21 contact hours per week in all mechanical engineering subjects; classes could be 60 or 70 strong. This work was to stand him in good stead. In 1952 he moved to the Mechanical Engineering Department at Sheffield University, researching metal forming under the encouragement of Professor H. W. Swift—the field in which Bill would establish his international reputation. In two papers published in 1955 (1, 2) he acknowledged the permission of the British Iron and Steel Association (BISRA), based in Sheffield, to publish the contents of two reports written by himself. This was presumably a consequence or their support.

It was in Sheffield that he first made contact with the work of Rodney Hill (FRS 1961), primarily through the publication of Hill's classic book, *The mathematical theory of plasticity*, which had been published in 1950, and through Rodney's early work with Green (Green & Hill 1952).

Manchester/UMIST

After four years at Sheffield, Bill was appointed in 1956 to the staff of the Engineering Department of Manchester University, in the Simon Engineering Building, under the headship of Professor Jack Diamond. Although now publishing at a rate of six papers per year, he decided not to pursue a PhD; instead, he acquired a DSc from Manchester University in 1960. The up-and-coming Bill (aged 38 years) was appointed in 1960 to the Chair of Mechanical Engineering at the (then) Manchester College of Science and Technology ('Tech), which was to become UMIST. He succeeded Professor Henry Wright-Baker, famous for unwrapping the Dead Sea scrolls from Qumran.

Encouraged by the Principal, Lord Bowden, Bill reconfigured the Mechanical Engineering Department into a broad, nationally—indeed, internationally—recognized department with both a research profile and a recognized teaching capability. He built up the research ethos in the department, which grew through the introduction by Bill of a set of divisions to produce a comprehensive coverage of the subject.

While the initial Head of Department, Bill also headed the Applied Mechanics Division; he was also responsible for the appointment of two other new professors, Roland Benson to head the Thermo-Fluid Mechanics Division and, somewhat unconventionally, Franz Koenigsberger to head a Machine Tools Division. The Department was plainly designed to provide a comprehensive academic support for British industry.

In the Applied Mechanics Division he assembled a formidable capability in experimental and theoretical solid mechanics. This combination of theory and experiment/testing was the hallmark of much of his research.

Over the period 1960–79 he wrote several books, for example *Plasticity for mechanical engineers* (3) in 1962 (later to become *Engineering plasticity* (8) in 1973) with Peter Mellor, whom he had first met in Sheffield. There then followed *Impact strength of materials* (6) in 1972. These remain classics, as well-referenced engineering reference texts in solid mechanics. These books are in contrast with, but in a supportive and complementary way, the more overtly mathematical texts of Hill, and with W. Goldsmith's *Impact* (Goldsmith 1960).

Never one for limiting his horizons, he was also instrumental in setting up a History of Science and Technology Department and a Medical Engineering Unit in the college.

Bill's other major achievement was the establishment of *International Journal of Mechanical Sciences* (*IJMS*) in 1960 and *International Journal of Impact Engineering* (*IJIE*) in 1983. Both of these journals contributed to the growing international research profile of the college and, indeed, of Manchester.

IJMS was first published by Pergamon Press under the ownership of Robert Maxwell, for whom Bill had a great respect, probably due to their common military background during World War II.

Cambridge and retirement

In 1975 Bill, to the surprise and some consternation of his colleagues, particularly in the Applied Mechanics Division, was elected to the Chair of Mechanics at Cambridge University. There he was heavily involved in starting the Production Engineering Tripos, acting as its Director. This heralded the official embracing of manufacturing engineering at undergraduate level at both Cambridge and Oxford. His involvement in manufacturing clearly stemmed from his own interest in plasticity and his earlier establishment of the Machine Tools Division in Mechanical Engineering in UMIST. It was clear to me as a colleague of his in Cambridge from 1976 that, notwithstanding Bill's success in broadening the engineering perspective of Cambridge into manufacturing, he never really integrated totally there.

Having gained international recognition and with the *imprimatur* of the Chair of Mechanics in Cambridge, he was elected a Fellow of the Royal Society in 1981, much to the delight of family and friends. The citation on his election is as follows:

Distinguished for basic studies of the mechanics of metal forming and for pioneering investigations of novel technological processes. Johnson's 230 papers and five books have established an international reputation in metal-working theory and design. His experimental work is imaginative and wide-ranging, and is supported by effective mathematical calculations. He has made substantial contributions to the fundamental understanding of metal flow in extrusion, forging, deep-drawing, blanking, and machining processes. In recent years he has systematically explored difficult and hazardous techniques of explosive forming and cutting. His latest ventures are in speculative fields such as ring-rolling, rotary forging, bubble-casting, electro-magnetic and magneto-hydraulic shaping, and energy-absorption devices. Johnson is the founder-editor of the International Journal of Mechanical Sciences, and has served as a consultant to many companies and government bodies. He has been for many years the inspiring leader of an extremely active and productive group of research engineers.

He had an interesting mix of supporters. The proposer and seconder were Sir Hugh Ford and Rodney Hill; other signatories were D. W. Holder, D. T. N. Williamson, Sir William Hawthorne, R. N. Haszeldine, E. H. Mansfield, J. H. (now Sir John) Horlock, W. H. Wittrick, A. R. Collar, Sir Bernard Crossland, Sir Frederic Williams, G. Gee and M. F. Ashby.

I believe that the account of Bill's research that follows underpins this citation of over 30 years ago.

Bill was elected to the Royal Academy of Engineering in 1983.

He retired from British university life in 1982, after which he and Heather travelled the world. In 1984 he spent several months at Purdue University, Indiana, where he was a Distinguished Visiting Professor. He then retired back to the UK, first in St Austell in Cornwall and then, after Heather's death in 2004, to Cambridge: he returned to Hathersage in his beloved Derbyshire in 2009, where he died.

RESEARCH

Engineering plasticity and manufacturing processes

Bill Johnson had wide research interests, principally in the field of plasticity, concerning the permanent deformation of material beyond the elastic (recoverable) limit, which is particularly relevant in manufacturing processes. These interests were initially focused on metal-forming plasticity, in which he has been acknowledged as a prime contributor. This view is supported by the success of his very popular academic textbooks with Peter Mellor (3, 8) and his more specialized slip-line field texts with Jim Haddow and Bob Sowerby (5) and with Hideaki Kudo (4). Some brief examples of his studies in plasticity are given in figure 1.

Figure 1 summarizes the essence of his research ethos as described in the Royal Society citation above, even from an early stage with a mix of experimentation and calculation. This is what can truly be described as the 'Johnson method'. These early studies concerned the extrusion of a cylinder to produce a longer one of a reduced diameter. This was an early study into the essence of wire and sheet drawing, a basic industrial manufacturing process. Technically this was directed to an investigation of the forces involved and the internal effect on the material resulting from this permanent (that is, plastic) distortion.

This is an area that both Bill and Rodney Hill explored. Both published some of their early work in the early volumes of Hill's new *Journal of the Mechanics and Physics of Solids* (*JMPS*); see, for example, Green & Hill (1952) and (1, 2).

Bill had a long-term acquaintanceship with Hill, whose work he first encountered in Sheffield, although Hill had already moved to Bristol when Bill arrived there. They were both early proponents of plasticity theory (the understanding and modelling of the permanent deformation of materials, particularly steel, in manufacturing processes) in the UK, Rodney from the mathematical perspective and Bill from the much more pragmatic and manufacturing design perspective.

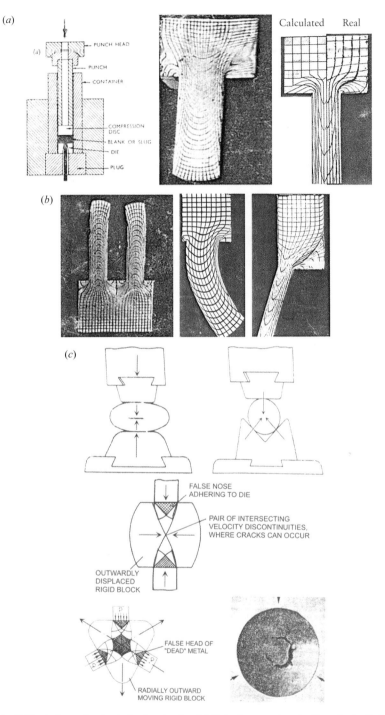

Figure 1. (*a*, *b*) Illustrations of early studies in extrusion. (*a*) Extrusion experiment with scribed cylindrical specimens. (*b*) Extrusion of thick sheets, showing influence of orifice location. (*c*) Illustration of the use of slip-line field theory and upper-bound methods. (From (15), pp. 242, 243 and 167, respectively.)

As an aside, in 1949 Hill, after taking a PhD at Cambridge with a thesis entitled *Theoretical studies of the plastic deformation of metals*, had moved to Sheffield to head a new section in the Metal Flow Research Laboratory at BISRA. The publication of *The mathematical theory of plasticity* (Hill 1950) in the following year established him as a leading authority in the field. In 1950 Hill moved to Bristol University to take up a three-year research fellowship in the departments of Physics and Mathematics, and in 1952 he founded *JMPS*, published by Pergamon Press as a forum for applied mathematics linked with experimentation in engineering science. Clearly this journal was an attraction to Bill in publishing his own research work, and Bill followed Rodney with the founding of *IJMS* in 1960. *IJMS* had a broader scope than *JMPS*, though including the mechanical engineering treatment of plasticity as a major topic. Interestingly, the name for *IJMS* arose from Bill's appreciation and recognition of the Mechanical Sciences Tripos in Cambridge.

The association between Bill and Rodney continued when the latter was appointed Professor of Applied Mathematics in Nottingham and when he moved to become a University Reader in the Department of Applied Mathematics and Theoretical Physics, Cambridge; later, Rodney was appointed to a personal chair there. Although in regular contact over the years, Bill and Rodney resumed a closer association when Bill moved to Cambridge in 1975.

The two were very different characters: Bill was clearly engineering oriented, although with a mathematical string to his bow, and Rodney was the more punctilious applied mathematician responsible for identifying and developing several major advances in continuum mechanics. To an observer they seemed very different characters who related well, possibly as a result of their commitment to their similar technical interests in plasticity.

According to (15) (p. 145), slip-line field theory was their common interest. Some of Bill's early works, as noted above, were published in BISRA reports and others in Hill's new *JMPS*. Bill in (15) generously acknowledges that he learned much in the early days of his research from Hill's comments and advice on his early draft submissions. Briefly, slip-line field theory stems mathematically from a solution of the governing partial differential equations (which are hyperbolic) for plane-strain plastic deformation of a rigid, perfectly plastic (that is, with no strain hardening) material. Such a material has a constant yield stress, the stress at which plastic or permanent deformation begins. This idealization is used extensively as a simplification for material behaviour beyond the elastic (recoverable) range. The use of this material model is extensively described in the books by Hill and by Johnson & Mellor (3, 8). Mathematically, the method uses a solution technique for the equations governing plane plastic 'flow' called the 'method of characteristics'. This method leads to the formulation of equations that, in two dimensions, apply along particular lines, called α and β lines, that cover the region in question; the equations enable the non-uniform stresses throughout the region to be computed. There are many examples of its use in the literature, of which (1, 2) provide early examples.

To obtain a better understanding of the problem, Bill used observations of the distortion of a square grid stamped onto the central plane of an extruded cylinder using a single, central die (figure 1*a*), or alternatively a pair of symmetrical orifices or, indeed, an offset orifice (figure 1*b*); these result in different flow patterns, which have manufacturing implications.

Theoretical modelling of these types of process developed from simple methods into the use of slip-line fields (1, 2), which gave a more detailed account of the non-uniformity of both the stresses (internal loads) and strains (internal deformation); the latter is of prime interest to industrial applications, in which the possibility of internal cracks during the manufacture of a product is a concern. The use of slip-line field methods can produce very useful information,

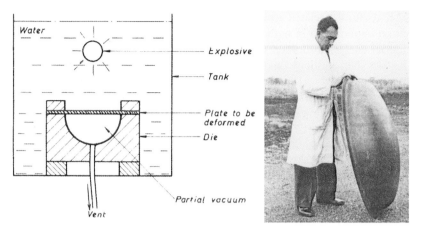

Figure 2. Explosive forming of a dished end-cap for a pressure vessel (15).

as exemplified in figure 1*c*. This method readily lent itself to graphical methods, which Bill and his students (such as Nawnit ('Neville') Chitkara) investigated extensively. In the main, this method has now been superseded by finite-element or other computational methods. Bill also used simplified, less accurate, techniques for studying problems of this kind, based on the upper-bound theorem of plasticity theory.

A mark of Bill's international influence on the subject of plasticity as a basis for manufacturing can be seen in his recognition by the inception in 1993 of the W. Johnson Gold Medal by the organizers of Advances in Materials and Processing Technologies (AMPT), an annual conference series for academics and industrialists. AMPT was founded in 1990 at Dublin City University, Ireland; AMPT conferences were held there in 1993, 1995, 1999 and 2003. Other conferences have been held in Portugal, Malaysia, Spain, Poland, the USA, Korea, Bahrain, Malaysia, Paris, Istanbul, Wollongong and Sydney; in 2013 the conference was held in Taipei, Taiwan.

The AMPT conference series provides a forum for academics, researchers and practising engineers to meet and exchange innovative ideas and information on all aspects of material processing technologies. Following Bill's general ethos, the award of the medal is 'to recognize and appreciate distinguished academic achievements', and is made to 'a most distinguished academic in materials processing research and teaching'. Recipients of the medal since 1993 have been senior academics from the UK, Japan, Poland, South Korea, Saudi Arabia, Singapore, Turkey, France and Australia.

Explosive metal forming

Figure 2 indicates an early study at Manchester College of Technology on the explosive forming of a dished end-cap, roughly 4 feet in diameter, for a pressure vessel. Many such tests were performed with Frank (now Professor) Travis in a quarry near Macclesfield, about which there were countless interesting stories!

Impact mechanics

As noted above, Bill's interest in methods of metal forming and manufacture led him to investigate the constructive use of explosive energy release for metal forming, of which figure 2 is one of many examples.

This led him into the related area of impact mechanics and engineering, which also has clear structural implications in terms of topics such as ballistics and penetration mechanics (13) and impact energy absorption (11); these references are two of his most highly cited papers. The fact that plasticity, and other forms of inelastic behaviour, have a dominant effect in the dynamic loading (impact and blast loading) of structures and materials generally became a major interest of Bill in the 1970s and led to Bill's writing the book *Impact strength of materials* (6). This title reveals Bill's bias towards applications rather than to the mathematical foundations of the subject.

Penetration mechanics

As an example of Bill's broader work on impact mechanics, figure 3 shows some work in penetration mechanics (12), which is concerned with the ballistic interaction between a projectile and a target. Bill and his group have published many papers, some being reproduced in *Impact strength of materials* (6). Figure 3 (12) shows one of several examples of how Bill informed the mechanics of very-high-velocity impact by the novel use of Plasticine as a model material. As shown in Figure 3*a*, *b*, this was achieved in a laboratory environment. Similarity between specimens of Plasticine and metal was achieved by the use of the non-dimensional parameter $\rho V^2/Y$, sometimes termed the Johnson damage number. Here, ρ, V and Y are respectively the density, impact velocity and yield stress of the projectile material. In the appropriate regime of this parameter, materials can display even fluid-like behaviour on impact.

This example shows the 'inversion' of a cylindrical 'long rod' projectile on penetration, a phenomenon achieved by using a very simple device to fire a Plasticine projectile into a Plasticine target at a velocity of a few hundred metres per second. This was Bill's basic idea. The set-up judiciously uses the properties of Plasticine as encapsulated in the Johnson damage number to simulate, in essence, phenomena similar to that produced by a metal (high-density) projectile striking a thick metal target at speeds of several thousand metres per second, requiring a gas gun or similar device.

The outline mechanism, in which the long rod projectile's material properties at high impact velocity become more like a fluid jet, is shown in Figure 3*c* alongside photographs of real tests of penetration into steel by tungsten-based projectiles with a length:diameter ratio of 10:1, fired at speeds in excess of 1500 m s^{-1} (compare this with the few hundred metres per second for the Plasticine cylinder). Several details, such as the increased diameter of the resulting cavity and the clear inversion of the projectile, are obvious in the simple Plasticine experiments (12). Long-rod penetrators are in current use by the military. This experiment also demonstrates the 'mushrooming' of the projectile at lower impact velocities and the transition into jetting behaviour.

Impact energy absorption

Another area of impact mechanics to which Bill contributed was impact energy absorption. This is concerned with the design and modelling of structures to absorb kinetic energy by means of dissipation in large structural plastic deformation. Figure 4 shows stages in energy absorption by a ring or tube. This scheme led to much research by Bill and his collaborators (11).

This area of study required Bill's movement into the field of structural plasticity, involving the plastic deformation of elements such as beams, plates and shells, usually regarded as the province of civil engineers. However, the interest here is in the displacement or crushing behaviour of the structure.

Many other such studies are contained in Bill's publications.

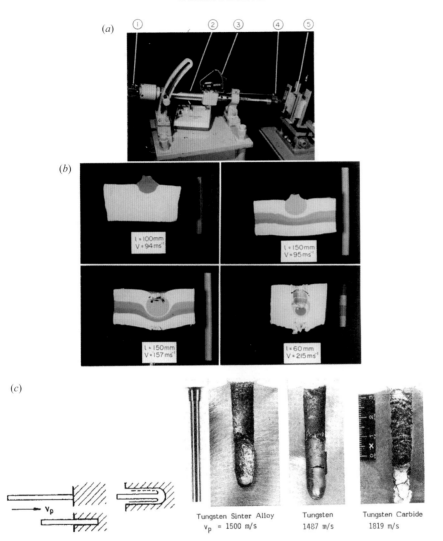

Figure 3. (*a*, *b*) Experimental arrangement using Plasticine for modelling penetration tests. Sequence of behaviours at increasing impact velocity up to inversion of the projectile. (From (12); © Crown Copyright, Ministry of Defence [Procurement Executive].) (*c*) High-velocity penetration mechanism for inversion and actual high-velocity penetration for penetration of a long tungsten rod into a steel target. (From Zukas (1990).)

Sport

In addition to his two major fields of study—the mechanics of plasticity and impact—Bill was a prolific writer on many topics. These had a mechanics root and often involved the application of his well-tried formula of combined experiment and mathematical modelling.

One example in which his writing reflected his range of interests was sport, and in particular football. His paper 'The impact, rebound and flight of a well inflated pellicle as exemplified in Association Football' (7) covered the mechanics of bouncing, heading and kicking a football. The stated aims of the paper were typical of Bill's approach to engineering: 'to furnish engineering science teachers with attractive examples which are close to students' interests' and 'to

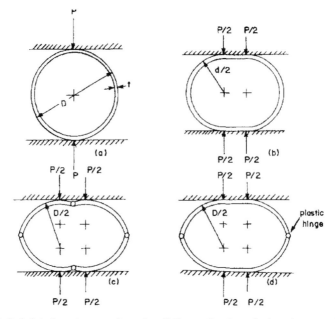

Figure 4. Prelude to impact energy absorption. Collapse of a tube under lateral compression (10).

Figure 5. Measurement of the Gadd severity index when heading a football (9).

enrich the appreciation of the game of football'. This was clearly a success because, although it was first presented in 1973, it remains one of the most accessed papers of the Manchester Association of Engineers.

At a more technical level, figure 5 illustrates the associated investigation into the mechanics associated with heading a football by measuring the acceleration pulse delivered to the head while heading a football, and the calculation of the Gadd severity index, used in assessing the

Figure 6. Three editors at Fort St David, Cuddalore, India. From left to right: Professor N. Jones (Editor-in-Chief, *IJIE*), Professor W. Johnson (founding Editor-in-Chief) and Professor S. R. Reid (Editor-in-Chief, *IJMS*). (From (15).)

effect on the driver of a car in an impact. In football, such impacts to the head were thought possibly to be responsible for generating subsequent brain damage in professional footballers in the 1950s. In the photograph, the 'dummy' was me! Fortunately the work showed that single blows of this type when heading a football were not threatening.

Further sport-orientated papers covered pole vaulting, rock climbing and head injuries in boxing.

History of science and technology

Bill Johnson never lost his early interest in the History of science and technology, which he pursued more vigorously towards the end of his career, particularly after his election to the Royal Society. He wrote papers about various eminent people; examples are Voltaire and Edward Gibbon FRS. Perhaps as a result of his interest in military mechanics, he paid special attention to Benjamin Robins FRS (14), who died in 1751 at Fort St David near Cuddalore in East India. Bill's influence resulted in his arranging for himself, Professor Norman Jones and me to share in a visit to several places key to the Robins story in a memorable post-conference journey, commemorated in figure 6.

PERSONAL REFLECTIONS

Having first seen Bill Johnson when I was a PhD student in the Department of Mathematics at the University of Manchester, attending a seminar organized by Bill at UMIST, he and I became properly acquainted when I was appointed to a lectureship in mechanical engineering there in 1970. We became senior and (very) junior colleagues then, and later good friends for the rest of his life.

Perhaps because of our similar social backgrounds, he became a trusted confidant and mentor throughout my career, both in teaching and in research, and particularly with our involvement as editors of *IJMS*, of which he was the founding editor. Bill performed his duties as editor with the strong support of Heather and me, as his successor, with Sue (my wife) as our editorial secretaries, duties that were superseded by the current electronic editorial system. Our paths first crossed professionally as colleagues at UMIST (the demise of which he deeply regretted); we then both moved to Cambridge, Bill in 1975 and I in 1976. I then moved on to Aberdeen in 1980, back to UMIST in 1985, thence to Manchester University after the merger in 2004. In 2006 I returned to Aberdeen, all the time retaining my link with Bill, mainly by telephone.

Bill's enthusiasm and drive were infectious, characterized by his aphorism that he would 'sooner write the first paper on a topic than the last'. This led him to publish a prolific number of papers and to open up several areas for investigation such as metal-forming plasticity and impact engineering. This attracted both admiration and, from some quarters, criticism; however, no one did or could criticize his commitment and his contributions to the broad field of mechanics. I believe that he recruited me in 1970 as someone with a mathematical background (first as a mathematics undergraduate in the University of Manchester, then completing a PhD there under the supervision of David Bland in elastic wave propagation up to 1969), which led me, after 1970, into impact mechanics/engineering and ultimately led Bill to found *IJIE*, the sister journal to *IJMS*.

As noted in the introduction, several academics from across the world owe their start in their academic careers to their interaction with Bill, and the tributes in the two 'Johnson' journals *International Journal of Mechanical Sciences*, vol. 53, pp. 155–163 (2011) and *International Journal of Impact Engineering*, vol. 38, pp. 265–274 (2011), are most appropriate.

I trust that these two academic organs, *IJMS* and *IJIE*, will remain as worthy and lasting testimonies to Bill's work and influence.

Bill Johnson's life can certainly be summarized by amendment of the title of his autobiography: 'Record and services, *more than* satisfactory'.

HONOURS AND AWARDS

1965	Bernard Hall Prize, Institution of Mechanical Engineers
1966	Bernard Hall Prize, Institution of Mechanical Engineers
1969	Commendation for services in mechanics by the US Department of the Army
1972	James Clayton Fund Prize, Institution of Mechanical Engineers
1974	President and Honorary Member, Manchester and Salford Medical Engineering Club
1975	President and Honorary Member, Manchester Association of Engineers
	Honorary Member, Institute of Diagnostic Engineers
	Honorary Member, Japan Society for Technology of Plasticity
1976	DTech (*honoris causa*), University of Bradford
1977	James Clayton Fund Prize, Institution of Mechanical Engineers
1980	Safety in Mechanical Engineering Prize, Institution of Mechanical Engineers
1982	Fellow of the Royal Society of London
	Fellow of University College, London
	Foreign Member of the Academy of Athens
1983	Fellow of the Royal Academy of Engineering
1986	DEng (*honoris causa*), University of Sheffield
1991	Safety in Mechanical Engineering Prize, Institution of Mechanical Engineers

1993 Foreign Member of the Russian Academy of Sciences (Urals Branch)
First recipient of the AMPT Johnson Gold Medal
1995 DEng (*honoris causa*), University of Manchester Institute of Science and Technology
1999 Fellow of the Indian National Academy of Engineering

ACKNOWLEDGEMENT

The frontispiece photograph was taken in 2002 and is copyright © The Royal Society.

REFERENCES TO OTHER AUTHORS

Goldsmith, W. 1960 *Impact*. London: Edward Arnold.
Green, A. P. & Hill, R. 1952 Calculations on the influence of friction and die geometry in sheet drawing. *J. Mech. Phys. Solids* **1**, 31–36.
Hill, R. 1950 *The mathematical theory of plasticity*. Oxford: Clarendon Press.
Zukas, J. A. 1990 *High velocity impact dynamics*, ch. 5. New York: John Wiley & Sons.

BIBLIOGRAPHY

The following publications are those referred to directly in the text. A full bibliography is available as electronic supplementary material at http://dx.doi.org/10.1098/rsbm.2014.0001 or via http://rsbm.royalsocietypublishing.org.

(1) 1955 Extrusion through wedge-shaped dies. Part I. *J. Mech. Phys. Solids* **3**, 218–223.
(2) Extrusion through wedge-shaped dies. Part II. *J. Mech. Phys. Solids* **3**, 224–230.
(3) 1962 (With P. B. Mellor) *Plasticity for mechanical engineers*. London: Van Nostrand Reinhold.
(4) (With H. Kudo) *The mechanics of metal extrusion*. Manchester University Press.
(5) 1970 (With J. B. Haddow & R. Sowerby) *Plane-strain slip-line fields: theory and bibliography*. London: Edward Arnold.
(6) 1972 *Impact strength of materials*. London: Edward Arnold.
(7) 1973 (With S. R. Reid & R. E. Trembaczowski-Ryder) The impact, rebound and flight of a well inflated pellicle as exemplified in Association Football. *Manchester Engr*, no. 5.
(8) (With P. B. Mellor) *Engineering plasticity*. London: Van Nostrand Reinhold. (Second edition published in 1983 by Ellis Horwood.)
(9) 1975 (With J. Skorecki) The Gadd Severity Index and measurement of acceleration when heading an Association Football. In *Proc. Int. Conf. on Biokinetics of Impacts, IRCOBI, Birmingham*, pp. 187–196. International Research Council on Biomechanics of Injury (IRCOBI).
(10) 1977 (With S. R. Reid & T. Yella Reddy) The compression of crossed layers of thin tubes. *Int. J. Mech. Sci.* **19**, 423–437.
(11) 1978 (With S. R. Reid) Metallic energy dissipating systems. *Appl. Mech. Rev.* **31**, 277–288.
(12) 1981 (With A. K. Sengupta, S. K. Ghosh & S. R. Reid) Mechanics of high speed impact at normal incidence between plasticine long rods and plates. *J. Mech. Phys. Solids* **29**, 413–445.
(13) 1996 (With G. G. Corbett & S. R. Reid) Impact loading of plates and shells by free-flying projectiles: a review. *Int. J. Impact Engng* **18**, 141–230.
(14) 2001 The Watts Academy, 1715–1750: Robins' probable involvements and opportunities. *Int. J. Impact Engng* **25**, 607–614.
(15) 2003 *Record and services, satisfactory*. Langley Park: The Memoir Club.

GEORGE BELLAMY MACKANESS

20 August 1922 — 4 March 2007

Biogr. Mems Fell. R. Soc. **60**, 277–298 (2014)

GEORGE BELLAMY MACKANESS

20 August 1922 — 4 March 2007

Elected FRS 1976

By Philip B. Carter

North Carolina State University, Raleigh, NC 27695-8401, USA

George Mackaness was an Australian immunologist, educated in Sydney, London and Oxford, who spent his professional career working in Australia and the USA. He is prominently recognized for his work elucidating the life history of the macrophage, the cell in animals so important in combating infection. Mackaness is credited with coining the term 'activated macrophage' to denote the enhanced abilities of a macrophage subset that he defined as particularly significant in controlling intracellular infections, of which tuberculosis (TB) is perhaps the most important. In collaboration with students and colleagues over many years, Mackaness built a body of work that better characterized the cellular immune response as complementary to the previously known humoral, or antibody, response and contributed to an understanding of the intercellular communications necessary in initiating and maintaining an effective immune response. In the end, he brought broad attention to the process by which blood monocytes gain increased destructive attributes as a necessary part of the immune response to intracellular infectious agents. Mackaness began his research career during the dawn of antibiotics and contributed importantly to the development of several novel antibiotics for the treatment of TB, among them isoniazid, which is still used to great effect. Less appreciated were his mid-career contributions to heart disease and his later role in bringing the first new class of therapeutics to clinical practice that changed and greatly improved the prevention and treatment of hypertension, stroke, kidney disease, heart attack and congestive heart failure.

Introduction

It was Sunday morning, 4 March 2007, while I was driving home from Cornell University after the celebration of the 75th birthday of Professor Douglas McGregor MD DPhil, when my mobile phone rang. The caller was George Mackaness's only child, Miles, to

http://dx.doi.org/10.1098/rsbm.2014.0017

Figure 1. George Mackaness as a child with his younger brother, James (left), *ca.* 1932, aged about 10 years. (Courtesy of the Mackaness family.)

say that his father had died that morning at the extended care facility near Charleston, South Carolina, where he had been living for almost a year. Miles expected me, his father's associate and friend of almost 40 years, to inform others that the life story of one of the most influential immunologists of the twentieth century had ended. A greatly respected scientist, extraordinary experimentalist, professor, author, public speaker, and administrator, George Mackaness was also known as a refined and caring gentleman in every sense of the word.

Only four days later (reports in her native Sydney state five days because of the International Date Line), Gwynneth ('Gwyn') Mackaness, George's wife of more than 61 years, passed away in the same extended care facility as George. Together they had formed a wonderful, mutually supportive team. There was never a presentation or manuscript by Mackaness that did not pass his wife's scrutiny before being shared publicly; that was the level of respect he had for Gwyn's exceptional command of the English language. It also undoubtedly contributed to the reputation that Mackaness had as a public speaker, as one who could present complex new concepts with such clarity that even those outside his field could grasp the points on a single pass.

What follows is a short synopsis of the person and the scientist who was George Mackaness FRS, with a perspective on the factors that contributed to his success in advancing the understanding of immune responses to infectious diseases and cancer, the work that led to discoveries in the antibiotic age, and his achievements as an administrator.

FORMATIVE YEARS

George Bellamy Mackaness was born and raised in Sydney, Australia (figure 1); he was the third child of James Vincent Mackaness and Eleanor Frances Bellamy Mackaness. As he grew to adulthood, it was important to use his middle name or initial to distinguish him from his uncle, George Mackaness OBE DSc (hon., Sydney), a respected Australian educator, author and historian. Two of his father's sisters were also recognized scholars who became teachers in the local girls' high school, but his father did not seem inclined towards academic pursuits: he established a large grocery business on Sussex Street in central Sydney. Although his extended family may have been an important influence on his inclination towards academics, it is not clear when or why young George chose to pursue medicine and, ultimately, medical research. He attended local primary schools and the Fort Street Boys' High School, Sydney, founded in 1849 and considered the best selective high school in New South Wales. Mackaness was then accepted to study medicine at the University of Sydney.*

UNIVERSITY

Mackaness successfully completed the requirements for his MBBS degree† with honours in the Faculty of Medicine of the University of Sydney during the most tumultuous years of his life, the war years of the early 1940s (figure 2). It was during that time that he developed a close relationship with the person who would become his life partner, Gwynneth Patterson, but he would not consider marriage until he had fulfilled his goal of receiving his medical degree. Family members recount how Gwyn was not certain whether marriage was in the offing until the final grades were posted, such was Mackaness's anxiety and concern about failure. His anxiety, which he transferred to Gwyn, was unfounded as he ended up graduating with honours and he and Gwyn, who had been an Army nurse, were married in 1945. Mackaness served as a resident medical officer at Sydney Hospital for a year, and then did a second year as a resident pathologist at the Kanematsu Institute of Pathology at Sydney Hospital. He was Demonstrator in Pathology at the University of Sydney before heading to England for advanced study.

THE OXFORD EXPERIENCE

After the end of World War II, Mackaness travelled with Gwyn to England for the purpose of completing a Diploma in Clinical Pathology (DCP) at the University of London. This Mackaness did in a year, but he also took some time to travel to Oxford to meet the most distinguished Australian scientist of the day, Sir Howard (later Lord) Florey FRS, Professor of

---

* Information provided in the Mackaness obituary in the *Sydney Morning Herald* (http:www.smh.com.au) of 28 March 2007 by Donelle Wheeler, a relative, and in conversation on 10 June 2014 with Mackaness's niece, Caroline Mackaness, was most helpful in gathering this history.

† It is worth clarifying, because of misstatements in North American and European publications about Mackaness, that the MBBS (also written MB BS) degree of the time in the British university tradition was a Bachelor of Medicine, Bachelor of Surgery degree (in the last decade, the University of Sydney changed this to a graduate degree). The BS degree has been often misconstrued as the American Bachelor of Science (BSc in the British system).

Figure 2. George Mackaness as a university student, *ca.* 1942, aged about 20 years.
(Courtesy of the Mackaness family.)

Pathology. From its beginning, the new School of Pathology on South Parks Road in Oxford, established as the result of a bequest from the Sir William Dunn Trust (Sidebottom 2013), had an Australian influence: starting with Florey, each subsequent Professor of Pathology was Australian. The string was broken with the appointment of Professor Herman Waldmann (FRS 1990) from Cambridge in 1992 after the death of Professor Alan Williams FRS at the age of 46 years. Florey's international reputation was the result of his success, through collaboration with the talented chemist Ernst Chain (FRS 1949) in developing a fungal product, discovered by Alexander (later Sir Alexander) Fleming (FRS 1943) in the 1930s, as a clinically useful therapeutic in the treatment of bacterial infections. Fleming observed that bacterial culture plates contaminated by an airborne mould, *Penicillium notatum*, showed zones of inhibition of the bacterial colonies proximate to the mould growth. Actually, such an observation was not unique to the time; others had reported such inhibition in culture plates having a variety of contaminants. However, in what may be the first instance of what is now termed 'translational medicine', the Oxford group of Florey, Chain and colleagues focused on the isolation and purification of the active component of *Penicillium* to produce a medically important therapeutic to treat bacterial infections. In association with the US Department of Agriculture laboratory in the small town of Peoria, Illinois, experienced in fungal cultivation, the production of the drug called penicillin was scaled up to the point that it was available in time to treat wound infections as World War II was coming to an end. Because of penicillin,

Figure 3. George Mackaness as a DPhil student at Oxford University, *ca.* 1952, aged about 30 years.
(Courtesy of the Sir William Dunn School of Pathology, Oxford.)

for the first time in recorded history, combatant deaths resulting from wound infections such as gas gangrene were less than those attributed directly to wounds or trauma. For their work Florey (who later became a very effective President of the Royal Society), Chain and Fleming shared the 1945 Nobel Prize in Physiology or Medicine.

Mackaness was most intrigued by the excitement of the early antibiotic era and the pioneering work being done at Oxford, so it was not a difficult decision to accept an offer from Florey to do graduate work in his laboratory. Mackaness matriculated in 1948 at Lincoln College (figure 3), where Florey had an appointment. An English colleague and contemporary in the laboratory, who was to become a lifelong friend, was James (now Sir James) Gowans (FRS 1963). A couple of years later, these two were joined by another Australian, and future Regius Professor of Medicine, Henry (now Sir Henry) Harris (FRS 1968).

According to Dunn School lore, the three graduate students were to study the cells involved in the immune response to infection; the way in which Professor Florey divided up responsibilities in the study of anti-infection immunity among the students would seem extraordinarily simplistic in today's world. Supposedly, Florey told Gowans to study the lymphocyte, Mackaness was assigned the monocyte/macrophage, and Harris was given the neutrophil. Except for Harris, who ultimately went in a different direction, Gowans and Mackaness pursued their assignments with such enthusiasm and diligence that their names became virtually synonymous with the cell lineages they began studying as DPhil students.

In actual fact, Gowans initiated his lymphocyte studies, at the suggestion of Florey, in his postdoctoral year, 1953, after returning from the Pasteur Institute. Gowans's thesis topic was more in keeping with Florey's interest of the time, antibiotics, and was entitled 'The mode of action of antibiotics *in vivo*'.

Gowans and Mackaness became close and lasting friends, as did their spouses, with admiration for each other's abilities as scientists. Gowans particularly recalls how creative and adept Mackaness was in designing and executing experiments, that he 'was the star among the research students in the lab' (Sir James Gowans, personal communication, 2013). Florey, however, was notoriously parsimonious in his praise of graduate students and it is unlikely that Mackaness, who was very self-critical to begin with, would have suspected that his mentor, as Gowans relates, greatly admired him for his achievements. A former Dunn School student and future Mackaness colleague at the Trudeau Institute, Al Volkman, attests to the same. On a flight shared with Florey from Canberra to Sydney in the latter half of the 1960s, Volkman recalls how Florey expressed his high regard for Mackaness as a scientist and viewed him as a leader in his field (Alvin Volkman, personal communication, 2014).

As a graduate student, Mackaness's interests were somewhat divided between his study of monocytes and macrophages, and how they could phagocytose and kill *Mycobacterium tuberculosis*, and his lingering desire to search out better antibiotics. His thesis (3)* focused on the subject assigned by Florey, but a presentation on the 50th anniversary of the discovery of gramicidin by René Dubos betrays the amount of time he dedicated to the search for novel antibiotics (10). Although this was originally something of a sideline, Mackaness's work on the search for anti-tuberculous antibiotics and their mechanism of action was one of the two bases for his election to the Royal Society. The increased interest in antibiotics resulted from a timely visit to the Dunn School by Sir Frank Macfarlane Burnet FRS of the Walter and Eliza Hall Institute of Medical Research in Melbourne. Mackaness described his work using *Listeria monocytogenes* to generate large numbers of blood monocytes with the goal of isolating a factor that might enhance the response of such cells to microbial infection *in vivo*. On hearing this, Burnet disclosed that Neville Stanley, working in Perth, Western Australia, had already submitted a paper on just that subject. Florey soon suggested that Mackaness alter the focus of his studies, which Mackaness did by using the *in vitro* monocyte culture techniques he had already developed to study the intracellular and extracellular action of putative anti-tuberculous drugs. These drugs included micrococcin, *p*-aminosalicylic acid, streptomycin, terramycin, neomycin, viomycin, nisin and, the most exciting of all, isonicotinic acid hydrazide (isoniazid). The last of these, which was first synthesized in 1929 but was only in 1952 being tested for its anti-tuberculous activity, was found to be extraordinarily effective. Mackaness was among the very first to investigate the action of isoniazid on tubercle bacilli, as well as many of the other antibiotics mentioned; this work was published in two important papers in 1952 (1, 2). The real significance of this work was the use of the techniques that Mackaness had developed in pursuing the central problem of his thesis, the study of the life history of monocytes and macrophages, to demonstrate that, to be effective, anti-tuberculous drugs had to be active intracellularly in macrophages.

The year 1952 was one of prodigious output. Mackaness had begun writing his thesis just as isoniazid became available to him, causing him to put the thesis writing aside and publish the two papers referenced above. He did finish his thesis, defended it successfully and

---

* Numbers in this form refer to the bibliography at the end of the text.

received his DPhil in 1953. He spent a further year with Florey at the Dunn School before heading back to his native Australia and a position in the newly established John Curtin School of Medical Research.

THE JOHN CURTIN SCHOOL

The John Curtin School of Medical Research (JCSMR) was established as part of the Australian National University in Canberra in 1948. This was the result of a proposal attributed to the former Australian Prime Minister John Curtin who, in response to a Florey suggestion, wanted Australia to have its own centre for medical research that would be distinguished enough to keep Australia's best scientists at home. Australian universities did not grant PhD degrees before the JCSMR did so.

The history of the JCSMR is well documented thanks to the efforts of Frank J. Fenner FRS, one of the original JCSMR department heads as Professor of Microbiology, co-author David R. Curtis, appointed Professor of Neuropharmacology in 1966, and their colleagues (Fenner & Curtis 2001). Many of the planning meetings for the new school were held in Oxford (Fenner was at Cambridge at the time) and it is likely that George Mackaness, who was near the end of his thesis work and would spend an extra year with Florey as a research associate, would have been privy to the workings of the planning committee.

The plan for the school was to have Australia's distinguished son, Sir Howard Florey, return home from Oxford and lead the new endeavour. Early on, Florey showed considerable interest in and dedication to the project. Florey's plan was to recruit many of his students to help staff the Department of Experimental Pathology of the new school. He was successful only up to a point because even a native Australian would have found the Canberra of the day little more than 'brown field', a barren place of a few trees and Parliament buildings. One such native, the Grande Dame of Australian higher education, Dame Leonie Kramer, a future chancellor of the University of Sydney, was not enthused by the thought of moving to Canberra. She describes her view of husband Harry's decision to accept an appointment as Senior Research Fellow at the JCSMR in 1953, after receiving his DPhil at the Dunn School that year, in disparaging terms: 'I warned Harry that after Oxford Canberra would be something of a wasteland, but beggars couldn't be choosers' (Kramer 2012, p. 99). Even so, Harry Kramer could not refuse an offer from Sir Howard Florey, a member of his thesis committee, to be the first member of the Department of Experimental Pathology at the new school. Knowing that his colleague, Mackaness, would be joining him in Canberra a year later probably made it easier for Harry, a South African, to make the move. (George, Harry and Leonie all received their DPhil degrees in 1953, and their Oxford friendship only grew as they worked to establish the school in Canberra. A phone conversation facilitated by the author, between Mackaness and Dame Leonie during the latter's visit to Cornell University in June 1997, confirmed that the friendship remained very warm after four decades.)

Mackaness was actually appointed to staff before leaving Oxford, having been made an Australian National University Research Fellow in Experimental Pathology in July 1951 and then promoted to Senior Fellow, a tenured position, in July 1953. He left Oxford for Canberra in 1954, undoubtedly expecting Florey to be moving there soon afterwards, along with Henry Harris, whom Florey intended to appoint as Professor of Cytology (Fenner & Curtis 2001). Harris decided to remain in Oxford and ultimately succeeded Florey as the Professor of Pathology.

At age 32 years, Mackaness took up his position as the acting head of the Department of Experimental Pathology at the JCSMR (holding the chairmanship open for Florey), where he was soon joined by several distinguished, or soon to be distinguished, scientists in the fields of microbiology, immunology and pathology. Fenner reports that the four JCSMR professors (John Carew (later Sir John) Eccles FRS, the Professor of Physiology, Arnold Hughes ('Hugh') Ennor, the Professor of Biochemistry and later Dean, and Adrien Albert, the Professor of Medicinal Chemistry, and himself) and Mackaness were surprised and disappointed when Florey resigned as adviser in the latter half of 1955 (Fenner & Curtis 2001; see especially ch. 2 and p. 35). Florey had early decided to remain in Oxford and run the school from afar but ultimately took the decision to stay in Oxford. Sadly, Florey's biographer, Gwyn Macfarlane FRS, shed little light on Florey's 1955 decision to remain in Oxford (Macfarlane 1979, p. 373). The real reason may have been that Mrs Ethel Reed Florey and her husband, although native Australians, were disinclined to leave England for health reasons (Abraham 1971) as much as for concern over the anticipated spartan living conditions mentioned above. Florey's decision left the five department leaders having to decide how to proceed, and they ultimately agreed to continue with the plan in place.

The next five years were exciting times as the Australian National University grew in size and reputation, and the JCSMR along with it. The laboratories became well established and the research was moving in new directions and attracting graduate students. By the time that Mackaness left for the Rockefeller Institute on sabbatical leave in 1959 (see below), he had been promoted to Professorial Fellow (equivalent in status to Reader) in August 1958 and things were well under way at the JCSMR. Mackaness (figure 4) had already produced a large number of research papers—many, surprisingly, in the field of hypertension, the first evidence of his interest in a field that became more important to him late in his career.

Before Mackaness resigned his position at the JCSMR in December 1962 to accept a professorship in microbiology at the University of Adelaide, he submitted an unusually lengthy manuscript, the culmination of years of work, to *Journal of Experimental Medicine*. Robert Blanden, JCSMR scientist and a former Mackaness student, was able to provide a first-hand account of Mackaness's possible motivations for moving to Adelaide (Robert V. Blanden, personal communication, 2014), such as promotion to a professorship and better facilities, but also to give an informed reflection on the importance of Mackaness's seminal paper in the early enhancement of the reputation of the JCSMR (Blanden 2001). The paper (4) effectively introduced Mackaness to the scientific world as an independent scientist worthy of notice by the novelty of his ideas about the cellular immune response, the clarity of his data in supporting the hypotheses put forth, and the strength of his arguments and plans for future work expressed in the discussion. This paper made his reputation in immunology and was the strongest argument at the time for a scientific basis for understanding the enhancement of killing of phagocytosed bacteria and other pathogens by macrophages—that is, macrophage activation—which was independent of antibody or any serum-transferable product. The paper is especially notable for Mackaness's observation that enhanced killing of intracellular bacterial pathogens by macrophages appeared concurrently with the conversion of the host to delayed skin hypersensitivity towards the microbial antigens. Because such a delayed skin reaction had long been used to diagnose infection with TB in humans, the same finding in the *Listeria* model indicated an important similarity to TB. It is likely that the journal editors, having come to know Mackaness during his year at the Rockefeller in 1959–60, were inclined to grant him more space than might otherwise

Figure 4. George Mackaness as a faculty member at the John Curtin School of Medical Research, Australian National University, Canberra, ACT, 1957, aged 35 years. (Courtesy of the Australian National University.)

be permitted for a single paper of such extraordinary length (26 pages with nine graphs or text figures and ten tables; 37 pages with the eight photographic plates included). The paper also contained an unusual curiosity that perplexed readers. Although the paper was submitted with a single author (Mackaness), which was not unusual for the time, there appeared, at the heading of section III (out of four sections), the name of Valentine Ackerman next to that of Mackaness. The mystery was explained by Ackerman himself years later (Valentine P. Ackerman, personal communication, 2005). As it happened, the great mass of work that constituted the published report was that of Mackaness himself, but George considered including an experiment by his new graduate student, 'Val' Ackerman. Neither Mackaness nor Ackerman thought the small contribution merited authorship and Ackerman thought his name should be left off altogether, but Mackaness proposed a partial authorship as co-author of a section. It is not known what the journal editors thought of this arrangement, but it was obviously approved. Ackerman recalled his own feelings (Valentine P. Ackerman, personal communication, 2005) thus:

> The conversation [by telephone with the author] brought back memories of what were three of the best years I spent. I thought afterwards that I should have made it clearer that I had no quarrel with the form of the final publication. I had been George's PhD student for only about a year when the papers were drafted and I thought it was generous of him to include my name on what looked like being a very significant paper.

The authorship issue may be further clarified by a copy of Mackaness's curriculum vitae from about 1964, with accuracy certified by his signature, in which the 1962 paper is referenced thus: ' "Cellular resistance to infection" I–IV. *J. exp. Med.* 116:381'. Mackaness's reference to four sections, never cited by others or the official PubMed reference in this manner, suggests that he clearly viewed the publication as having four distinct units.

ANOTHER TURNING POINT: ROCKEFELLER

It was only one year, a sabbatical year from the JCSMR, but it had a profound effect on Mackaness's career and personal life. In remarks delivered as a eulogy to his friend, Jim Hirsch (9), George Mackaness mentions the specific date on which he arrived at the Rockefeller Institute for Medical Research (it became the Rockefeller University in 1965) as being 'June 10th, 1959'. It is clear from what followed that Mackaness did not have to refer to his diary to reference the date: that day was indelibly imprinted on his mind as much as his own wedding date. Mackaness had come to the Rockefeller to work with René Jules Dubos*, whom Mackaness had met almost a decade before when Dubos sought him out in Oxford during a visit to England. Dubos had come to meet Mackaness rather than Florey because of a shared interest in identifying novel antibiotics for the treatment of TB. This field had become a passion for Dubos, having lost his first wife, Marie Louise, to the disease, and his own investigations into antibiotics followed on his doctoral work with Selman Waksman at Rutgers University in New Jersey. (Dubos had left his native France as a young man with the express purpose of studying under Waksman, never imagining that he would spend his entire adult life in that region, mostly in New York City, less than 50 miles from Rutgers. Even so, Dubos never relinquished his ties to France, and late in life would practise his French pronunciation in front of a mirror every night out of fear that he would lose his native accent (Jean Dubos, personal communication, 1967).)

As Mackaness relates (9), when he arrived at Rockefeller Dubos advised him to work with Jim Hirsch. The two were the same age and had shared interests in anti-infection immunity, and they became fast and lasting friends. Beyond a paper submitted in 1960 to *Journal of Experimental Medicine* from Rockefeller about the phagocytosis of staphylococci, it is not obvious how scientifically productive the year at Rockefeller was for Mackaness. Nonetheless, the personal relationships formed and solidified that year certainly affected George and Gwyn's decision to accept an invitation to move from their native Australia to the new Trudeau Institute several years later, in March 1965. As Mackaness said (9):

> In addition to being a most agreeable experience, my sabbatical at the Rockefeller had a most salutary effect on my spirits, profoundly changed the direction of my research, and ultimately brought me and my compliant family permanently back to the United States, four years later. It was, in fact, Jim Hirsch who found the position that brought me to the Trudeau Institute in 1965.

---

* The Dubos obituary in the *New York Times* for 21 February 1982 provides relevant information.

THE TRUDEAU INSTITUTE: THE HOUSE THAT MACKANESS BUILT

If the Sir William Dunn School of Pathology was effectively the house that Florey built, notably through his success in developing penicillin, the Trudeau Foundation Research Laboratories (later the Trudeau Institute) owed its successful establishment, after the building's dedication in August 1964, to the leadership, creativity and foresight of George Mackaness.

Waksman's streptomycin, and especially the subsequent development of isoniazid, brought to a swift close the era of TB sanatoria as the treatment for TB (10). The oldest of these was the Trudeau Sanatorium, established in 1884 as the Adirondack Cottage Sanitarium by a New York City physician, Dr Edward Livingston Trudeau, in the small village of Saranac Lake near Lake Placid in New York State. The closure of the Trudeau Sanatorium came on 1 December 1954. Partly to save the town from economic ruin and partly to extend his grandfather's legacy in the study and treatment of TB, E. L. Trudeau's grandson, Francis B. Trudeau MD, sold the buildings and grounds of the sanatorium. With funds from the sale, as well as the generous assistance of the National Institutes of Health and private donors of funds and land, he established a research institute in the village. The new institute was to be a centre for the study of TB and a repository of TB strains for use by investigators around the world. It was ready for occupancy in the summer of 1964 and the Laboratories' first director, Hollis Boren MD, was a clinician rather than a researcher. The work of the institute actually began within months with the appointment of Mackaness as Chief of Experimental Pathology in March 1965. He was nominally hired as an expert in TB to fill the void left by the retiring William Steenken, who had been associated with the Trudeau Sanatorium laboratories for decades. By 1966, Dr Boren had left and Mackaness was appointed director of the Laboratories (figure 5).

Mackaness moved quickly to bring in colleagues from Australia to serve as initial staff. Notably, these included Mr Allan Logie, a native Scotsman who had moved to the JCSMR as Frank Fenner's laboratory manager, to be the laboratory manager for the new Trudeau Foundation Laboratories. Also joining the original staff was Robert Blanden, a graduate student at the University of Adelaide who had studied dentistry but was now working towards a PhD, and Frank Collins PhD, a junior faculty colleague of Mackaness at Adelaide. Not long afterwards, Robert North, having finished his doctoral work at the JCSMR, joined the group as a postdoctoral fellow. The heavy, and relatively sudden, influx of Australians had the locals soon referring to the new Trudeau Laboratories as the 'Australian Research Institute'.

Although it proved most propitious that the new institute was able to recruit a person of Mackaness's talents, reputation and international connections who also had research interests that so closely aligned with the mission of the Laboratories, it was far from luck that brought Mackaness and the Trudeau together. Like all career moves, and especially one that meant moving a family from its native land, there was a push and a pull. For Mackaness the push was a less than satisfying environment in his department at the University of Adelaide, where the senior professor and department head, Derrick Rowley, was rather obstinate in his perspective of the importance of the humoral immune response against *Salmonella* infection and other infectious agents. Mackaness's focus on the emerging apparent necessity for a cellular component, a view shared by Collins, was not well received by Rowley. In contrast, the pull was particularly attractive. It is generally acknowledged that it was René Dubos, a member of the Trudeau Foundation Board of Trustees, who convinced the board to recruit Mackaness and who then, with the help of Jim Hirsch, did the necessary arm-twisting to convince George to

Figure 5. George Mackaness as director of the Trudeau Institute, 1969, aged 47 years.
(Courtesy of the Trudeau Institute.)

accept the offer. Undoubtedly, Mackaness's warm relationship with Hirsch, who would soon be appointed the dean of the newly renamed Rockefeller University, was a most important factor. Mackaness secured Hirsch's appointment to the Trudeau scientific advisory council and Board of Trustees in 1966.

Solidly in charge, Mackaness began a second wave of professional staff recruitment. In an almost 'Pied Piper of Hamelin' approach, Mackaness travelled to recruit particular individuals to work at the new institute. Specifically, he sought people who had studied at the Sir William Dunn School of Pathology and searched for students of his friend and Florey laboratory colleague, James Gowans. Mackaness travelled to Cleveland and successfully seduced fellow Lincoln College alumnus Douglas McGregor to surrender his faculty appointment at the Western Reserve University School of Medicine for the excitement of building a new research institute along the lines of the Dunn School (Douglas McGregor, personal communication, 2014). In like manner, Mackaness travelled to New York City to find Alvin Volkman, a recent Magdalen College graduate, having lunch at a favourite Kosher delicatessen with colleagues from the Department of Pathology at the College of Physicians & Surgeons of Columbia University (Alvin Volkman, personal communication, 2014). Like McGregor, Volkman could not pass up the opportunity to be part of a grand new enterprise. In addition to staff, Mackaness relied on his friends at Rockefeller, specifically Jim Hirsch and Zanvil Cohn, and a friend from Oxford, Irwin ('Lee') Lepow, to join the scientific advisory council along with other internationally known immunologists and experts in infectious disease.

The 10 years as director of the Trudeau Institute were particularly enriching for Mackaness because he was essentially the head of a department that he himself had staffed. Virtually every member of the professional staff was doing some work on different aspects of cellular immunity to infectious agents and, later, cancer. Robert North has written a particularly informative obituary of Mackaness that focused on his decade-long directorship (North 2007). North mentions that the expression most often associated with Mackaness was that he was the person 'who coined the term, "activated macrophage", to describe the enhanced antimicrobial function acquired by macrophages in response to infection'. It is not clear whether Mackaness did coin the term 'activated macrophage', something even North later questioned (Robert J. North, personal communication, 2014). Emanuel ('Manny') Suter, a Swiss student who worked with Dubos on TB in the late 1940s and 1950s, danced around the term, as did others of the day. But it was not something that Mackaness made a fuss about because he never made claims about the term but used it in the same context as he would say or write 'sensitized lymphocyte'; in fact, he preferred the term 'angry macrophage' (Alvin Volkman, personal communication, 2014). Nevertheless, it is not surprising that others ascribed the term to his invention because he certainly brought broad attention to the process by which blood monocytes gain enhanced destructive attributes as a necessary part of the immune response to intracellular infectious agents. In a superbly succinct yet detailed retrospective in 2005, Heather Van Epps brings clarity to this issue of 'macrophage activation' (Van Epps 2005). Beginning with the Metchnikoff reference to enhanced macrophage killing of bacteria (Metchnikoff 1905), the reviewer concisely summarizes the series of Mackaness papers in *Journal of Experimental Medicine* in the 1960s that brought him to the forefront of the field in which he was truly a pioneer.

The data came fast and furious out of the laboratories of most of the researchers at the institute during the years that Mackaness was there. Although there was some overlap, perhaps even competition, for the most part the various laboratories were doing complementary work that revealed different aspects of the cellular immune response. The best example of this is contained in the special presentation that Mackaness gave at the Eighth Annual Meeting of the Infectious Diseases Society of America held in Chicago on 18 October 1970. In the presentation, entitled 'Resistance to intracellular infection' (5), Mackaness mentioned work from virtually every laboratory then active at the Trudeau Institute in making his case for the proposed processes necessary in mounting a cellular immune response. This included postulating a cytokine secreted by sensitized lymphocytes; not long afterwards, this was shown to be interferon γ (Van Epps 2005). At the time, Mackaness was focused on the antiviral 'interferon' of Alick Isaacs FRS, later designated interferon α. The lymphocyte class was eventually shown to be a T lymphocyte, primarily through the work of J. F. A. P. Miller (FRS 1970) (Miller & Mitchell 1967). But even Miller, in an oral history provided to the Australian Academy of Science in 1999 (Miller 1999), admitted the strong bias of the 1960s in stating that, even after his extensive work elucidating the function of the thymus and of cells processed through the thymus, he was still searching for how these cells themselves produced antibody. His comments in this interview inadvertently demonstrated how prescient Mackaness was in conceiving of a special class of lymphocytes that could interact with monocytes to produce tissue macrophages with an enhanced ability to destroy intracellular parasites without the involvement of antibody. Miller's comments actually exposed the weight of bias that Mackaness had to overcome in convincing fellow immunologists of the reality of cellular immunity to infectious agents.

The end of the 1970 presentation in Chicago disclosed a budding area of interest for Mackaness: the relevance of his work to anti-tumour immunity. His last reference in the published form of his presentation (5) was to work by Bert Zbar and colleagues at the National Cancer Institute (NCI). The work cited was an extension of discoveries made at the Roswell Park Memorial Institute in Buffalo, New York, which showed some success in curing patients with melanoma after the injection of lesions with Bacille Calmette–Guérin (BCG), the live bovine TB organism attenuated for use as a human TB vaccine. Mackaness was soon collaborating with the NCI, with funding from an NCI contract, on studies of different BCG strains as a means of non-specifically killing tumour cells in BCG-sensitized animals. The NCI group was using guinea-pigs, so the Trudeau Institute soon began breeding two different inbred lines of these animals. Later, actual pigs were used as test animals after someone at NCI read about the similarities of pig skin to human skin and the possibility of using scarification of the skin as an effective way of administering BCG in trying to stimulate an anti-tumour response.

The cancer studies at Trudeau were joined in 1972 by Martin Scott, a young scientist from the Wellcome Research Laboratories in Beckenham and funded by a two-year fellowship from the Cancer Research Institute of New York City, who had established a reputation through his studies of *Corynebacterium parvum* as a non-specific immunostimulant. Clearly, the Wellcome Foundation would have had a profit motive for pursuing studies of *C. parvum*, which, unlike BCG, was a killed preparation and could be used in patients without regard to their tuberculin sensitivity. The pros and cons of the use of BCG over *C. parvum* were often a topic of enthusiastic debate between Mackaness and Scott during coffee breaks at Trudeau in the early 1970s.

The introduction in 1962 of Mackaness's concept of how a cellular-based response to TB and other intracellular infectious agents might work spawned more than a decade of work in a host of laboratories. His publication in *Journal of Experimental Medicine* showed how *Listeria monocytogenes* infection in rodents provided an ideal model for experimentally testing the hypotheses that he and others proposed (4). Even so, it was the considerable amount of work done at the Trudeau Institute that resulted in the shower of awards and accolades that Mackaness ultimately received, including a session chairmanship at the First International Congress on Immunology, which focused on his work (6, 7). Even the citation on his election to the Royal Society pays little homage to his 1949 work on antibiotics at Oxford, instead focusing on his decades of work elucidating the nature of immunity to TB and intracellular parasites generally.

In a way, 'Camelot'* came to an end at the Trudeau Institute in 1975, when Mackaness announced his intention to leave Saranac Lake and accept the appointment as president of the E. R. Squibb & Sons Research Institute (figure 6). The offer apparently came as a result of the recommendation of a Squibb board member at Harvard who was aware of Mackaness by reputation as well as perhaps through the encouragement of Sir Henry Harris, who was working at Harvard at the time (Sir Richard Sykes FRS, personal communication, 2014). Some junior staff moved with Mackaness on his departure, and senior staff, notably McGregor and Volkman, departed for opportunities in academia.

---

* A reference to a lyric in the 1960 Lerner and Loewe musical 'Camelot', also in use at the time to describe the Kennedy administration (*London Herald*, 23 November 1963, 'Kennedy assassinated: America mourns Camelot dream') and popularized following a comment by Jacqueline Kennedy to Theodore H. White in a *Life* magazine article on 6 December 1963, pp. 158–159. White ended his article with the sentence: 'For one brief shining moment there was Camelot.'

Figure 6. Gwynneth and George Mackaness just before leaving the Trudeau Institute. Saranac Lake, New York, June 1976. (Online version in colour.)

SQUIBB

The move to the presidency of the Squibb Research Institute in Princeton, New Jersey, in 1976 was the first experience that Mackaness had in private enterprise or for-profit industry but, by all assessments, he made the change without missing a beat. Located in the environs of Princeton University, the Squibb Institute of the time possessed characteristics and an environment that made it something of a hybrid between industry and academia, similar to the then Wellcome Research Laboratories. This allowed Mackaness to adapt more easily from his background in academia and the not-for-profit Trudeau Institute to a place that had a profit motive. Initially, the major adjustment was to industry's more structured reporting line. Mackaness preferred to keep his hand in some of his own pet research projects and give his research associates and assistants direct access to his office. For several reasons, not the least of which were the broader responsibilities that came with the position of president, Mackaness had to change the manner in which he had been used to working and adapt to the new reality. Although change was to be expected, it did not slow Mackaness down and his leadership had a profound effect on Squibb's fortunes almost from the very beginning.

Squibb scientists and pharmacologists were the first to adapt the findings of John (later Sir John) Vane FRS and colleagues relating to the angiotensin system, to create a drug for the treatment of hypertension, congestive heart failure and the effects of cardiac infarction. The drug was captopril, marketed as Capoten by Squibb. In his recent book, Eugene Cordes well describes the uniqueness of the drug and its importance in pharmacology (Cordes 2014). Captopril was the first angiotensin-converting enzyme (ACE) inhibitor and the first of an entirely new class of drugs. It is also distinctive in that it was developed through the process of

Figure 7. Official photo of George Mackaness by Squibb, 1985, aged 63 years. (Courtesy of Bristol-Myers Squibb.)

'rational design' for which Sir James W. Black FRS, Gertrude B. ('Trudy') Elion (ForMemRS 1995) and George H. Hitchings ForMemRS received the 1988 Nobel Prize in Physiology or Medicine. When Mackaness arrived at Squibb, the discovery had only recently been made, and patent and investigational new drug (IND) applications were under way. Work was proceeding for Phase I and II testing. Although Mackaness was not trained as a cardiologist, he took issue with the drug dosages being tested as far too high. His position received significant opposition from the established Squibb researchers and the company pursued an application to the US Food and Drug Administration (FDA). As it happened, the FDA denied the application on the basis of unacceptable adverse drug reactions (ADRs), the most serious being aplastic anaemia. Squibb stock value plummeted. This allowed Mackaness to gain the high ground, insisting that the dosage be cut significantly, by about 50%, which proved effective and without significant ADRs. The product received FDA approval, captopril was saved, the path to a long line of ACE inhibitors was opened, and profits soared. In the words of Sir Richard Sykes, then Mackaness's subordinate at Squibb and later chairman of Glaxo, Mackaness became a 'hero' within the company (Sir Richard Sykes, personal communication, 2014*). It should be mentioned in this context that, although Mackaness's lifelong research had been in the area of anti-infection immunity and therapeutics, he did take a curious diversion from this field in the late 1950s at the JCSMR to investigate and publish several papers on renin, 'hypertensinogen',

* Actual historic data and stock values are contained in 'Squibb Corporation', *International Directory of Company Histories*, 1988. (http://www.encyclopedia.com/doc/1G2-2840500264.html, accessed 23 June 2014.)

renal function in pregnancy, and hypertension. It is possible, then, that Mackaness harboured a lingering interest in cardiology and hypertension and was much better informed about the field before taking the position at Squibb than most of his colleagues would have imagined.

The administrative chain for the Research Institute was very strong and talented. This was especially so during the latter half of Mackaness's tenure when Charles Sanders MD, a cardiologist who had been running the Massachusetts General Hospital, joined Squibb as executive vice president of the corporation and was the person to whom Mackaness reported. Mackaness already had the talented Richard Sykes reporting to him in creating a smooth-running administrative structure conducive to research. At about the same time as Mackaness decided to retire (figure 7), Sykes was drawn to return to Britain and ultimately became chairman of GlaxoSmithKline plc (GSK) and, after retiring from the pharmaceutical industry, Rector of Imperial College, London. A few years later, Sanders was hired to run Glaxo, Inc. in Research Triangle Park, North Carolina, as CEO and later chairman.

Because so much of the work at Squibb was proprietary (two patents were assigned to Mackaness (11, 12)), and time was occupied with administration, scientific publications by Mackaness declined. His last was a review paper about ACE inhibitors (8).

The retirement years

After George's retirement from Squibb in 1985, he and Gwyn Mackaness moved to live near their son's family in a beautiful new home on Seabrook Island, South Carolina, just south of Charleston. This provided many years of happiness giving additional love and nurture to their three granddaughters and taking pride as they watched them grow into young women. Mackaness focused on family during these years and eschewed offers to serve on boards and the like, saying that he did not want to be one of those people who was occupying space on such committees or boards while not being sufficiently current in the field to contribute effectively (George Mackaness, personal communication, *ca.* 1986). His term on the Josiah Macy Foundation board began before he left Squibb, as a favour to Jim Hirsch, who was the chairman, as did his accepting the chairmanship of the Trudeau Institute Board of Trustees, after Hirsch, in 1982. Mackaness's decision not to serve on boards was almost certainly based on conviction, as well as dedication to family, and unrelated to memory loss due to the Alzheimer's disease that developed later in retirement. One of his last presentations followed the loss of his 'best friend', Jim Hirsch, from cancer; Mackaness presented a most moving and heartfelt eulogy at the memorial service held at the Rockefeller University on 7 December 1987, six months after Hirsch's death (9). Two years later, on 23 October 1989, Mackaness again felt compelled to leave his retirement home to travel to the Rockefeller University to honour a cherished mentor, René Jules Dubos, on the occasion of the 50th anniversary of the discovery of gramicidin, a milestone achievement initiating the 'era of antibiotics'. The presentations of that day were published by the Rockefeller University Press; Mackaness's paper, one of seven with introductory remarks by Joshua Lederberg ForMemRS, then Rockefeller's president, details his own attempts at discovering novel antibiotics, especially those effective against TB. In his address, Mackaness discussed the work performed at the Dunn School in the early 1950s that ultimately drew him to Dubos's laboratory in 1959 (10).

The first hint of memory loss to those outside the family was when friends and former colleagues approached Mackaness about celebrating his 75th birthday in 1997. George begged

Figure 8. The author with George Mackaness at his retirement home in Charleston, South Carolina, December 2004, aged 82 years. (Photograph by Mikayla Mackaness, edited by the author.) (Online version in colour.)

off without giving a reason, but his son later related that the real reason was his father's fear of embarrassing people at such an event when he might not remember their names (Miles Mackaness, personal communication, 1997). Mackaness was aware of his progressive memory loss at the time and worked assiduously to stimulate his mind with memory exercises thought to delay the inevitable. Through the decade from 1997 until his death, Mackaness maintained a positive attitude and was a happy person even when the time came that he could not remember names in his own family. An event on 21 June 2000 provides an example of his acceptance of the disease, which also came to afflict his wife, while still fighting to slow its progress. A scientific meeting in Charleston provided an opportunity for a dinner with George and Gwyn, the author and his wife, and a mutual friend and former colleague from the Trudeau Institute days. An early evening dinner was held at the historic Francis Marion Hotel in old Charleston. Mackaness was still able to drive, and he and Gwyn arrived on time, both impeccably dressed (Stephen Boyden, personal communication, 2014*). Because it was the summer solstice, it remained light late into the evening, which allowed Mackaness to decline an invitation to be driven to the dinner. Mackaness was forthright about his memory loss and apologized for not remembering the name of our colleague. In the course of conversation, Mackaness asked me what the current exciting frontier in immunology might be. When the response was 'xenotransplantation', Gwyn, sitting to George's left, gently punched his shoulder and said, 'There you go, George; you could have a pig brain transplanted into you!'

---

* Boyden specifically mentioned how Mackaness always dressed well: 'Unlike many of us in the department, he was always immaculately dressed and groomed.'

They both laughed heartily at the thought while the rest of the party looked on in astonishment, amazed that George and Gwyn could express such dark humour for the disease they faced.

George and Gwyn were able to live in their own home well into their eighties, thanks to the support of their daughter-in-law and granddaughters who lived nearby as well as to in-home care (figure 8). They ultimately moved to a senior care facility in the Charleston area, where they both died with their son, Miles, by their side.

Awards and honours

In addition to election as a Fellow of the Royal Society in 1976, George Mackaness received the Paul Ehrlich and Ludwig Darmstaedter Prize (1975) and the Novartis Prize in Clinical Immunology (1998). He was also elected a Fellow of the American Association for the Advancement of Science and a member of the American Academy of Arts and Sciences.

Acknowledgements

This memoir could not have been completed without the assistance of the following people, many of whom responded to requests most expeditiously to meet deadlines. These are: Valentine P. Ackerman PhD, Robert V. Blanden MDS PhD, Stephen Boyden BVSc PhD, Ms Karen Edwards (Australian National University Archives), Ms Lori Franklin, David R. Fraser BVSc PhD, Sir James Gowans FRS, Professor Dr.med. Helmut Hahn, Sir Henry Harris FRS, Lee Hiltzlik PhD (Rockefeller University Archives), Mr Robert A. Ingram, Professor W. K. Joklik DPhil, Mr Walter V. Kipp (Archivist, Bristol-Myers Squibb Co.), Ms Brenda Mackaness, Ms Caroline Mackaness, Ms Christiana Mackaness, Ms Jessica Mackaness, Ms Mikayla Mackaness, Mr Miles Mackaness, Douglas D. McGregor MD DPhil, Herbert B. McGuire Jr CPA, Ms Jane Mitchell and Lincoln College Archives, Carol Moberg PhD, James R. Murphy PhD, Madeleine Nicol PhD, Robert J. North PhD, Professor Christopher Parish PhD, Ms Jo M. Peel, Charles Sanders MD, Martin T. Scott PhD DSc., Eric Sidebottom MB DPhil and the Sir William Dunn School Archives, Ms Kelly Stanyon and the Trudeau Institute Archives, Ms Claudia Steinman, Sir Richard Sykes FRS and Alvin Volkman MD DPhil. Gratitude is expressed to all of the above; however, whatever shortcomings persist in this memoir remain the fault of the author.

The frontispiece photograph was taken in 1970 by the Trudeau Institute and is reproduced with permission.

References to other authors

Abraham, E. P. 1971 Howard Walter Florey, Baron Florey of Adelaide and Marston. *Biogr. Mems Fell. R. Soc.* **17**, 255–302.

Blanden, R. V. 2001 Immunology. In *The John Curtin School of Medical Research: The first fifty years, 1948–1998*, by F. Fenner & D. Curtis, pp. 319–322. Gundaroo, NSW: Brolga Press. (Available online at http://jcsmr.anu. edu.au/about-us/first-fifty-years-1948-1998.)

Cordes, E. H. 2014 Hallelujah moments: tales of drug discovery. Oxford University Press.

Fenner, F. & Curtis, D. 2001 *The John Curtin School of Medical Research: The first fifty years, 1948–1998*. Gundaroo, NSW: Brolga Press. (Available online at http://jcsmr.anu.edu.au/about-us/first-fifty-years-1948-1998.)

Kramer, L. 2012 *Broomstick: personal reflections of Leonie Kramer*. Melbourne: Australian Scholarly Publishing Pty Ltd.

Macfarlane, R. G. 1979 *Howard Florey: the making of a great scientist.* Oxford University Press.

Metchnikoff, E. 1905 *Immunity to infective diseases.* Cambridge University Press.

Miller, J. F. A. P. 1999 Professor Jacques Miller, Pathologist, interviewed by Professor Frank Fenner. In *Interviews with Australian scientists* (http://www.sciencearchive.org.au/scientists/interviews/m/jm.html). Canberra: Australian Academy of Science.

Miller, J. F. A. P. & Mitchell, G. F. 1967 The thymus and the precursors of antigenic reactive cells. *Nature* **216**, 659–663.

North, R. J. 2007 Obituary: George B. Mackaness, M.D., D.Phil., F.R.S. *Tuberculosis* **87**(4), 391.

Sidebottom, E. 2013 Who was Sir William Dunn? *Fusion* **12**, 19–20.

Van Epps, H. L. 2005 Macrophage activation unveiled. *J. Exp. Med.* **202**, 884.

Bibliography

The following publications are those referred to directly in the text. A full bibliography is available as electronic supplementary material at http://dx.doi.org/10.1098/rsbm.2014.0017 or via http://rsbm.royalsocietypublishing.org.

(1) 1952 The action of drugs on intracellular tubercle bacilli. *J. Path. Bact.* **64**, 429–446.

(2) (With N. Smith) The action of isoniazid (isonicotinic acid hydrazide) on intracellular tubercle bacilli. *Am. Rev. Tuberc.* **66**, 125–133.

(3) 1953 *The reactions of the mononuclear phagocytes to various forms of stimulation.* DPhil thesis, University of Oxford.

(4) 1962 Cellular resistance to infection. *J. Exp. Med.* **116**, 381–406.

(5) 1971 Resistance to intracellular infection. *J. Infect. Dis.* **123**, 439–445.

(6) Delayed hypersensitivity and the mechanism of cellular resistance to infection. In *Progress in immunology: First International Congress on Immunology, Washington DC, August 1971* (ed. B. Amos), pp. 413–424. New York: Academic Press. [Pagination in the Registrant's Copy edition.]

(7) (With S. Raffel) Macrophages: role in resistance to microbial parasitism. Workshop 27. In *Progress in immunology: First International Congress on Immunology, Washington DC, August 1971* (ed. B. Amos), pp. 1279–1282. New York: Academic Press. [Pagination in the Registrant's Copy edition.]

(8) 1985 The future of angiotensin-converting enzyme inhibitors. *J. Cardiovasc. Pharmacol.* **7** (Suppl. 1), S30–S34.

(9) 1987 Eulogy for James G. Hirsch. Hirsch Memorial Service, Rockefeller University, New York, 7 December 1987. Rockefeller University Archives. Special Events, James G. Hirsch Memorial Service, Folder 3, Record Group 600-19.

(10) 1990 New remedies for an ancient infection: antibiotics and tuberculosis. In *Launching the antibiotic era. Proceedings of the Symposium Commemorating the Fiftieth Anniversary of the Discovery of Gramicidin by René J. Dubos, 23 October 1989* (ed. C. L. Moberg & Z. A. Cohn), pp. 57–68. New York: Rockefeller University Press.

Patents assigned

(11) 1980 (With Joseph P. Hou) *Contrast media containing liposomes as carriers.* E. R. Squibb & Sons. US Patent 04192859, 11 March 1980.

(12) 1981 (With Kathryn A. Losee) *Reaction products of pyrazolo[1,5-c]quinazoline derivatives and proline derivatives and methods for reducing blood pressure while inhibiting allergic reactions with them.* E. R. Squibb & Sons. US Patent 04307099, 22 December 1981.

JOHN LENNOX MONTEITH

3 September 1929 — 20 July 2012

JOHN LENNOX MONTEITH

3 September 1929 — 20 July 2012

Elected FRS 1971

By Michael H. Unsworth

College of Earth, Ocean and Atmospheric Sciences, Oregon State University, Corvallis, OR 97331, USA

John Monteith fundamentally changed the way in which physical and biological scientists explore the interactions between living organisms and their environments. Trained in physics and meteorology, he pioneered innovative ways of measuring and analysing exchanges of heat, water vapour and carbon dioxide between leaves, crops, animals and the atmosphere. Building on the work of Howard Penman, with whom he worked for almost two decades, he developed the Penman–Monteith equation that is widely used in planning irrigation and water resource development. Subsequently, as the first Professor of Environmental Physics at the University of Nottingham, he brought together multidisciplinary groups to study the growth of temperate and tropical crops and the heat balance of animals. His Environmental Physics group trained graduates and postdoctoral scientists who have joined research establishments and universities worldwide. The final phase of his long career was spent at the International Crops Research Institute for the Semi-Arid Tropics, where he directed teams applying his experimental methods and analyses to benefit crop production in developing countries—a topic that epitomized his desire to have his science make an impact for the good of mankind. In addition to his exceptional ability in research and teaching, John Monteith was an outstanding communicator and leader who made substantial contributions to many national and international organizations.

EARLY LIFE AND EDUCATION

John Lennox Monteith was born in 1929 in St Margaret's Manse, Fairlie, a small village on the Firth of Clyde in Ayrshire, Scotland. He was the only son of the Reverend John and Margaret Lennox Monteith. His father was a minister of the Church of Scotland; his mother had been an English teacher before her marriage. When he was three years old, the family moved to

http://dx.doi.org/10.1098/rsbm.2014.0005

Bridge of Weir, Renfrewshire. John began school at the age of six years in the primary section of Paisley Grammar School; his mother had home-schooled him during the previous year.

His interest in science was first stimulated when his primary class visited the upper school science laboratory to see a teacher make a mercury-in-glass thermometer. It may be coincidental that one of his first scientific publications (1954) was concerned with errors in temperature measurement! He had hours of fun with electricity and chemistry sets during his school days and with homemade instruments. These included an induction coil, with which he could 'electrocute five or six of his friends simultaneously'—practical joking was part of John's nature, as was his interest in building instruments.

When John was 11 years old, his father developed multiple sclerosis and the family moved to Edinburgh, where his father died shortly afterwards. John was enrolled at George Heriot's School, where his mother had taught in the 1920s. Heriot's, one of Edinburgh's merchant schools founded in the seventeenth century, is one of the most distinguished in Scotland. He proved to be an academic all-rounder, winning prizes in mathematics, applied science, English literature and public speaking, and was active in drama, debating and music. He was 'Dux' of the school in 1946–47, but no sportsman—he reported holding a place in the lowest rugby team only on the basis of his height. In his final years John specialized in mathematics, physics, chemistry, English and Latin, having abandoned biology after one year because of his ineptitude in drawing specimens. Fortunately he discovered later in life that there were more exciting aspects of biology. English and Latin left him with a love of language and composition, so that later his publications, and those of colleagues for whom he reviewed drafts (with heavy use of his red pen), were exemplary in clarity and style.

University student years

In 1947 he began as an undergraduate in the Physics Department at the University of Edinburgh. He greatly enjoyed project work in the laboratory, where he could tinker with instruments. James Paton's lectures on heat and thermodynamics and on meteorology (Paton was the sole meteorologist in the University at that time) particularly stimulated him, and he decided that specializing in meteorology as a postgraduate student would lead him to a career in which physics could be applied outside the laboratory. An uncle, David Cuthbertson, who was Director of the Rowett Research Institute in Aberdeen, further focused John's interest by suggesting that agricultural meteorology might be a satisfying career; the idea of applying physics to improve food production appealed strongly to the young man.

After graduating from Edinburgh with first-class honours in 1951, he was awarded a two-year scholarship of £250 a year by the Department of Scientific and Industrial Research (DSIR) and began a postgraduate course for the Diploma in Meteorology at Imperial College, London, intending to continue on to a PhD. At that time the Department of Meteorology at Imperial College, led by Sir David Brunt FRS, was extraordinarily strong and included P. A. Sheppard (FRS 1964) and B. J. (now Sir John) Mason (FRS 1965) among its seven faculty members. The others, R. Scorer, E. T. Edie, F. Ludlam and R. Goody, were also highly respected meteorologists, so the class of about 11 students received outstanding tuition and research advice. A taught postgraduate-level course was very unusual in the UK at that time, and the Meteorology Diploma attracted students from throughout the Commonwealth, several of whom became John's lifelong friends. The sound grounding that he received in meteorology served him well, particularly during his term as President of the Royal Meteorological Society.

Early in his first year, John visited Rothamsted Experimental Station in Harpenden to seek advice from Howard Penman (FRS 1962) in the Physics Department about suitable PhD problems in agricultural meteorology. Penman suggested the physics of dew deposition, because the influence of leaf wetness on the development of plant disease was an important interest at Rothamsted, particularly with the microbiologist P. H. Gregory (FRS 1986) and his team. This proved an ideal topic for John, because it combined the opportunities of designing and building sensitive equipment to measure dew deposition and its associated microclimatic factors, with the analytical challenge of elucidating the heat balance of vegetation at night. Between lectures he frequented the Meteorology Department workshops, where he became a competent user of lathes, milling machines and other equipment. The training in workshop techniques that he received there from E. G. (Ted) Jennings provided him with the skills necessary to build equipment for micrometeorology at a time long before specialized manufacturers existed. When he later became Professor of Environmental Physics at the University of Nottingham all research students in his group were expected to construct some of their own equipment.

His PhD project proceeded rapidly, and by the spring of his second year, with the help of Jennings, he had built an ingenious recording dew balance that provided a sensitive record of the rate of dewfall (1)*. A concurrent theoretical analysis of errors and accuracy associated with the use of thermocouples for measuring atmospheric temperature profiles during dewfall yielded a second publication (2). He did not realize at the time that having two publications in prestigious journals so early in a PhD programme was highly unusual.

Throughout the summers of 1953 and 1954 he collected data from his instruments, which were installed on the Imperial College playing fields at Harlington 'a bit off the edge of the cricket pitch'. On nights when dew was likely he would ride to the site on his bike and attempt to stay awake all night to tend the instruments. A careful look at the published data, in a paper 'Dew' (3) that must vie for the shortest title on record, reveals occasional gaps when his resolve failed.

When John's DSIR grant ran out at the end of his second year at Imperial College, Penman made the unusual arrangement of appointing him to the staff of the Rothamsted Physics Department but permitted him to remain in London to complete his PhD research.

FIRST POST AND MATRIMONY

With his thesis complete, John finally moved to Rothamsted Experiment Station late in the summer of 1954, taking his dew balance and other paraphernalia with him. But first priority was marriage. In his second year as an undergraduate in Edinburgh he had met Elsa Wotherspoon at a youth fellowship in Greenbank church; the romance was cemented by weekly letters while he was in London and she was completing her teaching certificate at Moray House in Edinburgh. They became engaged in 1953 and married in July 1955, beginning a long and happy partnership that they shared for the next 57 years. In Harpenden they settled initially into a rented flat with no running hot water; over the next 12 years they had five children and moved house twice to accommodate the growing clan.

* Numbers in this form refer to the bibliography at the end of the text.

Figure 1. Morning coffee in the Physics Department, Rothamsted Experimental Station, in about 1955. Penman is in the right foreground; Monteith is sipping coffee. (Photograph supplied by Elsa Monteith.) (Online version in colour.)

Soil physics had been the focus of research in the Physics Department up to the 1950s, an emphasis dating back to the first department head, Bernard Keen FRS. Monteith received little guidance in choosing his research topics—the philosophy 'decide what you think you'd be interested in and get on with it' had long been embedded in the department. John was initially disappointed that he did not receive much guidance from his senior colleagues, but, as he later typically understated it, 'Fortunately I managed to find one or two things that led me into very interesting areas of agricultural meteorology.'

The Physics Department was small (figure 1) and remained so throughout the 1950s and 1960s, probably because Penman focused on the quality of staff and had no interest in 'empire building'. There was a shortage of space, so John was initially allocated a desk in Penman's large office, relative luxury for the new junior Scientific Officer. A few months later, Penman was promoted to Head of the Physics Department when R. K. Schofield moved to become Head of the larger Chemistry Department; as Penman would now occupy the Department Head's office, Monteith successfully made a case for staying put and converting the room into a combined workshop and office. This workshop space was certainly needed, because John had thrown himself enthusiastically into new research projects. At first he continued his interest in practical microclimatology, which required building his own instruments to measure the components of the energy balance. His familiarity from his student days with the many stores around Tottenham Court Road in London specializing in military surplus electrical equipment enabled him to find cheap motors, relays and other components for his instruments. Twenty years later it was still possible to rummage in cupboards of his office at Sutton Bonington and find a treasure trove of components and prototype instruments that he had hoarded 'just in case they should turn out useful'. This was a far cry from the present day in which several specialist companies make highly sophisticated microclimatological instruments.

It soon became clear that John needed an assistant to help him with the instrumentation and field measurements. Penman advertised and almost immediately received an application from a Hungarian, Geza Szeicz, who had worked in the meteorological section of the Hungarian

Figure 2. At the Rothamsted weather station, in about 1955. (Photograph supplied by Elsa Monteith.)

Air Force and had left the country after the 1956 uprising was crushed. Unable to find other employment, Geza was working as a waiter at London's Savoy Hotel. After a brief meeting, he was appointed on faith because he had no documentation proving his qualifications. John reminisced, 'that … turned out to be exactly the right thing to do because he was excellent both at making equipment and getting it running in the field.' With a like-minded assistant in place, John's relative isolation in the department was relieved, and the pair thrived both intellectually and socially. Their studies of the radiative components of the heat balance of soils and crops led to six publications on short-wave and long-wave radiation between 1959 and 1962, for which Monteith was awarded the Buchan Prize of the Royal Meteorological Society in 1962.

Inevitably John's interest in crop heat balance led him to thinking about evaporation, a topic he had tended to avoid because it was Penman's forte. In seeking ways of extending Penman's formula to explicitly separate the physical and physiological controls of evaporation from vegetation, he developed the idea of using a one-dimensional electrical analogue to describe the aerodynamic and canopy transfer of heat and water vapour, with resistances dependent on atmospheric turbulence and canopy properties (figure 2). His treatment of the canopy as a 'big leaf', with a canopy resistance analogous to the resistance imposed by stomata on transpiration by individual leaves, was both novel and controversial. In 1962, when he was invited by Lloyd Evans to present these ideas at a symposium in Australia (6), he found that several respected micrometeorologists, including R. J. Taylor, W. C. Swinbank, C. B. Tanner and J. R. Philip (FRS 1974) were highly critical of his one-dimensional model. The principal concern, voiced by Swinbank among others, was that assumptions in the 'big leaf' model ignored the complexity of turbulent transfer in canopies. These exchanges were the start of a long-running feud between practitioners and theoreticians, of which Philip was the most prominent. In a characteristically forthright review, 'Plant water relations: some physical aspects' (Philip 1966), he made several attacks on one-dimensional models and the 'big leaf' analogy, criticizing 'work which is superficially mathematical-physical, but which contains loose thinking, non-rigorous calculations, uncoordinated physical measurements in the field, and overinflated claims, [that] may temporarily impress our colleagues less familiar with mathematical-physical concepts.' Philip opined that Monteith's canopy resistance 'is an artifact of a somewhat unrealistic analysis, and its physiological significance is questionable.' The criticism of canopy resistance clearly stung, but in print Monteith allowed himself only the relatively mild riposte in his first edition of *Principles of environmental physics* (16): 'No more appropriate index (of the physiological control of water loss) has yet been devised despite attacks which are based on armchair speculators divorced from experience in the field.' Although Philip never completed the theoretical paper that he hoped (Philip 1966) would demonstrate the unreliability of canopy resistance, over the years experimental and theoretical advances by Philip's colleagues Denmead & Bradley (1985) and Raupach & Finnigan (1988), among others, have better defined the conditions when canopy resistance can be used appropriately, and elucidated other situations in which the concept fails.

By 1964, Monteith had developed his resistance analysis considerably further, applied it to data from several crops, and addressed some of the earlier criticisms. The time had come to publish the results. Rather than split the material into several papers, he took advantage of an invitation to speak at a meeting of the Society for Experimental Biology in Swansea, and submitted the entire work as a paper in the published proceedings (8). With some trepidation he had asked Penman to review the draft paper; unusually, it had come back with none of Penman's often severe editing, only a note at the end—'Bit of a Mahler symphony isn't it John?' (Penman, who was an accomplished member of the BBC Choral Society, would have been well aware of the large scale and complexity of Mahler's symphonic scores.)

The Swansea meeting was also significant for John's career path in another way. Fred Milthorpe, Professor of Agricultural Botany at the University of Nottingham's School of Agriculture (located near the small village of Sutton Bonington, and generally referred to as SB) mentioned at a chance meeting over coffee that Nottingham hoped to appoint a Professor of Environmental Physics in about three years. He encouraged John to consider a move when the opportunity arose. The distant prospect hardly registered with Monteith at the time.

The next three years passed quickly with the dual demands of a growing family at home and a multi-pronged research operation at work. John was also increasingly involved in international committee work. In particular, he was appointed to the Photosynthesis Subcommittee of the International Biological Program, and to the World Meteorological Organization (WMO) Working Group on Micrometeorology, organizations through which he made many lasting friendships around the world.

In the spring of 1967 the University of Nottingham contacted him. The Environmental Physics position mentioned by Milthorpe had materialized and, rather than advertising in what would have been a very sparse field, the university invited John to interview for the chair. He and Elsa struggled over what to do: their growing family was settled in Harpenden; they had just moved into a comfortable Edwardian house of which they were very fond; John's research at Rothamsted was productive and highly respected; and the prospect of taking over as Head of the Physics Department when Penman retired was implicit. On the other hand, a university position would open prospects of expanding his research group (opportunities for hiring at Rothamsted were very limited) and for developing new research lines such as animal heat balance. There was also a base on which to build: Milthorpe and John Hudson, Professor of Horticulture, had already established an MSc course on water relations, and the School of Agriculture had several staff interested in crop–atmosphere interactions: Jerry Clark, a physicist, recently hired to replace Ian Cowan, who had departed for Australia; Mike McGowan, a soil scientist with research interests in crop water use; and Keith Scott, an agronomist studying crop growth and the weather. Unfortunately, Fred Milthorpe left in 1968 to take the Chair in Biological Sciences at Macquarie University in Australia.

John and Elsa concluded that after 18 years at Rothamsted it might be a good time to explore fresh fields, so John went to the interview, was offered the chair and accepted it on the spot. John recollected that telling Penman of his decision to leave Rothamsted was the most awkward situation he had ever encountered. Penman sat shocked and silent, gazing out of the window for what seemed an interminable time; he had clearly not foreseen this loss of his most productive staff member and his likely successor. But over the next few weeks he came to terms with the departure and gave the Monteiths a rousing and convivial send-off; he and John maintained their friendship and professional interactions, but Penman still wrote a scathing letter to Nottingham accusing them of baby-snatching!

Just before John moved to SB he made an overseas trip that turned out to have a major influence on his future career path, although it took more than a decade to develop to fruition. Hugh Bunting, Professor of Agricultural Botany at the University of Reading, arranged for him to visit Ahmadu Bello University in Nigeria, where Bunting had established a strong collaboration studying semi-arid cropping systems. Jeremy Elston, on the staff at Reading (and later Professor of Agriculture at the University of Leeds), was working there; he became one of John's closest lifelong friends. Their respective individual strengths in biology and physics led to several insightful joint reviews over the years (13, 32). On this visit John became aware of some of the unique challenges of unravelling crop–environment interactions in semi-arid agriculture, in contrast to the moist temperate cropping systems that he had so successfully studied at Rothamsted.

ENVIRONMENTAL PHYSICS AT THE UNIVERSITY OF NOTTINGHAM

The Monteiths moved to SB in the summer of 1967 and the family settled into a comfortable university-owned house, St Michaels, in the village. A few years later they purchased the family house, Hillcroft, at the edge of campus. John quickly wrote successful grant proposals to support three lines of research. The Nuffield Foundation supported a large programme on the microclimate and carbon balance of barley crops, using the micrometeorological methods he had developed at Rothamsted but adding physiological, agronomic and hydrological studies through collaboration with Keith Scott and Mike McGowan. Two postdoctoral scientists, Paul Biscoe and Keith Gregson, were employed to develop physiological research and data acquisition, respectively, and several PhD students also contributed. The Natural Environment Research Council supported a project to study the water balance of the local catchment (watershed); Mike McGowan took responsibility for the hydrology, and Monteith supervised the microclimatological measurements, again with several PhD students involved. And John began a completely new line of research on animal heat balance through a grant from the Science Research Council, employing a Polish postdoctoral research assistant, Kris Cena. Each topic required major investment in new equipment and the construction of other instrumentation that was not commercially available, using a new workshop staffed by several technicians.

Shortly after arriving at SB, John received permission to hire an additional Assistant Lecturer in Environmental Physics. He advertised the position, indicating that an interest in

Figure 3. Monteith at his desk in the Environmental Physics Section, University of Nottingham School of Agriculture, Sutton Bonington, in 1980. (Photograph supplied by Elsa Monteith.) (Online version in colour.)

radiation measurement would be advantageous. (He hoped to encourage work that would continue his interest in the radiation budget at the surface.) He always joked that I was the only applicant for the job, and that I had probably misunderstood the wording, as I had just completed a PhD on the measurement of therapeutic X-radiation. However, the appointment turned out to be a wonderful opportunity for me; John helped me adapt to studying radiation of longer wavelengths than I had been used to, and we began a close working relationship and a friendship that continued until his death.

The formation of an Environmental Physics Section as part of the Department of Physiology and Environmental Studies (later the Department of Physiology and Environmental Science) at SB also required that the subject be taught to undergraduates. The three-year course leading to the honours BSc in agricultural science was structured so that students devoted the final term of their second year and all of their third year to the study of only three topics that formed a cohesive set (the 'triad'); an honours research project was undertaken in one of the subjects. John set to work developing an environmental physics option to be offered as a triad subject; he was determined that it would include a substantial amount of practical work, much of it outdoors, to reinforce the lecture material. As there was no appropriate textbook, John compiled extensive notes (figure 3). He proved to be a superb teacher. The first environmental physics class (1968) consisted of four undergraduates and several postgraduates, postdoctoral workers and members of staff. Shortly afterwards the publisher Edward Arnold approached John, and the class notes formed the basis of *Principles of environmental physics*, published in 1973 (16). The book was immediately successful (although the first undergraduate class to use it at SB delighted in finding several minor mathematical errors!); the International Biological Program (IBP) had created a worldwide group of young scientists applying physics to biology, and the book's approach was unique. It quickly became a much-used text on researchers' bookshelves and was adopted at several universities for undergraduate teaching. Translations into German, Japanese, Polish and Portuguese followed. John invited me to join him in co-authoring the second edition (1990); a third (2008) and fourth (2013) ensued.

With his main research areas at SB thriving and producing an increasing stream of publications as the research teams grew, Monteith was able to undertake more foreign travel in addition to serving terms as Department Head (1970–73 and 1979–82) and Dean of the School of Agriculture (1985–86). An IBP/UNESCO meeting in Kampala (1970), at which he spoke on 'Solar radiation and productivity in tropical ecosystems' (14), allowed him to visit Malawi, Kenya and Nigeria, further strengthening his enthusiasm for applying environmental physics to tropical agriculture. The prospect of making a significant impact on food production in developing countries had a great appeal for John.

A visit to the Cocoa Research Station in Brazil raised questions of how microclimate influenced fungal infection on cocoa pods. The solution that Monteith and David Butler (one of the first environmental physics graduates from Nottingham) found (24) lay in a rather subtle mechanism for condensation, harking back to John's PhD research. But in the Section we suspected that John's notorious sweet tooth was what particularly attracted him to this work— there was always much amusement when 'the men from Mars' visited (the Mars chocolate company funded the work).

The Brazilian project was the forerunner of other tropical research for which John was awarded grants from the Overseas Development Agency (ODA). In each case a postdoctoral scientist undertook the work, spending time at SB before and after undertaking research in the field. Geoff Squire studied the microclimatology and environmental physiology of tea in Malawi, including designing a controlled environment glasshouse for aspects of the research (foreshadowing later developments at SB); Rob Sunderland investigated the gas exchange of plantation forest in Malaysia; and John Littleton used a field-based controlled-environment chamber in West Africa to study the environmental physiology of cowpeas.

In 1974 John made his first visits to the recently established International Crops Research Institute for the Semi-Arid Tropics (ICRISAT) in Hyderabad, India, and the International Rice Research Institute (IRRI) in the Philippines. Both institutes had been funded by the Rockefeller and Ford Foundations and the World Bank to exploit advances from the 'Green Revolution' and develop methods of increasing crop production in developing countries. Monteith had already demonstrated that the methods and analyses that his group at SB had developed could be applied with similar benefits to study crop–environment interactions in the tropics, and he now saw the potential for further collaboration. On his return to the UK he began discussions with R. K. Cunningham, Head of the Natural Resources Division of the ODA, about establishing a unit at Nottingham for research on tropical crop microclimatology.

In 1976 the ODA decided to fund Monteith's proposal, which called initially for the hiring of four postdoctoral scientists and two technicians, and the construction of major facilities for growing tropical crops in field-like conditions at SB. The grant also covered 50% of Monteith's salary, allowing him to spend the mornings in his professorial duties on campus and the afternoons at the ODA Unit, which was accommodated by reconfiguring St Michaels House. John and his ODA team set about planning the tropical growth facilities and settling on the crops to be studied. The main research facility for the Unit was a suite of five glasshouses with temperature and humidity controls in which realistic stands of tropical crops could be grown to maturity. A key concept was that the SB facilities would be used to investigate how the crops responded to radiation, temperature and humidity in a controlled and intensively monitored environment, and then the team members would conduct field experiments with staff at ICRISAT to compare responses in real tropical conditions.

The plan worked extremely well: over the next 11 years the ODA Unit produced almost 100 papers and trained a large number of postgraduate students and institute researchers at Nottingham and ICRISAT. Postdoctoral research scientists employed in the Unit included

Peter Gregory, Nick Gallagher, Geoff Squire, Bruce Marshall, Dave Harris, Robin Matthews, Chin Ong, Sayed Azam-Ali and Lester Simmonds.

Although most of John's plant environment research was now focused on tropical crops, studies of the physics of the animal environment progressed well in the University Section. Alastair McArthur, another physics graduate from Scotland, had joined the Section in 1972 to study the heat balance of sheep outdoors. After the award of his PhD he was hired as the fourth environmental physics lecturer. The appointment of Lawrence Mount from the Institute of Animal Physiology, Babraham, as a visiting Special Professor brought expertise that supported teaching and research in animal heat balance and the microclimatology of animal housing. He was succeeded on his retirement by his colleague Doug Ingram.

Encouraged by another visiting Special Professor, Arthur Chamberlain, from the UK Atomic Energy Research Establishment, Harwell, I began to develop work on micrometeorological and physiological aspects of air pollution, and this topic quickly expanded to support its own group of PhD students and postdoctoral researchers.

The Environmental Physics Section was now large enough to support three main thrusts of research: Monteith on microclimate and crop productivity (temperate and tropical), Clark and McArthur on the microclimatology of animals (housed and in the field) and Unsworth (followed in 1983 by Jeremy Colls) on air pollution.

In 1984 the Monteiths decided that, with their family all 'out of the nest', it was time to take a long-postponed sabbatical year. They spent the first five months at ICRISAT, where John relished the freedom from administration that allowed him to ruminate on how he might apply his knowledge of temperate and tropical crop microclimatology to crop models. He had often complained that most crop–climate models were far too complex and could not be tested in the conventional sense; now he taught himself to program and began to develop parsimonious models that built on his well-known penchant for linear relationships and the principle of Occam's Razor.

After their stay at ICRISAT the Monteiths moved on to spend five months at NASA's Goddard Space Flight Center, outside Washington DC—a startling cultural contrast. Here John worked with Robert Gurney and Bhaskar Choudhury, again on models, but this time extending a canopy heat balance model (36) appropriate for remote sensing applications.

ICRISAT, Hyderabad

A year after returning from sabbatical, Monteith was contacted by the Director General of ICRISAT, advising him that there was a vacancy for Director of the Resource Management Division, and encouraging him to apply. Mirroring their quandary 20 years previously, John and Elsa struggled to balance the attractions of this position and its potential to influence crop production in the developing world with the satisfaction of heading an established research group and being part of village life at SB. The lure of the tropics won, and in the summer of 1987 Monteith resigned from the university and he and Elsa moved to Hyderabad (figure 4).

The Resource Management Division at ICRISAT had about 80 staff, distributed between atmospheric and soil science, crops and cropping systems, and the economics of human resources; thus Monteith's management responsibility was a lot more than he had been used to. Perhaps the institute was not quite as convinced as John that he was up to the challenge, as they promptly sent him for three weeks of management training in The Netherlands. There he suffered a barrage of personality tests, discovering, as all of us who worked with him knew

Figure 4. John and Elsa Monteith at a street market near Hyderabad, India, in about 1988.
(Photograph by Ed Potter.) (Online version in colour.)

already, that he was exceptionally intuitive in problem solving (for example finding elegant solutions but often with mathematical errors), and was a finisher rather than a procrastinator (as seen by his extensive publication list).

During his tenure at ICRISAT he designed experiments to study the interaction between irrigation and nitrogen in determining sorghum yield, using the unique advantage of having many willing field workers to undertake weekly growth analyses including detailed measurements of root growth and development. Such work put into practice many of the techniques and interpretations that his ODA Unit had perfected on a smaller scale in more controlled conditions. The outcome was a satisfying understanding of how maximum yields could be secured when water and fertilizer were in short supply. Although most of his responsibility was at ICRISAT, he also supervised teams at outstations elsewhere in the semi-arid tropics, for example Niger in the sub-Sahel. The Monteiths quickly became immersed in the community; they rented a comfortable house to the west of Hyderabad and adjusted to the vagaries of life in a developing country: frequent losses of electrical power, dubious drains and an unreliable water supply that they circumvented by stocking the refrigerator with large numbers of water-filled gin bottles. The Monteith house became known as a place where local school children were always welcome to bring their unanswered questions about many aspects of science, literature, history and life, explaining that at school they were 'not allowed to have doubts' (in other words, question the teachers). John and Elsa became members of a nearby English-speaking church congregation where John occasionally substituted for the regular organist, the delightfully named Isiah Comfort.

However, after five enjoyable years John began to feel that he was losing touch with the wider field of science, and both he and Elsa missed being close to their children and grandchildren. So in 1991 they left ICRISAT and returned to their Scottish roots, settling in Edinburgh close to the university. He accepted the offer of an office at the Institute of Terrestrial Ecology (Natural Environment Research Council), where a former environmental physics student, David Fowler (FRS 2002), was head of the biogeochemistry group. John imagined that he would ease into retirement, but colleagues thought differently. At that time the Natural Environment Research Council had launched a large research programme named TIGER (Terrestrial Initiative in Global Environmental Research). Several groups included John as a consultant on their TIGER research proposals to develop and test soil–vegetation–atmosphere transfer (SVAT) models. When the grants were announced he found that he had eight months of salary funded, working with Robert Gurney (Reading University, ex-NASA), Paul Jarvis (University of Edinburgh) and Melvin Cannell (Institute of Terrestrial Ecology, Edinburgh). During almost 10 years as a Senior Visiting Fellow at the Institute of Terrestrial Ecology he made progress on several aspects of the Penman–Monteith equation applied at regional scales, and took part in several international meetings. He also tackled some of the mountain of unpublished work that he had accumulated, publishing on the topics that he saw as most valuable. When spotted in the car park disposing of remaining papers in the waste bins, his response was that the only really important products of 'our research' are in peer-reviewed journals, and he was content that his most important findings 'are out there'.

NATIONAL AND INTERNATIONAL WORK

Monteith served on committees, councils and as an officer of several scientific societies. He was Vice-President of the Royal Meteorological Society from 1977 to 1978, and its President from 1979 to 1980. He was also Vice-President of the British Ecological Society (1977–78), probably the only time a person was simultaneously a Vice-President of these two societies. During his tenure as President of the Royal Meteorological Society he led the negotiations with the publisher John Wiley to establish the *International Journal of Climatology* under the Society's aegis.

He served on the Meteorology Sub-Committee and the Hydrology Sub-Committee of the Natural Environment Research Council, chaired its Applied Climatology Research Group, and was a member of its Council (1980–84). He was a governor of both the Grassland Research Institute (1975–83) and Silsoe Research Institute (1993–97), and was a member of the Lawes Agricultural Trust Committee (1983–86), overseeing developments at Rothamsted Experimental Station. He was an external advisor to the Physics Department at the University of the South Pacific, Fiji, an Honorary Professor at the University of Edinburgh and an Adjunct Professor at the University of Florida.

Possibly his international committee work with the most enduring outcome was his participation in 1990 in the Working Group of the UN Food and Agriculture Organization (FAO), which revised the FAO recommendations on 'Estimation of irrigation need' (figure 5). These discussions led to the adoption of the Penman–Monteith equation with specified crop resistances to provide estimates of water use by so-called 'reference crops' in relation to local weather parameters. The document known as FAO56 has been widely accepted worldwide for irrigation planning (Allen *et al.* 1998). (For details of the Penman–Monteith formula and crop resistance see below.)

Monteith was also a regular and active participant in national and international conferences. Contributions of particular significance were made at the 1962 Canberra conference 'Environmental Control of Plant Growth' mentioned above, in which canopy resistance

Figure 5. Participants in the FAO Expert meeting that led to the adoption of the Penman–Monteith 'reference crop evapotranspiration' method, Rome, Italy, in 1990. Front row, left to right: J. L. Monteith (UK), W. O. Pruitt (USA), R. Francaviglia (Italy), J. Doorenbos (FAO); second step, right: M. Smith (FAO); next row: M. Jensen (USA), H. Gunston (UK), L. Cavazza (Italy); second row from top: R. Feddes (The Netherlands), E. Romani (Italy), A. Perrier (France), P. Fleming (Australia), R. Gommes (FAO), L. Pereira (Portugal); top row: A. Segeren (FAO), R. Allen (USA), D. Rijks (WMO, The Netherlands). (Photograph supplied by R. Gommes.) (Online version in colour.)

models were introduced (6); the 1963 Symposium of the Society of Experimental Biology (the Penman–Monteith formula (8)); the 1967 UNESCO Symposium 'Functioning of Terrestrial Ecosystems' (micrometeorological analysis of carbon dioxide exchange of crops (10)); the 1969 Symposium of the American Society of Agronomy and the Crop Science Society of America, 'Physiological Aspects of Crop Yield' (radiation absorption in crop canopies (11)); the 1973 University of Nottingham Easter School 'Heat Loss from Animals and Man' (physical analysis of animal heat balance (17)); and the 1986 Royal Society Discussion Meeting 'The Scientific Basis for Irrigation' (integrating atmospheric and soil controls of crop water use (32)).

John's presence at a meeting, usually in the front row, could be rather daunting to new presenters, but even his most searching questions were asked in a polite and encouraging style. A distinguished American professor once described him as 'the classic British gentleman— smooth as goose grease'. His penchant for humour often lightened discussion sessions. One tongue-in-cheek interjection occurred at a British Ecological Society conference in Cambridge in 1974 on 'Light as an Ecological Factor'. Monteith was asked during the discussion to comment on the origin of the term 'albedo', used to describe the reflection coefficient of surfaces. He launched straight-faced into a spurious story about an American astronomer Al Bedo who had studied the reflectivity of stars; the rapporteur dutifully recorded the information, and it is preserved for posterity in the conference proceedings (Evans *et al.* 1976).

HONOURS AND AWARDS

Monteith's contributions to meteorology and agricultural science were recognized in numerous medals, prizes and awards. The Royal Meteorological Society awarded him the Buchan Prize (1962), the Symons Memorial Medal (1995) and the James Paton Prize for Photography (1988). This last particularly pleased him because it was named after his mentor while he was an undergraduate at Edinburgh University, and recognized his perceptive photographs and interpretations of meteorological phenomena, a lifetime interest.

For his contributions to agriculture he received the Solco Tromp Award for Biometeorology (1983), the Rank Prize for Nutrition and Crop Husbandry (1989) and an honorary doctorate from the Agricultural University of Athens (1993).

He was elected a Fellow of the Royal Society in 1971, a Fellow of the Royal Society of Edinburgh (1972), an Honorary Member of the British Ecological Society (1991), an Honorary Member of the European Geophysical Society (1992) and an Honorary Fellow of the Royal Meteorological Society (1997). In 1989 his alma mater, the University of Edinburgh, awarded him an honorary DSc.

RECREATION

Music played a large role in John's life. It was a catalyst in bringing John and Elsa together and was always an important feature of their home. John was an accomplished pianist and organist, and played the organ at the Methodist church in SB and at churches in Hyderabad and Edinburgh. He also loved to sing; each Christmas he would assemble a choir of students at SB and put on a concert for the village and university communities. True to their heritage, the Monteiths organized occasional Burns Night celebrations with other Scottish exiles at their home in SB, complete with traditional songs and dramatic poetry readings.

He was an accomplished photographer who always kept a camera close by to capture interesting observations. Several of his photographs illustrating environmental topics (including coalesced fog drops on my beard) appear in *Principles of environmental physics*, and others, particularly of clouds, were published in the journal *Weather*.

Walking, particularly in the Scottish mountains, was John's favourite form of exercise (figure 6). Their annual family summer holiday was always taken in Scotland and usually involved the ascent of a Munro or two (Munros are all the Scottish mountains with elevations exceeding 3000 feet (914 m)). Science was not always entirely put aside on these trips: several of John's excellent cloud photos were taken then, and one memorable family ascent of Scotland's highest mountain Ben Nevis (1344 m) involved multiple stops to make measurements. At the time, John and I were studying the influence of atmospheric aerosol on the intensity of solar radiation. A rare cloudless day in the Highlands was too much to miss, so the family carried a Linke–Feussner radiometer, microvoltmeter and sling psychrometer up

Figure 6. A relaxed moment in the Scottish Highlands, in about 1970. (Photograph supplied by J.L.M.)

the mountain, taking radiation and humidity measurements every 200–300 m. The effort in carrying the 20 kg or so package of instruments may not have been popular with the family, but the results were a valuable addition to the subsequent publication (15).

RESEARCH AND WRITING

With a publication record extending over 50 years, including almost 200 papers, it is not easy to give the reader an adequate flavour of Monteith's research and its impacts on science. In his publication list, John classified his publications into six broad headings (plus 'reviews' and 'miscellaneous'), and the following adopts that classification.

Instrumentation

Three examples of John's work on instrumentation are discussed here because each contains aspects that arise again in later work.

Much of his early research required measurements for which there were either no commercial instruments made or for which the principles of instruments were poorly understood. As a postgraduate student he and his mentor Ted Jennings built a recording dew balance on which the change of weight of a block of turf and soil was detected by the photographic record when light from a spot galvanometer struck photographic paper on the rotating drum of a cannibalized barograph (1). With this device, and concurrent measurements of wind speed and surface energy balance, Monteith discovered that both distillation (water evaporating from the soil and depositing on leaf surfaces) and dewfall (the turbulent transfer of water vapour from the atmosphere and its condensation on leaves) could be significant sources of 'dew' on clear nights (3). The relative importance of the two processes depended on the surface heat budget, which Monteith studied by measuring air temperature, humidity and wind speed profiles and net radiation.

In designing fine wire wet-and-dry-junction thermocouple systems (psychrometers) for the temperature and humidity profiles, Monteith needed to assess errors associated with such thermocouple psychrometry. This led to his earliest theoretical paper (2) in which he considered how the classical theory of psychrometry needed to be modified in practice because of the boundary layer existing around finite thermocouple sensors. He presented a new derivation of the psychrometer equation by using an approach to heat transfer that employed non-dimensional numbers (Reynolds, Nusselt and Prandtl), a style that he often used in later work. This choice may well have been influenced by his academic supervisor, B. J. Mason, who was studying heat transfer from water drops and ice crystals. Monteith also considered the exchange of radiation between thermocouple psychrometers and their surroundings, and he adopted a linearized radiative transfer equation that also appeared in several of his later publications. The resulting linear equations took a form similar to Ohm's law and although Monteith did not at this time take the step of explicitly using an Ohm's law analogue, this analysis may have sown the seeds for the development of resistance models later.

A second area in which instrumentation was needed arose shortly after Monteith began work at Rothamsted. He needed to understand how solar radiation was absorbed and transmitted through tall crop canopies. This knowledge was also needed for investigating how canopy light distribution influenced photosynthesis. However, there were no suitable instruments. He seized on a technique first used by Wilson & Epps (1919) to construct thermopiles by electroplating copper onto constantan wire wound around a former. In this way Monteith and Szeicz built 'tube solarimeters', consisting of a thermopile up to 1 m long enclosed in a glass tube (7). The linear sensor allowed the instrument to average the irradiance in sunflecks and shade, and arrays of tube solarimeters at various heights in a canopy allowed Monteith and Szeicz to investigate radiation absorption in relation to leaf distribution and spectral properties. Tube solarimeters were also built with gelatin filters inside to separate photosynthetically active (visible) and near-infrared radiation (Szeicz 1974).

Knowledge gained from tube solarimeters allowed Monteith to develop and test mathematical models of radiation absorption by plant canopies (9), and ultimately supported the adoption of a simple model of crop and forest productivity based on measurements of radiation interception that can be made from aircraft and satellites (36) (Landsberg & Waring 1997; Choudhury 2001).

A third example of Monteith's influence in employing new instruments in environmental physics is his contribution to diffusion porometry to study evaporation from leaves. Plant physiologists use porometers to investigate the stomatal control of transpiration. Calibration of early instruments that measured the relationship between air pressure and the viscous flow of air through part of a leaf clamped in the porometer cup was a problem until Penman, collaborating successively over a period of 25 years with F. G. Gregory FRS, O. V. S. Heath FRS and F. L. Milthorpe, derived and eventually improved a theoretical relation between the resistance to flow and stomatal aperture (Milthorpe & Penman 1967). However, making absolute measurements in the field remained a problem. In the mid 1960s small humidity sensors became available, allowing the development of a new generation of dynamic diffusion and steady-state porometers. After a visit by C. H. M. van Bavel to Rothamsted, at which he discussed new approaches to porometry, W. Stiles and T. A. Bull built a prototype diffusion porometer, and Monteith authored a paper with Bull on the theory, calibration and performance of the instrument (12). When Monteith moved to Nottingham he continued his interest in porometer design; P. V. Biscoe and other postgraduate students brewed foul-smelling potions in the laboratory to make miniaturized sulphonated polystyrene humidity sensors, and then used the porometers in their field studies of sugar beet and barley. These measurements helped to confirm the validity of Monteith's canopy resistance parameter as a measure of stomatal control. By 1972 a prototype automatic porometer had been built in the Section and was field tested by Geoff Squire in Malawi. He recalls that its slow-response sensor needed considerable nursing to obtain reliable measurements in humid conditions.

The availability of porometers also allowed Biscoe and Unsworth, supervising an undergraduate student project, to begin investigations of the influence of the air pollutant sulphur dioxide on stomatal behaviour (Unsworth *et al.* 1973). The research field of air pollution transfer and effects blossomed into one of the main themes of work in the Section over the next three decades. Much later, Monteith's understanding of the theory of porometry allowed him (with his PhD student Anne Wheldon) to improve the interpretation of measurements made with a 'skin evaporimeter', used to assess water loss from premature babies as discussed below (28).

In 1973 Monteith wrote to E. A. (Ed) Potter, who had recently set up a small instrument manufacturing business, Delta-T, near Cambridge, asking whether his company would be interested in making commercial versions of tube radiometers and porometers. The venture was highly successful, and since then Delta-T has sold large numbers of both instruments around the world. The first commercial Delta-T porometer (1975) was fully automated and much easier to use than the version that Geoff Squire had used. The design continued to be improved in sensor design and electronics with advice and encouragement from Monteith; in 1988, Monteith, Campbell and Potter published an extension of the theory behind the instrument, taking into account the sensor time response and adsorption of water on the cup materials (35).

Monteith also helped found Campbell Scientific Ltd, the European subsidiary of the environmental instrumentation company Campbell Scientific Inc. The impetus for the venture was a sabbatical year spent by Gaylon Campbell in the Environmental Physics Section in 1977–78. Gaylon was an extraordinarily stimulating and productive visitor. He introduced new ideas from soil science, animal science and electronics in a string of eight publications co-authored with Monteith and other members of the Section, and he taught short courses on special topics in instrumentation such as sonic anemometry and thermocouple psychrometry. After Gaylon returned for a second sabbatical at SB in 1984, Campbell Scientific Ltd was established; Dick Saffell from the ODA Unit was recruited as its first chief executive officer. The fledgling company initially set up offices on the School of Agriculture campus.

Radiation climatology

In an extension of the research that Monteith and Szeicz undertook on the radiation budget of crops, Monteith took a wider interest in radiation climatology, recognizing that better understanding of the causes of spatial variation in components of the radiation budget would improve the accuracy of estimations of potential evaporation. In the 1950s there were no robust net radiometers, and few weather stations made routine solar radiation measurements. Penman had circumvented this problem in his classic paper (Penman 1948) by using an empirical expression correlating daily solar radiation receipt at Rothamsted with sunshine hours (which were also widely measured elsewhere) and estimating the long-wave radiation balance of the surface from records of temperature, humidity and cloud cover.

From 1960 onwards Monteith published several papers in the *Quarterly Journal of the Royal Meteorological Society* on estimating long-wave radiation exchanges and on the climatology of solar radiation in the British Isles. His resulting estimates of the surface heat budget, compared with hydrological data that Penman had analysed, revealed a puzzle (4). It appeared that Penman's estimates of potential evaporation in Scotland were about 25% too low. The answer lay in an analysis that Monteith made of observations from the five locations in the UK and Ireland where solar radiation was measured directly. The remote western coastal stations of Valentia in Ireland and Aberporth in Wales recorded more solar radiation per hour of sunshine than elsewhere (5). Monteith suspected that smoke and other aerosol pollutants in the atmosphere at Rothamsted and elsewhere in central England reduced the amount of solar energy reaching the ground, and consequently Penman's Rothamsted-derived correlation between radiation and sunshine hours underestimated radiation receipt in cleaner parts of the UK. With the correction that Monteith proposed, potential evaporation estimates for Scotland increased and the discrepancy disappeared.

The aerosol explanation was not accepted by some meteorologists who argued that cloud distribution and/or density might differ between coastal and inland sites. So, when I joined the Environmental Physics Section in 1968, John suggested that we take a closer look at the influence of aerosols on radiation to see if it explained what Penman liked to call 'the excesses at Aberporth'. For several years we used a Linke–Feussner pyrheliometer to measure solar beam irradiance and the angular distribution of long-wave radiation whenever there were cloudless skies. To avoid missing those rare cloudless days, the instrument accompanied John and me on several family holidays (for example the Monteiths on Ben Nevis; see above) and on business trips. On one occasion in Nigeria, when John stopped by a busy road near an airport to take measurements, he was quickly surrounded by armed soldiers who suspected him of setting up a mortar.

When the data were analysed in terms of an aerosol turbidity coefficient (15) it emerged that aerosol associated with different air mass origins (maritime or continental) accounted for large variations in diffuse and direct solar radiation and in downward long-wave radiation at the surface (Dalrymple & Unsworth 1978). Coastal sites where clean arctic maritime air masses were common received much more radiant energy per hour of sunshine than sites in heavily populated parts of the country. More recent spectral measurements at the surface and from satellites are consistent with those early observations.

Evaporation and condensation

If there is one piece of work with which Monteith's name is most closely identified, it is the Penman–Monteith equation that is firmly embedded in agriculture, ecology, hydrology, and meteorology. His PhD research on dew had given him a firm grasp of the physics of evaporation and condensation processes and their role in the surface energy balance. Now, as he worked on the radiation budget of cereal crops at Rothamsted, it became clear that the next step was to understand how the absorbed net radiation was partitioned between evaporation and transpiration, sensible heating of the atmosphere, and heat storage in the soil. He needed to solve the heat balance of plant canopies, and thus he sought to extend the physical analysis that Penman had so successfully pioneered.

Penman had combined the surface energy balance and aerodynamic equations to develop a formula for estimating evaporation from a surface where water was freely available (Penman 1948). A valuable feature of his 'combination method' was that it eliminated the need to know the temperature of the evaporating surface (a difficult measurement with the instruments then available). The amount of the available energy H at the surface that was used in evaporation E depended on a function of wind speed $f(u)$, the saturation deficit of the air $(e_s - e_d)$, and two thermodynamic constants, the rate of change of saturation vapour pressure with temperature Δ, and the psychrometer constant γ. Thus

$$E = \frac{\Delta H + \gamma f(u)(e_s - e_d)}{\Delta + \gamma}.$$

Penman showed that estimates of evaporation using his formula agreed well with measured evaporation from wet surfaces, but evaporation was overestimated from drying soil and vegetation where air at the surface was not saturated with water vapour.

Around 1962 John began to extend the Penman formula for application to vegetation. Somewhat surprisingly, he chose to publish his main report of the work in the proceedings of the 1964 annual meeting of the Society for Experimental Biology (8). Despite its relatively obscure location, the work has become a Citation Classic, with almost 4000 citations.

He began by rewriting the Penman formulation in a form applicable to single leaves, emphasizing the fundamental thermodynamic principles. He then extended the concept so that diffusion from saturated surfaces *within* leaves became part of the transfer pathway to the atmosphere. Thus, with an additional parameter describing the restriction to diffusion imposed principally by stomata, the modified Penman formula could be applied to estimate rates of transpiration from individual leaves.

In the thermodynamic analysis Monteith replaced Penman's aerodynamic transfer function by a parameter r_a, representing the time in which a unit volume of air exchanged heat with a unit area of the surface. Values of r_a for single leaves could be estimated as a function of wind speed and leaf size by using empirical equations from fluid dynamics (drawing on his earliest paper). If the (unsaturated) vapour pressure at a leaf surface is e_0 and in the free atmosphere is e_d, then the transpiration rate is proportional to $(e_0 - e_d)/r_a$; by analogy with Ohm's law, Monteith called r_a an external diffusion resistance, because it controlled the flux of water vapour (current) that was driven by the potential difference $(e_0 - e_d)$. The principle of continuity also requires that the flux of water vapour from saturated surfaces inside the leaf is proportional to $(e_s(T_0) - e_0)/r_1$, where $e_s(T_0)$ is the saturation vapour pressure at leaf temperature T_0, and r_1 is the internal resistance of the leaf. With these modifications and some algebraic manipulation to eliminate T_0, Penman's formula became

$$E = \frac{\Delta H + \rho c_p (e_s - e_d)/r_a}{\Delta + \gamma(1 + r_1/r_a)},$$

where ρc_p is the volumetric heat capacity of air. This has become known as the Penman–Monteith (PM) equation. For a single leaf adequately supplied with water, the value of r_1 closely approximates the resistance imposed by the stomata, which is governed by the size and number of pores per unit leaf area. This simple equation demonstrates the dependence of transpiration rates on meteorological variables: available energy (net radiation), wind speed, air temperature and atmospheric saturation deficit $(e_s - e_d)$, and on the physiological variable stomatal resistance.

The next stage of Monteith's analysis was more controversial. He assumed that a uniform crop canopy fully covering the ground could be treated as a 'big leaf', with an external (aerodynamic) resistance r_a associated with the canopy roughness and wind speed, and an internal resistance r_c associated with the stomatal resistances of all the leaves in the canopy. When he first presented this idea at a conference in Canberra in 1962 he was severely criticized, as discussed above. There were two main objections: first, the aerodynamic resistances for water vapour and heat transfer are different from that for momentum because there is no mechanism for heat and mass transfer that is equivalent to drag caused by pressure gradients in momentum transfer. This results in values of r_c that are not independent of r_a. Second, the analysis does not yield a unique value of internal resistance r_c unless the spatial distributions of heat and water vapour sources in the canopy are identical.

Monteith addressed the first issue by introducing an additional aerodynamic resistance r_b in series with r_a to parameterize the separation of the heat, mass and momentum sinks (16, 25). The work of his PhD student Alastair Thom (Thom 1975) underpinned much of the analysis. Monteith argued that the second issue was unlikely to invalidate the analysis when the canopy was sufficiently dense for all incident radiant energy to be absorbed by foliage, but he accepted that values of r_c deduced from measurements above more open canopies would be influenced by physical restrictions on evaporation from the soil as well as by the physiologically controlled resistances of stomata. His 1965 paper, and many publications since, presented compelling evidence from field observations that, for many agricultural crops and forest stands with closed canopies, r_c varies diurnally and seasonally in the same way as stomatal resistance.

The PM equation incorporating Monteith's concept of canopy—or, more generally, surface—resistance has been widely used. As mentioned earlier, the UN FAO recommends the equation to estimate crop water requirements (Allen *et al.* 1998, 2006); canopy and surface resistances of different vegetation classes and land cover types have been tabulated (Wilson & Henderson-Sellers 1985; Kelliher *et al.* 1995) and may be used to estimate the hydrological consequences of a change in land use (such as deforestation); the PM equation has been manipulated and applied in many different ecosystems to demonstrate how vegetation is 'coupled' to the atmosphere (Jarvis & McNaughton 1986); and several models of general circulation and climate change use surface resistance in parameterizing surface heat balance (Cox 1999; Cox *et al.* 2001).

Monteith recognized the implicit circularity of the PM equation: evaporation rate calculated from the equation depends on air temperature and humidity, but at sufficiently large scales temperature and humidity in the atmospheric convective boundary layer (CBL) are influenced by the heat balance at the surface, creating a feedback mechanism. Priestley & Taylor (1972) theorized that the feedbacks were such that, over extensive uniform surfaces, the evaporation rate should attain an equilibrium value $E_{eq} = \Delta H/(\Delta + \gamma)$. In practice they found that actual evaporation in such situations was αE_{eq}, where α was an empirical factor. In some of his final research publications Monteith addressed these feedbacks: he reanalysed published reports of stomatal responses to humidity to assert that transpiration rate rather than atmospheric humidity itself controlled the responses (38), and he elegantly combined the PM equation with a simple CBL model to show that there is a nearly linear correlation between the surface resistance and α^{-1} (39, 40), which must have been satisfying because he so often sought linear relationships in his analyses.

Microclimate and crop growth

The prospect of using agricultural meteorology to benefit crop production drove much of Monteith's research. At SB and ICRISAT he assembled teams of physicists, biologists and soil scientists to tackle such problems; one of his great strengths was his ability to build bridges and communicate across these disciplines.

He had begun linking physics and biology at Rothamsted in the early 1960s as he tried to explore crop productivity by drawing together measurements of leaf photosynthesis in the laboratory and field measurements of the light distribution in crops. He used his binomial model of light interception in crops ((9), another Citation Classic) to explore how light distribution in the canopy, influenced by leaf angle and spectral properties, could be related to crop carbon assimilation. But what was needed was an experimental method to measure the CO_2 exchange of field crops.

At that time Lemon at Cornell and Inoue in Tokyo had shown that new, sensitive CO_2 analysers could be used to make micrometeorological measurements of crop CO_2 exchange. With support from the Rockefeller Foundation, Monteith and Szeicz persuaded a British company, Grubb-Parsons, to construct a prototype CO_2 analyser that was sufficiently sensitive. Although it required a replacement sensor every two weeks and considerable nursing in the field, John and Geza succeeded in making the first CO_2 flux measurements in Europe over a crop (10) and related their results to canopy light interception. However, there were unanswered questions about how the assimilation of individual leaves was related to crop growth, and addressing these needed a larger research team than Rothamsted could muster.

Arriving at SB in 1967, Monteith assembled a multidisciplinary team of staff and postgraduate students to study the carbon budget of barley crops with the use of micrometeorological, physiological and agronomic techniques to explore carbon sinks and sources on timescales from minutes to weeks. This was the first time that a crop had been studied continuously in this way over whole growing seasons. The measurements were challenging: infrared gas analysers for carbon dioxide and water vapour were the size and weight of large microwave ovens and required frequent calibration; one analyser was mounted on a rail track so it could be moved through the crop to study leaf photosynthesis; another was kept in a trailer alongside an early minicomputer that stored records of gas concentrations and microclimate data on punched tape, taken each day to the university's only mainframe computer for analysis. A neutron probe was used to measure changes in the soil water profile over the season.

The project revealed how the growth of the crop was related to the weather over a timescale fine enough for mechanisms of assimilation, transpiration and resource allocation to be identified. For example, relationships between solar irradiance and net CO_2 fixation of the canopy (light response curves) were developed throughout the life of the canopy and compared with the responses of single leaves, and excellent agreement was achieved between estimates of crop dry matter production based on integrated CO_2 flux measurements and those based on harvested plants (18).

In addition to demonstrating the power of combining micrometeorological and physiological measurements in relating crop growth to microclimate, this work also led Monteith towards a series of groundbreaking analyses concerning weather, climate and the efficiency of crop production (22, 23, 29–31).

He pioneered a way of thinking about the environment and crop growth. Historically, agronomists and crop physiologists had used factors such as net assimilation rate and relative growth rate to seek correlations with weather elements, with little general success. Now Monteith endeavoured to build simple models that related crop yield to factors that were, as far as possible, independent of each other. To begin, his measurements and his theoretical models of radiation transfer in canopies confirmed that the rate at which crops produced dry matter for much of the growing season was proportional to the rate at which radiant energy was intercepted by the canopy. Crop yields were also linearly related to the total intercepted radiation over a growing season (30). This relationship led to a valuable practical application: intercepted radiation measurements from satellites or aircraft can be used to deduce growth and yield (37) (Waring *et al.* 2010).

The concept that intercepted radiation is a major discriminant of crop growth therefore provides a framework for analysing crop yields and for identifying how breeders and growers can increase yields in a given environment. In essence, the amount of intercepted radiation and the efficiency with which it contributes to yield must be maximized by the following: lengthening the growing season; decreasing time lost at the beginning and end of the season when interception is reduced by sparse leaf cover or by senescing foliage; breeding and managing for optimal leaf light response, both to increase maximum growth rate in bright light and to maintain photosynthetic efficiency in low light; and breeding and managing to optimize the proportion of assimilated dry matter that the plant allocates between light-capturing leaves and harvestable yield.

Between 1976 and 1987 the UK Overseas Development Agency supported Monteith in a major project to gain a better understanding of how the weather affects the yield of tropical crops. As described above, he set up a Unit for research on the microclimatology of tropical crops, involving research in tropicalized glasshouses at SB and in the field at ICRISAT. The design criteria for the glasshouse system were novel: crops would be grown in stands mimicking an extensive crop canopy; the crop area would be large enough to allow sequential harvests without significant effects on plant population density; the system would control mean temperature and saturation deficit over ranges experienced in the tropics but would allow the range of these factors to vary throughout each day as they do in nature; and experiments would consist of a set of treatments covering a range of a single factor, with other environmental factors kept constant.

The Unit decided to focus on investigating how solar radiation, temperature and humidity affected the growth and yield of a cereal crop (millet) and a legume (groundnut). Stages in growth and yield were studied in 'developmental periods', focusing on rates of change in the numbers, size and weight of crop structures (such as leaves and grains). Three processes were followed in this way: expansion of the canopy and root system, the production of dry matter, and the partitioning of dry matter between crop elements (such as leaves, roots and fruiting structures).

Over the 11 years that the Unit operated, close to 100 papers were published in refereed journals. Their findings from glasshouse and field experiments can be summarized in terms of two distinct situations: when the soil was moist, yield depended on the amount of solar energy intercepted by the canopy (as in moist temperate climates); when the soil was drying over the season, yield depended on the amount of water that a crop stand could extract from the soil and on the amount of dry matter produced per unit of water transpired. Common to both situations were an expansion process that generated both a canopy and a root system to capture the limiting resource (light or water), and a conversion process generating dry matter, of which the yield is a part.

Monteith's team adopted several concepts that allowed them to simplify the analysis of environmental influences on growth and yield. They made extensive use of the concept of 'thermal time', the integral of time and temperature (degree-days) above a threshold temperature at which a process begins, and showed that the concept greatly simplified their analysis of rates and durations. In particular they emphasized the importance of thermal time in determining the rate of expansion and the duration of crop canopies and quantified the restriction imposed by low humidity on these processes (34) (Squire 1990). Coupled with the relationship relating yield to intercepted radiation, a simple model of crop growth when water supply was not limiting could be developed. When water *was* limiting, Monteith's principal contribution was in demonstrating how the rate at which the root system descends into the soil and proliferates governs the rate at which the stand transpires (33). The time available for growth thus depends on atmospheric and soil factors. Later, during his time at ICRISAT, he directed even more intensive studies of environmental controls of root system dynamics, including interactions with nutrition.

When Monteith began his tropical microclimatology work in the mid 1970s, many of the concepts mentioned above relating crop growth to microclimate were relatively new. The progress he made in experimental science and in communicating his results to the wider community has resulted in agronomists, crop physiologists, soil scientists and microclimatologists having a common framework to describe the responses of crops to the environment. The simple models resulting from his analyses have enabled breeders and crop managers to target their efforts more effectively to increase yields.

Microclimate and animal heat balance

When Monteith was appointed to the Chair of Environmental Physics at Nottingham in 1967 he began research into the physics of animal heat balance. At the time, the main centres for livestock/environment research were the Rowett Research Institute, Aberdeen (K. L. (later Sir Kenneth) Blaxter FRS), the Institute of Animal Physiology, Babraham (L. E. Mount), and the Hannah Dairy Research Institute, Ayr (J. A. McLean). Their main focus was on calorimetry in a controlled environment to study the metabolic rates of sheep, cattle and pigs. Animal heat losses were partitioned into the sensible and evaporative components, and there were some attempts to quantify insulation. Monteith and Blaxter had corresponded in the mid 1960s on solar radiation interception by sheep, and John was probably struck by the similarity between the physics of radiation interception in animal coats and in crop canopies.

John saw that a better understanding of the thermal insulating properties of animal coats would allow knowledge gained in calorimeters to be applied to heat balances in the more complex outdoor environment. He appointed a Polish physicist, Kristof Cena, to begin measurements of transfer processes in animal coats; the results for radiative transfer, heat conduction and convection, and water vapour transfer were reported in three groundbreaking papers in *Proceedings of the Royal Society* (19–21) in which an elegant physics-based approach to the heat transfer analyses was adopted. This work provided a theoretical basis for specifying the physical properties of animal coats and for determining how the state of the underlying skin surface was related to the thermal environment. The next stage was to apply the principles to whole animals indoors and outdoors, and this topic became the focus of research by Jerry Clark and Alastair McArthur.

Alastair recalls Monteith getting him started on his PhD research with the Rothamstedesque advice 'Go and sort out the physics of heat loss for sheep.' Fortunately McArthur turned out to be very effective and he, Monteith and Jerry Clark built a strong research group in the Section, with several postgraduate students studying the heat balance of sheep, cattle, goats, poultry, newborn foals and infants. McArthur's full-sized model sheep, a fleece-covered cylinder, was displayed at an exhibition reviewed by the Queen to mark the centenary of the Royal Meteorological Society; her remark 'But it hasn't got a head!' fortunately did not impact the scientific value of the work that McArthur and Monteith published in *Proceedings of the Royal Society* (26, 27).

Monteith became a regular attendee at meetings of the UK Climatic Physiology Group. As one of the few physicists in the group he encouraged a more rigorous analysis of environmental aspects of animal heat balance. Traditionally, animal scientists quantified insulation in units that obscured the similarity of heat and mass transfer, and there was often confusion between the insulation of the coat and that of the boundary layer surrounding it. Monteith advocated using resistance analogues to distinguish between tissue, coat and boundary-layer controls of heat transfer, as had become accepted in flux analysis in plant science and ecology. It proved a struggle to encourage some entrenched experimentalists to accept the elegance and utility of resistance analogues, and there is still a much greater mix of units used in animal heat balance studies than there is in the plant sciences.

In 1973 Monteith and L. E. Mount (Special Professor in Environmental Physics) organized an influential Easter School at Nottingham entitled 'Heat loss from animals and man'. In a complementary pair of papers in the proceedings, Monteith expounded his physics-based approach to the specification of the environment in thermal physiology (17), and Mount, with input from conference participants, reviewed the concepts of thermoneutrality and demonstrated how its physical and physiological aspects could be brought together (Mount 1974); these remain classic references for those entering the field.

Although most of Monteith's research on animal–environment interactions focused on agriculture, a chance meeting at a university committee with David Hull, Professor of Child Health, led to a valuable input of environmental physics into human health. It had proved extremely difficult to keep premature babies warm in normal incubators, with the result that survival rates were compromised. Monteith, Hull and his colleague N. Rutter received funding from the Medical Research Council to study the heat balance of babies, and an environmental physics postgraduate student, Ann Wheldon, was recruited for the work. Rutter had observed that the water loss through skin of premature babies was much larger than for full-term babies, and the group recognized that this evaporative loss equated to a large heat loss. To quantify this term, Wheldon and Monteith took the theoretical principles that Monteith had developed for leaf porometers and applied them to a commercial skin evaporimeter. Using resistance analogues they showed that the calibration supplied by the manufacturer severely underestimated skin permeability in premature babies (28). Applying their new calibration, the large evaporative heat loss from the premature babies was confirmed; improvements to incubator design have followed, and there is now much greater attention paid to the heat balance of babies in incubators and the maintenance of thermoneutral environments.

PERSONAL QUALITIES

John Monteith is particularly remembered by his colleagues and students for his personal qualities of patience and approachability and his belief in doing science that benefited society. Known to many as 'JLM', he was a great listener and a great communicator. On dropping by his office, staff and students marvelled at his ability to switch instantaneously from a mundane administrative task to a thoughtful discussion of a challenging problem in their research. His intuition could be humbling—he would see a solution to a problem that his visitor had struggled with for days, although his enthusiasm often ran ahead of mathematical thoroughness so that one left the office with a few scribbled equations on a scrap of paper that took the rest of the week to prove. In some of his theoretical publications these intuitive leaps between equations could be challenging to follow, and readers of the first edition of *Principles of environmental physics* with non-mathematical backgrounds also confessed that they found some sections hard going. His lectures were delight to those fortunate enough to attend. For many years he delivered the introductory science lecture to all first-year undergraduates at SB. Relatively few of the students were strong in physics, but on one occasion he was so taken aback by the speed and accuracy with which a student answered a challenging question that he felt compelled to part company with his much-loved Royal Society booklet *Quantities, Units, and Symbols* as a prize!

His writing is memorable for its clarity, brevity and style, the title of a short course on scientific writing that he regularly gave to postgraduate students. He was generous in supporting the preparation of publications, always willing to review drafts and offer suggestions. Manuscripts that he returned were always dismayingly heavily annotated in red ink in his almost indecipherable script, but this was a result of his enthusiasm and insight, not an attempt to impose a standard style. Those of us who continued as teachers inherited his 'tough love' style of editing for our own students' work.

As Head of the Environmental Physics Section at Nottingham he set an example with his well-mannered non-confrontational style and his professional planning. Everyone got a chance to speak at department meetings; dissenting views were listened to and consensus was always sought. These same skills served him well when he chaired much more exalted committees at learned societies and research councils. He applied the same style at conferences and seminars—he might disagree strongly with a presentation or interpretation and could demolish an argument with one or two rapier-like comments, but these were usually made in such an elegant style that the victim sometimes did not realize he was being skewered.

However, his reputation was not always recognized; he was left bemused on one occasion when he returned home to Hillcroft to find his 12-year-old daughter setting up a rain gauge immediately adjacent to the house for a school project. When he gently pointed out that this sheltered location was inappropriate, she reportedly retorted 'Oh go away, Dad, what do you know about it?'

He was a modest man, always ready to give credit to his colleagues, students and others where it was due. Although his name is firmly associated with the Penman–Monteith equation, he regularly pointed out that the resistance model had been proposed by several others, including Penman, who had developed an equation similar to the PM equation in a little-known publication but with different interpretation of the terms (Penman 1952); and Rijtema in the Netherlands had independently formulated a resistance model in his PhD thesis (Rijtema 1965). John claimed that his contribution was only in clarifying the meaning of the crop resistance term.

He was also very inclusive. The Environmental Physics Section received a large number of visitors, obviously wanting particularly to meet him, but he always made sure that visitors spent time with all his colleagues and research students. Similarly, when junior colleagues attended meetings with John he made a point of introducing them to his eminent contemporaries.

John was a very social animal. Environmental Physics parties that he hosted were memorable for the initiations of new members of the Section—a balding student planning a thesis on solar radiation might have his head decorated with a radiometer design, and a faculty member might be teased for some embarrassing event in their research (Monteith himself was a victim one year when he contaminated the gold-lined tubes of a gas analyser with mercury during an overenthusiastic attempt at calibration). The Christmas party at John and Elsa's home was always a highlight, with John's holly-shaped bow tie making its annual appearance. During their time in Hyderabad the Monteith home became a popular place for social gatherings that integrated newcomers into the community.

John's Christian beliefs were very important to him and underlay his career decisions and his treatment of others. Elsa and John were active members of their churches in SB and Hyderabad. In 1994 he visited me at Oregon State University, and over two days we taped his personal record of his life (available as electronic supplementary material at http://dx.doi.org/10.1098/rsbm.2014.0005). In the final minutes he reminisced about some of the happiest memories of his professional life: the guidance he believed God had given him to follow the career path described in this memoir; his pleasure at his election to the Royal Society at the age of 41 years, the award of his Rank Prize for 'contributions to crop husbandry and nutrition' while at ICRISAT, and the award of an honorary DSc by his alma mater, the University of Edinburgh, 38 years after his graduation in physics. But most particularly he valued the satisfaction of teaching and encouraging the careers of his students and colleagues to develop; many went on to hold senior positions in universities and research institutes in the UK and overseas.

One of his final comments was: 'The work is never finished but I managed to get a reasonable number of things done.'

In his last few years John was cruelly affected by an Alzheimer's-like decline. He died in Edinburgh on 20 July 2012 at the age of 82 years.

ACKNOWLEDGEMENTS

I am most grateful to the many people who have helped in providing material and memories for this review. Elsa Monteith and the family provided many personal details about John and his life. The taped record of his life that John made with me in 1994 is the source of many of the anecdotes and personal memories that are included in this memoir. Conversations with Jeremy Elston, Paul Jarvis FRS and Jim McCulloch gave insight into their interactions with John and his contributions to agriculture, forestry and hydrology. Fraser Sim, the archivist at George Heriot's School, Edinburgh, sent me details of John's school career. Many of John's former colleagues and friends provided reminiscences and anecdotes, and helped give perspective on the wide-ranging impact of his work: Gaylon Campbell, Jerry Clark, Tom Denmead, David Fowler FRS, Keith Gregson, Alastair McArthur, Geoff Squire, David Spittlehouse, Christopher Wathes and others. In particular Alastair McArthur, David Fowler and Geoff Squire read drafts of this manuscript, provided valuable suggestions for improvements, and corrected several examples of stylistic and grammatical errors at which John would have cringed.

The frontispiece photograph was taken in 1980 by Godfrey Argent and is reproduced with permission.

REFERENCES TO OTHER AUTHORS

Allen, R. G., Pereira, L. S., Raes, D. & Smith, M. 1998 *Crop evapotranspiration (guidelines for computing crop water requirements)* (FAO Irrigation and Drainage Paper no. 56). Rome: UN Food and Agriculture Organization.

Allen, R. G., Pruitt, W. O., Wright, J. L., Howell, T. A., Ventura, F., Snyder, R., Itenfisu, D., Steduto, P., Berengena, J., Yrisarry, J. B., Smith, M., Pereira, L. S., Raes, D., Perrier, A., Alves, I., Walter, I. & Elliott, R. 2006 A recommendation on standardized surface resistance for hourly calculation of reference ETo by the FAO56 Penman–Monteith method. *Agric. Water Mgmt* **81**, 1–22.

Choudhury, B. J. 2001 Estimating gross photosynthesis using satellite and ancillary data: Approach and preliminary results. *Remote Sens. Envir.* **75**, 1–21.

Cox, P. 2001 *Description of the TRIFFID Dynamic Global Vegetation Model* (Hadley Centre Technical Note no. 24). Bracknell: UK Met Office.

Cox, P., Betts, R., Bunton, C., Essery, R., Rowntree, P. & Smith, J. 1999 The impact of new land surface physics on the GCM simulation of climate and climate sensitivity. *Clim. Dyn.* **15**, 183–203.

Dalrymple, G. J. & Unsworth, M. H. 1978 Longwave radiation at the ground. IV. Comparison of measurement and calculation of radiation from cloudless skies. *Q. J. R. Met. Soc.* **104**, 989–997.

Denmead, O. T. & Bradley, E. F. 1985 Flux-gradient relationships in a forest canopy. In *The forest–atmosphere interaction* (ed. B. A. Hutchinson & B. B. Hicks), pp. 421–442. New York: D. Reidel.

Evans, G. C., Bainbridge, R. & Rackham, O. (eds) 1976 *Light as an ecological factor: II*. Oxford, UK: Blackwell Scientific.

Jarvis, P. G. & McNaughton, K. G. 1986 Stomatal control of transpiration: scaling up from leaf to region. *Adv. Ecol. Res.* **15**, 1–49.

Kelliher, F. M., Leuning, R., Raupach, M. R. & Schulze, E. D. 1995 Maximum conductances for evaporation from global vegetation types. *Agric. Forest Meteorol.* **73**, 1–16.

Landsberg, J. J. & Waring, R. H. 1997 A generalised model of forest productivity using simplified concepts of radiation-use efficiency, carbon balance and partitioning. *Forest Ecol. Mgmt* **95**, 209–228.

Milthorpe, F. L. & Penman, H. L. 1967 The diffusive conductivity of the stomata of wheat leaves. *J. Exp. Bot.* **18**, 422–457.

Mount, L. E. 1974 The concept of thermal neutrality. In *Heat loss from animals and man: assessment and control. Proceedings of the Twentieth Easter School in Agricultural Science, 1974 University of Nottingham School of Agriculture* (ed. J. L. Monteith & L. E. Mount), pp. 425–439. London: Butterworths.

Penman, H. L. 1948 Natural evaporation from open water, bare soil and grass. *Proc. R. Soc. Lond.* A **194**, 120–145.

Penman, H.L. 1952 The physical bases of irrigation control. In *Proceedings of the 13th International Horticultural Congress*, pp. 913–924. London.

Philip, J. 1966 Plant water relations: some physical aspects. *Annu. Rev. Plant Physiol.* **17**, 245–268.

Priestley, C. H. B. & Taylor, R. J. 1972 On the assessment of surface heat flux and evaporation using large scale parameters. *Mon. Weather Rev.* **100**, 81–92.

Raupach, M. R. & Finnigan, J. 1988 'Single-layer models of evaporation from plant canopies are incorrect but useful, whereas multilayer models are correct but useless': discuss. *Aust. J. Plant Physiol.* **15**, 705–716.

Ritjema, P. 1965 *An analysis of actual evapotranspiration*. PhD thesis, Agricultural University, Wageningen.

Squire, G. R. 1990 *The physiology of tropical crop production*. Wallingford: CAB International.

Szeicz, G. 1974 Solar radiation for plant growth. *J. Appl. Ecol.* **11**, 617–636.

Thom, A. S. 1975 Momentum, mass and heat exchange of plant communities. In *Vegetation and the atmosphere* (ed. J. L. Monteith), pp. 57–109. London: Academic Press.

Unsworth, M. H., Biscoe, P. V. & Pinckney, H. R. 1973 Stomatal responses to sulphur dioxide. *Nature* **239**, 458–459.

Waring, R. H., Coops, N. C. & Landsberg, J. J. 2010 Improving predictions of forest growth using the 3-PGS model with observations made by remote sensing. *Forest Ecol. Mgmt* **259**, 1722–1729.

Wilson, M. & Henderson-Sellers, A. 1985 A global archive of land cover and soils data for use in general circulation climate models. *J. Climatol.* **5**, 119–143.

Wilson, W. H. & Epps, T. D. 1919 The construction of thermocouples by electro-deposition. *Proc. Phys. Soc. Lond.* **32**, 326.

Bibliography

The following publications are those referred to directly in the text. A full bibliography is available as electronic supplementary material at http://dx.doi.org/10.1098/rsbm.2014.0005 or via http://rsbm.royalsocietypublishing.org.

(1)   1954   (With E. G. Jennings) A sensitive recording dew-balance. *Q. J. R. Met. Soc.* **80**, 222–226.
(2)   Error and accuracy in thermocouple psychrometry. *Proc. Phys. Soc.* B **67**, 217.
(3)   1957   Dew. *Q. J. R. Met. Soc.* **83**, 322–341.
(4)   1961   An empirical method for estimating long-wave radiation exchanges in the British Isles. *Q. J. R. Met. Soc.* **87**, 171–179.
(5)   1962   Attenuation of solar radiation: a climatological study. *Q. J. R. Met. Soc.* **88**, 508–521.
(6)   1963   Gas exchange in plant communities. In *Environmental Control of Plant Growth* (ed. L. T. Evans), pp. 95–112. New York: Academic Press.
(7)   1964   (With G. Szeicz & J. Dos Santos) Tube solarimeter to measure radiation among plants. *J. Appl. Ecol.* **1**, 169–174.
(8)   1965   Evaporation and environment. *Symp. Soc. Exp. Biol.* **19**, 205–234.
(9)   Light distribution and photosynthesis in field crops. *Ann. Bot.* **29**, 17–37.
(10)   1968   Analysis of the photosynthesis and respiration of field crops from vertical profiles of carbon dioxide. In *UNESCO Symposium on Functioning of Terrestrial Ecosystems at the Primary Production Level, Copenhagen, July 1965* (ed. F. E. Eckhardt), pp. 349–358. UNESCO.
(11)   1969   Light interception and radiative exchange in crop stands. In *Physiological aspects of crop yield* (ed. J. D. Eastin, F. A. Haskins, C. Y. Sullivan & C. H. M. van Bavel), pp. 89–115. New York: Academic Press.
(12)   1970   (With T. A. Bull) A diffusive resistance porometer for field use. II. Theory, calibration and performance. *J. Appl. Ecol.* **7**, 623–638.
(13)   1971   (With J. F. Elston) Microclimatology and crop production. In *Potential crop production* (ed. P. F. Waring & J. P. Cooper), pp. 129–139. London: Heinemann.
(14)   1972   Solar radiation and productivity in tropical ecosystems. *J. Appl. Ecol.* **9**, 747–766.
(15)   (With M. H. Unsworth) Aerosol and solar radiation in Britain. *Q. J. R. Met. Soc.* **98**, 778–797.
(16)   1973   *Principles of environmental physics*, 1st edn (241 pages). London: Edward Arnold.
(17)   1974   Specification of the environment for thermal physiology. In *Heat loss from animals and man: assessment and control. Proceedings of the Twentieth Easter School in Agricultural Science, 1974 University of Nottingham School of Agriculture* (ed. J. L. Monteith & L. E. Mount), pp. 1–17. London: Butterworths.
(18)   1975   (With P. V. Biscoe & R. K. Scott) Barley and its environment. III. Carbon budget of the stand. *J. Appl. Ecol.* **12**, 269–293.
(19)   (With K. Cena) Transfer processes in animal coats. I. Radiative transfer. *Proc. R. Soc. Lond.* B **188**, 377–393.
(20)   (With K. Cena) Transfer processes in animal coats. II. Conduction and convection. *Proc. R. Soc. Lond.* B **188**, 395–411.
(21)   (With K. Cena) Transfer processes in animal coats. III. Water vapour diffusion. *Proc. R. Soc. Lond.* B **188**, 413–423.
(22)   1977   Climate and the efficiency of crop production in Britain. *Phil. Trans. R. Soc. Lond.* B **281**, 277–294.
(23)   1978   Reassessment of maximum growth rates for C_3 and C_4 crops. *Exp. Agric.* **14**, 1–5.
(24)   1979   (With D. Butler) Dew and thermal lag: a model for cocoa pods. *Q. J. R. Met. Soc.* **105**, 207–215.
(25)   1981   Evaporation and surface temperature. *Q. J. R. Met. Soc.* **107**, 1–27.
(26)   1980   (With A. J. McArthur) Air movement and heat loss from sheep. I. Boundary layer insulation of a model sheep, with and without fleece. *Proc. R. Soc. Lond.* B **209**, 187–208.
(27)   (With A. J. McArthur) Air movement and heat loss from sheep. II. Thermal insulation of fleece in wind. *Proc. R. Soc. Lond.* B **209**, 209–217.
(28)   (With A. E. Wheldon) Performance of a skin evaporimeter. *Med. Biol. Engng Comput.* **18**, 201–205.
(29)   1981   Climatic variation and the growth of crops. *Q. J. R. Met. Soc.* **107**, 749–774.
(30)   Does light limit crop production? In *Physiological processes limiting plant productivity. Proceedings, Easter School in Agricultural Science, University of Nottingham* (ed. C. B. Johnson), pp. 23–38. London, Elsevier.
(31)   1982   (With R. K. Scott) Weather and yield variation of crops. In *Food, nutrition and climate* (ed. K. L. Blaxter & L. Fowden), pp. 127–149. Barking: Applied Science Publishers.

(32) 1983 (With J. F. Elston) Performance and productivity of foliage in the field. In *The growth and functioning of leaves* (ed. J. E. Dale & F. L. Milthorpe), pp. 499–518. Cambridge University Press.

(33) 1986 How do crops manipulate water supply and demand? *Phil. Trans. R. Soc. Lond.* A **316**, 245–259.

(34) 1987 (With G. R. Squire & C. K. Ong) Crop growth in semi-arid environments. In *International Pearl Millet Workshop, Patancheru, India, 7–11 April 1986*, pp. 219–231. ICRISAT Open Access Repository. (See http://oar.icrisat.org/4435/1/CP_375.pdf.)

(35) 1988 (With G. S. Campbell & E. A. Potter) Theory and performance of a dynamic diffusion porometer. *Agric. Forest Meteorol.* **44**, 27–38.

(36)   (With B. J. Choudhury) A four-layer model for the heat budget of homogeneous land surfaces. *Q. J. R. Met. Soc.* **114**, 373–398.

(37) 1989 (With G. Russell & P. G. Jarvis) Absorption of radiation by canopies and stand growth. In *Plant canopies: their growth, form and function* (ed. G. Russell, B. Marshall & P. G. Jarvis), pp. 21–39. Cambridge University Press.

(38) 1995 A reinterpretation of stomatal responses to humidity. *Plant Cell Environ.* **18**, 357–364.

(39)   Accommodation between transpiring vegetation and the convective boundary layer. *J. Hydrol.* **166**, 251–263.

(40) 1998 (With C. Huntingford) The behaviour of a mixed-layer model of the convective boundary layer coupled to a big leaf model of surface energy partitioning. *Boundary-Layer Meteorol.* **88**, 87–101.

SIR KENNETH MURRAY

30 December 1930 — 7 April 2013)

Biogr. Mems Fell. R. Soc. **60**, 331–348 (2014)

K. Murray

SIR KENNETH MURRAY

30 December 1930 — 7 April 2013)

Elected FRS 1979

By W. J. Brammar[1] and W. B. Gratzer[2]

[1]*Department of Biochemistry, University of Leicester, Leicester LE1 7RH, UK*

[2]*King's College London, Randall Division of Cell and Molecular Biophysics, New Hunt's House, Guy's Campus, London SE1 1UL, UK*

Sir Kenneth Murray—Ken to his friends—was held in high esteem and affection by all who knew him. In a remarkable career, which began after he left school at the age of 16 years, he played a prominent part, through his elegant and meticulous research, in the evolution of biotechnology; he trained and inspired generations of students entering this bright new discipline; he developed the means of diagnosing, preventing and treating a feared disease, thereby saving many thousands of lives; he was one of a small coterie that founded the first Europe-based biotechnology company; and he used the profits that this yielded to enrich his university and promote, through the charity that he founded, the careers of promising young scientists. He remained, throughout, modest, unassuming and ever willing to give of his time and knowledge to all who asked.

Early life

Ken Murray was born in the village of East Ardsley near Wakefield in Yorkshire, the younger of two sons of Allen and Elizabeth. The family were devout Christians, and Allen Murray was a preacher in the local chapel. Religion, though, did not seem to have left any imprint on Ken. When Ken was four years old, his father, a miner and member of the mine rescue team, was injured in a colliery accident and had to give up his work. The family moved south to Nottingham, where the father found employment as a school caretaker. The move was to prove fortunate for the young Ken, who showed early intellectual promise at school and gained a scholarship to the local Henry Mellish Grammar School. But the family's means did not stretch to the cost of a higher education, and so Ken left school at the age of 16 years.

http://dx.doi.org/10.1098/rsbm.2014.0008

Drawn to science, Ken joined the Nottingham company of Boots the Chemist (as it was then called) as a laboratory assistant. From Boots he moved to an outstation of the Glaxo pharmaceutical concern in Ulverston in the Lake District, where he was able to indulge his love of hillwalking and climbing. During this time he evidently reasserted his scientific promise, for his supervisor encouraged him in his ambition to improve his prospects by gaining a degree. And so, with the help of a scholarship from Glaxo, he enrolled as a part-time undergraduate in chemistry at the University of Birmingham, and in due time was awarded a first-class honours degree. In his introductory foray into research, while still an undergraduate, he took part in projects of Maurice Stacey FRS, the head of the department, exploring arcane corners of saccharide chemistry (especially an anomalous reaction resulting in the synthesis of isomers of a complex condensation product, mannosyl-D-glucosamine hydrochloride). That led to a pair of reports, published some years later in *Nature* (1, 2)*.

It was 1956 when Ken took his first step in the direction of biology as a PhD student, although still in the Chemistry Department. His supervisor was the genial Arthur Peacocke (later the Rev. Canon A. R. Peacocke, theologian and prolific writer on science and religion, winner of the Templeton Prize, *inter alia*), and Ken was set to work on the composition and properties of what is now called chromatin (3). During this time, as his nephew, Keith, recalls, he supplemented his meagre grant by occasional work as a labourer on building sites. It was during this period also that he met a fellow PhD student, Noreen Parker, a protégée of the noted geneticist, David Catcheside FRS. Ken and Noreen married in 1958, and so began a happy union and close scientific partnership that endured until Noreen's death in 2011. In late 1959 Ken emerged a freshly minted PhD, as did Noreen (figure 1), and took ship for America to begin his independent career in research.

POSTDOCTORAL YEARS: STANFORD AND CAMBRIDGE

Ken's choice of a laboratory for his postdoctoral work was dictated by his PhD research. J. Murray Luck at Stanford University in California was a biochemist, one of whose interests lay in the histones, the family of basic proteins associated with DNA in eukaryotic cells. Little was then known about the function of these proteins, and not a great deal about their structure. Noreen also found a position at Stanford, and the Murrays' intention was to remain there for a year or a little more. In the event they stayed for five profitable years, enjoying, among other things, climbing in Yosemite (figure 2). Ken was left largely to his own devices, and he set out to purify and characterize the histones from one source, the calf thymus gland (6). His definitive review in *Annual Reviews of Biochemistry* (5), encompassing the state of knowledge on the basic proteins of chromatin, appeared in 1965.

The Murrays had returned to England the year before that, he to join the division under Fred Sanger FRS at the Medical Research Council's Laboratory of Molecular Biology in Cambridge, she to the Botany Department of the university. Life with Sanger was once again a happy and enlightening experience, for which Ken remained grateful ever after. He formed lasting friendships, the most important of which was probably with César Milstein (FRS 1975), who shared the 1984 Nobel Prize in Physiology or Medicine with Georges Köhler for the discovery of monoclonal antibodies. Murray and Milstein published a paper on an

* Numbers in this form refer to the bibliography at the end of the text.

Figure 1. Noreen and Ken's PhD graduation, University of Birmingham, December 1959.
(Reproduced courtesy of Birmingham University.)

Figure 2. Climbing on the Sierra's Cathedral Peak, Yosemite National Park, California, in 1963.
(Online version in colour.)

unsuspected source of errors in amino acid analyses (7). Although never losing his fascination with histones, Ken took an active interest in the epoch-making DNA sequencing techniques that Sanger was then developing. What he learned during this time was to stand him in good stead years later in the work that made him famous.

But the Murrays' stay in Cambridge was not without its vicissitudes, and as the duration of Ken's fellowship drew to a close it became a matter of urgency to find a more durable berth; he therefore applied for a lectureship, and Noreen for a fellowship, at the recently established University of York. Both were successful and they prepared to leave Cambridge. At this point the hand of providence intervened, for shortly before the appointed date the Murrays had a car accident. It was serious enough for Ken to request a short delay in their arrival in York. He would in the interim commute from Cambridge to deliver his lectures. In reply he received the following missive from the University Secretary:

> Dear Murray—Postponement is unacceptable. You will be in York by 30 September.
> Yours faithfully …

Ken related that the first and only time he saw Sanger angry was when he was shown this uningratiating letter. Sanger responded by finding further support for Ken to remain in Cambridge until something more desirable should turn up. Meanwhile, he said, Ken should discharge his lecturing obligations in York and then resign. It was to be another two years before the hoped-for opportunity came. It arrived in the form of a letter from Martin Pollock FRS, founding Professor in the Department of Molecular Biology at the University of Edinburgh, the first such department in Britain. Moreover, the thriving MRC Microbial Genetics Unit, directed by William (Bill) Hayes FRS, was due shortly to move from Hammersmith Hospital in London to Edinburgh, and would accommodate Noreen. All were to be housed in a new building. This was the best possible solution for the Murrays, and a cause for gratitude that the car crash and the churlish secretary at York had combined to deflect them from joining a vestigial department with minimal laboratory facilities and as yet no library.

EDINBURGH

And so in 1967 Ken took up his position as Senior Lecturer in Molecular Biology in Edinburgh, eventually becoming a reader in 1973, and a professor in 1984. He and Noreen found the university and also the city congenial from the beginning, and remained loyal to both for the rest of their lives. For a time Ken continued to occupy himself with the histones, as he had done in Cambridge, and in 1969 produced a comprehensive study on successive stripping of the different histones from chromatin, and the structural effects on the residual complex (8). But his focus had been shifting to the histone genes and the mechanism of their expression in the cell (9, 17). He also published, starting from his time in Stanford (4), some of the first observations on postsynthetic modifications of histones in the cell, a topic that was later to acquire huge importance in relation to the control of gene expression and imprinting.

It was nevertheless something quite different that was starting to grip Ken's imagination, probably helped along by the turn that Noreen's research was taking (see the memoir of Noreen Murray in this volume (Gann & Beggs 2014)). Ideas about the production of proteins by gene cloning and expression in bacteria—still regarded by many as akin to science fiction—were taking shape. Moreover, it had become clear that restriction endonucleases, discovered not long before, were the key to success. These enzymes are produced by bacteria as a protection against bacteriophages. In some cases the nuclease is encoded in the bacterial genome; in others it derives from a plasmid, an independently reproducing body in the bacterial cell. The property that makes the restriction nucleases so indispensable to molecular biologists, as much as to the bacterium, is the highly selective nature of the targets on which they act. All restriction nucleases recognize a site in an alien DNA comprising a defined sequence of generally four to six nucleotides, and the enzyme will cut the chain at this point, or in some cases elsewhere in the vicinity. The DNA is broken into pieces (restriction fragments), their number and sizes depending only on how many times the critical short nucleotide sequence appears in the chain. At that time, however, these properties had been only sketchily defined, and none of the enzymes had been isolated.

Noreen, a botanist by training and inclination, had specialized in the genetics of fungi, in particular *Neurospora crassa*, a bread mould. While still in Cambridge she became dismayed at the disdain of the molecular biologists for the organism she loved, and decided to re-train in something closer to current trends. She consulted her friend Frank Stahl, and they agreed that she would spend her evenings in his laboratory to learn phage genetics. The phage she chose to study, called lambda, is a parasite of the geneticists' favourite bacterium, *Escherichia coli*, and was to serve as the vector that would carry a piece of DNA containing the foreign gene of choice into the bacterium. Then the bacterium would be cultured, the expressed protein harvested, and the task accomplished.

Ken and Noreen were not of course alone in entertaining this alluring vision, and the ferocious competition that soon erupted was wholly alien to Ken's temperament. The principal tools for the enterprise would be a suitable vector, an appropriate restriction endonuclease and a ligase, an enzyme already available, that joins apposed DNA strands end to end. But the challenges were formidable, a major one being the lack of any preparation of a pure restriction endonuclease. The lambda vector proved an inspired choice. Noreen had made herself a virtuoso in its manipulation, and it had, moreover, several properties that made it peculiarly suited to the purpose. It has a linear genome that assumes a closed circular form when it enters its host bacterium, which can belong to any of several strains of *E. coli*. It achieves this transformation by bringing into apposition a pair of short single-stranded complementary DNA sequences at its ends. As Ken envisaged it, a restriction nuclease would induce a break in the lambda phage DNA, modified to contain only one cleavage site, and the gene would be inserted into the gap. But that still presupposed knowledge of how and where a given restriction enzyme would cut a long DNA molecule. Ken occupied himself (figure 3) with these and many other related problems for the next few years.

The most felicitous feature of some, although not all, restriction enzymes is that they make staggered cuts in the two strands of a DNA duplex, thereby leaving a single-stranded overlap at the ends of the fragments. These 'cohesive ends' allow a segment of DNA containing a gene of interest, with single-stranded overlaps at its ends that are complementary to those created by the restriction enzyme, to be spliced in. The inserted fragment is then sealed in place covalently by the ligase. Thus the extraneous gene has been slipped into its recipient DNA—one that can function as a vector to carry the ensemble into a bacterium or other suitable cell—and the encoded foreign protein can then be expressed. This simple concept (illustrated in figure 4) evolved into the refined technology that was to transform biomedical and pharmaceutical research and much of diagnostic and therapeutic clinical practice.

Figure 3. Ken Murray in his laboratory in Edinburgh (*ca.* 1979), examining bacterial colonies on a Petri dish.

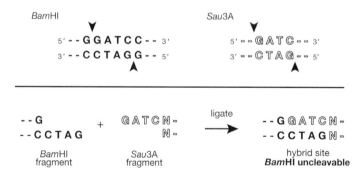

Figure 4. Cohesive ('sticky') ends: the use of restriction endonucleases for splicing a segment of foreign DNA into a host DNA. The bold letters denote the nucleotide sequence of a piece of DNA to be spliced into the DNA (open letters) of a recipient, such as a lambda phage DNA. The arrows (upper left) show the cutting sites of the restriction nuclease, here BamHI, a Type II enzyme, which recognizes a six-nucleotide sequence and makes staggered cuts in the two strands. This leaves one strand of the DNA duplex truncated and terminating in G, and a single-strand overlap on the other strand. The recipient DNA is cut by another restriction nuclease, Sau3A, which has a four-nucleotide recognition site, leaving a single-stranded overlap on one strand of the duplex, as shown (below left; N denotes any of the four nucleotides). The two pieces of single strand have complementary sequences, and when the two DNAs are mixed they cohere by making a duplex. The ligase enzyme is then added and seals the insert into the host covalently. (Diagram taken from Gann & Beggs 2014.)

CONSUMMATION: THE FIRST RECOMBINANT DNA

It had taken no little time, skill and effort to run a restriction enzyme to earth. The report from Meselson's laboratory at Harvard announcing the isolation of *Eco*K from a strain of *E. coli* appeared in 1968, a year after Ken's arrival in Edinburgh, and seemed to come at an opportune moment for the Murrays. In the event it was a poisoned gift. Noreen created lambda phage variants with only a single target site to receive a restriction fragment generated by the enzyme, and Ken began to determine terminal sequences. It presently transpired that all was not as it seemed. *Eco*K was the first member of the Type I class of restriction nucleases. Although these enzymes recognize a specific target sequence in DNA as expected, they cut the chains of the double helix at many random points. This was a disappointment, and occasioned a considerable loss of time.

The Murrays did not repine. Another leading American group purified a more promising restriction endonuclease from a different *E. coli* strain. This was *Eco*RI, and it drove Ken to trawl the *E. coli* plasmids (for one of these had been the source of *Eco*RI), and thus *Eco*RII came to light (10). The search for restriction enzymes became frenetic, because the greater the choice of sequence elements at which DNA chains could be severed, the greater the chances of isolating an intact (for instance human) gene and of splicing it into a vector. Ken and his small team purified two more restriction enzymes and were approached by Hamilton Smith (awarded the 1978 Nobel Prize in Physiology or Medicine for his work in this area), who had found restriction activity in a strain of the bacterium *Haemophilus influenzae*. Ken and his colleagues found that the extract sent by Smith contained not one but two enzymes. Smith had given the presumptive enzyme the name *Hin*dII, to which Ken now added *Hin*dIII. Ken and his group purified both enzymes and determined their cutting sequences (11). Later another restriction enzyme emerged from Ken's labours. This was *Sau*3a—a further addition to the molecular biologist's toolbox.

The outcome of this painstaking work inevitably thrust Ken into the turbulent waters of recombinant DNA and genetic engineering. The intoxicating promise that the emerging tech-nology so obviously held attracted leading molecular biologists from around the world. The mounting pressure of competition would have been borne in on Ken when, in 1972, he and Noreen attended a conference at which he announced the discovery of *Eco*RII and *Hin*dIII, giving full details of their recognition sequences and other properties. This meeting was also the occasion on which two workers from the University of California in San Francisco reported on the isolation of *Eco*RI and *Hin*dII, but the characterization was incomplete and they asked Ken to hold up publication of his results until they had completed their own work, so that the two reports could appear together. Ken chivalrously acceded to their wish, and six months later the two papers were submitted for simultaneous publication.

Ken and Noreen learned at this conference that *Eco*RI was a Type II restriction enzyme, which made staggered breaks in the two DNA strands within its recognition region, therefore leaving the desired single-stranded tails on the severed duplex. This set the Murrays on the path to a recombinant DNA. The first step was to modify the phage genome by eliminating all except one *Eco*RI target site, at which the enzyme would create a break with 'sticky' ends. This being accomplished, it did not then take Ken long to construct the first recombinant DNA based on the lambda phage. The resulting paper was published some time later, in 1975 (12), followed by two more on the creation of nuclease recognition sites in lambda DNA (13, 14). The Murrays' route to the expression of protein-encoding genes, by way of the lambda phage cloning vector, came into general use and remained so for some years (N. E. Murray 2006). It secured for the Murrays a place among the architects of the new science.

The wild surmise of a few years before, that bacterial cultures would soon be producing any desired proteins at will, now seemed a reality. Yet there were still difficulties to be confronted. The means were already available, at least in principle, of generating pieces of DNA containing a selected gene, but complementary cohesive ends had to be contrived. The phage vector carrying its burden had not only to invade the bacterium but also to fulfil the need, having entered, to multiply and destroy its host. It remained essential that the vector genome contain only a single restriction site for any restriction enzyme to be deployed. Then there was the constraint on the amount of DNA that the phage head—the globular structure containing the DNA—could accommodate. This placed a strict limit on the permissible size of the inserted material and therefore of the protein that could eventually be expressed. The efforts of many laboratories contributed to the resolution of these problems. Noreen and Ken made good use of the discovery that the lambda phage could dispense with as much as 40% of its genome without detriment to its invasive function. This meant that the space vacated by the endogenous DNA could be filled by an additional length of the foreign DNA. In the period after 1974, the year in which the Murrays published their first reports on the creation of a recombinant DNA, cloning and expression techniques were evolving rapidly, and the 'insertion cloning' devised by the pioneers was being supplanted by other more versatile and efficient procedures. The most important of these innovations was the use of plasmids to carry an inserted gene. Plasmids are abundant in bacteria (and occasionally also appear in other unicellular life forms). Plasmids replicate independently of the host DNA, and their DNA is generally, like that of the lambda phage, a closed circular double helix. The use of plasmids as cloning vehicles circumvents much of the heroic labour that went into the manipulation of phages, and plasmids were used by Ken Murray in his later work (below) on the hepatitis B vaccine. Today all constituents involved in protein expression, if not the whole procedure itself, are bought from biotechnology companies. The pioneering achievements of the Murrays in genetic engineering are discussed in much greater and authoritative depth by Gann & Beggs (2014).

VIRUS AND VACCINE

In the late 1970s Ken Murray took the decision to enter new territory: he would work on something with an explicit medical thrust. In 1978 he and a small group of like-minded individuals formed a plan to set up a commercial enterprise. Among them were leading biologists and enlightened investors, and their vision was to exploit new discoveries judged to hold therapeutic or diagnostic promise. Thus Biogen came into being (figure 5). It was the first biotechnology company based in Europe. Ken proposed viral vaccines as one line of research that could profitably be pursued, and it was hepatitis B that he mainly had in mind. A motivating factor was undoubtedly the sense that hazards and uncertainties inseparable from the classical methods of vaccine development could become a thing of the past. These methods had, to be sure, given the world the poliomyelitis vaccine, among many others, but recombinant DNA technology should now have the capacity to supersede them. Whether Ken was influenced by the recollection of a devastating outbreak of hepatitis B nearly 10 years earlier in the Edinburgh Royal Infirmary is not clear, but the disease and its consequences were in any case often in the news. The infection had struck

Figure 5. Occasion of the establishment of Biogen NV at a restaurant near Zürich, Switzerland, in 1978. Back row, standing: Molone?, Philippe Kourilsky, Moshe Alafi, Bernard Mach, Charles Weissmann. Middle row: Heinz Schaller (seated), Brian Hartley FRS, Dan Adams, Ray Schaefer. Front row, seated: Wally Gilbert, Phil Sharp, Ken Murray. (Online version in colour.)

in the renal unit, apparently spread through dialysis machines contaminated with traces of exchanged blood, and 40 people had been affected. Of these, eleven had died directly from the disease: seven patients, two laboratory technicians and two transplant surgeons. This resulted in 1970 in the temporary closure of the only dedicated transplant unit in Britain. But the Royal Infirmary was by no means the only medical centre touched by hepatitis B: the renal unit at Guy's Hospital in London recorded 69 cases, 32 of them in members of the staff, and was closed; and there were lesser outbreaks in hospitals around the country. The reported deaths underestimate the full impact, for the infection all too commonly leads to liver cancer.

There were at the time two possible routes to a vaccine: antibodies could be raised against either killed or attenuated virus. A virus could be killed chemically or by heat. Attenuation meant passaging the virus several times through animals or through cells in culture until it mutated (so it was hoped) into a harmless form. Both methods had their disadvantages. Isolation of the virus and the succeeding steps were both laborious and dangerous. The killed virus must be free of even the minutest residuum of live particles and yet retain enough of its antigenic potency. Attenuated virus could sometimes revert to the virulent state. The traditional methods assuredly had their successes, most famously the elimination of smallpox and poliomyelitis, but not all viruses responded so well, and vaccination against hepatitis B had achieved only limited results. The only animals susceptible to infection are humans and monkeys. Thus the available hosts and cell lines in which the virus could be propagated were severely restricted. A vaccine made from the killed virus was developed in the USA and approved by the Food and Drug Administration (FDA), but it was expensive and of limited efficacy. Ken judged that the time had come to apply the methods of genetic engineering to the problem.

There were now tolerably reliable cloning and expression procedures, and the sequencing of short pieces of DNA and the synthesis of oligonucleotides were both routine. There were still at this time relatively few genetic engineering practitioners, and Ken was one of the leaders. Yet the task was daunting, and compounded at the outset by the requirement—unaccountable as it now seems—that all genetic manipulations involving the construction of genetic hybrids between two species (in this case the virus and the bacterium, *E. coli*, for the purpose of cloning and expression) had to be performed under conditions of high physical and biological containment. This ruling arose from a wave of concern over the creation of new life forms, and the fear they might leak into the environment and cause mayhem. In 1975, in the wake of a meeting on recombinant DNA (the Asilomar Conference), the containment restrictions on, in essence, all recombinant DNA experiments were promulgated. In particular, the laboratory had to be maintained at negative pressure, so that airborne particles could get in but not out; in addition, the host bacteria had to be genetically enfeebled, so that even if they did escape into the outside world they would not survive. Few universities in any country could boast the necessary facilities, and so Ken was compelled, until the ban was lifted, to travel to the Microbiological Research Establishment at Porton Down on Salisbury Plain to continue his work. He pressed on.

The first inescapable step on the way to a vaccine had been to procure a virus sample from the blood of a seriously ill patient. This was provided by colleagues in the Department of Bacteriology in Edinburgh, and Ken could set out on his first task, a comprehensive analysis of the viral genome to identify possible antigenic targets. The initial plan was to isolate segments of DNA that might contain genes or parts of genes encoding coat proteins—the essential constituents of the outer layer of the virus—splice each into a suitably engineered lambda phage vector, insert that into *E. coli*, and search for antigenic activity in the polypeptides produced by the bacteria. Ken, in collaboration with his friend Peter Hans Hofschneider and members of his laboratory in Munich, succeeded (15) (as, almost simultaneously, did workers in France and in America) in cloning pieces of the viral DNA. In doing this they departed from Ken's lambda-based procedure, using instead a plasmid as cloning vehicle. Expression in *E. coli* led to an illuminating result: the product, in some cases, harboured a polypeptide that reacted with an antibody directed against an antigen (HBcAg) in a coat protein of the virus. This was an encouraging pointer to a vaccine.

A collaboration between Ken and his colleague Walter Gilbert and his research group at Harvard led to the next major advance, which eliminated to a large extent the hit-and-miss nature of the foregoing methods. The virus DNA fragments were inserted into the vector at a restriction site within the gene for an enzyme (β-lactamase), easily identified by its nucleotide sequence. Therefore an expressed polypeptide with antigenic activity would emerge fused to a β-lactamase protein sequence. It follows that the β-lactamase gene would be adjacent to or at least very close to the gene specifying the virus antigen. The sizes and terminal sequences of the coat and core (that is, internal) proteins of the virus being known, the complete sequences of the proteins could now be determined. The hope then was that both proteins could be made in quantity by expression in *E. coli*. In the event, the expectation was fulfilled only for the core protein; the coat protein, whose coding sequence was undeniably present in the bacteria, obstinately failed to express—a source of frustration all too familiar to researchers to this day. But to compensate, the work—presented in a landmark paper (16) in *Nature* in 1979—included an additional eye-catching observation: the expressed core protein had been used to generate antibodies in rabbits, and those antibodies had recognized an antigen in the blood of human hepatitis B patients.

The virus released into the blood of infected people (or chimpanzees) is accompanied by several other kinds of particle. They include viral capsids—intact spherical heads of the virus, emptied of their DNA—and globular or filamentous aggregates of single proteins or fragments of proteins, and, at a later stage, also antibodies against them. One such protein fragment—the one designated HBcAg—had proved highly immunogenic, but it was expressed in *E. coli* in only low yield. Changes introduced in the DNA sequence led to a much higher expression level and to a product with intact immunogenicity. This became the basis of a commercially disseminated diagnostic kit, which proved highly efficient, not to say profitable for Biogen. However, Ken wanted treatment and prevention, not mere diagnosis. Now that he and Gilbert had defined the genome structure, a wide choice of possible antigenic targets presented themselves. Another antigen, HBsAg, appeared especially promising, but again produced a minimal yield in the *E. coli* plasmid system. This time, moreover, it resisted all attempts to find a solution by genetic manipulation. Ken therefore turned to a different expression system, which had more recently come into favour. He and his group modified the DNA to render it compatible with a yeast vector. Yeast strains affording optimal expression levels had been developed; yeast cells can be grown almost as easily as *E. coli*, and in greater bulk. The microbially produced HBsAg gave rise to antibodies when injected into chimpanzees. These antibodies protected the animals against infection by high doses of a virulent hepatitis strain (18). This was a giant leap, and more revelations followed.

The observation (19) that immunity could be developed against the very reactive antigen, HBcAg, derived (as its designation implies) from the virus core, was unexpected, indeed counterintuitive. It implied that antibodies against an internal, therefore presumptively shielded, protein in the virus could give protection against the disease. This would have been an incentive to prepare antibodies against other hepatitis B proteins, such as the viral DNA polymerase (the enzyme responsible for DNA replication), a direction that was later followed. Ken and his colleagues preferred instead to explore the effects of single and multiple mutations in the HBsAg gene sequence. The object was to determine the extent to which the antigenic specificity could be altered, or more especially broadened to encompass two or more epitopes (separate antigenic elements in the molecule), and thus evade any suppression of immunogenicity through spontaneous mutation of the virus. This exacting work was performed with the uncompromising thoroughness that was so characteristic of Ken's style. The outcome was remarkably successful, and the strategy probably new to immunological practice. For a lucid survey of this and the foregoing work, see reviews by Ken and his co-workers (20, 22).

Ken further enlarged the scope of this general approach by generating antibodies against fusion hybrids containing epitopes of both a coat and a core protein. This exposed a striking synergy between the two antigenic sites. Ken also struck out in yet another direction—the use of oligopeptide homologues of protein interaction sites as competitive inhibitors of virus assembly in the host cell (23)—but this line of inquiry was not taken beyond the exploratory stage. There were more studies aimed at maximizing the efficacy and specificity of the diagnostic and therapeutic materials. Ken maintained his interest in hepatitis B until the vaccine became commercially established, and also in the application of the techniques that he and others had developed to viral pathogens more generally (21). The hepatitis B vaccine, based on Ken's anti-coat protein antibody, received the blessing of the FDA in 1982, and was marketed that year by Biogen. It was the first genetically engineered vaccine. It later transpired that a group of virologists at the Pasteur Institute in Paris had been working along similar lines, and were close on the Edinburgh team's heels. Neither side was apparently aware that it was in a race for the patent rights, and of course the glory. But it had been, as Ken later observed (quoting the Duke of Wellington), 'a damned close-run thing'.

Despite the success of the endeavour to produce hepatitis B viral antigens in *E. coli*, the Biogen patent was the subject of an extensive legal dispute that inevitably occupied much of Ken's time and nervous energy. In 1992 Biogen began infringement proceedings against Medeva plc, which was proposing to market a hepatitis B vaccine made by recombinant DNA technology and produced in cultured mammalian cells. Medeva counterclaimed for revocation of the Biogen patent on the grounds of both obviousness and insufficiency of disclosure. The 1978 priority date of the patent was also challenged. The UK High Court held that the claims in the 1990 European patent were supported by matter disclosed in the 1978 priority document. The obviousness and insufficiency objections were dismissed, and the patent was adjudged valid and infringed. An appeal was granted, and the Court of Appeal ruled that the priority document did *not* support the claimed invention, that it was obvious at the earlier date and that the descriptions were insufficient to support the claims. A third reiteration in the House of Lords essentially supported the decision of the Court of Appeal, although on the basis of a different legal argument. Fortunately for Biogen, in July 1994 the European Patent Office's Technical Board of Appeal dismissed the opposition proceedings against the European Patent.

The hepatitis vaccine set Biogen on the path to commercial ascendancy. Sales now amount to more than US$1 billion per year, and more than one billion doses have so far been dispensed. The vaccine has saved an incalculable number of lives, among which should be included those of patients who survived the infection but would have contracted cancer, because it has been estimated that some 80% of liver cancer cases result from hepatitis B infections. In this sense the Biogen vaccine counts as an anti-cancer vaccine.

TEACHING AND THE EMBL INTERLUDE

In 1979 Ken and Noreen took what amounted to a three-year sabbatical at the European Molecular Biology Laboratory (EMBL) in Heidelberg. It was no rest cure: the Murrays did not reduce the pace of their research activity while exerting themselves to offer instruction and advice to members of the institution. They had made the move in response to an invitation from Sir John Kendrew FRS, the director of the parent European Molecular Biology Organization (EMBO), who paid tribute to the invigorating effect of their presence. But they exerted a wider influence by designing and teaching a laboratory course on genetic engineering, in association with several other experts whom they recruited. The beneficiaries were mainly young researchers from around Europe, and many were the tributes from those whose careers the course helped to launch. Ken took a deep interest in scientific education. He was, in his low-key style, a fluent and stimulating teacher. He set great store by the ability of a lecturer to communicate the allure of his subject. He reminisced on one occasion about the inspiration he had drawn as an undergraduate in Birmingham from an introductory lecture by the eminent saccharide chemist, Maurice Stacey. Stacey, he recalled, wrote the formula of glucose on the blackboard three times, each time differently and each time incorrectly, but it was the enthusiasm that shone through and engaged his listeners.

At the end of their stint in Heidelberg, Ken and Noreen returned to Edinburgh, Ken to occupy the newly founded Biogen Chair of Molecular Biology. He continued to work on vaccines and to supervise students. Much of the research outlined above was performed between that time and his retirement in 1998, although retirement did not put an end to his immersion in work. Science remained central to his life, and he was still to be found in his office daily until very shortly before his death.

Ken's science was marked, like his written and spoken communication, by an unfailing clarity and precision. Ken was meticulous in all things. Even his handwriting—he preferred a fountain pen—was small, flawless and elegant. He made clear to his students that worthwhile research demanded persistence and hard work, and he, like Noreen, led by example. Throughout their careers they worked with immense application. Long days at the bench, and seven-day weeks, were not unusual when demanding experiments dictated. Ken was a man of strong principles and convictions. In engaging with the commercial world as a founder of Biogen, he incurred a good deal of obloquy from academic colleagues. The very idea of a spin-off company, now such a commonplace, was then widely seen as a betrayal of trust, but Ken persisted and was vindicated. Biogen was a huge success, and the royalties accruing from sales of the hepatitis vaccine made Ken rich. But Ken had little interest in personal wealth, and apart from a pied-à-terre in London, and a few pictures to decorate the walls, he devoted the proceeds to good works. He donated a large proportion of the income—about half of his total charitable donations—to the University of Edinburgh, for example to fund improvements of the university library facilities. He also gave support to a programme for bringing science to local schoolchildren. But above all he founded and funded a charity, the Darwin Trust of Edinburgh, dedicated to education and research in the biological sciences and to promoting the careers of aspiring young scientists of high promise. Since its inception in 1983 the trust has flourished, having funded more than 350 PhD students and some 50 undergraduates, mainly but not exclusively in Edinburgh. It has also supported faculty and building projects at Edinburgh and elsewhere. It continues in this work today and it is hoped that it will survive in perpetuity as an extraordinary legacy.

Ken Murray was a much-loved and admired figure, unpretentious and self-effacing. He received many honours in the course of his illustrious career, including a knighthood conferred on him in 1993 (figure 6) and the Royal Society's Royal Medal in 2012 (figure 7). Many felt that Ken could justly have been awarded the Nobel Prize. According to his perceptive obituarist, Tam Dalyell (Dalyell 2013), no less an authority than Lord (George) Porter FRS, former President of the Royal Society, opined that had Ken been less reticent and 'more pushy', that apotheosis might have come to him. Ken had a legion of friends around the world. He and Noreen offered a warm welcome and generous hospitality to their many visitors in Edinburgh and London. In retirement they found more time to indulge their pleasure in music and theatre, and Ken read widely, but especially nineteenth-century and twentieth-century history. In his younger days he had been a keen hiker and rock-climber, and later in life he and Noreen still enjoyed long country walks, until he was smitten with rheumatoid arthritis, which severely impaired his mobility. Noreen died in 2011, leaving Ken's nephew, Keith, as his only close relative.

Figure 6. Investiture at Buckingham Palace, January 1994. (Reproduced by permission of Charles Green.) (Online version in colour.)

HONOURS AND DISTINCTIONS

1979   Elected FRS
1983   Willem Meindart de Hoop Prize
1989   Elected FRSE
1991   Elected Fellow of the Royal College of Pathologists
1992   Saltire Society's Scientific Award
1993   Knighted
1995   Honorary doctorate, University of Birmingham
       Honorary doctorate, UMIST
1998   Honorary doctorate, University of Edinburgh
2000   Royal Medal of the Royal Society of Edinburgh (figure 7)
       Honorary doctorate, University of Dundee
2008   Honorary doctorate, University of St Andrews
2010   Honorary doctorate, University of Sheffield
2012   Royal Medal of the Royal Society
       Honorary doctorate, Cold Spring Harbor Laboratory

Figure 7. Sir Kenneth Murray receiving the Royal Medal of the Royal Society of Edinburgh from Her Majesty The Queen in 2000. (Reproduced by permission of The Royal Society of Edinburgh; copyright © Ian Marshall.) (Online version in colour.)

ACKNOWLEDGEMENTS

We are grateful to Sir Kenneth Murray's nephew, Keith Murray, for much illuminating information and reminiscences of his uncle's early life and career, and to Professor Alex Gann, Professor David Finnegan and Professor Jean Beggs for much indispensable advice, criticism and elimination of errors.

The frontispiece photograph was taken in 1985 by Godfrey Argent and is reproduced with permission.

REFERENCES TO OTHER AUTHORS

Dalyell, T. 2013 Professor Sir Kenneth Murray: scientist who developed the vaccine against hepatitis B. *The Independent*, 16 April.

Gann, A. & Beggs, J. 2014 Noreen Murray CBE. *Biogr. Mems Fell. R. Soc.* **60**, 349–374. (This volume.)

Murray, N. E. 2006 The impact of phage lambda: from restriction to recombineering. *Trans. Biochem. Soc.* **34**, 203–207.

BIBLIOGRAPHY

The following publications are those referred to directly in the text. A full bibliography is available as electronic supplementary material at http://dx.doi.org/10.1098/rsbm.2014.0008 or via http://rsbm.royalsocietypublishing.org.

(1)   1961   (With S. A. Barker & M. Stacey) *N*-Mannosyl D-glucosamine hydrochloride. *Nature* **191**, 142–143.

(2)   (With S. A. Barker, M. Stacey & D. B. E. Stroud) 6-*O*-Mannosyl D-glucosamine hydrochloride. *Nature* **191**, 143–144.

(3)   1962   (With A. R. Peacocke) Thymus deoxyribonucleoprotein. 1. Preparation and thermal denaturation. *Biochim. Biophys. Acta* **55**, 935–942.

(4)   1964   The occurrence of ε-*N*-methyl lysine in histones. *Biochemistry* **3**, 10–15.

(5)   1965   Basic proteins of cell nuclei. *Annu. Rev. Biochem.* **34**, 209–246.

(6)   The acid extraction of histones from calf thymus deoxyribonucleoprotein. *J. Mol. Biol.* **15**, 409–418.

(7)   1967   (With C. Milstein) Esters of serine and threonine in hydrolysates of histones and protamines, and attendant errors in amino acid analysis of proteins. *Biochem. J.* **105**, 481–485.

(8)   1969   Stepwise removal of histones from native deoxyribonucleoprotein by dilute acid at low temperature, and some properties of the resulting partial nucleoprotein. *J. Mol. Biol.* **39**, 125–144.

(9)   1971   (With P. I. Greenaway) Heterogeneity and polymorphism of chick erythrocyte histone fractions. *Nature New Biol.* **229**, 233–238.

(10)   1973   (With C. H. Biggar & N. E. Murray) Recognition sequence of a restriction enzyme. *Nature New Biol.* **244**, 7–10.

(11)   1974   (With N. E. Murray) Manipulation of restriction targets in phage lambda to form receptor chromosomes for DNA fragments. *Nature* **251**, 476–481.

(12)   1975   (With R. Old & G. Boizes) Recognition sequences of restriction endonucleases from *Haemophilus influenzae*. *J. Mol. Biol.* **92**, 331–339.

(13)   (With N. E. Murray & G. Bertabi) Base changes in the recognition site for functions in lambda phage DNA. *Nature* **254**, 262–265.

(14)   (With N. E. Murray) Phage lambda receptor chromosomes for DNA fragments made with restriction endonuclease III of *Haemophilus influenzae* and restriction endonuclease I of *Escherichia coli*. *J. Mol. Biol.* **98**, 551–564.

(15)   1979   (With C. J. Burrell, P. Mackay, P. J. Greenaway & P. H. Hofschneider) Expression in *Escherichia coli* of hepatitis B virus DNA sequences cloned in plasmid pBR322. *Nature* **279**, 43–47.

(16)   (With M. Pasek, T. Goto, W. Gilbert, B. Zink, H. Schaller, P. MacKay & G. Leadbetter) Hepatitis B virus genes and their expression in *E. coli*. *Nature* **282**, 575–579.

(17)   1983   (With M. M. Smith) Yeast H3 and H4 histone messenger RNAs are transcribed from two non-allelic gene sets. *J. Mol. Biol.* **169**, 641–661.

(18)   1984   (With S. A. Bruce, A. Hinnen, P. Wingfield, P. M. van Erd, A. de Reus & H. Schellekens) Hepatitis B virus antigens made in microbial cells immunize against viral infection. *EMBO J.* **3**, 645–650.

(19)   1987   (With S. A. Bruce, P. Wingfield, P. van Erd, A. de Reus & H. Schellekens) Protective immunization against hepatitis B with an internal antigen of the virus. *J. Med. Virol.* **23**, 101–187.

(20)   A molecular biologist's view of viral hepatitis. (The Leeuwenhoek Lecture, 1985.) *Proc. R. Soc. Lond.* B **230**, 107–146.

(21)   1988   Application of recombinant DNA technology in the development of viral vaccines. *Vaccine* **6**, 164–174.

(22)   1989   (With S. Stahl & P. G. Ashton-Rickardt) Genetic engineering applied to the development of vaccines. *Phil. Trans. R. Soc. Lond.* B **324**, 461–476.

(23)   1995   (With M. R. Dyson) Selection of peptide inhibitors of interactions involved in complex protein assemblies: association of the core and surface antigens of hepatitis B virus. *Proc. Natl Acad. Sci. USA* **92**, 2194–2198.

NOREEN ELIZABETH MURRAY CBE

26 February 1935 — 12 May 2011

Biogr. Mems Fell. R. Soc. **60**, 349–374 (2014)

Noreen E. Murray

NOREEN ELIZABETH MURRAY CBE

26 February 1935 — 12 May 2011

Elected FRS 1982

By Alexander Gann[1] and Jean Beggs[2] CBE FRS

[1]*Cold Spring Harbor Laboratory, 1 Bungtown Road, Cold Spring Harbor, NY 11724, USA*
[2]*Wellcome Trust Centre for Cell Biology, University of Edinburgh, Edinburgh EH9 3JR, UK*

Noreen Murray was one of the architects of the recombinant DNA revolution that transformed the study of biology from the early 1970s. Her particular prowess for genetic manipulation of bacteria and their phage was critical in developing the bacteriophage lambda vectors that were a vital part of the early genetic engineering toolbox. Her skill as a microbial geneticist had earlier become apparent through her work on genetic recombination and complementation in the fungus *Neurospora*, especially as a postdoctoral researcher at Stanford where her work brought her to the attention of some of the giants of early molecular biology. Back in the UK, first at Cambridge and then, for the bulk of her career, at Edinburgh, she produced a remarkable body of work focused on uncovering the mechanisms and biology of restriction enzymes, and their adaptation as tools underpinning modern biological research and the rise of the biotechnology industry. Much of this work was done in collaboration with her husband Ken Murray FRS, whose biographical memoir accompanies this one. Together they were known not only for the quality of their research but also for their vast generosity both on a personal level and on a larger canvas through their philanthropy.

Early life

Noreen Elizabeth Murray (*née* Parker) was born on 26 February 1935 in the village of Read near Burnley in Lancashire, the second child (figure 1) of a local headmaster, John Parker, and his wife, Lilian Grace Parker (*née* Sutcliffe). Both branches of Noreen's family were from Lancashire, her maternal and paternal grandfathers having both worked in the cotton mills as

http://dx.doi.org/10.1098/rsbm.2014.0009

Figure 1. Noreen with her parents and brother, Neil.

'tacklers', the overseers who supervised looms operated by 25 weavers. Despite having left school at the age of 12, her maternal grandfather was committed to self-improvement—learning languages, writing poetry and becoming a skilled draughtsman; throughout her life, Noreen treasured notebooks filled with his writings and drawings. Her paternal grandfather rose to become a 'boss' (a manager, not an owner) at the mill, enabling Noreen's father, John, to attend grammar school at Accrington and then St John's training college at York. After a relatively short spell as a schoolteacher, John became headmaster of the local school at Read before taking up a similar position at the larger school in Bolton-le-Sands in 1940.

Only five years old when they left, Noreen remembered little of Read beyond the noise of clogs on the pavement as the workers walked to the mill early each morning; collecting fresh milk daily in a jug from the adjacent farm; and attending matches at the nearby cricket ground where she had the unforgettable thrill of seeing the great West Indian player—and, later, first black peer—Learie Constantine. But it was in Bolton-le-Sands that Noreen spent the bulk of her happy childhood, in a house looking out over Morecambe Bay and across to the hills of the Lake District beyond.

Noreen was a self-confessed tomboy, and life in Bolton-le-Sands was enriched by numerous outdoor activities: frequent bicycle rides—ranging as far as the Lake District, some 20 miles distant—long walks, gardening (a lifelong passion), swimming in the bay, rowing on Lake Windermere and in the canal at the bottom of the family's garden, and—favourite of all—climbing trees. Climbing was also practised on a large rock that the local children called

Figure 2. Early experiments with mouse genetics. Noreen (middle), with her brother and a cousin.
(Photograph restored by Peter Reid.)

'Jumbo' on the shore near the house. Her father—a powerfully set, rugby-playing man—was a strict disciplinarian, but also fair and companionable. For example, although he instilled in Noreen a lasting commitment to strict punctuality, he also fostered her enthusiasm for gardening and built her a seat in a tree overlooking the canal from which she could observe the fish below. Known locally as 'Pop' Parker, he was fondly remembered by former pupils. Many years later, when Noreen received an honorary degree from Lancaster University, she met the Mayor of that city and discovered that he, too, had grown up in Bolton-le-Sands and been a pupil at 'Pop' Parker's school, memories of which he recalled cheerfully.

Noreen's mother dedicated herself to looking after the children. As was common at that time, and especially during World War II, which was then in progress, she was an expert cook and preserver of produce from their garden and other local sources. Her skill in sewing and knitting also allowed her to make many of Noreen's clothes, or adapt those of her older brother Neil for her use.

Neil was three years Noreen's senior and a keen naturalist. Indeed, it was he who first awakened Noreen's interest in genetics (figure 2). Noreen had won a scholarship to Lancaster Girls' Grammar School when she was still only 10 years old, and was put in the top stream among girls a year ahead of her. With the benefit of excellent teachers, she prospered. By the fifth year, she had to choose between Latin or physics and chemistry (biology was offered only to students in the third stream). She chose physics and chemistry, and her ambition was to be a Domestic Science teacher until her brother, revising for his higher School Certificate (A-level) exams, taught her Mendel's laws, an experience that inspired her, aged 15 years, to switch her allegiance from domestic to biological science.

Her lack of Latin precluded an Oxbridge application, and only during the sixth year did she take a maths O-level (at the time necessary for an application to any science degree outside the University of Hull). She won a London Intercollegiate Scholarship for entry to King's College, London, where she arrived in 1953 to read for a BSc in botany. Among her classmates on the course that year was John Ellis (FRS 1983). Noreen graduated in 1956 with an upper second-class degree, which rather bothered her, and she kept the note sent to her by the head of department, Professor T. A. Bennet-Clark FRS, which read: 'Congratulations. A IIi but you *should* have done better.' She had been thrown by questions on the university exam papers (which had to be taken in addition to those set by the college). These turned out to be on topics not covered in her courses at King's, and included one on bacterial genetics which she could answer only on the basis of what she had gleaned from an article by J. B. S. Haldane FRS in the popular magazine *New Biology* (to which she had, as with Mendel's laws, been introduced by her brother).

BIRMINGHAM AND *NEUROSPORA*

Despite the disappointment of her 2.i, she had nevertheless already been offered a PhD place at Birmingham University in the laboratory of David Catcheside FRS, himself a former graduate of Botany from King's. Catcheside had recently returned from the University of Adelaide to set up a new department at Birmingham. Although called Microbiology, the forward-looking department he assembled brought together geneticists, biochemists and even a physical chemist interested in DNA. A few years later, it might well have been called a department of molecular biology.

Catcheside encouraged his students to be independent—to devise and plan their own experiments—but was at the same time happy to share his knowledge and insights. Noreen took on a research project designed to find out whether genes involved in a given biochemical pathway in a eukaryote were linked in the manner then just being described in the operons of bacteria. For this she chose the fungus *Neurospora*. At Catcheside's suggestion, she focused on the genes involved in methionine biosynthesis and proceeded to isolate many mutants defective in this pathway, and to sort the genes that she found into complementation groups. But mapping the genes revealed no clustering, even between complementation groups on the same chromosome. Further work on one locus, *me-2*, showed interallelic complementation and provided an insight into recombination within a gene, showing in particular that gene conversion was influenced by the position of a mutation within the locus (1, 2)*.

During her first year as a graduate student, Noreen was often invited to the Catchesides' home when an interesting geneticist was visiting (Herschel Roman and George Beadle (ForMemRS 1960), for example). She would help Catcheside's wife, Kathleen, and meet the eminent visitor. But this practice fell victim to Catcheside's disapproval when Noreen became engaged to a fellow graduate student, Kenneth Murray (FRS 1979), who was then working with Arthur Peacocke, the DNA chemist in the department. (Peacocke was later to become the Reverend Cannon Peacocke, Master of Pusey Hall in Oxford, and proponent of the view that no conflict existed between evolution and Christianity, as expounded in his essay 'Evolution: the disguised friend of faith?') Catcheside explained to Noreen that if she were to marry, her career would come second to that of her husband. His dictum caused Noreen some distress and severely limited her subsequent interactions with both Catcheside and his wife. Later in her career she came to understand the significance of Catcheside's reaction, but also knew that he 'forgave her': years afterwards he supported her election to the Royal Society; and even during her final year as a graduate student, when Ken secured a postdoctoral position at Stanford University, Catcheside wrote to David Perkins, the Stanford *Neurospora* geneticist,

---

* Numbers in this form refer to the bibliography at the end of the text.

to ask whether he could accommodate Noreen in his laboratory so that she could continue her research project. Perkins complied, and even offered funding—a minimal top-up to Ken's salary for the first year, and her own stipend thereafter. And so in late 1959 Ken and Noreen set off, travelling by boat to New York, and thence by train across the continent to California, taking up their postdoctoral positions at Stanford in January 1960.

STANFORD: A WHOLE NEW WORLD

During five exhilarating years at Stanford, Noreen continued her successful studies on *Neurospora*, publishing a further three papers (3–5). Like those published during her graduate studies with Catcheside, these were all single-author papers: both Catcheside and Perkins felt their contributions insufficient to justify co-authorship. Nowadays, in the era of relentless quantitative assessment, it is hard to imagine such a state of affairs, and even in the early 1960s it was far from the norm. But it attests to the level of independence that Noreen brought to her projects, in both their conception and their execution.

Beyond this research success, Noreen's time at Stanford was even more influential because it was here that she was introduced to bacterial and phage genetics, the field in which her future career lay. She heard many inspiring lectures (including Sydney Brenner (FRS 1965) presenting the phage experiments that he and Francis Crick FRS had carried out to define the general nature of the genetic code, before that beautiful work was published), attended courses given by the acclaimed Stanford-based prokaryotic geneticists Charles Yanofsky (ForMemRS 1965) and Dale Kaiser, and took part in the Yanofsky laboratory journal club. It was at one of these journal clubs that Naomi Franklin presented the work of Daisy Dussoix and Werner Arber that began to expose the mechanistic basis of the phenomenon of restriction and modification that became so central to Noreen's later career and to the evolution of recombinant DNA technologies. Dussoix and Arber had shown that restriction—the decrease in plating efficiency of a phage on one strain after it had been propagated on another—worked at the level of DNA degradation in the absence of strain-specific protection, protection that a few years later was shown to be due to DNA methylation (Dussoix & Arber 1962; Arber 1965).

While at Stanford, Noreen was invited to California Institute of Technology to give her first scientific seminar, in front of a daunting crowd that included Max Delbrück (ForMemRS 1967), Ed Lewis (ForMemRS 1989), George Beadle, Norm Horowitz and Sterling Emerson. Also while at Stanford she met Frank Stahl (figure 3), who invited her to Oregon to give a talk on her work on polarized gene conversion. Stahl became a lifelong friend and influential supporter. Although they worked very hard, Ken and Noreen also enjoyed life in California, especially escaping to the mountains; they took particular delight in visits to Yosemite.

CAMBRIDGE AND THE FIRST PHAGE EXPERIMENTS

Ken and Noreen returned to the UK only in 1964 when Ken was offered a position in the laboratory of Fred Sanger FRS at the Medical Research Council (MRC) Laboratory of Molecular Biology (LMB) at Cambridge. Noreen received a fellowship allowing her to continue work in another *Neurospora* laboratory—that of Harold Whitehouse, in Cambridge University's Botany Department. After Stanford, life in Cambridge had its challenges: the

Figure 3. With Frank Stahl (left) and David (Arnold) Catcheside, the son of Noreen's PhD supervisor, David Catcheside. The photo was probably taken in the summer of 1977, when Catcheside was in Edinburgh learning to use lambda vectors and Stahl attended a meeting on recombination at nearby Nethy Bridge. The photo may have been taken in Edinburgh, but more probably at Nethy Bridge. (Photograph restored by Peter Reid.) (Online version in colour.)

facilities made available to Noreen were vastly inferior to those she had become accustomed to at Stanford, and as her Birmingham PhD was not recognized by Cambridge University she was expected to work for a Cambridge degree. Thus, in her sixth postdoctoral year, she appeared in the photograph of Cambridge PhD students.

On the plus side, Frank Stahl was by then on sabbatical leave at LMB, and he was happy to have Noreen do some experiments with him. As Stahl has recently written (Stahl 2013):

> Then, late one afternoon, Noreen Murray, an acquaintance with a background in fungal genetics, appeared in my lab and asked if there was anything going on that she might help with. She wanted to take part time off from her work in the botany department if I had anything for her. Did I! The search for co-adapted genes would use (over and over) all the elementary moves of phage genetic analysis, making it an ideal project for a beginner, especially for one familiar with sterile technique. Noreen signed on once I convinced her that her lack of experience would be more of an asset than a problem.

Noreen relished the experience, to the extent even of overcoming her anxiety about working in a laboratory to which she had no formal connection—a discomfort that led her to hide beneath the bench whenever Sydney Brenner came into the room. The experiments that she and Stahl completed at this time on mapping genes on the circular T4 genome were her first with phage and marked the start of her transition from fungal to bacterial systems. They also resulted in a pair of papers, published with Stahl in 1966, which established her as a *bona fide* phage geneticist (6, 7). The first of these papers presented evidence that the clustering of genes of related function within the phage genome might be driven by adaptive constraints (*à la* R. A. Fisher) rather than regulatory constraints (as the recent operon model suggested). Thus, clustering might ensure that recombination events between phages during co-infection would be more likely to produce viable progeny than if those genes were not clustered and so more susceptible to reassortment by recombination events. Stahl asked Francis Crick and Sydney Brenner for comments on the manuscript before he submitted it for publication. In reply, Crick jokingly wrote that he thought the work 'is nearer theology than science. In fact I think you would have made an excellent Jesuit' but concluded: 'Are you nevertheless permitted to publish? Certainly. But I would suggest the Journal of Theological Biology. Sydney's lips are sealed. We enjoyed having you here, awake or asleep.' (Stahl had regularly slept through performances at the Aldwych.)

Looking now at a reprint of that paper, two features characteristic of Stahl stand out: a humorous footnote appended to Noreen's name gives her affiliation as 'On loan from the Botany School'; and in the middle of the circular genetic map of phage T4, Stahl stamped 'US Get Out Of Vietnam' on every copy he sent out.

The experience, so influential in Noreen's life, was also special to Stahl, as he noted in the recent memoir of his year at LMB (Stahl 2013):

> The entire, memorable experience was topped up by the opportunity to work with Noreen years before she was honoured for her contributions to phage-based genetic engineering. Unforgettably, on my sabbatical leave at LMB I had the pleasure of teaching Noreen Murray (1935–2011) the ABC of phage genetics using Dick Epstein's (1929–2011) amazing amber mutants. How blessedly lucky can a guy be? Serendipity indeed!

EDINBURGH AND THE MRC UNIT

Ken was due to take up a position as a lecturer at the new University of York in October 1965. However, neither his laboratory there nor even the library was ready and, after Ken and Noreen were involved in a car accident just a few weeks before their planned move, Ken requested to postpone their relocation for three months. When his request was curtly denied—see the memoir of Ken Murray (Brammar & Gratzer 2014)—Sanger provided sanctuary in his laboratory and they remained in Cambridge until, in 1967, Ken was appointed a Senior Lecturer at the University of Edinburgh, in the new Department of Molecular Biology.

The situation at Edinburgh was in many ways ideal for Ken and Noreen. As well as the department itself, under the leadership of Martin Pollock FRS, there was soon to be an MRC Unit of Bacterial Genetics headed by Bill Hayes FRS, which relocated from the Hammersmith Hospital in London in 1968. Noreen wrote to Bill Hayes who, after an interview, offered her a position in his Edinburgh-bound Unit; her time working with phage had paid off.

Pollock had also previously been employed by the MRC (at the National Institute for Medical Research, Mill Hill) and had moved with some colleagues to Edinburgh in 1965. Generous MRC funding was critical in combining Hayes's unit, with its expertise in microbial genetics, with Pollock's biochemists to create the first Department of Molecular Biology in the country. Michael (later Lord) Swann FRS, himself an eminent cell biologist, and at the time Principal of Edinburgh University, was the other key figure in driving the formation of this exciting new department.

Noreen moved to Edinburgh in January 1968, ahead of the arrival of Bill Hayes's Unit, and at first had no bench to work on, just a desk she shared with Bill Brammar's technician. (Bill Brammar was a member of the new department and would later collaborate closely with

Noreen.) In July the new building, subsequently called the Darwin Building, was completed, providing three floors for molecular biology. Noreen had a tiny room on the eighth floor, while Ken's laboratory was on the sixth floor. Initially she continued her *Neurospora* work—the fine-structure analysis of genes and the mechanisms of genetic recombination, in particular the study of polarized gene conversion. A decade of these studies had led her to the idea that genetic exchange might be preferentially initiated at certain sites on the chromosome, perhaps at specific sequences found at the ends of genes. She realized that to take this analysis to a deeper mechanistic level—to approach a molecular understanding of what was going on—she would need to move into systems more amenable to that sort of study, bacteria or phage. So during the early part of 1968 she was already familiarizing herself with other systems, even as she continued her *Neurospora* work. She decided that site-specific recombination in phage lambda, or restriction enzymes, might provide propitious systems in which to investigate how specific sites on DNA are recognized.

RESTRICTION ENZYMES

The first restriction enzyme (*Eco*K) was purified at Harvard by Matt Meselson (ForMemRS 1984) and Bob Yuan, a feat published in *Nature* (Meselson & Yuan 1968) in a paper that Noreen always claimed was one of the most impressive she ever read. This breakthrough opened up the possibility that Noreen might combine her genetic manipulations with Ken's biochemical prowess to analyse how these enzymes act on phage genomes. Towards the end of his time in Sanger's laboratory, Ken had started to deduce short DNA sequences at the ends of DNA molecules (he had used the lambda genome) by end-labelling. So the plan was for Noreen to genetically manipulate lambda to generate a series of phage genomes each with just a single recognition site for *Eco*K, each at a different location. The purified phage genomes could then be cut by *Eco*K, and polynucleotide kinase used to add ^{32}P phosphate to the 5′ terminal nucleotides. The sequence of a few nucleotides at those ends could then be determined with the technique that Ken had developed in Sanger's laboratory. This would hopefully reveal the precise sequence recognized by *Eco*K.

The approach was a good one, but the Murrays were unlucky in their choice of the enzyme *Eco*K. This is a Type I restriction enzyme, not one of the Type II enzymes that later became so well known for their role in recombinant DNA manipulations. Type II enzymes recognize specific DNA sites ('target sites') and cut at a defined place within those sequences. Although Type I enzymes also recognize specific DNA sequences, they cut, not within those target sites, but apparently randomly, some distance away. Thus there was no sequence similarity between the ends of DNA molecules generated by *Eco*K digestion.

The collaborative studies were greatly facilitated when Noreen moved from her rather isolated room on the eighth floor down to the sixth floor, in response to the arrival of Frank Stahl, who, together with his wife, Mary, came to Edinburgh for a sabbatical year in 1969. Noreen shared an office with Stahl, and her bench and facilities were contiguous with those in Ken's laboratory, at which Frank and Mary were working.

Daisy Dussoix, the student in Werner Arber's laboratory involved in early dissection of restriction mechanism as mentioned above, was by now at University of California at San Francisco in the laboratory of Herb Boyer. There she was involved in attempts to purify a plasmid-encoded (and, as it turned out, Type II) enzyme, *Eco*RI. Encouraged by discussions with her, Noreen and Ken turned their attention to that class of enzyme. They picked a different plasmid-borne system, *Eco*RII, and determined that this—like *Eco*RI—cut DNA into discrete fragments. Noreen and Ken (with his postdoctoral researcher Cynthia Biggar) were able to work out its target sequence in 1972. Not long afterwards, Hamilton Smith sent them the *Haemophilus influenzae* strain in which he had identified a restriction enzyme (*Hin*dII), using phage T7 as a substrate. In purifying the enzyme, Ken instead used lambda DNA; in that way he discovered there were in fact two enzymes present in the strain, and soon worked out the target sequence of the second enzyme, *Hin*dIII (which, fortunately for Smith, did not occur in the T7 genome) (Old *et al.* 1975).

THE DAWN OF RECOMBINANT DNA

In September 1972 there was a meeting of the European Molecular Biology Organization (EMBO) in Switzerland. This event was significant in several ways, not least because of an unscheduled extra session, chaired by Norton Zinder, to discuss the possibility that biohazards might attend recombining DNA molecules from different organisms. This was well before such concerns were raised in the famous 'Berg letter' to *Science* (Berg *et al.* 1974) and the subsequent well-documented Asilomar meeting, but it seems to have been largely overlooked. On the purely scientific front, Noreen spoke about her work manipulating the *Eco*K sites in lambda, and she and Ken presented the *Eco*RII target sequence (and possibly preliminary data on *Hin*dIII as well). Herb Boyer and Howard Goodman reported their results on *Eco*RI, indicating that they had identified its target site, but the data were not at that time quite complete; the sequence was published later that year (Hedgpeth *et al.* 1972). Boyer and Goodman were also engaged in attempts to find the target sequence of *Eco*RII and asked Ken to hold back on publishing his results until they were ready to submit theirs at the same time. Ken agreed, though this led to a six-month delay in publication (8) (Boyer *et al.* 1973).

Also at this fateful meeting, two other findings from Stanford were reported in an abstract. One, the finding, later published by Lobban & Kaiser (1973), that poly(A-T) tails could be attached to the ends of DNA molecules to create self-complementary 'sticky ends', thus allowing molecules to be joined. The second—even more exciting in Noreen's view—was the result from Ron Davis and Janet Mertz that *Eco*RI cleaved DNA to generate fragments with 5' single-stranded overhangs of four nucleotides that were complementary to one another and could be joined by DNA ligase. This allowed different molecules cut with *Eco*RI to be joined efficiently in new combinations (Mertz & Davis 1972).

At about this time, Bernard Allet, at Cold Spring Harbor Laboratory, used the recently invented gel separation and ethidium bromide staining system to show that *Eco*RI cut the lambda genome into six fragments, revealing that it bore five sites for that enzyme. But he was not at the EMBO meeting, and so Noreen discovered this fact only when it was published in January the following year (Allet *et al.* 1973). She then immediately realized that manipulation of those *Eco*RI sites, in the way that she had already done for *Eco*K, would generate lambda phage able to carry foreign DNA generated by digestion with *Eco*RI. This would enable the power of transducing phages—naturally occurring recombinant phages carrying parts of the bacterial genome long used by bacterial geneticists—to be extended to the analysis of DNA from any source.

However, at this time, life in Edinburgh became less secure. Threats of closure fell upon the MRC Unit, triggered in part by the desire of its director, Bill Hayes, to accept an attractive post-retirement position in Australia. The threats came despite a piece entitled '*Escherichia* at Edinburgh' that was published in *Nature New Biology* (anonymously, but possibly with Werner Arber's input) in March 1972, praising the work of the department, including what Ken and Noreen were doing with restriction enzymes (described at the time as a way to study protein–DNA interactions rather than to generate recombinant DNA molecules) (Anon. 1972). There was also an MRC report that extolled the work going on in Edinburgh and recommended that the Unit be kept alive after Hayes's retirement, if on a smaller scale. However, the MRC subsequently set up a subcommittee review that recommended closure on Hayes's retirement.

Noreen felt the stress. She was one of six members of the department without tenure who faced the axe. To evade the oppressive atmosphere caused by this uncertainty over the future, she escaped back to Stanford for a few months and there took up her *Neurospora* work again. This, she later came to believe, was a mistake. The task of eliminating the *Eco*RI sites from lambda she left in Edinburgh in the hands of a new technician, who, lacking phage-handling experience, struggled to make headway. When Noreen returned some months later (in September 1973), it took her only three weeks to create phages with single and double *Eco*RI sites—derivatives that could serve as receptors for foreign DNA—the first lambda vectors. Another regret was the decision not to mention her plans for *Eco*RI when she gave a seminar during her stay at Stanford on the manipulation of *Eco*K sites in lambda. This, she felt, would have established a public precedent for her idea, which was soon taken up by others.

That autumn, Ken created their first recombinant molecules using these new lambda vectors, but the paper describing this success was not published (or even submitted) until the following year (9). The delay was of course largely because of Noreen's flight to Stanford, but also her insistence, as a geneticist, that she map each of the *Eco*RI sites accurately within the genome before they published the paper. This was not critical to their main findings and unfortunately took some time. The significance of these delays lies in the fact that their cloning paper appeared in 1974, whereas Boyer and Cohen's paper describing cloning in plasmid vectors came out in 1973 (Cohen *et al*. 1973).

The future of the MRC staff was clarified in the autumn of 1973. Although the Unit was to close, Noreen and several other members were granted MRC tenure. Noreen believed that her case was bolstered by strong supporting letters from Frank Stahl and John Fincham FRS. Tenure did not immediately guarantee that they could stay in Edinburgh (they could have been moved to an MRC Unit elsewhere), but within a year that tenure was transferred to the university department and so at last their security in Edinburgh was assured. One consequence of this was that in April 1975 Noreen was at last able to submit her first grant application, entitled 'The generation of transducing phages by *in vitro* recombination and their amplification of gene products'. This was funded after very favourable review. Noreen subsequently remembered that even Sydney Brenner had been very supportive—although she would also wryly observe just how long it had taken her to reach this level of independence.

Despite the continued success of her research and her commitment to teaching, her rank in the department rose rather slowly. When she was first nominated as a candidate for Fellowship of the Royal Society she was still just a Senior Lecturer. On a visit to Edinburgh the following year, John Fincham suggested she should get a promotion. This duly happened, and she became a Reader in 1978. But even though she was elected to the Royal Society in 1982 she was appointed professor only six years later, in 1988. Not being a professor meant she was not able to make long-distance phone calls from her office, a restriction that caused her

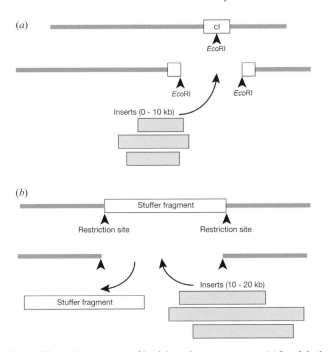

Figure 4. Schematic diagram illustrating two types of lambda replacement vectors. (*a*) Lambda 'insertion vector' with a unique *Eco*RI site in the *cI* gene into which DNA fragments were ligated. (*b*) Lambda 'replacement vector' in which a non-essential 'stuffer' fragment could be replaced, allowing larger DNA fragments to be cloned.

some inconvenience (not to say embarrassment) when she became President of the Genetical Society, particularly during negotiations with Cold Spring Harbor Laboratory over investment in the journal *Genes & Development*. She had to resort to using Ken's phone. (Her predecessor as President—David (now Sir David) Hopwood FRS—had been mortified to discover he could not introduce her as 'Professor Murray' when she took over.)

Noreen liked to tell this story more as a positive reflection on the Royal Society than as a negative one on the university. Indeed, she felt that the Royal Society was less gender-biased than people, and the media, at times maintained. Rather, she believed strongly that it did—as it should—reward people for their science irrespective of gender.

OVEREXPRESSION OF CLONED GENE PRODUCTS

By 1975 Noreen had created both insertion vectors (able to incorporate additional DNA) and replacement vectors (containing regions that could be replaced by foreign DNA). Replacement vectors had the virtue that they could accommodate larger DNA fragments, because there is a limit to how much DNA the lambda heads can accommodate (figure 4). These vectors could accept DNA fragments generated by either *Eco*RI or *Hin*dIII (10).

A particularly neat trick applied to the insertion vectors. Insertion was at a site within the lambda *cI* gene, which encodes lambda repressor, and so recombinant phage (containing insertions) could not form lysogens. As a result, the recombinant phage could readily be discriminated from empty vectors because, when plated on a bacterial lawn, recombinants produced clear plaques, whereas the empty vector formed turbid plaques (11). This discrimination was later enhanced by the use of *Hfl* (high frequency of lysogeny) bacterial host strains. When grown on a lawn of these cells, *cI*⁺ phages (for example vector) always formed lysogens, and so produced no visible plaque at all; only recombinant phages, unable to form lysogens, grew lytically and produced plaques.

The next few years were very exciting for Noreen. She collaborated not only with Ken but also with Bill Brammar, with whom she by now shared an office. Brammar's student Ann Moir was working with classical λ*trp* transducing phage, examining (by assaying the products of the *trpD* and *E* genes) expression from the lambda P_L promoter. This started them thinking about how one might not just clone genes, but also overexpress their products. Noreen and Bill also generated libraries of *Escherichia coli* DNA in lambda vectors and identified clones of various genes by complementing mutant host cells lacking that function.

Edinburgh quickly became a Mecca for recombinant DNA technology. In those days very few people had direct access to the protocols and reagents required to clone genes. Two features of the department at Edinburgh fostered its role in the dissemination of recombinant DNA techniques. First, many researchers were taken in and taught the lore, including John Atkins, Jean Beggs (FRS 1998) and Alan Hall (FRS 1999). Another local colleague, Ed (now Sir Edwin) Southern (FRS 1983), benefited from the new technologies introduced by Ken and Noreen; these were critical to his developing, in 1975, Southern blotting, a powerful technique that added to Edinburgh's reputation as a centre for recombinant DNA (Southern 1975). Second, in working out how to express genes cloned in lambda vectors, Noreen realized it would be useful if they experimented using genes whose products were needed for recombinant DNA techniques, thereby ensuring their plentiful supply. Thus, together with another visitor to the laboratory, Geoff Wilson, she cloned the gene encoding phage T4 ligase, the enzyme used to join recombinant DNA molecules, and, later, polynucleotide kinase, which is used in DNA end-labelling (12, 16). In addition, in response to a request from Bill Kelley (in Pittsburgh, Pennsylvania), she screened her *E. coli* libraries for a clone encoding DNA polymerase. She was in luck: the entire *polA* gene was within a small *Hin*dIII fragment and thus present as a clone in her library. This clone became the source from which the Klenow fragment was produced (13).

High-level production of T4 ligase was achieved by using a recombinant lambda prophage harbouring the gene in a region of the genome expressed from the late promoter P_R' upon induction; for *polA*, expression was driven from one of the early promoters, P_L, during lytic growth (just as with the *trp* genes in the earlier experiments). By overexpressing these genes, their products could much more easily be purified in large quantities. Indeed, Noreen gave the T4 ligase clone to the pharmaceutical firm Boehringer, who used it to produce commercial ligase for years. (A characteristic tale: in the late 1980s Boehringer discovered that their ligase strain had died, and sheepishly asked whether Noreen could replace it. Of course she could; her stocks were always carefully preserved. As reward for this kindness the company offered her a choice of laboratory equipment. When those present in her laboratory picked from the list a gel-dryer, she replied, 'Oh I can't ask for that, it's the most expensive item on the list!')

Ken and Noreen did not patent any of these constructs, although it was suggested that they might have tried to. However, Noreen had talked publicly about the *Eco*RI vectors at an EMBO meeting in Ghent in 1974, and the UK patent office therefore decided not to take the matter further.

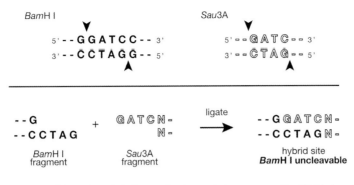

Figure 5. Schematic diagram illustrating DNA cleavage by the restriction enzymes *Bam*HI (six-base target sequence) and *Sau*3A (four-base target sequence) to produce DNA fragments with four-base single-stranded ends that are complementary and 'cohesive' or 'sticky' and therefore can be combined to form hybrid sites. Most of these hybrid sites are uncleavable by *Bam*HI.

IMPROVED LAMBDA VECTORS

The discovery of the restriction enzyme *Sau*3A enhanced the quality of DNA libraries. This enzyme recognizes target sequences only four nucleotides in length, but cuts them in such a way that they generate sticky ends compatible with those generated by another enzyme, *Bam*HI, which recognizes a six-nucleotide target sequence. An enzyme that recognizes a target site of six nucleotides (as *Eco*RI and *Hin*dIII also do) will cut on average once in every 4096 base pairs (bp). In contrast, an enzyme that has a target site of four nucleotides will cut on average every 256 bp. By choosing conditions in which the enzyme only partly digests the donor DNA—that is, it cuts only a subset of its sites in any given molecule—*Sau*3A can generate a set of overlapping fragments that can then be cloned into a vector designed with an appropriate *Bam*HI site. The benefit of this is that even if a gene of interest has a site for *Sau*3A within its coding region, a clone containing the entire gene can still be present in the library (figure 5).

So there arose a demand for a lambda vector with a suitable *Bam*HI site. But there was a problem: of the five *Bam*HI sites found in lambda, one lies within an essential gene and so could not be removed by genetic deletion (which is how Noreen had typically removed other restriction sites). As a solution, she took advantage of the recently developed system for packaging lambda DNA *in vitro*. The method for assembing lambda head proteins *in vitro* and packaging the phage DNA was originally devised by Dale Kaiser. This was further developed for packaging recombinant phage genomes by Ken and Barbara Hohn (ForMemRS 2008), with the help of participants in the 1976 EMBO course on recombinant DNA—see below (Hohn & Murray 1977). Until then, recombinant lambda genomes had been introduced into host cells by transformation, just as plasmid vectors had been. The efficiency of this process was low; packaging lambda DNA in viral coat proteins and using these to infect host cells was 100 times more efficient. This increased efficiency was critical.

To eliminate the troublesome *Bam*HI site, Noreen first generated a lambda carrying just that one *Bam*HI site in its genome. She then grew up the stock of phage, purified the DNA and incubated it with *Bam*HI. This treatment eliminated all genomes except for the rare cases in which the phage had picked up a spontaneous mutation that eliminated the *Bam*HI site. When

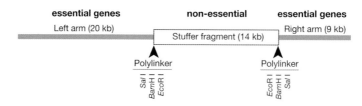

Figure 6. An example of an EMBL lambda vector, carrying polylinkers with sites for *Eco*RI, *Hin*dIII and *Bam*HI either side of a non-essential stuffer fragment that can be replaced.

the mixture was packaged *in vitro* and used to infect a host cell, the phage that emerged had indeed lost the *Bam*HI site (Klein & Murray 1979).

Unfortunately for Noreen, despite making this critical step, she was not able to finish the construction of the first *Bam*HI vector. Instead, the mutant phage resistant to *Bam*HI was taken on by Sydney Brenner, who completed the job at LMB (Karn *et al.* 1980). For Noreen, the project was interrupted by another stint abroad. Ken had been invited to spend a few years at the new European Molecular Biology Laboratory (EMBL) in Heidelberg, and moved there in the autumn of 1979, with Noreen following in early 1980 after she had fulfilled her teaching commitments for the year at Edinburgh. This move, while highly beneficial in many ways, was also—like her return to Stanford in 1973—rather disruptive for Noreen, who, having just taken advantage of her first grant (1976–79) and having two graduate students and her first postdoctoral researcher, would now have to curtail the development of her laboratory at Edinburgh for a few years. However, she had excellent technical assistance at EMBL and it was a productive time. In collaboration with Hans Lehrach's laboratory, she created a series of new lambda vectors—the so-called EMBL vectors—carrying polylinkers bearing sites for *Eco*RI, *Hin*dIII and *Bam*HI, among others. These, which included replacement vectors (figure 6), were Noreen's most widely used cloning vectors, and the paper describing them was her most highly cited (14).

A RETURN TO TYPE I RESTRICTION AND MODIFICATION SYSTEMS

While at EMBL, Noreen also returned to Type I restriction–modification (R–M) systems, and these remained the focus of her research after her return to Edinburgh in late 1982, and for the rest of her career (26).

These large, multi-subunit enzymes can both modify (methylate) and restrict (cleave) DNA carrying appropriate target sites. Each enzyme includes a specificity (S) subunit responsible for recognizing that enzyme's specific DNA target sequence, R subunits for cleavage and M subunits for modification. We earlier noted that Type I enzymes do not cut DNA within their target sequences, but nevertheless initiate this action by first binding to those sites. The target sites are bipartite—that is, they comprise two defined regions separated by a non-specific linker. For example, *Eco*K recognizes the site 5′-AAC(N$_6$)GTCC-3′. Type I enzymes are grouped into families, with extensive sequence homology between members of the same family.

While still at Heidelberg, with the help of her technician Jill Gough, Noreen sequenced the genes encoding the S subunits of three members of the *Eco*K family, each with a different target sequence specificity. Comparing the different S genes revealed two regions of homology—100 nucleotides in the middle of the gene, and 250 at the end—and two non-conserved regions each of about 500 nucleotides, one at the beginning of the gene, and the other between the two conserved regions. This led to the proposal that each variable region encoded a domain that recognized one part of the bipartite target sequence (15).

This was demonstrated in experiments begun in Heidelberg with another technician, Francis Fuller-Pace, and continued later in Edinburgh by Fuller-Pace, who was by then a graduate student, and by other students who followed. These studies showed that reassorting domains between different S subunits within a family produced enzymes recognizing novel, hybrid (and predictable) target sites. Moreover, specificity subunits from different families (which typically show no homology with those from the *Eco*K family) do share strong homology in their variable regions when those enzymes recognize the same target sequence (17–19).

Noreen's laboratory also sequenced the R and M subunits of Type I R–M systems. There followed extensive mutational analysis and structural studies that revealed how the subunits interact with each other and with DNA, and identified regions associated with the various enzymatic activities, including ATPase and DNA cleavage (20–23). The structural studies finally produced a model for the entire complex—a feat achieved in 2011, soon after Noreen's death, by David Dryden, a former postdoctoral researcher who now has his own laboratory at Edinburgh. The work was published in a paper dedicated to her memory (Kennaway *et al.* 2012).

In the last phase of her work on Type I R–M systems, Noreen—together with her penultimate graduate student, Sveta Makovets—uncovered the unexpected and striking fact that cells protect themselves against restriction, not only through methylation of their target sites but also by ClpXP-mediated proteolysis of the restriction subunits of the enzyme after it has bound to its site and initiated DNA translocation (24, 25).

THE FIRST RECOMBINANT DNA COURSES

As already mentioned, Ken and Noreen contributed to the dissemination of recombinant DNA technology by taking in those desiring to learn and by helping to make the reagents more readily (and cheaply) available. They were also involved in the first formal courses offered in this technology. The very first such course was organized by Werner Arber (figure 7) under the auspices of EMBO and held in Basel in 1976. Ken and Noreen acted as instructors, as did Ed Southern, David Glover, Barbara Hohn and others. Among the students who took the course were Walter Gehring (ForMemRS 1997), Bernard Dujon and Martina Couterier. The course was repeated at Basel for the next three years before moving to EMBL, Heidelberg, in 1980, where Ken and Noreen were by then based. One of the students who took the course in the first year at EMBL was Paul (now Sir Paul) Nurse (FRS 1989; PRS 2010–), along with Chris Leaver (FRS 1986), Marilyn Monk and Peter Jackson. In his comments on the occasion of EMBO's 40th anniversary in 2004, Nurse recalled the huge influence that the recombinant DNA course had on his career (Nurse 2004, p. 132; 2014):

> EMBO has been very important to my scientific activities in a number of ways …. But the key role that EMBO played at a very crucial stage in my research career was a practical course held at EMBL around 1980/81.
>
> This course was organized by Noreen and Ken Murray, who I believe were spending some months in Heidelberg at the time. The course was designed to train participants in the basic procedures of gene cloning—how to construct and bulk up plasmid and phage vectors, to generate recombinant DNA molecules, to screen for inserts, to produce proteins in bacteria and so on: all

Figure 7. Noreen with Werner Arber at Bremen in 2010. (Photograph courtesy of Wil Loenen.)
(Online version in colour.)

common place now, but rather unusual then and certainly very exciting. As is often the case in practical courses, the work was intense and exhausting but was also enormously productive. We, the students, got lots of hands-on experience and also exposure to some of the great molecular geneticists of the time, who came and gave visiting lectures. …

My transition to molecular genetics was made vastly easier by this fine course and I am grateful to both EMBO and our inspirational teachers, Noreen and Ken Murray. I still remember it with affection and respect over 20 years later—thank you Noreen and thank you Ken!

Noreen as a Colleague

We would like to convey something of what it was like to work with Noreen. One of us (A.G.) was a graduate student in her laboratory from 1985 to 1989 and stayed in close touch with her afterwards. In Noreen's laboratory, he worked on Type I restriction enzymes, genetically characterizing their DNA recognition domains and investigating how new specificities arise. J.B. knew Noreen for longer, since her arrival as a postdoctoral researcher to learn recombinant DNA techniques in the mid 1970s, and later as a colleague on the staff of the Department of Molecular Biology at Edinburgh, and as a close friend and neighbour. Inspired by Noreen's success cloning genes in bacteria, she, together with John Atkins, cloned the 2 micron plasmid (the name refers to its circumference of 2 µm) from *Saccharomyces cerevisiae*, which she then used to develop the first yeast–*E. coli* (hybrid) shuttle system and an efficient method for cloning DNA sequences in budding yeast cells.

Noreen had only 17 graduate students in her career. This was partly because she never wanted her laboratory to get too large, but also because she was not allowed to supervise a

Figure 8. Noreen with members of her laboratory in about 1987. From left to right: Anne Daniel, Gill Cowan, Julia Kelleher and Alex Gann.

student until rather late in her career: her first student completed her thesis in 1975, close to Noreen's 40th birthday. She did help supervise a few earlier students, most notably Jeremy Brockes (FRS 1994), who arrived in 1969 and spent his first year learning bacterial and phage genetics with Noreen before returning to biochemistry with Ken, his official supervisor.

Noreen and Ken had no children, but Noreen thought of her students and postdoctoral researchers as her family and she earned their admiration and affection. To those in her research group, Noreen was a wonderful supervisor. Because she still worked in the laboratory every day (figure 8) one could learn directly from her—and as she was a virtuoso in the genetic manipulation of bacteria and phages, this was a huge bonus as well as a great pleasure. She was always available to chat about science or pretty much anything else. One could spend long hours in her cosy office beside her bench, talking about people, ideas, experiments and the intellectual history of molecular biology.

Noreen was remarkably conscientious and meticulous. This was reflected in many ways, none more so than in how she dealt with requests for bacterial and phage strains. She had an extensive collection of many hundreds of each, predominantly constructed by her, but including those from other masters in the field as well. Her collection was catalogued in little hardback notebooks. The broken spines were sellotaped and the oldest books had yellowing pages. All genotypes were annotated—sometimes impenetrably to others—in her small, spidery hand.

From the 1970s onwards, requests for *E. coli* and lambda strains arrived almost daily. Before sending a strain to anyone, Noreen would get the stock out and grow it up, pick a colony or plaque, and do whatever genetic tests were needed to confirm that it was indeed exactly the strain it was supposed to be. Some of these tests could be fairly involved and tricky, and she did them all herself—there was no dedicated technician to take care of this business.

There were also requests for entirely new strains, constructed by her from scratch to provide the ideal genetic background for specific experiments. Such bespoke strains were in great demand because her skills were held in such high regard. To watch her pick out just the right plaque or colony was a treat; she had an instinct, built on experience and careful observation, that made it seem almost mystical at times. While a postdoctoral researcher in Edinburgh, J.B. screened thousands of recombinant phage clones, searching for one encoding the *Eco*K restriction subunit. Noreen, who would often say 'show me the plate', looked at the results, tested a dozen or so that looked interesting and found one. Everyone would trust any strain Noreen made, and nothing would have mortified her more than sending out a strain that was not as she had described it.

She was also very generous and supportive. Perhaps following the example set by her own PhD supervisor, David Catcheside, Noreen made sure that young colleagues met interesting and influential scientists when they visited, often at dinner in her home. Among others we met in this way were Sydney Brenner, Alan Campbell, Frank Stahl, Jim Watson (ForMemRS 1981), Paul Nurse and the legendary local geneticist Lotte Auerbach FRS.

This level of generosity and friendship endured after one left Edinburgh. Noreen always stayed in touch, shared news of Edinburgh and liked to hear about one's own adventures. She visited A.G. in Boston, London, Lancaster and Cold Spring Harbor. While visiting A.G. when he was a postdoctoral researcher in Mark Ptashne's laboratory, Ken and Noreen sat in on one of Ptashne's undergraduate lectures. This, as Ptashne told the students, was rather nerve-wracking for him as 'those two sitting there are Ken and Noreen Murray, and they actually know a lot more about lambda than I ever did!'

On another occasion, while A.G. was a lecturer at Lancaster University, Noreen came to stay and the two toured round the places of her childhood—including Bolten-le-Sands, the village where she grew up. Seeing Jumbo—the rock so often climbed as a child on the shore of Morcambe Bay—her tomboyish enthusiasm resurfaced; she was confident she could still scale it, and was truly frustrated to discover she could no longer get quite to the top.

HONOURS AND COMMITTEE WORK

We have touched on some of the problems experienced by Noreen as a married woman in science, and these issues vexed her. Needless to say, they did not prevent her from achieving outstanding success and earning many honours, including the Gabor Medal of the Royal Society, the Royal Medal of the Royal Society of Edinburgh and six honorary degrees. In her collaborations with Ken (figure 9), the importance of her contribution was always evident. Her skills perfectly complemented Ken's, she being the geneticist and he the biochemist in their projects.

As well as serving as President of the Genetical Society from 1987 to 1990, she later took on other important committee work, much of it for the Royal Society, where she served on Council, as a Vice-President from 2002 to 2004 and, in 1998, chaired the Working Party on Genetically Modified Organisms. The latter produced the report on the controversial experiments conducted by Dr Arpad Pusztai. In addition to much other committee work, she served from 2005 to 2009 on the Science and Technology Honours Committee and between 2002 and 2007 on the Fellowship Committee for the Royal Commission for the Exhibition of 1851.

Figure 9. Noreen and Ken in 1995 (Copyright © Jonathan Littlejohn.) (Online version in colour.)

From 1990 until her death, Noreen also served as a Trustee of the Darwin Trust of Edinburgh. This trust was established by Ken and Noreen in 1984 with money from royalties that Ken received for the hepatitis B vaccine that he developed for Biogen (see Brammar & Gratzer 2014).

LIFE OUTSIDE SCIENCE

After science, Noreen's great love was gardening, a manifestation of her continued interest in botany and an activity she found very relaxing. She rejoiced in spending a sunny evening or weekend in the garden of their final home on Mortonhall Road in Edinburgh, which was magnificent and maintained to an exceptionally high standard (figure 10). As in many other aspects of life, she rejected new technology, pushing a manual lawnmower well into her seventies. She could often be found on her knees pulling weeds from the highly manicured lawn. Her gardening boots stood proudly outside the entrance to the house (figure 11).

Noreen and Ken were generous and delightful hosts. They frequently invited friends and colleagues to their home for dinner, when an exquisite meal and fine wines could be expected. Noreen liked high-quality ingredients, cooked simply. Favourites were venison or halibut, with roast vegetables. Many guests requested recipes, which Noreen would write out meticulously by

Figure 10. Noreen in her garden in Edinburgh in May 2010. (Photograph courtesy of
Sir Peter Lachmann FRS.) (Online version in colour.)

hand with tips for variations. They were also generous with invitations for dinner at restaurants
or, more often latterly, at the Edinburgh New Club, where they regularly dined themselves.

Noreen and Ken could often be spotted in art galleries and were discriminating collectors.
Their home was richly furnished and well endowed with work by artists including Renoir,
Anne Redpath, L. S. Lowry, Duncan Grant, Augustus John, John Singer Sargent and contem-
porary artists such as Victoria Crowe, who became a personal friend.

Noreen was also a keen follower of rugby. Her father had introduced her to the game, and she
kept on her office wall a caricature of him playing. As a student in London she attended international matches at Twickenham, and continued in later life to watch games during the annual Six
Nations tournament on television—one of the very few times that she watched television at all.

As already indicated, Noreen had an aversion to technology. Although she and Ken eventually bought mobile phones, they never used them. The shop obligingly set up the phones so
that Noreen had Ken's number on her list of contacts and Ken had Noreen's. But there was a
mix-up: Noreen's phone listed her own number under Ken's name and vice versa. Three years
later it was one of us who discovered the mistake. They had apparently never used them to
call each other, let alone anyone else!

Noreen was also reluctant to use a computer. She did learn to read emails on a computer set
up for this purpose in her office, but she always wrote a reply by hand and passed it to Ken's
secretary for emailing. It was therefore unfortunate that, when she developed a form of motor

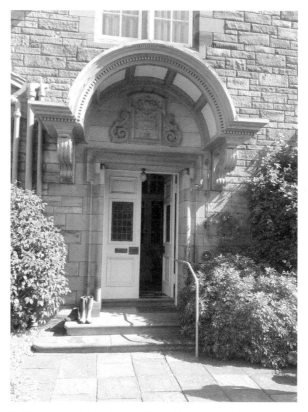

Figure 11. Noreen's gardening boots, still outside her house in Edinburgh two years after she passed away. (Online version in colour.)

neurone disease in 2010 and her speech deteriorated, she felt unable to use texting or other electronic means to facilitate communication. However, she confronted this affliction with courage and dignity. By the beginning of 2011 she could no longer speak but she continued to come into her office to deal with correspondence and she maintained a lively involvement in discussions by jotting in little notebooks that she carried everywhere. Noreen was fit and energetic until this illness developed, and then she seemed more concerned for the welfare of those around her than for herself. Noreen passed away on 12 May 2011, with Ken at her side. She is remembered with huge affection and admiration by so many, and is greatly missed. Ken died at home less than two years after Noreen, and their passing feels like the end of an era.

AWARDS AND HONOURS

1980   Elected to EMBO
1982   Fellow of the Royal Society
1987–90 President of Genetical Society of Great Britain
1989   Fellow of the Royal Society of Edinburgh
1989   Royal Society Gabor Medal
        Elected to Academia Europaea

1995	Honorary DSc, UMIST
	Honorary DSc, University of Birmingham
2001	Society of General Microbiology Fred Griffith Review Lecture
	Honorary DSc, University of Warwick
2002	CBE, Queen's New Year Honours List
2005	AstraZeneca Award from The Biochemical Society
2006	Fellow of King's College London
2008	Honorary DSc, University of Lancaster
2010	Honorary DSc, University of Sheffield
2011	Honorary DSc, University of Edinburgh
	Royal Medal of the Royal Society of Edinburgh

ACKNOWLEDGEMENTS

We thank Walter Gratzer, David Finnegan and Millie Masters for helpful suggestions, Frank Stahl for letting us quote from his letters in the Archives of the Cold Spring Harbor Laboratory, and Frank Stahl and Hugh Huxley FRS for permission to quote from Stahl's LMB memoir. We also thank Carrie Cowan for help with figures.

The frontispiece photograph was taken in 1985 by Godfrey Argent and is reproduced with permission.

REFERENCES TO OTHER AUTHORS

Allet, B., Jeppesen, P. G., Katagiri, K. J. & Delius, H. 1973 Mapping the DNA fragments produced by cleavage by lambda DNA with endonuclease RI. *Nature* **241**, 120–123.

Anon. 1972 *Escherichia* at Edinburgh. *Nature New Biol.* **236**, 33.

Arber, W. 1965 Host specificity of DNA produced by *Escherichia coli*. V . The role of methionine in the production of host specificity. *J. Mol. Biol.* **11**, 247–256.

Berg, P., Baltimore, D., Boyer, H. W., Cohen, S. N., Davis, R. W., Hogness, D. S., Nathans, D., Roblin, R., Watson, J. D., Weissman, S. & Zinder, N. D. 1974 Potential biohazards of recombinant DNA molecules. *Science* **185**, 303.

Boyer, H. W., Chow, L. T., Dugaiczyk, A., Hedgpeth, J. & Goodman, H. M. 1973 DNA substrate site for the *Eco*RII restriction endonuclease and modification methylase. *Nature New Biol.* **244**, 40–43.

Brammar, W. J. & Gratzer, W. B. 2014 Sir Kenneth Murray. *Biogr. Mems Fell. R. Soc.* **60**, 331–348 (This volume.)

Cohen, S. N., Chang, A. C., Boyer, H. W. & Helling, R. B. 1973 Construction of biologically functional bacterial plasmids *in vitro*. *Proc. Natl Acad. Sci. USA* **70**, 3240–3244.

Dussoix, D. & Arber, W. 1962 Host specificity of DNA produced by *Escherichia coli*. II. Control over acceptance of DNA from infecting phage lambda. *J. Mol. Biol.* **5**, 37–49.

Hedgpeth, J., Goodman, H. M., Boyer, H. W. 1972 DNA nucleotide sequence restricted by the RI endonuclease. *Proc. Natl Acad. Sci. USA* **69**, 3448–3452.

Hohn, B. & Murray, K. 1977 Packaging recombinant DNA molecules into bacteriophage particles *in vitro*. *Proc. Natl Acad. Sci. USA* **74**, 3259–3263.

Karn, J., Brenner, S., Barnett, L. & Cesareni, G. 1980 Novel bacteriophage lambda cloning vector. *Proc. Natl Acad. Sci. USA* **77**, 5172–5176.

Kennaway, C. K., Taylor, J. E., Song, C. F., Potrzebowski, W., Nicholson, W., White. J. H., Swiderska, A., Obarska-Kosinska, A., Callow, P., Cooper, L. P., Roberts, G. A., Artero, J. B., Bujnicki, J. M., Trinick, J., Kneale, G. G. & Dryden, D. T. 2012 Structure and operation of the DNA-translocating type I DNA restriction enzymes. *Genes Dev.* **26**, 92–104.

Klein, B. & Murray, K. 1979 Phage lambda receptor chromosomes for DNA fragments made with restriction endonuclease I of *Bacillus amyloliquefaciens* H. *J. Mol. Biol.* **133**, 289–294.

Lobban, P. E. & Kaiser, A. D. 1973 Enzymatic end-to-end joining of DNA molecules. *J. Mol. Biol.* **78**, 453–471.

Mertz, J. E. & Davis, R. W. 1972 Cleavage of DNA by R1 restriction endonuclease generates cohesive ends. *Proc. Natl Acad. Sci. USA* **69**, 3370–3374.

Meselson, M. & Yuan, R. 1968 DNA restriction enzyme from *E. coli. Nature* **217**, 1110–1114.

Nurse, P. 2004 *EMBO: 40 years of success.* Heidelberg: EMBO Publications.

Nurse, P. 2014 EMBO at 50. *Science* **343**, 117.

Old, R., Murray, K. & Boizes, G. 1975 Recognition sequences of restriction endonucleases from *Haemophilus influenzae. J. Mol. Biol.* **92**, 331–339.

Southern, E. M. 1975 Detection of specific sequences among DNA fragments separated by gel electrophoresis. *J. Mol. Biol.* **98**, 503–517.

Stahl, F. 2013 Me and Hills Road (1964–6). In *Memories and consequences: visiting scientists at the MRC Laboratory of Molecular Biology, Cambridge* (ed. Hugh Huxley), pp. 109–114. Cambridge: MRC Laboratory of Molecular Biology. (Available from http://www2.mrc-lmb.cam.ac.uk/about-lmb/archive-and-alumni/.)

BIBLIOGRAPHY

The following publications are those referred to directly in the text. A full bibliography is available as electronic supplementary material at http://dx.doi.org/10.1098/rsbm.2014.0009 or via http://rsbm.royalsocietypublishing.org.

(1)   1960   The distribution of methionine loci in *Neurospora crassa. Heredity* **15**, 199–206.

(2)   Complementation and recombination between *me-2* alleles in *Neurospora crassa. Heredity* **15**, 207–217.

(3)   1961   Polarised recombination within the *me-2* gene of *Neurospora. Genetics* **46**, 886.

(4)   1963   Polarised recombination and fine structure within the *me-2* gene of *Neurospora crassa. Genetics* **48**, 1163–1183.

(5)   1965   Cysteine mutant strains of *Neurospora. Genetics* **52**, 801–808.

(6)   1966   (With F. W. Stahl) The evolution of gene clusters and genetic circularity in microorganisms. *Genetics* **53**, 569–576.

(7)   (With F. W. Stahl, A. Nakata & J. M. Creaseman) Intergenic *cis–trans* position effects in bacteriophage T4. *Genetics* **54**, 223–332.

(8)   1973   (With C. H. Biggar & K. Murray) Recognition sequence of a restriction enzyme. *Nature New Biol.* **244**, 7–10.

(9)   1974   (With K. Murray) Manipulation of restriction targets in phage λ to form receptor chromosomes for DNA fragments. *Nature* **252**, 476–481.

(10)   1975   (With K. Murray) Phage lambda receptor chromosomes for DNA fragments made with restriction endonuclease III of *Haemophilus influenzae* and restriction endonuclease I of *Escherichia coli. J. Mol. Biol.* **98**, 551–564.

(11)   1977   (With W. J. Brammar & K. Murray) Lambdoid phages that simplify the recovery of *in vitro* recombinants. *Mol. Gen. Genet.* **150**, 53–61.

(12)   1979   (With G. G. Wilson) Molecular cloning of the DNA ligase gene from bacteriophage T4. I. Characterisation of the recombinants. *J. Mol. Biol.* **132**, 471–491.

(13)   (With W. S. Kelley) Characterisation of λ*polA* transducing phages; effective expression of the *E. coli polA* gene. *Mol. Gen. Genet.* **175**, 77–87.

(14)   1983   (With A. M. Frischauf, H. Lehrach & A. Poustka) Lambda replacement vectors carrying polylinker sequences. *J. Mol. Biol.* **170**, 827–842.

(15)   (With J. A. Gough) Sequence diversity among related genes for recognition of specific targets in DNA molecules. *J. Mol. Biol.* **166**, 1–19.

(16)   1985   (With C. A. Midgley) T4 polynucleotide kinase; cloning of the gene (*pse*T) and amplification of its product. *EMBO J.* **19**, 2695–2703.

(17)   1986   (With F. V. Fuller-Pace) Two DNA recognition domains of the specificity polypeptides of a family of type I restriction enzymes. *Proc. Natl Acad. Sci. USA* **83**, 9368–9372.

(18) 1987 (With A. A. F. Gann, A. J. B. Campbell, J. F. Collins & A. F. W. Coulson) Reassortment of DNA recognition domains and the evolution of new specificities. *Mol. Microbiol.* **1**, 13–22.

(19) 1989 (With G. M. Cowan & A. A. F. Gann) Conservation of complex DNA recognition domains between families of restriction enzymes. *Cell* **56**, 103–109.

(20) 1991 (With J. E. Kelleher & A. S. Daniel) Mutations that confer *de novo* activity upon a maintenance methyltransferase. *J. Mol. Biol.* **221**, 431–440.

(21) 1993 (With D. T. F. Dryden & L. P. Cooper) Purification and characterization of the methyltransferase from the type 1 restriction and modification system of *Escherichia coli* K12. *J. Biol. Chem.* **268**, 13228–13236.

(22)   (With L. M. Powell, D. T. F. Dryden, D. F. Willcock & R. H. Pain) DNA recognition by the EcoK methyltransferase: the influence of DNA methylation and the cofactor *S*-adenosyl-L-methionine. *J. Mol. Biol.* **234**, 60–71.

(23) 1994 (With D. F. Willcock & D. T. F. Dryden) A mutational analysis of the two motifs common to adenine methyltransferases. *EMBO J.* **13**, 3902–3908.

(24) 1998 (With S. Makovets & A. J. B. Titheradge) ClpX and ClpP are essential for the efficient acquisition of genes specifying type IA and IB restriction systems. *Mol. Microbiol.* **28**, 25–35.

(25) 1999 (With S. Makovets & V. A. Doronina) Regulation of endonuclease activity by proteolysis defends the bacterial chromosome from potential breakage by type I restriction enzymes. *Proc. Natl Acad. Sci. USA* **96**, 9757–9762.

(26) 2002 Immigration control of DNA in bacteria: self versus non-self. (The 2001 Fred Griffith Lecture.) *Microbiology* **148**, 3–20.

PHILIP GEOFFREY SAFFMAN

19 March 1931 — 17 August 2008

Philip Saffman

PHILIP GEOFFREY SAFFMAN

19 March 1931 — 17 August 2008

Elected FRS 1988

BY DARREN CROWDY[1] AND SALEH TANVEER[2]

[1]*Department of Mathematics, Imperial College London, 180 Queen's Gate, London SW7 2AZ, UK*

[2]*Department of Mathematics, Ohio State University, Columbus, OH 43210, USA*

Philip Geoffrey Saffman was born in Leeds on 19 March 1931 and died in Pasadena, California, on 17 August 2008. During an academic career lasting just over 40 years he became a world-renowned fluid dynamicist and applied mathematician. After completing his PhD in 1956, and a brief spell as a lecturer at Cambridge, he joined King's College, London, as a reader before moving to the California Institute of Technology (Caltech) in 1964 as a professor. He was to remain there for the rest of his career, retiring in 1998. His death followed 10 years later, after an extended illness.

The *Saffman–Taylor finger*, the *Saffman–Delbrück model*, *Saffman lift* and *Saffman turbulence* are now broadly recognized terms that have entered the general scientific vernacular. They are just four of an extensive array of scientific contributions attributable to Philip Saffman, whose scientific interests were broad. Theoretical fluid dynamics was his principal field. His published work in this area spans a startling array of subjects, including viscous fingering and porous media flows, the dynamics of drops and bubbles, water waves, low-Reynolds-number hydrodynamics, vortex dynamics and turbulence theory. He also made contributions in mathematical biology, astrophysics and plasma physics. Vortex dynamics became a particular expertise of his, spawned from his abiding interest in turbulence. In 1992 he published a research monograph, *Vortex dynamics*, which has since become a *sine qua non* of the subject. He became a Fellow of the American Academy of Arts and Sciences in 1978 and was elected to Fellowship of the Royal Society in 1988. He received the Otto Laporte Award from the American Physical Society in 1994.

Philip Saffman is survived by his wife, Ruth; children Louise, Mark and Emma; and grandchildren Timothy, Gregory, (Sarah) Rae, Jenny, Nadine, Aaron, Miriam, Alexandra and Andrey.

http://dx.doi.org/10.1098/rsbm.2014.0021

1. EARLY YEARS, BACKGROUND AND EDUCATION

Philip Saffman's grandparents were Eastern European Jews who immigrated to Britain. His father, Samuel Ralph Saffman, and his mother, Sarah Rebecca (*née* Leviten), were both born in Britain, with Philip becoming an addition to the family home in Savile Road, Leeds, on 19 March 1931. Philip had two brothers and, in his childhood household, the law was a dominant theme: his father and both his brothers were solicitors. His elder brother, Leonard, subsequently became a judge and he is survived by his younger brother, Simeon. Philip was the only scientist.

Philip received a solid education at Roundhay Grammar School in Leeds, which, coupled with his unusual academic precociousness, resulted in his admission to Cambridge University when he was just 15 years old. The university would not allow him to attend at such a young age, so, to fill time, he served a year of military service in the Royal Air Force as a teleprint operator. This turned out to be useful later in his academic career: it meant he could type up his own manuscripts, relying less on support staff. It was also during this period that Philip made his first extended visit to the USA, where he had cousins dotted around, including one in Culver City, California, and another in Baltimore, Maryland. This was his first taste of the country in which he would spend the major part of his career.

Telephones were not widespread in mid-century Leeds, and people tended to just drop in on their neighbours. It was in this way that Philip became acquainted with Ruth Arion, through his association with her older brothers who were Philip's academic contemporaries by virtue of his accelerated advancement through school. Ruth's parents were also immigrants to Britain, from Poland and Lithuania. Philip and Ruth married in 1954, just before Philip won a Prize Fellowship at Trinity College, Cambridge. 'If he'd known beforehand I don't think he would have married me', Ruth quips, in knowledge of how much Philip enjoyed the perks of a Trinity Fellow—the free meals, occasional feasts at high table, the stately rooms overlooking majestic College courtyards. Figure 1 shows Philip and Ruth in front of a fountain in the Villa d'Este, Tivoli, during their honeymoon in 1954.

Philip finished his Bachelors degree in mathematics in 1953, studied for Part III of the Cambridge Mathematics Tripos in 1954, and stayed on for graduate study under the supervision of George K. Batchelor (FRS 1957). It was after just two years of graduate study that Philip submitted his thesis for the Prize Fellowship. He also took his PhD in 1956, a degree largely viewed at the time to be something of a consolation prize for those not accomplished enough to secure a Prize Fellowship. Nevertheless, Philip wanted his PhD because he knew that Americans were generally unaware of what a 'Prize Fellowship' was. It was during his fellowship tenure that a long-standing association with Geoffrey I. Taylor FRS—or 'G.I.'—was born. G.I. was to play a significant role in Philip's life.

In 1960 Philip moved to King's College, London. The reasons for the move are not entirely clear but, according to Ruth, 'he was a young man in a hurry', and rapid professional advancement at Cambridge was not forthcoming. Owen Phillips (FRS 1968), with whom he was friendly at Cambridge, urged Philip to move on. The early 1960s saw an explosion in the institution of new British universities (for example Southampton and East Anglia), and Philip was not the only one to contribute to an exodus of talent from Cambridge at that time. Philip chose London as his destination, drawn by the appeal of a tolerant and cosmopolitan bigger city. One of his mentors at King's College was Hermann (later Sir Hermann) Bondi FRS and, with Ian Roxburgh, Philip wrote a paper on cosmology, but it was a subject with which he only fleetingly engaged.

Figure 1. Philip and Ruth in Italy in 1954.

An auspicious six months was spent, in 1963, as a visiting scholar at the Jet Propulsion Laboratory (JPL) in Pasadena. The invitation came from Janos Laufer, a member of Hans Liepmann's fluid dynamics group at JPL. Philip had met Laufer at the 'Mechanics of Turbulence' Symposium, held in Marseilles in 1961. Philip gave a lecture there on the effects of the molecular diffusivity in turbulent diffusion. 'Brilliant, it was', recalls Keith Moffatt (FRS 1986), a contemporary of Philip's at Cambridge, who was also present at the meeting. Philip's academic flair also impressed both fellow Englishman Gerald Whitham (FRS 1965) and Hans Liepmann during his visit to JPL: at the end of it Philip and Ruth returned to London, but Whitham and Liepmann had already offered Philip a permanant position at Caltech, which he immediately accepted. 'There was no question', Ruth recalls. A final year at King's College was spent merely to honour his contractual obligations there. Philip became a Professor of Fluid Mechanics at Caltech in 1964 and he was named von Kármán Professor in 1995.

His foresight in deciding to secure his PhD degree in Cambridge also paid off later in that, when he arrived at Caltech, he was allowed to dine at the Athenaeum, Caltech's faculty club and a respectable substitute for Trinity's high table. At the time, a PhD was an Athenaeum entry requirement.

Figure 2. (*a*) Philip Saffman outside his home in April 1969, tending the tree that would become the famous 'vortex filament tree'. (*b*). The 'vortex filament tree'. (Photos courtesy of R. Saffman.) (Online version in colour.)

2. Personal life, family, and interests

Philip and Ruth had three children, Louise, Mark and Emma, all born in the UK (in 1956, 1958 and 1964, respectively). Emma was very young at the time of the move to the USA. During its short spell in London the family lived in Twickenham; on their move to Southern California the Saffmans spent their first year in a rented home in Altadena before moving, in 1965, to Ninita Parkway, Pasadena, where Ruth still resides. The address is famous for what has become known colloquially among fluid dynamics colleagues as the 'vortex filament tree' (shown in figure 2), in reference to Philip's scientific interests. It is also known as a former home of the Caltech seismologist and inventor of the Richter scale, Beno Gutenberg, whom Albert Einstein frequently visited there. Philip used to joke to his house guests that if you looked hard enough you'll find mathematical equations etched on the bathroom walls.

The house is a very walkable two blocks from the Caltech campus, which Louise and Mark both attended as undergraduates. Emma, in contrast, went off to Yale to study biochemistry; she then transferred to Stanford to earn her PhD and she is currently a patent agent in Canada. Mark inherited his father's academic sensibilities and is a professor of physics at the University of Wisconsin–Madison. Louise is the entrepreneur of the family and credits her father with helping to shape her disposition:

> I remember his explaining logic problems to me when I was in sixth grade, always patient with homework questions, and having the particularly amazing ability to explain anything starting from first principles in a way that made it seem so clear; he taught me to think out of the box.

Philip and Ruth were from orthodox Jewish families with differing degrees of observance. Philip was never particularly interested in religion, but he was always respectful of it and, according to Ruth, 'did what his father expected of him'. This continued throughout his life, although the family often noticed Philip jotting down mathematics on napkins he had sneaked

Figure 3. The extended Saffman family outside the Athenaeum at the June 1998 event in celebration of Philip's retirement. (Online version in colour.)

into his pockets during services. When Philip was working at home, however, Louise recalls 'he had these really large clipboards which he would balance on his knee'.

He enjoyed classical music, but not in public spaces, preferring to listen to it in the privacy of his home. Reading was a long-time passion of his. Philip enjoyed history, war history in particular, drawn to it by the elements of strategy and calculated manoeuvres involved. Crime and detective novels also appealed to him, no doubt for similar reasons. He enjoyed Dick Tracy stories and the work of Raymond Chandler. One of us (S.T.) recalls Philip remarking in the mid 1980s that performing successful numerical computations in his scientific work was 'like being a detective', something he enjoyed very much. He also liked classic novelists such as Charles Dickens and Jane Austen, and he enjoyed watching Shakespeare's plays (he particularly enjoyed watching one of his own PhD students, James Gleeson, play Richard III in Caltech's Ramo Auditorium in 1999). Philip and Ruth shared a liking for the work of Anthony Burgess.

In his earlier years Philip would play golf with Ruth's brothers—Ruth recalls them all visiting St Andrews together—and his interest in golf persisted throughout the years. In later life he would play tennis, as a social sport, especially on Sundays in doubles matches with Ruth. Fred Culick and his long-time Caltech colleague Herb Keller were frequent opponents, as was Bengt Fornberg, who was Philip's Caltech colleague between 1974 and 1984. By the early 1990s he seemed to have lost interest in tennis; when asked why he was no longer playing, he responded by saying he did not find much point in hitting the ball! He enjoyed hikes to Mount Wilson and the Echo Trail, often inviting his current cohort of graduate students on day-long expeditions as an extracurricular activity. Both of us have fond memories of attending barbeques hosted by Philip and Ruth, for graduate students and colleagues, in the back garden in Ninita Parkway. Such a barbeque, organized to mark Philip's retirement in 1998, was attended by colleagues, as well as current and former PhD students, from all over the world. Figure 3 shows a photograph of the extended Saffman family taken on that occasion.

Los Angeles in the mid 1960s was a far cry from what the Saffmans were used to. Ruth, especially, found the transition difficult: 'There was smog, and you could see it; my senses were in shock.' G.I. visited Caltech in 1970, and Ruth, still adjusting to her new environs, found his presence 'very soothing'. He stayed at the Huntington Hotel, and the Saffman family has fond memories of showing him the attractions of Southern California, taking him sailing, visiting the arboretum in Arcadia (where G.I. apparently ran off, like a little boy, into a jungle-like enclosure with young Mark; G.I. enjoyed the fact that it was where the early Tarzan movies were filmed (20)*). Philip adjusted more quickly: he adored the warm, sunny climate of Southern California, and he revelled in the pervasive informality in the USA, although it took time for him to fully embrace it. Sheila Shull, the head administrative assistant of Applied Mathematics at Caltech since 1979, recalls that Philip asked that she address him as 'Professor Saffman' when she first arrived on the job. Later he asked her to use 'Philip', but after so many years, and with her respect for him firmly established, she could not bring herself to do it! 'He was a true gentleman', Sheila recalls.

Philip was an involved father who enjoyed discovering the national parks and forests of the USA with his children, especially on long car trips, where they would hike and camp as much as possible. Louise recalls that, in the few weeks immediately after Philip's visit to JPL, the family drove across the USA, along Route 66 as far as possible, in a Chevy station wagon and stopping overnight at Howard Johnson's or similar motels.

But, for all the attractions of the USA, Philip still missed certain aspects of British culture: the traditional ales, pub culture, *Hancock's Half Hour*, recorded BBC readings of Sherlock Holmes mysteries. His visit to London in 1988 to receive his Fellowship of the Royal Society and to sit for his official portrait photograph is a fondly remembered occasion for the family, and held special significance for Philip.

3. ACADEMIC CAREER AND ASSOCIATIONS

Although Batchelor was Saffman's supervisor, as a PhD student in Cambridge, Saffman became involved with G. I. Taylor on some pattern formation problems in viscous fingering (see §4.1). G.I. was the biggest scientific influence in his life, and he clearly revered him. Those visiting Saffman's office in the early 1980s were greeted with a picture of his baby grandson looking at a copy of Taylor's collected work. When asked what it was like to work with G.I., Philip would respond, 'he already knew the answer.' By this he meant that G.I. asked others to do the mathematics to confirm his intuition, rather than using mathematics to discover the underlying physics. By contrast, mathematics itself was of interest to Saffman, whose mathematical mastery was also matched by his commanding physical intuition.

Cambridge in the late 1950s was arguably the place to be if you had interests in fluid dynamics, and Philip rapidly gained the reputation of a rising star. Ruth vividly remembers an occasion when a certain Lord Rothschild, seeking to consult Philip on a scientific matter, casually knocked on the door of their Cambridge house to see whether Philip was home. The Department of Applied Mathematics and Theoretical Physics (DAMTP) was in its infancy. A photograph of the Cavendish Laboratory team taken in April 1955—it is reproduced in George Batchelor's biography of G. I. Taylor—features Philip in a line-up that includes Batchelor,

---

* Numbers in this form refer to the bibliography at the end of the text.

Figure 4. Philip Saffman circa 1955.

Owen Phillips, John S. Turner (FRS 1982) and Ian Proudman, with all of whom Philip was well acquainted. Figures 4 and 5 both show Philip in Cambridge around that time—the first is an official portrait taken by Trinity College; the photograph of Philip punting was taken by Ruth.

It was at Cambridge that Philip first met Derek Moore (FRS 1990), who was to become one of Philip's closest collaborators and a dear friend. Originating in the days before email (and beyond), the two regularly exchanged letters and other correspondence about science, mutual colleagues, family and friends, the general vicissitudes of life. Their scientific collaborations started in the late 1960s, and over the years Derek would make regular, extended, summer visits to Caltech. Derek was an avid—indeed, professional-level—jazz saxophone player, and the Saffman family became accustomed to sounds of his saxophone emanating from the basement of their house, where Derek would practise.

Max Delbrück (ForMemRS 1967) and his wife, Manny, probably also got used to Derek Moore's basement improvisations—they lived next door to the Saffmans and became good friends of the family. Delbrück was also at Caltech, and is now broadly viewed as one of the founding fathers of molecular biology; he shared the 1969 Nobel Prize in Physiology or Medicine for pioneering work studying the genetics of bacteria and their viruses. It was during

Figure 5. Philip Saffman punting in Cambridge.

a well-earned break in the mowing of front lawns in Ninita Parkway that the seeds of what is now known as the 'Saffman–Delbrück model' were sown (see §4.3).

Philip took several sabbaticals during his career. He spent time at the Massachusetts Institute of Technology (MIT) in the early 1970s, visiting his close colleagues David Benney and Harvey Greenspan. That trip was particularly memorable for the family in that it coincided with a large earthquake in the Los Angeles area and, although they were away, there was naturally concern for friends, and for the house! In 1982 another sabbatical year was spent with time divided between a return to MIT and a six-month sojourn at the University of Wisconsin—Madison.

To our knowledge, Philip supervised an impressive total of 41 PhD students during his academic career. His first students were in Cambridge and included Francis Bretherton and Ron Wooding, but most worked with him at Caltech. He enjoyed the task of research supervision, and he was an inspiring mentor, although in his productive mid-career phase he gained a reputation for not suffering fools gladly. He served as Executive Officer of Applied Mathematics at Caltech between 1985 and 1989, a role he took very seriously but, according to Ruth, did not particularly enjoy. In contrast, Philip did enjoy teaching, but only to students interested in learning. His typewritten lecture notes for the Caltech staple, course AMa 95 (now known as ACM 95/100), which he taught for many years, became a canonical set of notes for that course (his children, Louise and Mark, both took the course from their father). His graduate-level course, 'Vortex dynamics', served as the basis for an eponymous 1992 monograph (19) (see §4.5), which he was encouraged to write by his Caltech colleagues Hans Liepmann and Hans Hornung of the Graduate Aeronautics Laboratory. Saffman served as associate editor for both *Journal of Fluid Mechanics* and *Physical Review Letters* and was also an editorial board member for the journal *Studies in Applied Mathematics*.

4. SCIENTIFIC CONTRIBUTIONS

Given the breadth of Saffman's scientific contributions, space limitations alone preclude us from providing a comprehensive account. We have therefore picked out what we view as a representative showcase of his interests, including what we believe to be his most impactful contributions, and others that tell us most about the man, his methods, and his scientific principles and beliefs. Several articles have already been written focusing on particular aspects of his work, including an insightful survey by Howard Stone on Saffman's contributions to low-Reynolds-number hydrodynamics (Stone 2000), and a survey of his influence in turbulence theory by Daniel Meiron and Dale Pullin (Pullin & Meiron 2011), two of his close Caltech colleagues. The latter authors have also written an excellent account (Pullin & Meiron 2013) of Saffman's scientific contributions to the general field of fluid dynamics in a recent article for *Annual Reviews of Fluid Mechanics*.

4.1. 'Lambda equals a half'

One of the scientific problems with which Philip Saffman is indelibly linked is one he worked on very early in his career: the Hele-Shaw problem of viscous fingering. Taylor invited Saffman to perform some mathematical calculations associated with this problem, but Saffman was also directly involved with the laboratory experiments. Ruth recalls her husband's interactions with the Cavendish Laboratory assistant, Walter Thompson, and the purchasing of golden syrup from the grocery store on King's Parade: a 'Hele-Shaw cell' comprises two plates of glass with a thin layer of viscous fluid sandwiched between them.

This simple experimental set-up allows one to explore how a less viscous fluid, such as air, interacts with a more viscous fluid, such as oil or water, as the less viscous fluid is pumped into the cell. Mathematically, the equations governing the motion of the fluids in this Hele-Shaw cell are analogous to those governing the motion of water displacing oil in a porous rock. Consequently, an understanding of the toy Hele-Shaw problem provides insights into methodologies in the more important matter of drilling for oil. Taylor was motivated to study this problem after learning of the very real challenges faced by an oil company he had visited in the USA (20).

The Hele-Shaw problem is a so-called free boundary problem, in which it is the motion of an interface between two immiscible fluids that is of interest. In his now-classic 1958 paper with Taylor (4), Saffman considered the problem of displacement of a more viscous fluid by a less viscous fluid. Beyond the linear instability stages of the planar interface, their experiment revealed a competition process that eventually resulted in a steadily translating finger whose width was approximately half the channel width (except when the so-called capillary number was small). Theoretical calculations confirmed the linear instability and also revealed a class of analytical solutions to an idealized problem using complex variable techniques*—an area of mathematics that interested Saffman and would serve as an invaluable tool in many of his future endeavours. The idealization invoked is that one of the fluids is just a constant-pressure gas, with the boundary condition at the interface being that the pressure in the other fluid is constant on the boundary. The analytical solutions described a class of steadily travelling finger-like interfaces— now almost universally known† as the 'Saffman–Taylor fingers'. In his characteristically unassuming fashion Saffman downplayed his role in the joint work with Taylor, remarking in the 1990s: 'it shouldn't be Saffman–Taylor. It should be Taylor–Saffman. That happened because at that time the Royal Society would only publish names alphabetically' (Cohen 1999, p. 30).

The beautiful, and impactful, 1958 paper (4) was published, but the more important scientific story was only just beginning. There was an unresolved issue concerning the analytical solutions that Saffman and Taylor had found: the ratio of the width of the travelling fingers to the width of the Hele-Shaw cell, called λ in the original paper, was indeterminate. The analysis allowed λ to take any value between 0 and 1, in contrast with the value $\lambda = \frac{1}{2}$ observed in the experiment. Saffman and Taylor offered some explanations of why this was the case, but it was essentially left unresolved. Later on, Saffman recalled that when G.I. was asked if he slept well, G.I. replied that he usually did, except when puzzling over the discrepancy between theory and experiment in the Hele-Shaw problem.

This unresolved matter also bothered Saffman, who referred to it as 'lambda equals a half' (Cohen 1999). He re-examined the problem years later with several students. One idea was to include three-dimensional effects in the transverse direction to determine whether this made any difference. Another was to include capillary effects, although G.I. had found it difficult to imagine that these, which were estimated to be small, could make a difference. Being at Caltech, which was a centre for the study of singular perturbation methods including work by S. Kaplun, P. A. Lagerstrom, J. D. Cole and D. S. Cohen, many of whom were to become Saffman's immediate colleagues after the formation of the applied mathematics option at Caltech, Saffman was well aware by this time that apparently small terms in an equation can have unusually large ('singular') effects on a solution.

It turned out that capillary effects were indeed crucial. In joint work with a PhD student, John McLean, numerical calculations (18) were performed suggesting that the relative finger width λ was selected by capillary effects and it appeared to tend to $\frac{1}{2}$ in the small surface tension limit, although this was at odds with their perturbation analysis. It is interesting to recall their conclusions:

> Stringent checks of the numerical procedure were carried out and the internal consistency leads us to believe that the numerical results are correct and the perturbation expansion contains an undetected inconsistency.‡

Believing as they did that their numerical calculations were correct, the paper could easily have focused on the strong numerical evidence to support their conclusions. But instead they also chose to point out the discrepancy with the perturbative calculations, something that could have created doubts about those conclusions. In retrospect, one cannot but admire the intellectual fortitude needed to return to an old conundrum more than

---

* The 1958 paper (1) credits assistance from Fritz Ursell (FRS 1972).

† Unknown to Saffman and Taylor, Zhuravlev (1956) had also discovered the same steady solution.

‡ They had also concluded linear instability in contradiction to experiment, but this was later pointed out to be the result of mistakenly omitting a term in their calculation.

20 years later and publish another attempt to resolve it, only to conclude that it seemed at odds with perturbation theory. But Saffman acted with a conviction that something more profound was at work here. And he was right. In the 1980s, 'lambda equals a half' ignited a feverish flurry of scientific endeavour, in both physical scientists and mathematicians, extending methods of exponential asymptotics to integro-differential equations that arose both in this and in other related problems in pattern formation. These efforts paved the way to the understanding that their idealized mathematical model is structurally unstable (Tanveer 2000) to arbitrarily small physical effects such as surface tension and therefore need not lead to reliable physical predictions.

4.2. Saffman lift

The Hele-Shaw problem is fundamentally a viscous flow problem, but the confinement of the fluid to the thin region between two rigid plates renders the mathematical equations more akin to those describing the flow of an inviscid fluid. But it was not long before Saffman tackled the full viscous flow equations in trying to understand a puzzle concerning the shear-induced drift of particles in shear flows at low Reynolds numbers. In his 1965 paper on this subject he credits J. T. Stuart (FRS 1974) with 'reawakening his interest' (7) in such matters, a phrase perhaps alluding to work he had contributed a few years earlier on the effect of dusty gases on the stability of shear flows in a pipe (6).

It was known that spherical particles in steady low-Reynolds-number parabolic flows in a pipe drift laterally across streamlines. It was also known that such behaviour is disallowed for a particle in a unidirectional flow at zero Reynolds number when inertial effects are totally ignored. Saffman offered a theoretical rationalization of this phenomenon. It was natural to assess the effects of inertia, so, in an insightful singular perturbation analysis, Saffman was able to explain this conundrum and to produce an explicit formula for what is now known as the 'Saffman lift'. It is in response to this lift force that a particle experiences an inertia-induced velocity *across* the streamlines of the unidirectional flow in which it sits. The analysis requires a careful balancing of the inertial effects due to slip against that due to the local shear, together with a realization that particle effects manifest themselves in the far field as those due to a point singularity (a Stokeslet) at the particle centre. Saffman's consideration of this problem began in the UK and was completed at Caltech, which, as just noted, was a hotbed for the development of singular perturbation methods. Saffman's 1965 paper reflects both his interest in and proclivity for such methods and he would make repeated use of them throughout his career whenever a problem called for it.

Not only has Saffman's result on the lift velocity now been shown to give very good agreement with experiments, but the essence of the analytical approach he pioneered has also since been adopted in many other contexts. His original work assumed that it is the local shear that dominates over slip-induced inertial effects, and that the particle is rigid and far from any other boundaries. It has been generalized to spherical bubbles and drops (with an internal viscosity), to the case where boundary effects are important, and to general three-dimensional bodies. Stone (2000) has surveyed the impact of Saffman's work in more detail. It is reasonable to say that Saffman's 1965 paper had as much mathematical impact as it did in providing a physical explanation for the experimentally observed drift phenomenon.

A couple of years after his 1965 paper was published, Saffman opened his review of the monograph 'Low Reynolds number hydrodynamics' by Happel and Brenner by stating that 'The flow motions of a viscous fluid is one of the less fashionable branches of fluid mechanics. Yet....low Reynolds number flows are of enormous practical importance in many fields of science and technology'. With novel technological applications arising all the time in the modern areas of micro- and nano-fluidics, Saffman's observation continues to hold true, and the influence of his own impressive series of seminal contributions in this area still resonates to this day.

4.3 The Saffman–Delbrück model

Singular effects in flows at small Reynolds numbers also lie at the heart of the so-called 'Saffman–Delbrück model' (15). This concerns the motion of particles in a membrane or surface film neighbouring a viscous fluid phase. Many biological membranes comprise a lipid bilayer with fluid-like characteristics often containing protein molecules that essentially diffuse along it in a nearly two-dimensional motion. Although the particle motion is confined to this membrane layer, the latter often sits next to a less viscous subphase.

The biomechanical challenge is to understand the particle diffusion rate along the membrane. By invoking standard thermodynamic arguments, and by the use of the Stokes–Einstein relation, this problem of determining the translational diffusivity of the particle can be reduced to finding the translational mobility coefficient more familiar to low-Reynolds-number fluid dynamicists; this is the linear coefficient relating forces to velocities. At first sight one might think to model the motion of a single particle in the membrane as the two-dimensional uniform translation of a solid object in a Stokes flow. But the latter problem does not admit a mathematical solution (this is the so-called 'Stokes paradox'), and the sought-after mobility coefficient does not exist. Saffman and Delbrück's key contribution to modelling this scenario was to weigh up the possible competing physical effects deriving from the inescapable three-dimensionality of the flow and to identify the principal one affecting the membrane-bound particle motion. By a rational process redolent of those featuring in the fictional detective novels of which Saffman was so fond, the authors discounted inertial corrections, finite-size effects of the membrane, and far-field wall effects to conclude (17) that the most important determining mechanism is associated with the viscous dissipation in the neighbouring fluid subphase. Their arguments rely on a mixture of scaling arguments and an asymptotic analysis of the detailed velocity field. Once again, the original model has been developed in a variety of different directions (Stone 2000) and is viewed as a key contribution to biomechanical modelling.

It is a sign of Saffman's versatility, and his willingness to pitch in scientifically when he could, that he was able to turn his physical insights, and a casual conversation in the garden with his neighbour, into an invaluable scientific asset.

4.4. Turbulence

The challenge of finding an effective theoretical characterization of turbulence was a major theme running through the entire course of Saffman's career, and he studied several problems in this area. In some cases the relation to turbulence was only indirect, whereas others concerned turbulence itself.

In a study with Turner (1), which was completed even before Saffman received his PhD, they determined that it was spatial variation of the small-scale velocity field that was responsible for the collision of smaller drops to form larger ones. They obtained explicit expressions for the collision rate by using the kinetic theory of gas developed by Taylor (1935) and the pressure-fluctuation statistics in turbulence obtained by Batchelor (1951). Before this it had been known that the size of drops due to condensation itself was not enough for precipitation to occur. Saffman and Turner provided the first known explanation for the coalescence so vital to the precipitation process. This remains an influential work in environmental fluid dynamics.

Saffman's work (6) on dusty gases was motivated by experiments that suggested that the presence of dust particles reduces turbulence. Saffman showed how particulate matter changes the hydrodynamic stability features of an otherwise uniform parallel flow. Critical to the Orr–Sommerfeld-type analysis was the timescale τ of adjustment of a particle to the ambient flow relative to the timescale of that flow. Physically, the larger τ for coarser particles resulted in the transfer of energy that would otherwise have gone into unstable modes to the dust particles, thus delaying the onset of linear instability. This effect is not significant when τ is small, and the clean-gas transition Reynolds number is simply scaled down to lower values by the presence of particulate matter. Thus, fine enough particles hasten the onset of instability through a decreased critical Reynolds number, whereas coarser particles increase the critical Reynolds number. Saffman advanced this as an explanation of why dusty gases in experiment, which consisted of coarser particles, had less turbulent intensity. The 'Saffman dusty gas model' has inspired much subsequent work in both the physics and mathematics communities.

Saffman studied the effect of molecular diffusion on turbulent dispersion (5). He noticed that particles do not move with the continuum fluid velocity but have an additional random thermal component determined from the local one-molecule probability distribution. Using a local solution in time of the passive-scalar advection–diffusion equation in the presence of local straining and relative rotational motion, and assuming uncorrelated random and continuum motion, he came up with an expression for dispersion in which the effect of molecular diffusivity was to decelerate dispersion. Although experimental evidence for this phenomenon is not clear-cut, this was a startling and counterintuitive theoretical prediction based on well-accepted assumptions. Until then it was widely believed that in all cases molecular diffusivity enhanced dispersion rates.

His most enduring work in turbulence theory is likely to be his work on decaying turbulence at large scales (8); this has been a topic of interest for many decades. Before this contribution the prevailing view was that energy $E(k)$, where k is the wavenumber, scales as $E(k) \simeq C_4 k^4$ for small k. This resulted in the prediction that the mean square turbulent velocity $\langle u^2 \rangle \simeq t^{-10/7}$ for large time. This assumed that a so-called Loitsyanskii integral, which is time invariant, exists for all reasonable initial conditions. By initially taking a random distribution of impulsive forces whose spectral correlation with distance decreased exponentially, Saffman (8) showed that the Loitsyanskii integral did not exist in this case. Instead, he found a different invariant that led to the scaling behaviour $E(k) \simeq C_2 k^2$ and, as a consequence, a decay rate $\langle u^2 \rangle \simeq t^{-6/5}$. Much work followed and it appeared that different types of initial condition led to different decay rates—they are broadly classified into 'Batchelor turbulence' and 'Saffman turbulence' categories, although more recent work (Vassilicos 2011) has suggested that there can be an infinity of integral invariants, each corresponding to a different decay rate.

In hindsight, Saffman's contribution to decaying turbulence suggests that no universality in the decay rate independent of initial conditions can be expected. His own view of this work, given in the preface to his lectures on turbulence (9), is typically self-deprecating: 'The work … on the structure and invariance of the large eddies is believed to be both new and correct, but is of no real importance'.

His many other contributions to turbulence theory have been summarized in Pullin & Meiron (2011).

Notwithstanding his own work, he was a fierce critic of much of the prevailing research on turbulence. In his lectures (9) he quoted Shakespeare's 'Scottish play' to express his belief that many people at the time tended to overstate their results relative to what was actually accomplished (and which invariably depended on a string of untested implicit assumptions), suggesting that the current state of turbulence theory was 'full of sound and fury, signifying nothing.' He also expressed the hope that research over the next few decades would make this quotation inappropriate but, until his death, he still did not quite believe this had happened. This scepticism extended to his own work, in respect of which he once offered readers the caution (9) 'the ideas … are new and hopefully important, but are speculative, and quite possibly in serious error.'

Arguably, his role as a critic may have been as important as his own work in turbulence. His criticisms focused attention on implicit, untested assumptions that go into turbulence theories. He himself thought seriously about many of these assumptions and identified a few fundamental questions that he believed needed to be resolved before serious progress could be made. These include (i) the independence of Reynolds number of the dissipation rate, (ii) the dependence of the inertial range, small eddies and intermittency on Reynolds number, and (iii) long-time existence of solutions to the Euler and Navier–Stokes equations. These remain widely recognized important open theoretical problems, although there have been empirical advances (see, for example, Sreenivasan (1998) and Kaneda *et al.* (2003) concerning question (i), and Luo & Hou (2014) concerning the three-dimensional Euler equations).

Saffman recognized the challenges in these problems and was generally pessimistic about the pace of progress in turbulence research. However, he always held the belief that understanding structures in turbulent flows, like those demonstrated by the experiments of Brown & Roshko (1974), was a very worthwhile intermediate goal, and this led him to devote considerable time and energy to improving our understanding of vortex structures in fluid flows.

4.5. Vortex dynamics

The 1970s saw the blossoming of Saffman's interest in vorticity as a key to understanding complex fluid dynamical behaviour. This theme of his research continued well into the 1980s, and culminated in the publication of *Vortex dynamics*, the only monograph that Saffman would write in his career. Cambridge University Press published the first edition in 1992; the paperback edition appeared in 1995, and a Russian translation in 2000. Ruth reports that Philip found writing it 'exhausting'. But in the short time since its first appearance it has arguably already taken its place in the pantheon of influential fluid dynamics texts. Derek Moore once told one of us (D.C.) that he valued it so much that he kept a copy on his bedside table.

Indeed, Derek Moore can largely be credited with engaging Saffman in this area: Saffman's contributions to vortex dynamics started in earnest in the early 1970s, and mostly in collaboration with Moore. The two had published their first collaborative work together in the late 1960s—on the subject of particle motion in rapidly rotating flows in bounded domains (10)—and their first article on vortex dynamics appeared soon afterwards in 1972 (12). It was a skilful use of the techniques of matched asymptotic expansions and provided the first self-consistent formulation of the motion of a vortex filament with small but finite cross-sectional area and arbitrary internal flow structure, including axial flow effects and ambient irrotational strain. This paper helped to clarify several contradictory results in the literature concerning the speed of propagation of a thin-cored vortex ring. Two other important related papers appeared shortly afterwards (13, 14).

On surveying both Saffman's published work in vortex dynamics, and the topic choices for his monograph, several characteristics become apparent. He was convinced that the judicious study of reduced models, and exact solutions, can afford crucial insights into the study of more complex dynamical phenomena. The organization of his monograph into chapters devoted to the line vortex model, the vortex patch model, vortex sheets and vortex filaments is consonant with his belief that vorticity in its various guises constitutes 'the sinews and muscles of fluid motion'—a phrase (attributed to Küchemann 1965) that he enjoyed and would often repeat.

With his students and collaborators Saffman contributed many studies on vortex patches. His primary interest in them involved a careful analysis of their structure and stability, and he appreciated the remarkable numerical advantage, noticed by Zabusky and co-workers in the late 1970s, afforded by the reduction of their dynamical evolution to the methods of 'contour dynamics'. Inspired by the work of Brown & Roshko (1974), Moore and Saffman made use of an exact solution that they had found earlier* (11) for an elliptical vortex patch in equilibrium in a linear ambient straining flow to make arguments about the spacing of vortex structures in turbulent shear flows. They argued that this was controlled by the fact that there is an upper limit on the line density of a linear array of finite-cored vortices: vortices that are too close cannot continue to exist in equilibrium without breaking up (16).

As Saffman's interest in numerical methods grew, he used them to compute a wide range of vortex patch equilibria. For example, he got involved in the subtle question of the stability properties of von Kármán vortex streets, a hotly contested topic in the late 1970s and early 1980s. Despite the fact that such vortex streets are commonly observed in nature and experiments, a linear stability analysis of the point vortex street is well known to be stable to linear perturbations only at an isolated value of the street's aspect ratio. Saffman was interested in whether the vortex patch analogues of the von Kármán point vortex streets would help to clarify the stability question. In the end they did. The story of the developments is detailed, involving contributions by Saffman with his student James Schatzmann and with Daniel Meiron, as well as by Shigeo Kida, Robert MacKay (FRS 2000) and Javier Jimenez, but it was eventually found, from general arguments based on the stability structure of Hamiltonian systems, that the stability properties of the point vortex street are generic in all inviscid models that are not 'too far' from the point vortex case. Having spent much time and effort studying this problem, Saffman was impressed by the power of these Hamiltonian methods; he would come to make use of them in his work on water wave problems (see §4.6). In the early 1990s he took pains to try to understand the geometrical mechanics approach to the Euler equations developed by Arnold, Marsden, Weinstein, and others.

Saffman's interest in vortex patches continued to the end of his career. Indeed, his very last published paper revisited the subject of aircraft vortices; with his student David Hill he studied the structure and stability of a counter-rotating pair of vortex patches in a linear shear flow in an attempt to understand how ambient weather conditions might affect the safety of air traffic control protocols at airports. Given his long-standing interest in such problems it is fitting that Saffman's *Los Angeles Times* obituary states:

> In particular, he developed a precise mathematical understanding of wake turbulence caused by jets during takeoff. That analysis helped uncover the conditions that contributed to several aircraft accidents, including a Delta Air Lines crash in Dallas in August 1985, when the flight crew tried to

---

* Moore and Saffman were unaware that the exact solution they derived in (12) had been found much earlier by S. A. Chaplygin (Meleshko & van Heijst 1994).

land in a thunderstorm. Saffman's work helped convince airlines and airports that they must allow a minimum amount of time to pass between takeoffs to let the wake turbulence of the preceding jet to subside.

In this context, Saffman's 1972 contribution on the motion of a trailing vortex pair in a stratified atmosphere was particularly important. The distance between aircraft had to be sufficient to let the vortex pair migrate or dissipate enough to allow subsequent aircraft to avoid the turbulent trail. It is interesting to note that such concerns persist to this day and turned out to be one of the causes of delayed certification of the Airbus A380 in the USA.

4.6. Water waves

Water wave theory was the other topic that occupied most of Saffman's attention in the 1970s and 1980s. He worked on different aspects of water waves for a long time, typically with students. Initially he seemed to have been influenced by David Benney from MIT, with whom he collaborated on nonlinear wave interactions.

As already mentioned, by this time Saffman had become a firm believer in the power of scientific computation in achieving scientific goals. Graduate students seeking to work with Saffman at this time were actively encouraged to engage in computations. In regard to Saffman, Bengt Fornberg told us, 'if I recall correctly, he was the first faculty member in the Applied Math department to acquire a personal computer almost before the concept was known—a preassembled Heathkit, without hard drive, but remarkably with a simple Fortran compiler on a floppy disk.' Robert Mackay similarly recalls, 'Saffman was very proud of his VAX, which was named PGSaffVax.'

To an extent, Saffman believed that the use of analytical techniques in fluid dynamics had run its course and that unless you were a 'genius', as he put it, computation was about the only way in which one could expect to make significant scientific progress. Looking at the historical development of water wave theory, there were good reasons to hold such a view. The study of water waves had a long history involving some of the best-known mathematicians— Laplace, Lagrange, Cauchy, Poisson, Airy, Stokes and many others. Yet, by the late 1970s, when Saffman got involved, most of the theoretical work involved either weakly nonlinear models or rigorous analysis of the Stokes amplitude for two-dimensional steady water waves. Even in two dimensions, uniqueness issues were not settled. Observed water waves in nature are typically three-dimensional, and a two-dimensional theory was clearly inadequate. Saffman was particularly impressed by computational discoveries of M. S. Longuet-Higgins FRS and co-workers.

With collaborators, Saffman contributed a series of his own skilful computations on water waves: with Benito Chen he established a new branch of steady two-dimensional waves that arose from a period-doubling bifurcation from known two-dimensional solutions; with John McLean and others he found that the Benjamin–Feir instability was not as dominant as the three-dimensional instability for steep two-dimensional water waves; and in 1982 with Daniel Meiron and Henry Yuen he found three-dimensional steady waves that resulted from subharmonic bifurcation of relatively steep two-dimensional waves and which agreed very well with observations. This body of work, which was primarily numerical, is probably the most significant of Saffman's contributions to the theory of water waves. Saffman and his collaborators were guided in this research by calculations on water waves that he had performed in 1980, with Yuen, using the simplified integro-differential equations presented by Vladimir Zakharov. The Zakharov model also extended the range of validity of the results to steeper wave amplitudes. It could also be used to explore random wave fields that were of interest to Saffman and his colleagues at the TRW group in Redondo Beach, with whom he had an extended association, often performing consultancy work for them.

Overall, Saffman had a dim view of pure analysis—and pure mathematics in general—in its ability to contribute anything substantial to cutting-edge research problems; he believed for a time that analysts in the twentieth century strayed too far from application, unlike those in the nineteenth century. However, he was very impressed by the power of the methods that Robert MacKay brought to problems of mutual interest. Together, in 1986, they showed that a necessary condition for instability of Stokes waves is a collision of eigenvalues of opposite Krein signature in the linearized spectral problem. This criterion could be related to a quartet resonance condition between waves of different wavenumbers. In retrospect it is interesting to observe that Saffman's numerical water-wave computations have since served as inspiration to pure mathematicians interested in developing more rigorous approaches. John Toland FRS, for example, holds Saffman's work in very high regard (Toland *et al.* 2000).

5. FINAL THOUGHTS

Saffman's career spanned the decades during which the use of computation burgeoned into an inescapable tool for scientific enquiry, and he made strategic use of it in his own research. He was not, however, a believer in large-scale computation, especially if it involved many parameters and variables, which he thought of as a 'numerical wind-tunnel' in the sense that it would give results for only a limited set of parameter values. This may be the reason that he generally avoided computation of time-evolving flows because it would require a huge number of initial conditions before one could fathom, if at all, the overall dynamical behaviour of the system (although, in the mid 1970s, in close collaboration with Control Data Corporation, Saffman put extensive effort into direct simulation of three-dimensional turbulence by a new approach involving the computation of interacting 'vortons'—three-dimensional analogues of point vortices. There were technical issues with the method, but the project was also hampered by the unexpected passing of Saffman's collaborator Mike Kascic (Kascic 1984).) A mantra often voiced by Saffman was 'use the computer like a scalpel, not a sledge-hammer.' He was particularly wary of 'thoughtless number crunching' (20).

Saffman's scientific enquiries were almost always driven by the need to understand the underlying physics of a situation. In the spirit of G. I. Taylor he espoused the use of physical intuition to inform his investigations, but he was always open to the possibility that his intuition might be wrong; he relied on mathematics to help confirm a theory or to reject it. His career is testament to his willingness to embrace varied mathematical techniques (such as the Orr–Sommerfeld approach to stability theory, complex variable techniques, singular perturbation methods, and the theory of Hamiltonian systems) and numerical methods, in pursuit of nothing other than the scientific truth. In this respect, Saffman's collected body of work exemplifies an instinctive *style* of looking at problems, one that is not easily emulated.

As a mentor for other researchers, Saffman left lasting impressions, and invaluable lessons, with all those lucky enough to interact with him. He was a man of unflappable demeanour and of unerring principle and integrity, both in his scientific endeavours and in his personal associations. Greg Baker recalls challenging Saffman about the wisdom of including, in their joint paper (also with John Sheffield) on periodic hollow vortex arrays, the statement 'the purpose of this paper is to present the calculation as a contribution to the theory of vortices. We see no direct physical application of the results', to which Saffman immediately responded that one should always be honest about the limitations of one's work. We have already emphasized, in discussing contributions to turbulence theory by both himself and others, how stridently Saffman adhered to this principle.

On the occasion of Philip's retirement in 1998 the editors of *Journal of Fluid Mechanics* commissioned a special issue—volume 409—to honour the many years of scientific leadership, deep physical and mathematical insights, and inspiration that he had brought to the fluid dynamics community over his career. From the three landmark articles that Philip contributed to its very first volume (1–3), to the many he would subsequently publish there, he provided an ever steady hand and a guiding light for all its readers.

The California Institute of Technology organized a memorial workshop in Philip's honour on 31 May 2009. It was a spirited occasion with more than 100 attendees, including colleagues from around the world, family and friends all sharing reminiscences both scientific and personal. Ruth told us that, as Philip gradually succumbed to illness in his final years, 'he was saddened that he couldn't finish his list of problems'.

So are we all.

ACKNOWLEDGEMENTS

We thank the Saffman family, whose help was invaluable in the preparation of the memoir. D.C. is especially grateful to Ruth Saffman for many enjoyable and informative conversations on various occasions in 2013 and 2014. He also extends special thanks to Sheila Shull for her constant help.

Sincere thanks also go to Greg Baker, Tony Davis, Bengt Fornberg, John Gibbon, Philip Hall, Robert MacKay FRS, Keith Moffatt FRS, Daniel Meiron, Dale Pullin, Katepalli Sreenivasan, Trevor Stuart FRS and J. C. Vassilicos.

The frontispiece photograph was taken in 1988 by Godfrey Argent and is reproduced with permission.

REFERENCES TO OTHER AUTHORS

Batchelor, G. K. 1951 Pressure fluctuations in isotropic turbulence. *Proc. Camb. Phil. Soc.* **47**, 359–374.

Brown, G. L. & Roshko, A. 1974 Density effects and large structure in turbulent mixing layers. *J. Fluid Mech.* **64**, 775–816.

Cohen, S. K. 1999 Caltech Oral History Project: 'Philip Geoffrey Saffman'. (See http://oralhistories.library.caltech.edu/.)

Kaneda, Y., Ishihara, T. & Yokokawa, M. 2003 Energy dissipation rate and energy spectrum in high resolution direct numerical simulations of turbulence in a periodic box. *Phys. Fluids* **15**, L21–L24.

Kascic, M. J. 1984 Vorton dynamics: a case study of developing a fluid dynamics model for a vector processor. *Parallel Comput.* **1**, 35–44.

Küchemann, D. 1965 Report on the IUTAM symposium on concentrated vortex motions in fluids. *J. Fluid Mech* **21**(1), 1–20.

Luo, G. & Hou, T. Y. 2014 Potentially singular solutions of the 3D axisymmetric Euler equations. *Proc. Natl Acad. Sci. USA*, http://dx.doi.org/10.1073/pnas.1405238111 (published ahead of print 25 August 2014).

Meleshko, V. V. & van Heijst, G. J. F. 1994 On Chaplygin's investigations of two-dimensional vortex structures in an inviscid fluid. *J. Fluid Mech.* **272**, 157–182.

Pullin, D. I. & Meiron, D. I. 2011 P. G. Saffman. In *A voyage through turbulence* (ed. P. Davidson, K. Moffatt, Y. Kaneda & K. Sreenivasan), pp. 221–249. Cambridge University Press.

Pullin, D. I. & Meiron, D. I. 2013 Philip G. Saffman. *Annu. Rev. Fluid Mech.* **45**, 19–34.

Sreenivasan, K. R. 1998 An update on the energy dissipation rate in isotropic turbulence. *Phys. Fluids* **10**, 528–529.

Stone, H. A. 2000 Philip Saffman and viscous flow theory. *J. Fluid Mech.* **409**, 165–183.

Tanveer, S. 2000 Surprises in viscous fingering. *J. Fluid Mech.* **409**, 273–308.

Taylor, G. I. 1935 Statistical theory of turbulence. *Proc. R. Soc. Lond.* A **151**, 421–444.

Toland, J. Buffoni, B. & Dancer, E. N. 2000 The sub-harmonic bifurcation of Stokes waves. *Arch. Rat. Mech. Anal.* **152**, 241–270.

Vassilicos, J. C. 2011 An infinity of possible invariants for decaying homogeneous turbulence. *Phys. Lett.* A **375**, 1010–1013.

Zhuravlev, P. 1956 Shape of interface in fluids displacement. [In Russian.] *Zap. Leningrad. Com. Inst.* **133**, 54.

BIBLIOGRAPHY

The following publications are those referred to directly in the text. A full bibliography is available as electronic supplementary material at http://dx.doi.org/10.1098/rsbm.2014.0021 or via http://rsbm.royalsocietypublishing.org.

(1)   1956   (With J. S. Turner) On the collision of drops in turbulent clouds. *J. Fluid Mech.* **1**, 16–30.

(2)   On the rise of small air bubbles in water. *J. Fluid Mech.* **1**, 249–275.

(3)   On the motion of small spheroidal particles in a viscous liquid. *J. Fluid Mech.* **1**, 540–553.

(4)   1958   (With G. I. Taylor) The penetration of a fluid into a porous medium or Hele-Shaw cell containing a more viscous liquid. *Proc. R. Soc. Lond.* A **245**, 312–329.

(5)   1960   On the effect of the molecular diffusivity in turbulent diffusion. *J. Fluid Mech.* **8**, 273–283 (1960).

(6)   1962   On the stability of laminar flow of a dusty gas. *J. Fluid Mech.* **13**, 120–128.

(7)   1965   The lift on a small sphere in a slow shear flow. *J. Fluid Mech.* **22**, 385–400.

(8)   1967   The large-scale structure of homogeneous turbulence. *J. Fluid Mech.* **27**(3), 581–593.

(9)   1968   Lectures on homogeneous turbulence. In *Topics in nonlinear physics* (ed. N. J. Zabusky), pp. 485–614. Berlin: Springer.

(10)   (With D. W. Moore) The rise of a body through a rotating fluid in a container of finite length. *J. Fluid Mech.* **31**, 635–642.

(11)   (With D. W. Moore) Structure of a line vortex in an imposed strain. In *Aircraft wake turbulence and its detection: Proceedings of a Symposium on Aircraft Wake Turbulence held in Seattle, Washington, 1–3 September 1970* (ed. J. H. Olsen, A. Goldburg & M. Rogers), pp. 339–354. New York: Plenum.

(12) 1972   (With D. W. Moore) The motion of a vortex filament with axial flow. *Phil. Trans. R. Soc. Lond.* A **272**, 403–429.

(13) 1973   (With D. W. Moore) Axial flow in laminar trailing vortices. *Proc. R. Soc. Lond.* A **333**, 491–508.

(14)   Structure of turbulent line vortices. *Phys. Fluids* **16**, 1181–1188.

(15) 1975   (With M. Delbrück) Brownian motion in biological membranes. *Proc. Natl Acad. Sci.* **72**, 3111–3113.

(16)   (With D. W. Moore) Organized vortices in a turbulent mixing layer. *J. Fluid Mech.* **69**, 465–473.

(17) 1976   Brownian motion in thin sheets of viscous fluid. *J. Fluid Mech.* **73**, 593–602.

(18) 1981   (With J. McLean) The effect of surface tension on the shape of fingers in a Hele-Shaw cell. *J. Fluid Mech.* **102**, 455–469.

(19) 1992   *Vortex dynamics*. Cambridge University Press.

(20) 1997   Review of *The life and legacy of G. I. Taylor*, by George Batchelor. *SIAM Rev.* **39**(3), 546–549.

HARRY SMITH CBE

7 August 1921 — 10 December 2011

Harry Smith

HARRY SMITH CBE

7 August 1921 — 10 December 2011

Elected FRS 1979

By Alan Rickinson

School of Cancer Sciences, Vincent Drive, University of Birmingham, Edgbaston, Birmingham B15 2TT, UK

Harry Smith was the person who, more than any other in the latter half of the twentieth century, prompted a renaissance of interest in the pathogenesis of microbial disease. A chemist turned microbiologist, his work on *Bacillus anthracis*, the causative agent of anthrax, led to the discovery in the serum of infected animals of the tripartite toxin that brings about the death of the host. These studies not only identified the first bacterial toxin, inspiring parallel work in related fields, but were seminally important in two further respects: first, they showed that toxins can be complexes of multiple components that, when studied individually, are non-toxic; and, second, they emphasized that research into infectious disease pathogenesis needs to focus on the biology of infection *in vivo*.

EARLY YEARS

Harry Smith was born in Northampton on 7 August 1921. His father, also Harry, was a local bookmaker, and his mother, Annie (*née* Brown), was the daughter of a bookmaker. Both had been forced to leave school at an early age and so, when the time came, they were determined to send both Harry and his younger brother Alfred to Northampton Grammar School. It was here, helped by an excellent teacher, that Harry first developed his interest in chemistry. Having done well in the School Certificate Examination at the age of 15 years, he was keen to stay on for the Higher Certificate but, as so often in those days before free education, it was not to be. Luckily, however, he gained an apprenticeship with a local pharmacist and was able to study for three nights a week at Northampton Technical College for the Intermediate Examination of the Pharmaceutical Society, the first step on the way to qualification as a pharmacist. There he was again blessed with a supportive chemistry teacher who, recognizing Harry's talent, encouraged him to switch course and take a degree in pharmacy, which at the time was taught at University College, Nottingham, and awarded through the University of London.

http://dx.doi.org/10.1098/rsbm.2014.0014

Nottingham

Harry won a scholarship to Nottingham and arrived as a student in the School of Pharmacy in September 1940. Studies had to be dovetailed alongside wartime duties as a member of the Officer Training Corps, a harbinger of close engagement with the military that was to come much later in Harry's career. Harry excelled as a student in Nottingham and gained a BPharm (London) degree within two years, at the same time taking the Pharmaceutical Society's pharmaceutical chemistry examination and winning their Harrison Memorial Prize. But these student years brought a much more important reward than academic prizes. On the same degree course Harry met a fellow-student, Janet Holmes, the person who was destined to become his wife, soulmate and constant support over the ensuing 70 years of their life together. Janet's enormous contribution to the 'Harry and Janet' partnership cannot be overstated and, although mentioned *en passant* throughout the text covering Harry's scientific career, will have its own spotlight later in the piece. For the moment, suffice it to say that none of the following would have happened or been possible without Janet by Harry's side.

It was now 1942 and, under wartime regulations, Harry was directed to the analytical laboratories of the Boots Pure Drug Company in Nottingham and, after a time, was placed in charge of a small laboratory working on the production of pharmaceuticals. The work at Boots gave him valuable experience in volumetric and gravimetric analysis and the opportunity, at evenings and weekends, to study for a BSc degree in special chemistry from the University of London. Harry took these examinations in war-torn London in July 1944. They included a hair-raising episode when the practical chemistry paper was temporarily halted because of a 'doodle-bug' (V1 flying bomb) raid, all candidates being instructed to take cover under their laboratory bench; the practical eventually resumed but, afterwards, a large crater at the end of the road revealed just how close the examination had been to permanent cessation! Harry survived with a first-class honours degree to his name and, in 1945, was appointed Assistant Lecturer in Pharmaceutical Chemistry back at University College, Nottingham.

With the position came the opportunity to register for a PhD under the supervision of the head of department, Professor J. Masson Gulland (FRS 1945), whose interests lay in ribonucleic acid chemistry. Harry's project was to join two cytidine molecules together by a phosphate link at the 5′ position of the ribose moiety. Perhaps it was fortunate that his supervisor's frequent absence, through duties in postwar London, forced Harry back on his own resources, honing that streak of independence that came to characterize so much of his later research. The project was indeed completed with the successful synthesis of both cytidine and uridine dimers, leading to the award of a PhD in biochemistry from the University of London. One of his PhD examiners was Professor Alexander Todd FRS, who was then Professor of Chemistry in Manchester but would later move to Cambridge and, as Lord Todd, become President of the Royal Society. Indeed, Harry always suspected that it was Todd who made the recommendation that would soon change the course of his career from pure chemistry to microbiology.

At the end of his PhD in 1947, such a move was far from Harry's mind: in fact, he was on the point of accepting promotion from an assistant to a full lectureship in pharmaceutical chemistry in Nottingham. Then, unexpectedly, he received a letter inviting him to apply for a job as a Senior Scientific Officer in the Microbiology section of the Chemical Defence Establishment (CDE) at Porton Down, near Salisbury in Wiltshire. The salary was £800 per year, £100 more than the position in Nottingham, and with the added bonus of on-site accommodation, an attractive offer for the soon-to-be married couple. As Harry jokingly admitted later in life, he switched from chemistry to microbiology for an extra £100 per year and the promise of a house!

Porton Down

Harry arrived at Porton Down in September 1947 to join a team that the Head of Microbiology, Dr David Henderson (FRS 1959), was in the process of building. Several other recruits arrived at the same time, all, like Harry, without any formal training in microbiology. Indeed, at the time there was only one microbiology degree course in the entire country, at Reading. However, a training course in medical microbiology, primarily designed for medical graduates, was available at the British (later Royal) Postgraduate Medical School in Hammersmith, London. Harry and his new colleagues attended this course over the next three months. This provided some essential background for their future work at Porton Down, but also gave them the opportunity to hear occasional seminars by distinguished scientists from around the world. For Harry, the most memorable was that given by Linus Pauling ForMemRS, the American chemist whose work on the nature of chemical bonding was soon to be recognized by a Nobel prize. By that time, Pauling had moved from inorganic chemistry to biochemistry and to protein structures in particular. Great scientists do not stand still, was the message.

Initially David Henderson asked Harry to work on the chemical basis of a curious property of mucin, namely its ability to enhance the virulence of bacterial infection in several animal models. Knowing little or nothing about mucin, Harry acted on Henderson's suggestion to ask for help from an expert on respiratory mucus, none other than Sir Howard Florey FRS (PRS 1960–65), Director of the Institute of Pathology in Oxford and a Nobel laureate for his work on the development of treatment with penicillin. Florey invited Harry to Oxford and spent two full hours in conversation with the young researcher. As Harry recalled, he learned a lot about mucin but also a much more important lesson for future life: no matter how eminent you may become, never forget to find time for young scientists if they seek your help. As things turned out, the virulence-enhancing properties of mucin proved to be very complex. The activity was due to synergism between particulate matter, a viscous medium and several chemical components, including heparin, chondroitin and blood-group substances. This principle of cooperative actions underpinning biological activities was in Harry's mind as he moved to his next, and arguably his most important, project: *Bacillus anthracis* infection and anthrax.

Anthrax had been known as a scourge of both humans and animals since ancient times, and the disease has a special place in the history of microbiological research. Thus it was Robert Koch's demonstration of *Bacillus anthracis* as the cause of anthrax that enabled the establishment of Koch's postulates in 1877. Thereafter, researchers such as William Greenfield and Louis Pasteur, working on anthrax in the early 1880s, demonstrated the feasibility of using attenuated live vaccines to protect livestock from the disease, the second ever example of a bacterial vaccine. Two decades later, it was Elias Metchnikoff's studies of the interaction between *Bacillus anthracis* and macrophages that laid one of the foundation stones of a new science: cellular immunology. This bacterium is distinguished by an ability to form spores that can lay dormant in the earth for many years and then germinate on entry into a living host, typically through skin abrasion or inhalation. The capacity for dormancy is of inherent scientific interest but, in more recent years, has given anthrax some notoriety as a candidate organism of biological warfare. Even by 1950 there was no shortage of literature for the young researcher entering the anthrax field to read. As Harry did so, he became intrigued by one thing: despite the well-known signs of anthrax infection, namely oedema and haemorrhage, it was not clear how *Bacillus anthracis* produced these symptoms leading to the death of the host. In contrast with other microbial diseases such as tetanus or diphtheria, no lethal toxin had ever been identified *in vitro*, either in anthrax bacilli or in their culture filtrates. It was this paradox that led Harry to propose to David Henderson that they should search for a toxin not in bacterial cultures but directly in experimentally infected animals. Such work was not without risk, even by the standards of the time, because there was no anthrax vaccine yet available for use in humans. Henderson nonetheless approved the project, acting against the advice of his Safety Officer, but insisted that Harry be joined by a more experienced colleague. The colleague in question, Dr James Keppie, had worked on gas gangrene at the Lister Institute in London during the war and already had experience of animal work. So began a 15-year scientific partnership and lifelong friendship with the person whom Harry describes as a superb experimentalist and essential to their success.

Smith and Keppie decided to use the guinea-pig model for their work, taking advantage of the CDE's new animal laboratories that had been purpose-built for research on infectious disease. Large numbers of guinea-pigs could be infected with *Bacillus anthracis* and samples taken directly at death for toxicity testing. Safety precautions were rudimentary by today's standards. Post-mortems were performed wearing normal hospital operating gowns, face masks, gloves and rubber boots, and spins to separate bacteria from extracellular products were performed in ordinary refrigerated centrifuges, using non-sealed tubes. Despite this, there were no cases of anthrax infection among Smith, Keppie and their loyal team of four to six technicians in more than six years of experimental work. Rather than taking this as proof of their superb experimental technique, Harry came away with the impression that the bacterium was not as infectious as first thought and that anthrax might have been be overrated as a biological weapon!

The work on *Bacillus anthracis* gave fascinating results. Although the fatal phase of the infection was associated with massive bacterial replication, extracts of the anthrax bacilli taken at this stage did not induce toxicity in uninfected animals. Indeed, streptomycin given midway through the course of infection could avert this replication yet did not prevent the fatal outcome. Unexpectedly, the toxin responsible for fatality lay within the plasma of infected animals. This key observation, published in *Nature* in 1954 (1)*, marked the beginning of a long series of studies to characterize the factors involved. Smith and Keppie went on to show that the toxin was transiently detectable in bacterial culture filtrates, but only early in the course of infection, and that it consisted of three components, each of which was non-toxic when tested in isolation (2). Interestingly, one of those components was the Protective Antigen (PA), which Dick Strange and Frank Belton, colleagues at Porton Down, had begun to purify from bacterial culture filtrates and had shown could immunize animals against anthrax. The other components were Lethal Factor (LF) and Edema Factor (EF), both named after their pathogenic contributions. Their mechanisms of action are today largely understood from the work of many groups, with LF being a metalloprotease, EF a modulator of cyclic AMP, and PA a non-toxic, cell-binding ligand responsible for transporting the other components into the cell (Baillie 2009). But this whole field of endeavour owes its genesis to the classical early studies of Harry Smith and James Keppie.

---

* Numbers in this form refer to the bibliography at the end of the text.

The discovery of the anthrax toxin was a significant advance that, with the benefit of hindsight, marked a turning point in the field of microbial pathogenesis. As John Stephen, one of Harry's research fellows at Porton Down, subsequently wrote in his book on bacterial toxins (Stephen & Pietrowski 1987), 'it gave the kiss of life to a subject that was almost moribund'. Before then, no one had harvested bacteria and their products from infected animals in sufficient quantities to examine them chemically for virulence determinants. Now it was clear that other bacterial toxins could be discovered if they were looked for in more appropriate contexts and/or tested in more appropriate ways. Accordingly, the subsequent discovery by others of cholera toxin owed much to the stricture of testing for biological activity at the relevant site *in vivo*.

The work on anthrax was seminal in another respect. It showed for the first time that toxins could be multi-component complexes, a theme that would recur throughout much future work in this field. That realization spurred Harry to pursue an immunological approach to the identification of toxin components. Beginning 20 years before the onset of monoclonal antibody technology, Harry was actively immunizing rabbits with toxin preparations, setting up large diffusion gels to separate the individual complexes from toxin–antibody reactions, cooling the gels with solid carbon dioxide, and cutting out the component bands to obtain individual antigen preparations. A labour of love!

Most importantly, the anthrax work set the theme for Harry's future career as a microbiologist. While maintaining his interest in anthrax, Harry initiated new work at Porton Down on *Pasteurella pestis* and *Brucella abortus*, the causative agents of plague and brucellosis, respectively. Again with James Keppie as collaborator, bacilli were harvested from infected animals, and hitherto unknown aspects of their pathogenicity were revealed. Harry had nailed his colours to the mast: he was determined to study microbial pathogenicity by looking at the biology of the infection *in vivo* and, moreover, to encourage others to do the same. The point was forcefully argued, and much of his early research was summarized, in an article written for *Annual Review of Microbiology* in 1958 (3). Yet not everyone was convinced and it took more than a decade for the message to begin to be appreciated by the research community at large. Indeed, it was not until the 1990s that the study of pathogenicity *in vivo* mushroomed and assumed its present status as one of the most active areas of contemporary microbiology.

By the mid 1960s Harry had worked at Porton Down, in what had then become the Microbiological Research Establishment (MRE), for more than 15 years. During that time he had risen from Principal to Senior Principal and eventually to Deputy Chief Scientific Officer, one rank below that of David Henderson, whose retirement was imminent. Harry was one of those considered for the top position but, at a time when virology rather than bacteriology seemed to be in the ascendant, the selection went against him. Harry, ever proud of his record, felt the rejection keenly and made the decision to seek a leadership role elsewhere. This was the spur that led him to the University of Birmingham, whose offer of headship of the university's Department of Microbiology he accepted in January 1965. In retrospect, Harry considered this to be one of the best decisions that he ever made. The government of the day seemed to lose interest in biological warfare, and MRE was transferred, in reduced circumstances, into the Public Health Service. By contrast, Birmingham offered Harry the chance to build a thriving new research department focusing on his interests in pathogenesis. Much lay ahead, but first came a brief and formative interlude in the New World.

AN AMERICAN INTERLUDE

The importance of Harry's work at Porton Down in the 1950s and 1960s was recognized more immediately in the USA than in Britain. Accordingly in 1964, while pondering his future, Harry accepted an invitation to spend three months as a visiting professor in the Department of Microbiology and Immunology at the Berkeley campus of the University of California. The approach had come through Standford (Sandy) Elberg, a distinguished expert on brucellosis and by then a Dean at Berkeley. The brief was to deliver a broad-based lecture course on bacterial pathogenesis to PhD students, evening lectures being followed by question and answer sessions at the local beer parlour, a format exactly suited to Harry's tastes both in democratic debate and in refreshment.

As Harry freely admitted, the preparation for these lectures made him realize that he knew a great deal about anthrax, plague and brucellosis but very little about other areas of microbiology. Clearly he had some reading to do. As it happened, one of several members of staff at Berkeley with whom Harry formed a lifelong friendship was Roger Stanier (FRS 1978). He and his colleague Mike Doudoroff were renowned for their work on microbial metabolism, but they had also written a highly praised book on general microbiology that had become a standard undergraduate text in many countries. Harry admired Roger's academic breadth, not to mention his unconventional view of life and his active support of the student protest movement that, well before it became a worldwide phenomenon, was stirring in mid-1960s Berkeley. The experience convinced Harry of his responsibility, as an imminent Professor of Microbiology, to know the subject on which he would profess. As Harry later observed: 'I had not realized that I was in a rut at MRE … and that I needed to get out of it! The advantage of academic life is that having to teach students broadens one's view of the subject. I was glad that I was about to take a position at a University.'

BIRMINGHAM

Harry made the move to Birmingham in 1965 accompanied by three of his research fellows from Porton Down: John Pearce, Tony Williams and John Stephen. With these recruits and a small number of existing staff, Harry began to forge a unit that had microbial pathogenicity as its central theme. The existing Microbiology Department was housed in a building shared with other biological disciplines, and space was at a premium. Harry needed a new laboratory, purpose-built for microbiological research and complete with a secure animal house: this was no small request, yet somehow he persuaded the Vice-Chancellor of the day, Sir Robert Aitkin, to agree. Although the building took some years to complete, it left an indelible mark on the university landscape. From the outside, it looked like a large electricity transformer; inside, it provided a first-rate facility for research. Although his own work had until that time focused exclusively on bacteria, Harry's vision was to extend the study of disease pathogenicity to include both viral and fungal infections in the department's range. By way of example, in addition to his mainstream research, he personally initiated projects on a mouse model of Semliki Forest virus infection and on a plant pathogen, *Fusarium graminearum*, and encouraged other staff in their own independent ventures. Inspired by his experience in Berkeley and duly armed with Roger Stanier's textbook, he also taught an eight-week undergraduate course that served as a general introduction to microbiology.

Every course needs a catchphrase, and Harry's 'Johnny Bacillus' lectures will long be remembered by Birmingham students from that time.

Such was the beginning of more than two decades in which Harry led the Department of Microbiology in Birmingham, putting it firmly on the map as an internationally recognized centre for research in microbial pathogenesis. He had a canny knack of spotting talent and of nurturing it to independence. Long-term colleagues such as Jeff Cole, Charles Penn and Clive Sweet have testified to Harry's outstanding academic leadership in their contributions to a special issue of *Microbiology Today* published by the UK's Society for General Microbiology in his honour (Hoskisson (ed.) 2012). Although he had many other calls on his time during this period, Harry remained first and foremost a scientist devoted to his research. His métier was disease pathogenesis, although not specifically bacterial disease: he became increasingly interested in viral pathogenesis and was never shy in giving the virological community the benefit of his experience, either verbally or in print; see, for example, his 1972 article in *Bacteriological Reviews* (4). As if following his own advice, Harry developed interesting work with Clive Sweet on influenza virus pathogenesis in the ferret model. Comparing infections with virulent and attenuated virus strains, they tracked the spread of virus in the upper and lower respiratory tract in relation to the maturity of the host's immune system, and identified phagocytes rather than lymphocytes as the main source of a pathogenic cytokine storm (5). However, it was Harry's work on bacteria of the *Neisseria* genus, in particular on gonococci with Jeff Cole and on meningococci with Chris Tang (Imperial College), that stands out as his most enduring legacy from these later years.

Ever on the lookout for important but unexplained findings, in 1970 Harry's eyes had alighted on a seminal paper by Ward, Watt and Glynn in London reporting that gonococci *in vivo* are resistant to complement-mediated killing, whereas those grown in the laboratory are serum-sensitive (Ward *et al.* 1970). What could be the basis of such immune evasion? The question prompted 16 years of research, with its final resolution achieved in 1988, the year in which Harry relinquished the headship of the department and formally 'retired'. It turned out that gonococci exploit a host-derived nucleotide, cytidine monophospho-*N*-acetylneuraminic acid (CMP-NANA), to evade destruction. This nucleotide normally acts to deliver sialic acid to such host proteins as transferrin and blood-group antigens. On the surface of the gonococcus, the bacterial lipopolysaccharide antigen displays a tetrasaccharide sequence that exactly replicates CMP-NANA's target site on transferrin; CMP-NANA-induced sialylation of this site protects the organism from immune recognition and complement-mediated lysis. Smith, Cole and colleagues had unearthed a beautiful example of molecular mimicry in which the pathogen decorates its surface with a host-derived disguise (6). In their natural niche *in vivo*, gonococci have evolved to survive in a low-oxygen environment; indeed, others subsequently showed that gonococcal serum resistance is enhanced if grown under conditions of low oxygen, reinforcing Harry's argument that studies of microbial pathogenicity need to be guided by the biology of infection *in vivo*.

While pursuing the identity of CMP-NANA, Harry noticed that there was another moiety capable of enhancing gonococcal serum resistance, albeit less dramatically. This was identified as the metabolic by-product lactate, which ironically had been reported many years earlier as the preferred source of carbon and energy for gonococcal growth. Investigating further, Smith, Cole and colleagues found that the lactate effect was independent of CMP-NANA and was instead mediated by a stimulation of gonococcal metabolism, affecting in particular the synthesis of CMP-NANA's target antigen, lipopolysaccharide. Harry then drove the extension of this work to meningococci, a related organism but one whose niche *in vivo* is the well-aerated regions of the upper respiratory tract. Here lactate again increased serum resistance, in this case by enhancing both the synthesis of the capsule polysaccharide and its sialylation. The intriguing story of CMP-NANA, lactate and immune evasion by *Neisseria* formed the cornerstone of Harry's prestigious Royal Society Leeuwenhoek lecture, delivered in 1991, and its development was further traced as part of his review in *Philosophical Transactions* series B in 2000 (7). The work is a testament to the continued pursuit of research excellence that characterized his leadership of microbiology in Birmingham. Even more impressive is the fact that his commitment to laboratory work never wavered despite his increasing involvement in national and international scientific affairs, contributions to science that fully deserve their own place in the Harry Smith story.

Learned societies: SGM, FEMS and 'The Royal'

In 1955 the Society for General Microbiology (SGM) held a symposium on Mechanisms of Microbial Pathogenicity to which Harry was invited to describe his ground-breaking work on anthrax. Thus began a close involvement with SGM affairs that ran over the following quarter of a century. In 1960 Harry was elected to its Council and in 1965 the Council appointed him as Meetings Secretary, with responsibility for organizing both the annual April symposium and the publication of symposium articles. This was a useful, if demanding, way of getting to know the wider microbiological community and also the SGM staff. Harry saw at first hand the excellent work done by the Treasurer, Ken Cooper, in creating the group system that allowed the two main disciplines, bacteriology and virology, to have parallel sessions at SGM meetings and to run twin journals under the SGM umbrella. Subsequently, Harry succeeded Ken as Treasurer and served in that capacity from 1968 to 1975.

During his time as Treasurer, in his words, the SGM changed from an amateur society to a professional outfit with its own office and administrative structure. The proceeds of journal sales had put the society into a sound financial position and it was Harry who, with the Council's blessing, negotiated the purchase of Harvest House in Reading and helped with the appointment of a small permanent staff. Over the years the SGM grew to become Europe's premier microbiological society, and in 1975 Harry was greatly honoured to be elected as its President, succeeding David (later Sir David) Evans FRS. He recalled his three-year presidency as a hugely enjoyable experience, the culmination of many years of service to the society. Some indication of the high regard in which he was still held at the SGM came with the dedication of their August 2012 issue of *Microbiology Today* to articles detailing Harry's many contributions to the discipline.

The early 1970s also saw the SGM, through David Evans, make the first move that led to the formation of the Federation of European Microbiological Societies (FEMS). Andre Lwoff ForMemRS, the Nobel laureate from the Pasteur Institute, became the first President, and Harry became the first Treasurer. This ensured that the FEMS finances, initially pump-primed by the SGM, were in safe hands! The prospect of a FEMS journal was the logical next step, a project that reunited Harry with his old friend from Berkeley, Roger Stanier, whom the FEMS Council had elected as Editor. The two considered several options before brokering a deal with publishers Elsevier in Holland, and *FEMS Microbiology Letters* was launched in 1974. Now in its 40th year, the journal has been a great success, securing the finances of the federation and allowing it to grow from strength to strength. With his experience, Harry was naturally at the centre of things, as President and Chairman of the Organising Committee, when the 14th International Congress of Microbiology was held in Manchester in 1986. Three years in preparation, the congress turned out to be a success both scientifically and socially, with Harry claiming that he had chosen the very week in which there was not a drop of Manchester rain! His colleague Charles Penn recalls, 'Harry was in some ways at his best in this kind of role, energetic and focused on ensuring that everything was in its place and all contingencies allowed for, including personal oversight of the finances.' Harry had assumed the role of leading ambassador for UK microbiology, and many who felt the benefit remained in his debt.

Election to the Fellowship of the Royal Society, or, as he called it, 'The Royal', came in 1979. Harry admitted to being 'overjoyed' when the news came through and arguably he treasured this mark of recognition above all things. He served on a number of Royal Society committees and was a member of Council from 1989 to 1991. Building on his experience in matters of national defence (see the next section), he was a member of the Society's Group on Scientific Aspects of International Security and chaired a working party that produced a report on measures for controlling the threat from biological weapons. This much-praised report struck a fine balance, emphasizing that the threat of biological warfare needed to be taken seriously while cautioning against exaggeration and the dangers of an alarmist response. In 1991 Harry joined a select group of Fellows who have the additional distinction of giving one of the Society's prize lectures. In his case it was the Leeuwenhoek Lecture, named after Antoni van Leeuwenhoek, whose development of a simple one-lens microscope more than three centuries ago allowed him to see microbes for the first time, hence his epithet: the father of microbiology.

THE MINISTRY OF DEFENCE

Less well known is the important service that Harry gave to the UK's Ministry of Defence (MOD) in his later years. Interest in biological warfare had waned after he left Porton Down and he had had little contact for more than a decade when, in 1982, he was approached by one of the few microbiologists still working at the site. There had been an outbreak of anthrax in the USSR at a location, Sverdlosk, where there was a military institute suspected of working on biological warfare agents. This was prompting a resurgence of interest in biological weapons, and Harry was asked to advise on rebuilding Porton Down's research capacity in that area. Over the next few years he helped both to recruit staff and to offer guidance on research topics. As their range of research broadened, the establishment's advisory body duly changed its name from the Chemical Defence Establishment to the Chemical and Biological Defence Board. Harry was the first biologist appointed to that board and was later joined by two others. His term of office lasted from 1986 to 1992 during which time, besides completing an important report on the relevance of biotechnology to defence problems, he had some interesting, if hair-raising, experiences with the military: a guided tour of a nuclear submarine in Portland harbour, delivery by helicopter into the middle of a full-scale NATO exercise on Lüneburg Heath, and a Marines exercise on a fast-moving frigate that the 68-year-old Harry boarded by scrambling up a metal ladder on the outside of the ship!

This was all necessary training, it seemed, for Harry's subsequent appointment as the first biological member of the MOD's Defence Science Advisory Council. This dealt with the application of science to all military matters, except for nuclear weapons, which were dealt with at a higher level. This Council was attended by the Chief Scientist and representatives of all three services as well as by scientists of various disciplines, making it a forum for the type of vigorous debate that was very much to Harry's taste. He certainly took his Council and other MOD responsibilities very seriously, keeping classified documents in a locked safe in his office, maintaining a secure telephone link, and having not just himself but also his secretary sign the Official Secrets Act. All this was honorary work performed in the nation's interest, and it was fitting that Harry's long service to the MOD should be recognized by the award of a CBE in the Queen's 1993 Birthday Honours. But no episode in any Harry Smith story, however serious, is without its lighter side. In this case, the trip to Buckingham Palace to receive the award was thrown into confusion by an overnight storm that led to the cancellation of all trains from Birmingham to London. As a last resort, Harry and Janet set off in the family car, Harry driving at 90 miles per hour down the M1 and seemingly on schedule, only to be delayed yet further by the inevitable traffic jam on approaching London. The situation was not helped by a call of nature, forcing Harry to disappear down a motorway embankment in full morning dress, to the consternation of passing vehicles. Somehow they got to the palace just in time and received the award but, on finally returning to the car, realized that the keys had been locked inside!

JANET, THE FARM AND THE FAMILY

Central to the whole of Harry's career was the support of his wife, Janet, and the unshakeable strength of the bond between them. It was the bedrock on which everything else was built. They had met as pharmacy students in Nottingham, were married in 1947 just before the move to Porton Down, and remained together for more than 60 years. Janet came from a farming family, her father having rented a farm at Burton Lazars, a small village near Melton Mowbray in Leicestershire. Eventually her parents moved to their own small 42-acre farm nearby and grew cereal crops. As time passed, Janet and Harry had to take more responsibility for the management of the farm, acting largely at a distance but keeping in touch with the contractor on visits roughly every six weeks. This was a project for which Janet had the knowhow and Harry was the research assistant. They made two important changes that put the farm's finances on an even keel, increasing the acreage to give more capacity and building a grain dryer on site so that corn could be stored over winter and sold at a higher price in the spring. By that time, both of Janet and Harry's children had arrived, Mary Elizabeth in 1951 and John Harry in 1952, and the whole family would come to the farm for Christmas and Easter holidays and for three weeks in late August for the harvest. Harvest-time on the farm gave both parents and children some of their happiest memories.

With the move to Birmingham in 1965, the farm was now only 60 miles away, so contact could be more frequent. By this time Janet's mother was ageing and widowed, and so the decision was made to renovate the farmhouse, making it more comfortable for everyone to visit, and for Janet, Harry and the now teenage children to move to a spacious flat in the leafy suburb of Edgbaston, very near the University of Birmingham campus. This proved to be an ideal family base and, after the children had left, Janet and Harry remained there for all except the last few years of their married life. They had considered the possibility of returning to the farm when Harry formally retired in 1988, but they did not do so for two reasons: first, farm costs were rising, receipts were falling and the time had come to sell; and second, Harry had no intention of actually retiring—he considered himself a member of Jeff Cole's group and had work to do!

The Smiths enjoyed an active social life in Birmingham, much of it based on the wide circle of university friendships made either by Harry during his times on Senate and inter-Faculty committees, or by Janet though her work for the University Wives group, as it was then called. They had more than their share of personal grief, bearing with great fortitude the loss of their daughter Mary to a long battle with cancer while still in her thirties. Despite this, their positive spirit and joy of life always shone through. Their flat in Edgbaston was the site of many a memorable evening of eating, drinking, talking politics and generally putting the world to rights. They remained there until around 2006, when Janet had a fall that restricted her mobility, after which they moved together into a nearby retirement home. Harry's mobility, although not his mental acuity, also began to fail towards the end, and he died peacefully after a brief illness on Saturday, 10 December 2011 at the age of 90 years. He leaves behind his devoted wife, Janet, a son, a daughter-in-law and three grandchildren.

HARRY, THE MAN

To someone who was first befriended by Harry some 30 years ago, towards the end of his tenure as Head of Microbiology in Birmingham, he came across as a man still with a restless spirit of enquiry and driven by a deep love of science. He was determined in his opinions, fiercely competitive and revelled in the chase. He graphically likened the experience of making a truly novel finding to lifting one of Mother Nature's veils, pinning it back to the wall and revealing her colours for the first time. No doubt he could be a hard taskmaster if he felt that a colleague deserved reprimand, but at the same time he was fiercely loyal to colleagues who had gained his respect. His own memoirs are replete not with scientific detail but with pen-pictures, not always printable, of the many people whom he had met during a long and varied academic career; they reveal him as a man of action who may have been prone to snap judgements but who often revised them in the course of time. He was broad-ranging and sometimes unpredictable in his friendships; a lovely vignette from his time in Birmingham recalls one Mrs Downs, the wash-up lady and 'mother' of the department, from whom he would get the best advice on personnel matters and the firmest admonition when he got things wrong.

What came through most clearly in conversation with Harry was his honesty and straightforwardness; his views were rarely nuanced and he had no time for obfuscation. His loyalty to a cause was legendary and he cared deeply about the University of Birmingham, to the point where a succession of Vice-Chancellors were cajoled into action by Harry's regaling them with perceived sins of omission or commission. This reputation did not prevent the current Vice-Chancellor, Sir David Eastwood, from hosting a 90th birthday lunch in Harry's honour in 2011 and paying tribute to the enormous contribution he had made to the university. This was a richly deserved send-off for a man who had established Birmingham's leading position in a discipline, microbial pathogenesis, that is still thriving today. Perhaps the most memorable tribute came in epigrammatic form on the occasion of Harry and Janet's golden wedding celebrations, held at Winterbourne House in the university's botanic gardens in 1997. The address was given by Harry's good friend, Jim Boulton, Emeritus Professor of English at the university and a man of great eloquence and a mischievous wit. Taking the literal translation of Harry's common surname as a man who could take disparate elements and forge them into something strong and enduring, he pronounced Harry 'not just *a* Smith, nor even *the* Smith, but verily *the Smith of Smiths*'. How true!

ACKNOWLEDGEMENTS

The author gratefully acknowledges help received from former academic colleagues of Harry Smith, particularly Jeff Cole, Clive Sweet, Charles Penn and Les Baillie.

The frontispiece photograph was taken in 1979 by Godfrey Argent and is reproduced with permission.

HONOURS, DEGREES AND AWARDS

Civic honour

1993   CBE

Degrees (London University)

1942   BPharm
1944   BSc (special chemistry, first class)
1947   PhD (biochemistry)
1955   DSc (microbiology)

Fellowships

1968   Royal College of Pathologists (FRCPath)
1979   Royal Society (FRS)
1980   Institute of Biology (CBiol, FIBiol)
1994   World Academy of Arts and Sciences

Honorary degrees

1992   DSc, University of Leicester
2001   DSc, University of Nottingham

Honorary memberships

1986   Royal College of Physicians (Hon. MRCP)
        Society for Microbiology
1993   Royal Society of Veterinary Surgeons (Hon. Assoc. RCVS)

Other distinctions

1942   Silver Medal and Harrison Memorial Prize, Pharmaceutical Society
1991   Purkoyne Memorial Medal, Czechoslovak Academy of Sciences
1992   Bledisloe Veterinary Award, Royal Agricultural Society of England
1994   Stuart Mudd Award, International Union of Microbiology Societies

Special appointment

1986   President, 14th International Congress of Microbiology, Manchester

REFERENCES TO OTHER AUTHORS

Baillie, L. W. 2009 Is new always better than old? The development of human vaccines for anthrax. *Hum. Vaccin.* **5**, 806–816.

Hoskisson, P. A. (ed.) 2012 Harry Smith Memorial Issue. *Microbiol. Today* **39**, 143 and 154–169.

Stephen, J. & Pietrowski, R. A. 1987 *Bacterial toxins*. Wokingham: Van Nostrand Reinhold.

Ward, M. E., Watt, P. J. & Glynn, A. A. 1970 Gonococci in urethral exudates possess a virulence factor lost on sub-culture. *Nature* **227**, 382–384.

BIBLIOGRAPHY

The following publications are those referred to directly in the text. A full bibliography is available as electronic supplementary material at http://dx.doi.org/10.1098/rsbm.2014.0014 or via http://rsbm.royalsocietypublishing.org.

(1) 1954 (With J. Keppie) Observations on experimental anthrax; demonstration of a specific lethal factor produced *in vivo* by *Bacillus anthracis*. *Nature* **173**, 869–867.

(2) 1958 The basis of immunity to anthrax. *Proc. R. Soc. Med.* **51**, 375–377.

(3)   The use of bacteria grown *in vivo* for studies on the basis of their pathogenicity. *Annu. Rev. Microbiol.* **12**, 77–102.

(4) 1972 Mechanisms of virus pathogenicity. *Bacteriol. Rev.* **36**, 291–310.

(5) 1988 (With C. Sweet) Lessons for human influenza from pathogenicity studies with ferrets. *Rev. Infect. Dis.* **10**, 56–75.

(6)   (With N. J. Parsons, P. V. Patel, E. L. Tan, J. R. Andrade, C. A. Nairn, M. Goldner & J. A. Cole) Cytidine 5′-monophospho-*N*-acetyl neuraminic acid and a low molecular weight factor from human blood cells induce lipopolysaccharide alteration in gonococci when conferring resistance to killing by human serum. *Microb. Pathog.* **5**, 303–309.

(7) 2000 Questions about the behaviour of bacterial pathogens *in vivo*. *Phil. Trans. R. Soc. Lond.* B **355**, 551–564.

DAVID ALAN WALKER

18 August 1928 — 13 February 2012

DAVID ALAN WALKER

18 August 1928 — 13 February 2012

Elected FRS 1976

By Peter Horton FRS

Department of Molecular Biology and Biotechnology, University of Sheffield,
Western Bank, Sheffield S10 2TN, UK

David Alan Walker was born in Kingston upon Hull, England. He entered King's College, Newcastle, then part of the University of Durham, where he received his BSc, and subsequently his PhD under Meirion Thomas FRS in 1958. Later, in 1968 he was awarded a DSc at the University of Newcastle in recognition of his exceptional contributions of published work in his field. In 1991 he received a Humboldt Research Prize, and in 2004 the inaugural Communications Award from the International Society of Photosynthesis Research. He was the author of more than 230 publications, including several books. He made important contributions to the understanding of photosynthesis, in particular the fixation of carbon dioxide by the biochemical transformations of the Benson–Calvin cycle in the stroma of chloroplasts of higher plants. Based on the meticulous attention to detail and technical prowess derived from his earlier training as an enzymologist, his work prompted totally new thinking about how this cycle was regulated and how it interfaced with the synthesis of ATP and NADPH in the light reactions of photosynthesis. Later, he was one of a very small group of people to recognize that this regulation was observable in whole leaves through the changes in chlorophyll fluorescence, helping to open the door to one of the most widely used tools in plant physiology. After periods at Newcastle, Purdue, Cambridge, Queen Mary College and Imperial College, London, he spent the largest part of his academic career as a professor at the University of Sheffield. There he established a world-renowned photosynthesis research group that grew into one of the university's first semi-autonomous research institutes, the Research Institute for Photosynthesis, later renamed the Robert Hill Institute. This legacy persists more than 30 years later. He also distinguished himself in the wider aspects of being a scientist: long before it became fashionable, he wrote about the issues of food, energy and global change in his 1992 book *Energy, plants and man*. His enthusiasm for communicating both the joy of science and these serious issues led to many other imaginative schemes and endeavours, again long before the need for greater 'public understanding of science' became recognized.

http://dx.doi.org/10.1098/rsbm.2014.0007

Early life: becoming a plant biochemist

> I acquired an undeserved reputation as a fledgling chemist. Understandably, despite an excellent chemistry teacher, I didn't want to become a chemist. I wanted to go to sea like my father.*

But the young David Alan Walker did not go to sea, nor did he become a chemist, at least not in the way he might have imagined. David, the son of Cyril and Dorothy Walker, was born in Kingston upon Hull, England, in 1928. He attended the South Shields Boys High School (now Harton Technology College) from 1939 to 1946. When he left school with modest training in science, there was the question of what to do next. One of his school friends happened to be the son of a pharmacist and therefore came from a family that had experience of universities. Without such a background, neither he nor any of his immediate circle had even contemplated the possibility of going on to university. However, swept along by the pharmacist's son, he and four of his friends applied to read botany at King's College, Newcastle (then part of the University of Durham).

> What impelled the others towards botany I can't tell. Chemistry would have been my natural choice but this was precluded by accidents of school time-tabling.

However, entry was delayed by National Service: David served in the Royal Navy until 1948. His disdain for this experience was clear:

> being handed over to the tender mercies of The Royal Navy meant incarceration for two years of my young life in conditions more arduous, so far as I can gather, than those currently imposed on prisoners in British jails.

Fortunately, he was released early to take up his studies at King's College. Thankful for his 'second chance', he worked hard and did well, so much so that he was invited to stay on at Newcastle and continue his studies in botany. His supervisor was to be Meirion Thomas, who led one of the country's best plant biochemistry laboratories.

From Newcastle to Lafayette and back: organic acid metabolism

David Walker's research career in plant science thus began as a PhD student at King's College, Newcastle, in 1952 (figure 1). During his time there, and through a Fulbright Scholarship, he had the opportunity to work for several months as a research assistant in Harry Beevers's laboratory at Purdue University in Lafayette, Indiana. Beevers, who had emanated from the Thomas laboratory some years earlier, was carrying out world-leading research into plant metabolism. This was a highly productive visit for Walker, resulting in his first publications, in *Biochem. J.* (1, 2)†, but most importantly for the skills he acquired in how to conduct biochemical investigations of metabolism. Study of biochemistry and the metabolic transformations involved in energy transduction and biosynthesis in cells was an active area of research in biology at this time. In the 1930s Sir Hans Krebs (FRS 1947) had discovered major metabolic pathways involving a series of organic acids that were progressively oxidized and decarboxylated to release their redox free energy for oxidative phosphorylation.

---

* All unattributed quotations come from D. A. Walker, 'Tell me where all past years are', *Photosynth. Res.* **51**, 3–26 (1997).
† Numbers in this form refer to the bibliography at the end of the text.

Figure 1. The aspiring scientist—David Walker as a young student at Newcastle.

The Krebs cycle, as it became known, was also shown to be the starting point for biosynthesis of sugars, fatty acids and amino acids. This golden age of metabolic biochemistry was initially focused on animal (mostly mammalian) and microbial systems. Investigations of plant metabolism lagged behind, although some centres were increasingly active in the period after World War II, including the Beevers laboratory. Plant cells contain mitochondria as well as chloroplasts, where photosynthesis takes place, and there was a lot of interest in whether the metabolic processes in plants were the same as in animals and how they might be modified and integrated with photosynthesis. The 1950s also witnessed the discovery of the metabolic reactions leading to the fixation of carbon dioxide in photosynthesis, the Benson–Calvin cycle. Whereas the Krebs cycle used organic acids to release ATP and NADH, the Benson–Calvin cycle involved a series of sugar phosphates and consumed ATP and NADPH.

David's work at Purdue was part of the process of demonstrating the metabolic activities of the Krebs cycle in subcellular preparations of plant mitochondria, measuring the effects of various metabolites on the rate of O_2 uptake (measured using manometry). Particulate preparations were prepared from the endosperm of germinating castor beans (*Ricinus communis*), which under appropriate conditions were shown to oxidize the various intermediates of the Krebs cycle at high and sustained rates. Clear requirements were established, not only for adenosine triphosphate (ATP) and diphosphopyridine nucleotide (now called nicotinamide adenine dinucleotide, NAD^+) but also for the additional cofactor coenzyme A (CoA) and an acetyl-CoA regenerating system (1). David also discovered an induction period before the onset of O_2 uptake, a feature of pyruvate oxidation in certain circumstances, and possible explanations of this effect were discussed (2). It is interesting to note two aspects of this work that re-emerged in David's research a decade later: the measurement of O_2 exchange in isolated organelles in response to changes in experimental conditions, and the desire to understand observed changes in reaction rate over time, in particular lags or induction periods.

The PhD project assigned to David at Newcastle by Meirion Thomas was to identify the enzyme(s) responsible for the dark fixation of CO_2 in crassulacean acid metabolism (CAM). Plants performing CAM live in conditions of water shortage, typically in deserts. They were known to take up the CO_2 they needed for photosynthesis at night to prevent water loss through the pores in the leaf surface (stomata) through which both molecules pass during the day. The CO_2 fixed at night is released and re-fixed in photosynthesis in the daytime. It had been discovered that the CO_2 fixed at night was accumulated as organic acids, principally malate, which was interestingly one of the components of the Krebs cycle. David's task was to determine the enzymatic reactions involved, using the model CAM plant *Kalanchoe crenata*. With the biochemical skills acquired from his time at Purdue, Walker began to work on extracts from *Kalanchoe* leaves, proceeding to show that the dark acidification associated with CO_2 fixation was by the newly discovered enzyme phosphoenolpyruvate (PEP) carboxylase and malate dehydrogenase, producing malate. De-acidification and the release of CO_2 took place via the malic enzyme. The first results of this work were published in *Nature* (3); this paper was soon followed by others (4, 5). Much of Walker's PhD research formed the basis of a review, 'Pyruvate carboxylation and plant metabolism' (7).

These were formative years for David. He stayed on at Newcastle courtesy of an Imperial Chemical Industries Fellowship, carrying on his biochemical studies on *Kalanchoe*. He co-authored papers with his colleagues Stan Ranson and John Brown. Thus, in addition to laying the foundations for Walker's future research, the Thomas laboratory was populated by colleagues with whom he formed lasting professional and personal relationships. Other such colleagues included P. N. (Dhani) Avadhani, Mary Stiller and the three Bradbeer brothers, Bill, Clive and Phil. David had also married Shirley (*neé* Mason) in 1956, and their first child, Marney, was born in 1957. Their son, Richard, was born three years later, in 1960.

PHOTOSYNTHESIS, ROBIN HILL AND QUEEN MARY COLLEGE

The external examiner of Walker's PhD thesis was Robert (Robin) Hill FRS. In 1957 Hill invited David to move his fellowship to Cambridge to work on photophosphorylation in isolated chloroplasts. To David, Cambridge biochemistry seemed like a Mecca—crowded with some of the world's most prestigious scientists such as David Keilin FRS, Joseph Needham FRS and Frederick Sanger FRS. Hill himself was already renowned for his work on photosynthetic electron transport, having made the seminal discovery that light-induced O_2 evolution in leaf homogenates could be driven by oxidants such as potassium ferricyanide. This defined the light reactions of higher-plant photosynthesis leading to O_2 evolution as being separate from 'dark' CO_2 fixation, and the former became known as the 'Hill reaction'. Hill went on to investigate how ATP synthesis was driven by the Hill reaction, photophosphorylation, that had been discovered by Dan Arnon and co-workers in 1954. Walker and Hill contributed to this research through the characterization of the reactions by which various artificial molecules could act as catalysts of cyclic photophosphorylation (6). David's admiration for Hill was evident and lasted for 40 years:

> I have met and admired some very accomplished scientists and often felt out of my depth. With Robin it was more than that. Intellectually, I was a small child in the presence of an adult.

As we shall see, Hill was later to be involved in one of David's most important discoveries.

The association with Hill was a first step in David's future change in research direction towards photosynthesis and away from organic acid metabolism, but this would be catalysed by another meeting at Cambridge, with Charles Whittingham. When Whittingham took a chair at Queen Mary College in the University of London in 1958, he offered Walker a lectureship. Despite a career-long dislike of lecturing (although he was exceptionally good at it), David accepted, the start of a glittering career in academic research.

At Queen Mary, David at first continued his previous line of research, studying aspects of metabolism in *Kalanchoe*. He established his own small research group, his talented PhD students including Geoffrey Hind. He also worked with Doug Graham, who was a student of Whittingham's. Both Hind and Graham progressed to successful careers in plant science. Tom Delieu, who was to become a very close friend and influential colleague of Walker's for many years, was a workshop technician. In 1962 a six-month leave on a Kettering Fellowship to Israel Zelitch's laboratory in New Haven, Connecticut, saw David's one excursion into investigating the metabolism of stomata, the pores on the surface of leaves that allow the efflux of water and influx of CO_2, trying to uncover why and how these open in the daytime and close at night. Observation of the effect of various metabolic inhibitors on the stomatal aperture confirmed the new hypothesis that stomatal opening and closure were intricately controlled by cell metabolism (8).

INTACT CHLOROPLASTS AT IMPERIAL COLLEGE

On his return to London, David's research career was about to change forever. Whittingham had obtained a grant for work on the isolation of fully functional chloroplasts, proposing that David should do the actual work. Although it is obvious to us now, it should be remembered that 50 years ago it was not clear whether or not the process of photosynthetic CO_2 fixation took place in the chloroplast and how exactly it was linked to O_2 evolution. Suspensions of chloroplasts extracted from leaves usually failed miserably to fix CO_2, and any observed fixation occurred at a rate one-hundredth of that in whole leaves. It was not known that the chloroplast had an outer membrane envelope containing a stromal phase which surrounded the thylakoid membranes. In fact, the cell-free 'chloroplast preparations' were merely thylakoid membrane suspensions, being devoid of envelope and stroma.

Before starting the project, David sought the advice of his mentor, Robin Hill. Hill suggested the use of 0.3 M sugar as osmoticum: a simple, obvious but inspired idea. With the assistance of a skilled technician, Carl Baldry, David was soon to isolate chloroplasts that would fix CO_2 ten times faster, although still at one-tenth of the rate *in vivo* (9). Further progress was to be disrupted by Whittingham's move to Imperial College, the chloroplast project and David moving with him. But there, he was now a Reader in Enzymology, and able to attack the project with renewed force. In addition to Baldry, Chris Bucke was hired as postdoctoral assistant, later followed by Bill Cockburn. This small team set about the task of increasing the rate of CO_2 fixation in their chloroplast preparations. Aided by the electron microscopy of Dennis Greenwood it was demonstrated that only those chloroplasts surrounded by the double-envelope membrane, enclosing the stroma, were able to fix CO_2 (10). By improving the isolation methodology, the team approached 100 µmol of CO_2 per milligram of chlorophyll per hour, near to the rate *in vivo* (11). Unfortunately, the glory that might have gone with this landmark was taken by Dick Jensen and Al Bassham, who published first. Nevertheless, David's focus had by now shifted from this methodological preoccupation to seeking an understanding of why certain ingredients in the reaction mix were so critical, why fixation rates were so variable and why small amounts of sugar phosphate were needed. David concluded with great foresight that it was to do with the chloroplast envelope:

> Certainly some molecules pass easily in and out of the chloroplast but it is becoming increasingly evident that the properties of the envelope are such that there is some measure, perhaps a very large measure, of selectivity and control.

Further progress again came from Hill's intervention: Hill introduced David to the Clark electrode, which enabled continuous monitoring of O_2 concentration. Thus, the rate of CO_2-dependent O_2 evolution driven by light in isolated chloroplasts was recorded in 'real time' for the first time. David had also decided to see whether chloroplasts isolated from spinach, which he could buy from Covent Garden, would give more reliable CO_2 fixation rates than pea seedlings—a spectacularly successful decision. With spinach chloroplasts in an O_2 electrode chamber, a characteristic lag or induction period was observed: after illumination, the rate of O_2 evolution gradually increased until a consistently high maximum rate was shown after several minutes. Very significantly, the addition of 3-phosphoglycerate (PGA), a component of the Benson–Calvin cycle whose transformation into glyceraldehyde 3-phosphate consumes ATP and NADPH produced by the light reactions of photosynthesis, removed this induction period (12). This 'eureka moment', as David described it, answered many questions and opened many doors to future research.

What followed was one of those explosive periods of research associated with most successful scientists: a simultaneous technical advance and intellectual breakthrough leading to new experiments with exciting results. In the late 1960s several papers from the Walker group explained why there was an induction period, introducing the idea of autocatalysis, a basic principle of metabolic control, namely that in metabolic cycles, the attainment of maximum reaction rates of product formation requires the progressive build-up of concentrations of the reactants. In the case of the Benson–Calvin cycle, these are synthesized by the reactions of the cycle itself, but this requires time, explaining the induction period. Furthermore, Walker was able to determine why the concentration of orthophosphate (P_i) was so critical, showing the existence of a phosphate translocator in the chloroplast envelope that catalysed the simultaneous import of phosphate and export of triose phosphate (TP). Phosphate was needed for photosynthesis, in the measured stoichiometry $3CO_2 + 1P_i + 3H_2O \rightarrow 1TP + 3O_2$ (exactly as predicted), but if the concentration was too high there would be excessive export of TP, depleting the Benson–Calvin cycle of constituents and preventing or suppressing autocatalysis (13–16). This elegant demonstration of the dynamics of the Benson–Calvin cycle was arguably David's finest research achievement. David reviewed his work on photosynthetic induction in 1973 (19).

RECONSTITUTED CHLOROPLASTS AND THE MOVE TO SHEFFIELD

Despite this successful research, David was unhappy at Imperial College. As he put it himself,

> Queen Mary College had been small and friendly. Immediate friends and colleagues apart, Imperial College (also ostensibly part of the same University of London) was just the opposite, the most awful and soulless academic establishment that I have ever encountered. Travel, to and from my home in Epping, came a close second in disgust. It took three hours in total, two out of the three on the London underground. It became my greatest ambition to leave London.

In 1970 that ambition was achieved: Walker accepted an offer of Chair of Biology at the University of Sheffield. Life improved as the Walker family moved into a spacious Victorian house only 20 minutes' walk from the university. The work–life balance was much more satisfactory. With this came another productive period of research, aided again by a succession of gifted young postdoctoral researchers: David Stokes, Ross Lilley, Toni Slabas, Simon Robinson and Richard Leegood.

David's natural instinct as a biochemist was to understand more fully the mechanisms behind the phenomena he had discovered. Realizing the limitations of how much more could be discovered using intact chloroplasts, his team started the ambitious task of reconstituting CO_2 fixation in envelope-free chloroplasts. Without the selectively permeable barrier of the envelope, the dynamics and regulation of the Benson–Calvin cycle could be more incisively probed.

It turned out to be remarkably simple—merely osmotically shocking intact chloroplasts provided enough enzymatic activity, even though diluted (although a concentrated stromal extract improved activity). The addition of an appropriate selection of ions, ADP, $NADP^+$ and purified ferredoxin, and the use of the right pH, was all that was needed to observe PGA-dependent O_2 evolution (17, 20). David always maintained that he was never able to fully exploit the possibilities offered by the system he devised. Nevertheless, he showed the competition between the two ATP-consuming reactions in the Benson–Calvin cycle and the biochemical control mechanisms that enabled the cycle to run smoothly. He showed that the length of the induction period for O_2 evolution was also dependent on the length of time taken for the ATP/ADP ratio to increase sufficiently to drive the reduction of PGA to dihydroxyacetone phosphate. Thus, ribose 5-phosphate, acting as an ATP sink, inhibits the reduction of PGA (and so inhibits O_2 evolution), which subsequently recovers as the ribose 5-phosphate is itself depleted by phosphorylation to ribulose bisphosphate (21, 25).

David's assertion about the role of autocatalysis during photosynthesis was not without controversy. Detractors pointed to the documented activation of enzymes that also occurred during this period. Careful investigation of one such enzyme, fructose bisphosphatase, showed that its activity responds to limitations in utilization of NADPH, rather than being a regulator (26). This is a topic still argued about today.

Alongside this research aimed at understanding events inside the chloroplast, attention was also given to photosynthetic carbon assimilation occurring outside the chloroplast, in the cytosol. Alice Herold, a PhD student in the group, showed how the critical role of P_i played out in whole leaves: sequestration of P_i with mannose led to an increase in starch synthesis (22). This is consistent with the idea that the concentration of P_i controls the partitioning of photosynthate: the exchange of P_i for triose phosphate across the chloroplast envelope promotes the export of photosynthate to the cytosol; when this is suppressed, starch synthesis inside the chloroplast is stimulated. A visit to Sheffield by Gerry Edwards introduced the technique of isolating plant cell protoplasts from leaves, enabling photosynthesis by whole cells to be investigated biochemically (24). Walker's team used this system to demonstrate that sucrose was the product of photosynthesis occurring in the cytosol, as well as validating previous hypotheses concerning induction. A major statement could now be made about how photosynthesis was regulated by the transport of P_i across the chloroplast envelope, crucially determining the balance between the storage of carbohydrate in the chloroplast as starch, and the export from the chloroplast for the synthesis of sucrose. David, and his German colleagues Ulrich Heber (Würzburg) and Hans Heldt (Göttingen) together published a highly cited article on this topic (23).

THE AGRICULTURAL RESEARCH COUNCIL RESEARCH GROUP ON
PHOTOSYNTHESIS

In 1979 the next big change in David's career took place. Having been elected to the Royal Society in 1976, he was now acknowledged as one of the world's leading photosynthesis researchers, and certainly the top person in the UK for photosynthetic carbon metabolism. Thus, when the Agricultural Research Council (ARC) was drawing up plans for a research initiative in photosynthesis (tremendously visionary, given what we know now!) it turned to David Walker and Sheffield to play a major role. Two new university-based centres were established, at Imperial College under Jim Barber (FRS 2005), and at Sheffield, together with one at the John Innes Institute under Harold Woolhouse, which joined with the ARC institutes at Aberystwyth and Rothamsted. The ARC Research Group on Photosynthesis at Sheffield was based around existing personnel in Walker's group, but with some key additions. Tom Delieu was recruited from London to lead instrument development. I had been appointed a lecturer in the Department of Biochemistry a year earlier and was asked to join, an offer I accepted with great enthusiasm. Richard Leegood continued as an ARC postdoctoral researcher. For the first year, the group was virtual, as the construction of a new building was awaited. David, perhaps fondly remembering his days at Queen Mary College, where he was based in a small outpost at Dytchley, decided the new group would relocate away from the main Sheffield campus to the Tapton Experimental Garden, a mile away (and only a five-minute walk from his home!). Thus, the Robert Hill Laboratory was born: it was opened officially in 1980, fittingly by Robin Hill himself (figure 2). Also on site was a new greenhouse specifically designed to grow the world's best spinach! An adjacent coach house was renovated to become Tom Delieu's work-shop, and a house on site was similarly renovated to serve as a library and to provide accom-modation for visitors. New postdoctoral researchers were hired, including Christine Foyer and Denis Murphy. New PhD students appeared, including Ian Woodrow, Matthew Hills and Paul Quick. Efficient technical and administrative back-up was secured from the university. Visitors, both short term and long term, were frequent; in fact David saw this as a main *raison d'être* of the Robert Hill Laboratory.

By 1981 the results of this investment were starting to emerge, as the volume of high-quality research output increased. Between 1980 and 1983 David was the author of 40 papers, including 18 in 1983 alone. New and exciting research directions were opening up. Spurred on by the instrument building of Tom Delieu, he began to measure chlorophyll fluorescence from intact spinach leaves as a new way to explore the dynamics of photosynthesis uncovered by previous work on chloroplasts and protoplasts. Measurement of the changes in fluorescence emitted from chlorophyll in leaves, algal cells and chloroplasts had been a tried and tested methodology in photosynthesis research for several decades. In the 1970s and early 1980s there emerged a much clearer understanding of the processes underlying the changes in fluo-rescence, and there were significant breakthroughs in techniques to unravel the complicated mixtures of the processes involved. Initial studies confirmed David's prediction that the induc-tion of photosynthetic carbon assimilation was mirrored in the kinetics of chlorophyll fluo-rescence (27). These observations showed how changes in the two major factors controlling the yield of fluorescence, the use of light energy in photosynthetic electron transport, qP, and the dissipation of light energy as heat when the thylakoid membranes become over-energized, qE (hence reflecting the ATP/ADP ratio), could explain the change in fluorescence during induction or on the supply or withdrawal of CO_2. In the absence of CO_2, photosynthesis is

Figure 2. David presenting a bouquet to Mrs Priscilla Hill at the opening of the Robert Hill Laboratory, with Robin Hill looking on. Alongside David is Professor Arthur Willis, Head of the Department of Botany at the University of Sheffield.

inhibited, qP falls but qE rises; this is reversed when CO_2 is supplied. Similarly, David was able to interpret the changes in fluorescence resulting from manipulation of the P_i content of leaves by feeding with mannose.

THE RESEARCH INSTITUTE FOR PHOTOSYNTHESIS—OSCILLATIONS

In the early 1980s the remit of ARC was extended and it was renamed the Agriculture and Food Research Council (AFRC). As the Sheffield AFRC group evolved, it was clear that it was developing into a major international centre for photosynthesis research. There was additional inward investment not only from the university but also from other funding sources such as British Petroleum (BP) and the Science Research Council. In recognition of this, in 1983, the university created one of its first dedicated research institutes, the Research Institute for Photosynthesis, and David became its director and Professor of Photosynthesis. At its peak this housed 30–35 personnel (figure 3). The Institute became a beacon for excellence in photosynthesis research worldwide. Although the Institute pursued a variety of projects in photosynthesis, the measurement, analysis and understanding of chlorophyll fluorescence took centre stage. Assisted by me, Paul Quick, a new postdoctoral researcher Mirta Sivak and several visitors and new collaborators, David sought to get to grips with an in-depth understanding of the relationship between chlorophyll fluorescence and photosynthetic carbon assimilation.

When Tom Delieu had perfected the design of the leaf-disk O_2 electrode (see below), it was possible to measure photosynthetic oxygen evolution and chlorophyll fluorescence simultaneously in leaves. David revelled in the design and testing of this new apparatus and the ever more incisive experiments he was able to do to explore his favourite induction phenomenon. He found that under the conditions required for the operation of the electrode (a sealed chamber to prevent the equilibration of O_2 with the atmosphere), a high concentration of CO_2 was

Figure 3. Staff and students of the Research Institute for Photosynthesis in 1986. Standing next to David is his colleague and friend Tom Delieu. Several of this group have gone on to successful careers in plant science research, including Christine Foyer (end left, second row), Julie Scholes (third from right, front row) and Bob Furbank (third from right, standing). I am sixth from right, standing.

necessary. Under these conditions the induction of photosynthesis displays more dramatic and complicated changes in photosynthetic rate and in chlorophyll fluorescence: both signals undergo oscillations, but they are phase-shifted (29). Oscillations within metabolic pathways had been observed previously, for example in glycolysis in yeast, and were explained by the 'over-reaction' of feedback regulatory mechanisms when a steady state was abruptly perturbed. Thus, oscillations in photosynthesis were an expression of regulatory mechanisms in the Benson–Calvin cycle. Walker looked for clues as to what mechanisms were involved by collaborating with Agu Laisk, who had formulated a mathematical model of photosynthesis (31). Investigation of this model showed how the interplay between the two ATP-requiring reactions and limitations by P_i supply could promote oscillations. The possibilities of using the photosynthetic system to address the broader issue of mathematical approaches to understanding the control of complex systems led Walker and me into a second new collaborative project funded by the BP Venture Research Unit, this time with Harry Nicholson in the Department of Control Engineering at Sheffield. This work pre-dated current activity in plant systems biology by 20 years! Studying photosynthetic oscillations became David's preoccupation throughout the 1980s, exploiting the instrumental developments both in house to allow multiple measurements, and also pulse amplitude-modulated (PAM) fluorimetry being introduced by Uli Schreiber and the Walz company, which could separate the qP and qE components of chlorophyll fluorescence quenching. With meticulous attention to detail that was the hallmark of David's 30 years of research, state-of-the-art instrumentation and skilled co-workers including Trevor Brearley and George Seaton, a complete definition of how and why oscillations arise was uncovered, reviewed by Walker in several articles during 1990–95 (32).

Discussion meetings also formed an important part of the Institute. From the beginning, Walker was keen to make sure that the AFRC initiative in photosynthesis was for the benefit of the whole UK research community. Exciting meetings were organized, inviting international experts as keynote speakers or discussion leaders, first at Sheffield, and later at other partner institutions. One of these took place in Sheffield in 1982 with the title 'What limits photosynthesis?', a question of just as much importance nowadays as it was then. In discussions led by Charles Arntzen, Barry Osmond (FRS 1984), Olle Björkman and Ulrich Heber, David, with great insight, urged consideration of the term 'photosynthetic efficacy', which relates capacity to performance and therefore assesses the degree to which photosynthetic capacity is realized in a given circumstance. This meeting was accompanied by a workshop that I helped organize, on chlorophyll fluorescence measurement; this involved some of the world's leading experts, such as Neil Baker and Jean-Marie Briantais. David's enthusiasm for techniques-based meetings also gave rise to two Royal Society Discussion Meetings in 1989 and 2000, both co-organized with Barry Osmond.

OXYGEN ELECTRODES

A major activity of the Institute was instrument development, and the recruitment of Tom Delieu was an inspired decision by David. He realized, of course, that most of the major advances in science come when new ideas arise simultaneously with new technology. As in many areas of biology, this was the hallmark of photosynthesis research in the latter decades of the twentieth century. A principal method for the study of photosynthesis in isolated chloroplasts was the measurement of oxygen evolution. Oxygen electrodes had been developed in the 1940s (the Clarke electrode), and it was used as described above by Walker and Hill in their initial studies on isolated chloroplasts. But its deficiencies for the study of photosynthesis were many. In London, David, in collaboration with Tom Delieu, set about developing a new oxygen electrode and chamber purpose-built for photosynthesis research. The relationship between David and Tom was crucial:

> I made pencil drawings on the backs of envelopes. Tom, a master craftsman, turned these into physical reality.

With a newly designed electrode disk, which formed the base of the chamber and was highly sensitive, robust and easily set up using cigarette papers as part of the 'membrane', the new device enabled David to measure photosynthesis in 1 ml volumes of dilute chloroplast suspensions. He could now routinely and accurately monitor fluctuations in the rate of oxygen evolution that indicated the complex regulatory processes in the lag phase of CO_2-dependent oxygen evolution described above (18). The success of this oxygen electrode led David into a productive relationship with a newly emerging small UK company, Hansatech, who manufactured the device and supplied it to laboratories all over the world. The successful relationship between David, Tom, John Humby and others at Hansatech lasted for many years.

Continued refinement of the electrode some years later made it sensitive enough to measure oxygen evolution from leaf disks in the gas phase, fulfilling a long-standing desire of Walker's for a cheap and simple apparatus for measuring photosynthesis in leaves. The Leaf Disk O_2 Electrode was born (28). There followed numerous technical developments, prototyped by Delieu and Walker in the Sheffield workshops and manufactured commercially by Hansatech; principal among these were instruments for the simultaneous measurement of oxygen concentration and chlorophyll fluorescence that enabled the in-depth analysis of photosynthetic oscillations described above. Other notable innovations were a tunable light-emitting diode illumination system to allow automatic recording of the dependence of photosynthesis on irradiance, measuring quantum yield and photosynthetic capacity. As Walker put it,

> Measurements of quantum yield which once took giants of the world of photosynthesis many hours to perform could be done in as many minutes.

This device was used by Barry Osmond and David to characterize sun and shade acclimation and the effects of photoinhibition.

THE ROBERT HILL INSTITUTE

By the end of the 1980s further change was afoot. The AFRC ceased its block funding of photosynthesis research. Plant science was moving into a new era, that of *Arabidopsis* and molecular genetics. David had tired after 10 years of a managerial role he was never comfortable with, and was contemplating a few quieter years as he approached the prospect of retirement. His close friend Tom Delieu died in 1988, a great loss to the institute but particularly so to David. Senior postdoctoral researchers had moved on, and Richard Leegood and I had established independent successful research groups. Neil Hunter (FRS 2009) had been recruited from Imperial College. Reorganizations had taken place within biology at Sheffield, with various departmental mergers. All of these factors led to significant change for photosynthesis research at Sheffield in general and for David in particular: in 1989 the Research Institute for Photosynthesis was renamed the Robert Hill Institute. David stepped aside, and I became its first chairman. The new institute embedded itself within the core activities of the biology departments, developing new research areas in microbiology, ecology, molecular biology and structural biology. David continued to work in the Hill Laboratory in the Tapton Experimental Garden, developing new applications of the leaf disk electrodes, focusing particularly on computer-aided automation.

The Robert Hill Institute flourished throughout the 1990s as its principal academics developed their research programmes. New appointments were made, including Paul Quick, who returned to Sheffield after a successful period working with Mark Stitt. AFRC favourably reviewed the institute in 1992, and grant funding thereafter actually exceeded that of the former block grant. Two of its members, Neil Hunter and I, followed David in being elected Fellows of the Royal Society in 2009 and 2010, respectively. David's achievements were also further recognized, by the American Society of Plant Biology, by the International Society for Photosynthesis Research and by the University of Sheffield.

After a quiet period in the first decade of this century, the Robert Hill Institute was relaunched in 2013, as the university sought to stimulate new plant science research in the face of the global challenges of climate change and food security as part of its 'Project Sunshine' agenda. Research into C_4 photosynthesis has been reinvigorated. It was originally introduced to Sheffield during a visit by Gerry Edwards in the 1980s (in 1983 Walker and Edwards together wrote the book C_3, C_4: *mechanisms, and cellular and environmental regulation, of photosynthesis* (30)). Now the Institute contributes in a very significant way to achieving the goal of improving photosynthesis in C_3 crops by introducing elements of the C_4 pathway, which could eventually contribute in a major way to sustainable food security. Richard Leegood (at Sheffield), Paul Quick (at IRRI) and Bob Furbank (at Australian National University), who all cut their teeth in photosynthesis research in David's AFRC group, are principal figures in this global effort. The legacy of David Walker is both an immense and a lasting one.

Figure 4. David with Ulrich Heber and me in 1982.

AUSTRALIA AND GERMANY

David developed many close relationships, in which colleagues became friends and serious research was intermingled with social events and pleasure. There were many, and some have already been mentioned, in particular that with Gerry Edwards. However, the relationships he developed with colleagues in two countries deserves special mention. In Germany, Ulrich Heber shared the same research objectives, understanding photosynthetic regulation; potentially rivals, instead they became collaborators and friends (figure 4). Heber was a regular visitor to Sheffield, where he revelled in the availability of such wonderful apparatus. He had the same admiration for Robin Hill. He was tremendously popular with the members of the Sheffield group. A firm link between Sheffield and Würzburg was established and on numerous occasions joint group meetings involved mass transit of researchers between the two places. The social interaction and camaraderie were unique and highly productive. Hans Heldt's group from Göttingen and Irwin Latsko's at Munster were also involved. Heldt, Heber and Walker came together with a landmark paper on the role of P_i in the regulation of photosynthesis (23), and Heber and Walker were the first to show the crucial role of cyclic electron transport around photosystem 1 in generating qE (33). There were many visitors to Sheffield from the German laboratories, most notably including Karl-Josef Dietz and Mark Stitt.

The Australian connection was just as strong and important. David's first visit in 1970 was at a time of great excitement after the discovery of the C_4 pathway of photosynthetic carbon assimilation by M. D. (Hal) Hatch (FRS 1980), Roger Slack (FRS 1989) and their colleagues a few years earlier. Australia had become a hotbed of research into photosynthesis in the 1960s and a natural place for David to visit, but it became more than this to him:

> At a purely personal level, Australia itself was also a revelation. There can be few more beautiful campuses than that of the ANU to which Barry Osmond and Hal Hatch so kindly invited me so often. Shirley and I made many new friends and renewed many old friendships.

Figure 5. David with David Hall (left) and Richard Leegood (right) while taking part in an international training course in photosynthesis.

It is noteworthy that it was during one visit to Canberra in 1981 that David, together with Osmond, conducted his first measurements of chlorophyll fluorescence. Again, there was a constant stream of visitors to Sheffield from Australia, including long-term research visits by John Anderson, Peter Brownell, Graham Farquhar (FRS 1995), Bob Furbank, Roger Slack and Ian Woodrow.

SCIENCE COMMUNICATION AND EDUCATION

Most scientists of the Walker era regarded their research work only in the context of their specific scientific communities, and teaching as something done reluctantly as a part of a contractual obligation to their employers. David Walker was different. Although doing everything he could to shy away from undergraduate teaching, he more than made up for it in other ways. Together with his Sheffield colleague Richard Leegood he gave his time, enthusiasm and effort to contribute in a major way to the international training courses organized by David Hall (figure 5). These took David and a small number of similarly dedicated academics to the remotest areas of the globe, to teach enthusiastic students the art of photosynthesis research, in the most difficult environments and circumstances. He also made sure that the Sheffield Institute would play host to similar courses for students from all over the world.

He also made great efforts to share his joy of science in general and photosynthesis in particular to the lay public, as he put it 'from 9 to 90'. His books were always engagingly written, amusing where appropriate and illustrated imaginatively (aided by the artistic talent of his son, Richard). They also had a social conscience: they would describe the most fascinating aspects of photosynthesis, but in the context of the global problems that were emerging: of CO_2-related global warming and of supplying energy and food for a growing population. Two books stand out: *Energy, plants and man* (34), written in 1992, and *A leaf in time* (35), a 2002 book for children that was simply written but with powerful messages. In the last years of his life, engaged in the potential of interactive on-line technology, he was working on 'A new leaf in time' (http://www.hansatech-instruments.com/forum/uploads/david_walker/A New Leaf in Time.pdf) with hyperlinks to online sources. *Energy, plants and man* was perhaps his most personal book, and David was keenly aware of the effect that increasing population growth, the consumption of finite resources, and the impact of pollution such as CO_2 emissions were having in damaging the environment and contributing to global warming. His book set out to understand the crucially important interrelation between energy, plants, humans and the environment and to argue for alternatives to fossil fuel consumption and for a sustainable relationship with the environment. Even 20 years ago, when the book was published, David was sceptical about the extent to which we could reverse the damage we have already unleashed. Nevertheless, he argued, 'What does lie with Man's province, as a supposedly sentient animal, is his ability to recognize the problems as real and pressing and to do everything possible to make the last years of the great fossil fuel bonfire as painless as possible' (34). David's passionate views on the impact of global warming were a continuing preoccupation throughout his life. His letters on the subject were frequently published in the national press.

I am sure that David did not see this as an obligation to 'tick the box' of contributing to the 'public understanding of science', as nowadays demanded of holders of UK research council grants. Rather, I think he thought science, like art, was part of our cultural life, and scientists, like artists, should share their work with their fellow human beings. His most interesting endeavour in this regard, which brought together his love of the traditional English public house as a place to drink beer and engage in conversation, and his wish to share his love of science, was the beermat project, 'The pub understanding of science' (http://www.hansatech-instruments.com/forum/uploads/david_walker/pub understanding of science.pdf). In this project, beer mats were distributed, each having printed on them questions about science!

In 2004 David was awarded the inaugural Communications Award of the International Society of Photosynthesis Research to acknowledge all these outstanding efforts in communicating photosynthesis to the general public, and in 2006 he was similarly awarded an honorary DLitt by the University of Sheffield.

RETIREMENT AND MORE TIME IN BIDDLESTONE

Shortly before the start of the ARC group in 1979, the Walkers bought and then refurbished, with the help of Tom Delieu, a derelict cottage in Biddlestone, in rural Northumberland, some 175 miles north of Sheffield.

> Biddlestone became a refuge, a hiding place from the more unpleasant aspects of academic life and, in the words of my daughter Marney, the best thing that I have ever done.

This idyllic rural environment in a sheltered garden bordered by woodland with a burn running through it provided endless opportunity for David to indulge himself in a lifelong interest in messing about in water. He built a series of forges, dams and many prototype bridges and experimented with hydropower (figure 6). Despite the consternation of neighbours whose complaints prompted inspections from the local parish council, his design for a fish ladder, dam and the huge pool that it created earned him a grant for increasing the salmon trout

Figure 6. David and his wife, Shirley, at the dam in Biddlestone. (Online version in colour.)

population in the locality. It was also a place where David would take his close friends, such as Ulrich Heber and Barry Osmond, during their many visits to Sheffield. In 1993 he retired from the university, becoming Emeritus Professor. He and Shirley spent much more time in Biddlestone—it comes as no surprise to learn that a greenhouse had been added and a shed that housed a computer and equipment necessary for measuring photosynthesis and chlorophyll fluorescence! Retirement also gave David the opportunity to spend more time in writing. His love of language and literature, apparent even in early childhood, was able to blossom in the writing of books, commentaries and retrospectives. Such literary style is rare in scientific writings, and it made these not only informative and insightful but also enjoyable.

David remained active in photosynthesis research for almost 20 more years. His last paper was published in 2010, an authoritative and detailed analysis of the (spurious) claims being made about the contributions of biofuels to sustainable energy supply (36). David Alan Walker died after a long illness in February 2012; the tributes that followed indicated the fondness, admiration and respect felt by the photosynthesis research community, illustrated in the obituary compiled for *Photosynthesis Research* by Gerry Edwards and Ulrich Heber (Edwards & Heber 2012). This was clearly mutual: the final words of his 1997 autobiographical article are thus a fitting closure to this memoir:

> As a boy I thought longingly of the sea-going apprenticeship which, even before his sixteenth birthday, took my father to the far corners of the earth. However, in pursuit of my profession I eventually finished up in many more countries than he did, sometimes as a resident, always amongst colleagues and friends. This has meant much more than simple pleasure and satisfaction. To date, retirement has been pure bliss and I have a legacy of friends and memories of a sort that do not often flow from otherwise comparable professions. This is a century in which there have been many changes for the good. It has also been one in which the greatest atrocities have been perpetrated, atrocities fashioned out of religious bigotry and irrational prejudice. Clearly international science is not above and beyond human frailty but at least it is based on a degree of rationality and knowledge which recognizes no borders. As such, it often seems to engender

some degree of humility amongst its practitioners, perhaps knowing as they must, that they are at least as likely to be as wrong as the next man and that there is no way of repealing the laws of thermodynamics. Whatever the reasons, being a member of the photosynthesis community has been an immensely rewarding experience.

ACKNOWLEDGEMENTS

I am grateful to Barry Osmond FRS for help and encouragement in the preparation of this memoir. I also acknowledge the valuable input from my colleague at Sheffield, Richard Leegood. The comments and materials provided by David's children, Marney and Richard, are very much appreciated.

The frontispiece photograph was taken in 1979 by Godfrey Argent and is reproduced with permission.

REFERENCE TO OTHER AUTHORS

Edwards, G. E. & Heber, U. 2012 David Alan Walker (1928–2012). *Photosynth. Res.* **112**, 91–102.

BIBLIOGRAPHY

The following publications are those referred to directly in the text. A full bibliography is available as electronic supplementary material at http://dx.doi.org/10.1098/rsbm.2014.0007 or via http://rsbm.royalsocietypublishing.org.

(1)   1956   (With H. Beevers) Oxidative activity of particulate fractions from germinating castor beans. *Biochem. J.* **62**, 114–120.

(2)   (With H. Beevers) Some requirements for pyruvate oxidation by plant mitochondrial preparations. *Biochem. J.* **62**, 120–127.

(3)   Malate synthesis in a cell-free extract from a Crassulacean plant. *Nature* **178**, 593–594.

(4)   1957   Physiological studies on acid metabolism. 4. Phosphoenolpyruvate carboxylase activity in extracts of Crassulacean plants. *Biochem. J.* **67**, 73–79.

(5)   (With J. M. A. Brown) Physiological studies on acid metabolism. 5. Effects of carbon dioxide concentration on phosphoenolpyruvic carboxylase activity. *Biochem. J.* **67**, 79–83.

(6)   1959   (With R. Hill) Pyocyanine and phosphorylation with chloroplasts. *Plant Physiol.* **34**, 240–245.

(7)   1962   Pyruvate carboxylation and plant metabolism. *Biol. Rev.* **37**, 215–256.

(8)   1964   (With I. Zelitch) Role of glycolic acid metabolism in opening of leaf stomata. *Plant Physiol.* **39**, 856–862.

(9)   Improved rates of carbon dioxide fixation by illuminated chloroplasts. *Biochem. J.* **92**, 22c–23c.

(10) 1965   Correlation between photosynthetic activity and membrane integrity in isolated pea chloroplasts. *Plant Physiol.* **40**, 1157–1161.

(11) 1966   (With C. Bucke & C. W. Baldry) Some effects of sugars and sugar phosphates on carbon dioxide fixation by isolated chloroplasts. *Biochem. J.* **101**, 636–641.

(12) 1967   (With R. Hill) Relation of oxygen evolution to carbon assimilation with isolated chloroplasts. *Biochim. Biophys. Acta* **131**, 330–338.

(13)   (With W. Cockburn & C. W. Baldry) Photosynthetic oxygen evolution by isolated chloroplasts in presence of carbon cycle intermediates. *Nature* **216**, 597–599.

(14)   (With W. Cockburn & C. W. Baldry) Some effects of inorganic phosphate on O_2 evolution by isolated chloroplasts. *Biochim. Biophys. Acta* **143**, 614–624.

(15)   (With C. Bucke & C. W. Baldry) Photosynthetic carbon dioxide fixation by isolated chloroplasts in Good's buffers. *Phytochemistry* **6**, 495–497.

(16) 1968 (With W. Cockburn & C. W. Baldry) Photosynthesis by isolated chloroplasts—reversal of orthophosphate inhibition by Calvin-cycle intermediates. *Biochem. J.* **107**, 89–95.

(17) 1971 (With D. M. Stokes) Phosphoglycerate as a Hill oxidant in a reconstituted chloroplast system. *Plant Physiol.* **48**, 163–165.

(18) 1972 (With T. Delieu) Improved cathode for measurement of photosynthetic oxygen evolution by isolated chloroplasts. *New Phytol.* **71**, 201–225.

(19) 1973 Photosynthetic induction phenomena and light activation of ribulose diphosphate carboxylase. *New Phytol.* **72**, 209–235.

(20) 1974 (With R. M. Lilley) Reduction of 3-phosphoglycerate by reconstituted chloroplasts and by chloroplast extracts. *Biochim. Biophys. Acta* **368**, 269–278.

(21) 1976 (With A. R. Slabas) Transient inhibition by ribose 5-phosphate of photosynthetic O_2 evolution in a reconstituted chloroplast system. *Biochim. Biophys. Acta* **430**, 154–164.

(22) (With A. Herold & D. H. Lewis) Sequestration of cytoplasmic orthophosphate by mannose and its differential effect on photosynthetic starch synthesis in C_3 and C_4 species. *New Phytol.* **76**, 397–407.

(23) 1977 (With H. W. Heldt, C. J. Chon, D. Maronde, A. Herold, Z. S. Stankovic, A. Kraminer, M. R. Kirk & U. Heber) Role of orthophosphate and other factors in regulation of starch formation in leaves and isolated-chloroplasts. *Plant Physiol.* **59**, 1146–1155.

(24) 1978 (With G. E. Edwards, S. P. Robinson & N. J. C. Tyler) Photosynthesis by isolated protoplasts, protoplast extracts, and chloroplasts of wheat—influence of ortho-phosphate, pyrophosphate, and adenylates. *Plant Physiol.* **62**, 313–319.

(25) 1979 (With S. P. Robinson) Control of 3-phosphoglycerate reduction in isolated-chloroplasts by the concentrations of ATP, ADP and 3-phosphoglycerate. *Biochim. Biophys. Acta* **545**, 528–536.

(26) 1980 (With R. C. Leegood) Auto-catalysis and light activation of enzymes in relation to photosynthetic induction in wheat chloroplasts. *Arch. Biochem. Biophys.* **200**, 575–582.

(27) 1981 Secondary fluorescence kinetics of spinach leaves in relation to the onset of photosynthetic carbon assimilation. *Planta* **153**, 273–278.

(28) (With T. Delieu) Polarographic measurement of photosynthetic oxygen evolution by leaf-disks. *New Phytol.* **89**, 165–178.

(29) 1983 (With P. Horton, M. Sivak & W. P. Quick) Anti-parallel relationship between O_2 evolution and slow fluorescence induction kinetics. *Photobiochem. Photobiophys.* **5**, 35–39.

(30) (With G. Edwards) C_3,C_4: *mechanisms, and cellular and environmental regulation, of photosynthesis.* Chichester: Packard Publishing Ltd.

(31) 1986 (With A. Laisk) Control of phosphate turnover as a rate-limiting factor and possible cause of oscillations in photosynthesis—a mathematical model. *Proc. R. Soc. Lond.* B **227**, 281–302.

(32) 1992 Concerning oscillations. *Photosynth. Res.* **34**, 387–395.

(33) (With U. Heber) Concerning a dual function of coupled cyclic electron-transport in leaves. *Plant Physiol.* **100**, 1621–1626.

(34) *Energy, plants and man*, 2nd edn. Brighton: Oxygraphics Ltd.

(35) 2002 *A leaf in time*. London: Portland Press.

(36) 2010 Biofuels—for better or worse? *Ann. Appl. Biol.* **156**, 319–327.

SIR MAURICE VINCENT WILKES

26 June 1913 — 29 November 2010

Maurice V. Wilkes

SIR MAURICE VINCENT WILKES

26 June 1913 — 29 November 2010

Elected FRS 1956

BY MARTIN CAMPBELL-KELLY

Department of Computer Science, Warwick University, Coventry CV4 7AL, UK

Maurice Wilkes was head of the Mathematical Laboratory (later Computer Laboratory) at Cambridge University from 1945 until his retirement in 1980. He led the construction of the EDSAC (Electronic Delay Storage Automatic Calculator), the world's first practical stored-program computer, completed in May 1949. In 1951 he invented microprogramming, a fundamental technique of computer design. He subsequently led the construction of the EDSAC 2 and the Titan computers; he then established the CAP computer project, the Cambridge Digital Ring, and the Cambridge Distributed Computer System. Beyond Cambridge University, he was founding president of the British Computer Society. He was knighted in 2000 for services to computing.

EARLY LIFE

Maurice Vincent Wilkes was born in Dudley, Worcestershire, on 26 June 1913, the only child of Vincent Joseph Wilkes and his wife Ellen (*née* Malone). His father was an accounts clerk in the estate of the Earl of Dudley, which had extensive coal-mining interests. Wilkes senior was ambitious and capable, and was promoted to cashier of the estate; after nationalization of the coal industry in 1947 he became a regional director of the National Coal Board.

Wilkes was educated at King Edward's School, Stourbridge. He was a born tinkerer, starting at a young age with Meccano (which he described as 'every English boy's birth right') and graduating to wireless set construction. In the sixth form he learned Morse code, obtained an amateur radio licence and took out a subscription to *Wireless Engineer*, which he carefully annotated and from which he learned much. Wilkes was an able scholar, and his father agreed that he should go to Cambridge University. Because the family had no experience of higher education, they sought the advice of the school's head master, J. B. Boyt. In 1898 Boyt had graduated in mathematics from St John's College, Cambridge University, and so that was the path that Wilkes also took.

http://dx.doi.org/10.1098/rsbm.2013.0020

Figure 1. Maurice Wilkes in 1932 or 1933 operating a 5 MHz superhet receiver in an amateur radio experiment. (By permission of the Master and Fellows of St John's College, Cambridge.)

Wilkes went up to St John's College in October 1931. He was torn between mathematics and natural philosophy, and decided on the Mathematical Tripos. Although he was by temperament an engineer, for which he had a greater aptitude than his chosen subject, he never regretted reading mathematics, and it turned out to be a good preparation for a life in computing. In any case, he found outlets for his other interests by becoming a member of the Wireless Society and taking a course in wireless waves in his final year (figure 1). He graduated with first-class honours in June 1934, a distinction he shared with Alan Turing (FRS 1951), who completed his studies in the same year, although they barely knew one another as undergraduates.

Postgraduate studies and war service

Wilkes always viewed his undergraduate studies as nothing other than a preparation for a life in research. Immediately on graduating he became a research student in radio physics in the Cavendish Laboratory under the supervision of J. A. Ratcliffe FRS. He was assigned to a group studying the propagation of very long radio waves. The work involved excursions in a motor car, towing a caravan loaded with portable electrical measuring equipment, taking readings in the field, and undertaking a mathematical analysis afterwards. In every way Wilkes was in his element and it gave him a lasting interest in the physics of the atmosphere.

In his second year as a research student, Wilkes attended a lecture by Douglas Hartree FRS, Professor of Applied Mathematics at Manchester University, which changed the course of his life. A few years previously, Vannevar Bush at Massachusetts Institute of Technology (MIT) had invented an analogue computing machine for integrating differential equations, called a differential analyser. Hartree had built a model differential analyser in 1934 from Meccano that proved to be surprisingly accurate and useful. A copy of this machine had been built at Cambridge for John Lennard-Jones FRS, Professor of Theoretical Chemistry, and it was demonstrated at Hartree's lecture. This was the first Wilkes had heard of the machine and he asked Lennard-Jones if he might use it.

Wilkes found the differential analyser irresistible. His research threw up numerous differential equations and his early publications involved their solution (1, 2, 4, 5, 7)*. He was soon such an expert that Lennard-Jones invited him to take charge of the machine and provide technical assistance for users. By good fortune the appointment came with a stipend, just as Wilkes's research grant from the Department of Scientific and Industrial Research was coming to an end. In 1937 Lennard-Jones persuaded the university to establish a 'calculating laboratory'. At the last minute the facility was named the Mathematical Laboratory, perhaps to make its mission seem less prosaic; the name was changed to the Computer Laboratory in 1970. Lennard-Jones was appointed Director of the Mathematical Laboratory, and Wilkes became Assistant Director with the rank of University Demonstrator.

The Laboratory was located in the former Anatomy Laboratory, Corn Exchange Street. Wilkes set to work with characteristic energy—improving the Meccano differential analyser (3), installing a variety of calculating machines, and making himself known to the small world of computing experts. Before he took charge, the Laboratory had commissioned a one-of-a-kind analogue electric computing machine from the Cambridge Instrument Company, invented by R. M. M. Mallock of the university's Engineering Department. Wilkes used the Mallock Machine to solve a set of linear equations (6), but it never became a mainstay of the computing service. The Laboratory had a budget for a full-scale differential analyser, and a copy of the machine constructed for Manchester University was ordered from Metropolitan–Vickers. This necessitated Wilkes making a trip to Manchester, where he met Douglas Hartree in person for the first time. Hartree collected Wilkes from the railway station in his motor car, and put him up in his home. It was the beginning of a lasting friendship. When Hartree moved to Cambridge University after World War II, he became a kind of godfather to the Laboratory. However, no sooner was the differential analyser delivered than Britain was at war. The facilities of the Laboratory were taken over by the Ministry of Supply, and Wilkes was enlisted in the scientific war effort.

In the run-up to war, the Cavendish Laboratory had entered secret high-level talks with the Air Ministry as to its role if a conflict should come. In July 1940, not long after the fall of France, Wilkes was mobilized, along with Ratcliffe and several of his Cavendish colleagues. He was initially assigned to RAF Bawdsey Research Station, serving technical and operational roles in the Chain Home radar stations. He was a key member of the Air Defence Research and Development Establishment, working under John (later Sir John) Cockcroft FRS, and then of the Army Operational Research Group, and made important contributions to the development of radar, especially the radar cross-section of a target. Later he was transferred to the Telecommunications Research Establishment (TRE), where he undertook operations research into the effectiveness of radar equipment—his only war activity to result in a publication (9). Immediately after the end of the war, he was part of a technical mission in Germany to evaluate electronic developments. Like most scientific war work, that of Wilkes was highly specialized, and pragmatic rather than fundamental. He was unusual, however, in that his experience—involving both pulse electronics and practical computation—would prove an almost perfect background when it came to building the EDSAC computer after the war.

In spring 1945 the end of the war was in sight, and the Mathematical Laboratory at Cambridge University was re-established. The Ministry of Supply was prised out of its wartime occupation

---

* Numbers in this form refer to the bibliography at the end of the text.

Figure 2. Maurice Wilkes at his desk in the Mathematical Laboratory. (By permission of the Master and Fellows of St John's College, Cambridge.)

of the Laboratory and Wilkes resumed his duties as Acting Director with the rank of University Lecturer in October 1945 (figure 2). He had two remits: first, to conduct research into computing machines and methods; and second, to provide computing resources and assistance for users.

THE EDSAC AND THE DEVELOPMENT OF PROGRAMMING

Soon after the end of the war, three major British computer projects were established in Britain, at Manchester University, Cambridge University, and the National Physical Laboratory (NPL). The projects were led by F. C. Williams (FRS 1950) and T. Kilburn (FRS 1965) at Manchester, Wilkes at Cambridge, and Turing at the NPL. The starting point for all of the projects was a theoretical design for a computer known as the EDVAC (Electronic Discrete Variable Automatic Computer) developed by John von Neumann and others at the Moore School of Electrical Engineering at the University of Pennsylvania. (The EDVAC was the successor to an earlier special-purpose electronic calculator, the ENIAC (10).) Although the primary aim of all the projects was to build a practical computer, their secondary aims differed. At Manchester the focus was on engineering, at the NPL on numerical mathematics, but at Cambridge Wilkes lit on the development of programming.

Wilkes first learned in detail about the EDVAC in May 1946, when he received a visit from L. J. Comrie (FRS 1950), Britain's foremost computing expert. A former superintendent of the Nautical Almanac Office, in 1937 Comrie had founded the Scientific Computing Service, the world's first for-profit calculating agency in London, and had prospered during the war

(Croarken 1990). Comrie was helping Wilkes to re-equip the Laboratory. On this occasion, Comrie brought with him a copy of the *First draft of a report on the EDVAC*, dated June 1945, which von Neumann had written on behalf of the computer group at the Moore School. As Wilkes recalled, there were no photocopiers in those days, so he stayed up late into the night reading it. The *EDVAC Report* described the logical design of the stored-program computer on which almost all subsequent computers were based, up to the present day. Wilkes decided at once that the Laboratory should have one.

A few weeks later, Wilkes received a telegram from the Moore School. They were planning a summer school in computer design and would he like to attend? He did, but 1946 was not a good time for overseas travel. Because of bureaucratic and shipping delays he arrived in time for only the last two weeks of the eight-week course. Wilkes was unfazed by the delay, because most of the course was background material on numerical methods and electronics in which he was already well versed. The Moore School was not free from red tape either. At the time the summer school started, the EDVAC was still classified; security restrictions were not lifted until the final days of the course, when the students were shown the block diagrams of the EDVAC in a darkened room. Because of the security restrictions, the participants were allowed to take away nothing but their personal notes. But it was all that Wilkes needed. Returning to the UK on the *Queen Mary* he began to map out the design of the EDSAC. The name EDSAC was deliberately chosen to echo EDVAC so that there should be no doubt about its provenance.

At all times Wilkes was more interested in getting a computer up and running quickly than in having one with the highest technological performance. So, for example, he opted for a half-megacycle pulse rate. If he had been more adventurous he could have built a machine that was twice as fast. But he reasoned that since the computer would be a thousand times faster than anything previously available, users would be well enough satisfied and would be pleased to have the machine sooner rather than later.

The key technical problem facing all the early computer groups was designing a memory system that could store at least a thousand numbers and instructions. No one anywhere had built such a device. The Moore School advocated using mercury delay lines, which were a by-product of radar research and so—always taking the path of least difficulty—that is what Wilkes decided on. In October 1946 he had a great stroke of luck when he encountered a newly arrived Cavendish research student, Thomas Gold (FRS 1964), who subsequently became a distinguished astrophysicist. In the last year of the war, Gold had worked on a moving-target indicator based on a mercury delay line for the Admiralty's radar research programme (Gold 1951). He was able to give the constructional particulars to Wilkes, who followed them to the letter.

Before he could start construction in earnest, Wilkes needed to build up an engineering team. Gold again came to the rescue when he recommended a seasoned electronics engineer, William Renwick, with whom he had worked at the Admiralty Signals Establishment. Another key appointment was Eric Mutch, a meticulous project manager and administrator, whom Wilkes had worked with from time to time at the TRE. By the end of 1947, more technical staff had been recruited and construction went full steam ahead (figure 3). Always an outstanding communicator, Wilkes published several papers describing the machine's progress (see, for example, (12–15)).

Besides building the EDSAC, Wilkes had heavy administrative burdens. While Renwick and the engineering staff got on with building the EDSAC, Wilkes attended to the postwar

Figure 3. The EDSAC under construction, ca. 1948. In the foreground are Maurice Wilkes (left, inspecting the mercury delay line store) and William Renwick. (Courtesy Computer Laboratory, Cambridge University.)

reconstruction of the Laboratory. There was an academic programme to develop and a computing service to provide. In November 1947 he established a series of fortnightly colloquia, which became a focal point for all the computer groups working in Britain. A course on numerical analysis was initiated, with Douglas Hartree giving the lectures. The first three research students were recruited: John Bennett, David Wheeler (FRS 1981) and Stanley Gill. Ben Noble, and later R. A. (Tony) Brooker, were hired to manage the differential analyser. All of these individuals would become significant players in the rapidly evolving computing scene of the 1950s. In particular, Wheeler became a distinguished fixture of the Laboratory, and he and Wilkes would have complementary roles in its development.

In April 1947, at the age of 33 years, Wilkes married Nina Twyman, the classicist daughter of a diplomat. Wilkes had an enormous capacity for work at this stage of his life. Alongside the development of the EDSAC and the Laboratory, he picked up the threads of his prewar research in radio physics, publishing articles (8, 11) and a monograph, *Oscillations of the Earth's atmosphere*, for Cambridge University Press (16). Wilkes was as interested in using computers as in building them. In 1948 it was not foreseeable to Wilkes or anyone else that computing would become a 'science' and that computers would assume world-shaking importance. At this time the computer was primarily a scientific instrument—rather like an electron microscope or a radio telescope. For Wilkes, the computer represented not so much an end in itself as a means to advance research in his particular science, the physics of the atmosphere. He continued to be active in radio physics up to the early 1960s.

The EDSAC sprang into life on Friday, 6 May 1949, successfully printing a table of squares. It was the world's first practical EDVAC-type computer. Six weeks later there was an inaugural conference, attended by practically the whole of the British and European computing community—there were 144 delegates (Mathematical Laboratory 1950*a*).

After the conference, Wilkes assumed the role of a user, both to put the machine through its paces and to see how it might advance his personal research. His first real application program was for the integration of Airy's differential equation—a type that tended to arise in atmospheric physics. In writing this program he made one of the most profound discoveries in computing: that getting programs right was very difficult. His was a short program of 126 instructions, but it contained about 20 errors. It was only after at least a dozen attempts that he finally coaxed the correct results out of the machine. He subsequently recalled, in a much quoted passage of his memoirs ((37), p. 145):

> By June 1949 people had begun to realize that it was not so easy to get a program right as had at one time appeared. I well remember when this realization first came on me with full force. The EDSAC was on the top floor of the building and the tape-punching and editing equipment one floor below on a gallery that ran round the room in which the differential analyser was installed. I was trying to get working my first non-trivial program, which was one for the numerical integration of Airy's differential equation. It was on one of my journeys between the EDSAC room and the punching equipment that 'hesitating at the angles of stairs' the realization came over me with full force that a good part of the remainder of my life was going to be spent in finding errors in my own programs.

Something needed to be done about the programming problem. Capitalizing on this early insight, Wilkes turned the problem over to Wheeler, who developed the so-called Initial Orders (later known as an assembler). The Initial Orders read in a program written in a simple symbolic form and converted it into the binary instructions used by the circuits of the computer. Wilkes was bowled over by the system that Wheeler developed—he described it as a tour de force of programming. This Wilkes could never have done. On the other hand, Wilkes brought into being a practical computing service, which would never have interested Wheeler.

The Laboratory began to offer a university-wide computing service at the beginning of 1950. In September the programming system was described in *Report on the preparation of programmes for the EDSAC and the use of the library of sub-routines* (Mathematical Laboratory 1950*b*). Wilkes sent copies of the report to everyone he thought might be interested. At about this time he received a visit from Zdenek Kopal, who was then at MIT and later became Professor of Astronomy at Manchester University. Wilkes, hopeful that the report might be published, gave a copy of the report to Kopal, who brought it to the attention of Addison-Wesley in Cambridge, Massachusetts. Wilkes duly received an offer from Addison-Wesley, and the book appeared in 1951 under the title *The preparation of programs for an electronic digital computer* (18). The book was essentially the same as the September 1950 report, with the addition of a foreword by Hartree and Americanized spelling. Wilkes included as co-authors Wheeler and Gill (the latter had developed ground-breaking debugging techniques), and the book became known as Wilkes, Wheeler and Gill, or WWG for short. It was the first textbook on programming, and because it was published at a time when the first computers were just coming into operation it rushed in to fill the vacuum of knowledge about programming. The book influenced programming techniques almost everywhere (indeed, the subroutine library, organized in the manner invented by Wheeler, remains a fundamental principle of most programming systems up to the present day). WWG was perhaps the single most important outcome of the EDSAC.

The completion of the EDSAC attracted worldwide attention, and Wilkes was in constant demand to write articles and give lectures. He enjoyed writing for the lay person, and his direct, simple style was put to great effect in a full-length work, *Automatic digital computers*, published by Methuen in 1956 (24). In his personal research Wilkes still had a foot in two camps: in radio physics (17, 20) and computing (21); just occasionally the two came together (23).

In 1950 Wilkes instituted an annual summer school in programming, which continued for several years. At a time when it was very difficult to get first-hand experience of using a computer, this served a vital national purpose in manpower training. Many of the course participants went on to have important roles in the emerging computer industry, in user organizations and in academia. A one-year postgraduate Diploma in Numerical Analysis and Automatic Computing began in 1953. Numerical analysis was initially taught by Hartree, but Wilkes later took over and published a compact and successful textbook that stayed in print for many years (28).

Beyond the Laboratory, the EDSAC began to transform the nature of scientific research in the university, most spectacularly with the elucidation of the molecular structure of myoglobin by John Kendrew (FRS 1960), in which he was assisted by the Laboratory's John Bennett. Kendrew shared the 1962 Nobel Prize in Chemistry for this achievement (Kendrew 1962). The EDSAC also led to a commercial spin-off, the LEO computer built by the catering company of J. Lyons. The company subsequently established Leo Computers Limited, which became Britain's first manufacturer of commercial data processing computers (Ferry 2003).

EDSAC 2 AND MICROPROGRAMMING

The Mathematical Laboratory, like several other world-class academic computing centres (such as Manchester University and MIT), designed a succession of computers with the twin objectives of acting as a focus for departmental research and subsequently providing a computing service. This phase of the academic development of computing lasted until about 1970, after which it became impossible to combine these objectives. In the case of the Mathematical Laboratory, the successive projects were EDSAC, EDSAC 2 and Titan. (The next project, the CAP computer, was never intended to provide a general computing service.)

Wilkes began planning for a successor to the EDSAC as soon as it had settled down and begun to provide a regular computing service. Although the new machine would still use vacuum tubes, it was intended to achieve at least a tenfold speed improvement by using parallel rather than serial operation (that is, processing several bits at a time instead of one bit at a time). The idea of a parallel computing structure was well known and had been promulgated by von Neumann and Herman Goldstine at the Institute for Advanced Study, Princeton, in a series of reports during 1946–48.

Although by the early 1950s it was possible to buy a commercially manufactured computer, building a computer in-house enabled it to be used as a proving ground for new ideas in computer design. Thus the Manchester University Atlas innovated with virtual memory, MIT's Compatible Time-Sharing System pioneered online interaction, and EDSAC 2 demonstrated microprogramming. All of these were of fundamental importance in computer design and were adopted as standard techniques by industry.

In July 1951 Wilkes presented his initial thoughts at the Manchester University Computer Inaugural Conference, held to celebrate the arrival of the Ferranti Mark I computer (built to the university's design). Wilkes's paper 'The best way to design an automatic computing machine' (19) contained two key ideas, which later went under the names of bit-slicing and microprogramming. Both techniques were intended to reduce the amount of 'random logic' in computer hardware that made design and maintenance difficult. Wilkes proposed, where possible, the use of several chassis of identical construction so that the design process would be simplified and, in service, it would be possible to replace a faulty unit rapidly. Although the technique would entail the use of extra hardware, this would be compensated for by easier design and maintenance. This idea, under the name of bit-slicing, later became a standard technique in integrated circuit design, although probably owing more to reinvention than to Wilkes, as it was an idea that became somewhat obvious as the cost of electronics fell.

Microprogramming, however, was decidedly non-obvious. The idea was to use a set of internal 'micro orders' to implement the standard machine instructions (for example, a multiply instruction would be achieved by a microprogram that executed a series of primitive shift and add micro-instructions). In this way the heart of the machine would come to be defined by software rather than hardware, and would therefore be much easier and more flexible to design (22).

Wilkes entrusted Renwick with leading the hardware design of EDSAC 2, and Wheeler with undertaking the programming including the design of the microprogram. (Wheeler was now a research fellow and later became a professor of computer science.) Wheeler, assisted by a research student, David Barron, executed his part with characteristic brilliance. Interestingly, because Wheeler's original EDSAC programming system had been so satisfactory, the Laboratory was slow to develop programming languages, but an 'autocode' was at last developed for EDSAC 2 by Wilkes's research student David Hartley. EDSAC 2 came into service in early 1958, and the original EDSAC was dismantled a few months later. EDSAC 2 provided, for its era, a fast and reliable computing service (figure 4). However, of much greater significance to the outside world was the successful realization of Wilkes's microprogramming invention, which was undoubtedly his most significant technical contribution to the development of computing.

The EDSAC 2 microprogramming technique was described in detail in a joint paper by Wilkes, Renwick and Wheeler presented at a meeting of the Institution of Electrical Engineers (IEE) in March 1958, and subsequently published in its Proceedings as 'The design of the control unit of an electronic digital computer' (26). This got the idea into the mainstream. Microprogramming was capable of seemingly endless adaptation and refinement, and over the following decade some 50 papers were published on the topic (32).

The most important implementation of microprogramming occurred in IBM's System/360 range of computers announced in April 1964, which became the first standard computer platform. The idea was first picked up by John Fairclough at IBM's Hursley Laboratories in Winchester. Fairclough (later Sir John Fairclough, Margaret Thatcher's chief scientific advisor) was the only UK-based member of the System/360 design team. A key requirement for the new computer range was that it should be upwardly software compatible, so that a program written for one machine would be able to function correctly on a larger machine in the series. It was quite easy to achieve upward compatibility (the instruction set of each model just had to be a superset of the one below it in the range). Fairclough brought microprogramming into the picture, and this enabled the range to be both upward and downward compatible by giving every processor an identical instruction set (instructions were implemented by microprogram in low-end machines and by hardware in the high-end machines). This provided enormous cost savings in the design, manufacturing and system software for System/360 (Pugh *et al.* 1991, pp. 132–134). Microprogramming remains a cornerstone of computer design.

Figure 4. Program testing hour on EDSAC 2, May 1960. (By permission of the Master and Fellows of St John's College, Cambridge.)

As Wilkes anticipated, the development of EDSAC 2 spawned several interesting sub-projects. These included core memory, a fast paper-tape reader, and a magnetic-tape backing store. Although the age of the entrepreneurial start-up had not yet arrived in Britain, Wilkes used his contacts with industry to ensure that the ideas were developed commercially.

It had originally been intended to use a mercury delay line memory for EDSAC 2—reluctantly, but this was still the best option in the early 1950s. After visiting MIT in the summer of 1953, however, Wilkes saw its newly developed core memory in operation and on returning to the Laboratory decided that they would do the same. Wilkes negotiated with Mullard to obtain suitable cores (small magnetic ceramic toroids) and the Laboratory constructed a 1024-word store. The design was transferred to Mullard, which subsequently went into core memory manufacture. The staff developed a high-speed paper-tape reader, which was then developed and manufactured for many years by Elliott Brothers. Wilkes worked with a research assistant, Donald Willis, on a prototype magnetic-tape auxiliary store (25). Willis subsequently joined Decca, which went into magnetic-tape drive manufacture, and eventually equipped the EDSAC 2 with tape drives.

Not all of Wilkes's geese turned out to be swans, however, and one of his comparative failures was the WISP programming system. In the late 1950s there was a vogue for 'self-compiling compilers'—that is, programming language translators written in their own language. He was initially intrigued by a self-compiling system, NELIAC, developed for the US Navy and brought to his attention by Harry Huskey, a sabbatical visitor from the University of California, Los Angeles (Huskey *et al.* 1960).

At this time Wilkes's personal research had languished somewhat as other activities took over. Besides the administrative load of running the Laboratory, he was the most publicly engaged of Britain's senior computing academics. After his election as a Fellow of the Royal Society in 1956, he had become chairman of its Mathematical Tables Committee, and presided over its gentle dissolution. (The computer had made mathematical tables largely obsolete, and an older generation of table-makers had to be appraised of the new world order.) He was heavily involved in the creation of the British Computer Society (BCS), the learned society for computing, and served as its first president from 1957 to 1960. His presidency also obliged him to serve as the British representative of the International Federation of Information Processing Societies (IFIP), the umbrella organization for national computing societies. He was no longer active in radio physics, and his hope was that the self-compiling compiler project would get him back into the swing of research.

WISP was a small but rather elegant system that used both self-compilation and the newly invented list-processing data structures (27). He intended that WISP should serve as an implementation system for a scientific programming language for the up-coming Titan computer. However, this proved quite impracticable, and a conventional autocode compiler was eventually produced by Peter Swinnerton-Dyer (FRS 1967) of the Mathematics Department. Whereas Wilkes had a seemingly infallible instinct for electronics (he likened it to green fingers), he lacked the same intuitive sense for software and never personally ventured into a programming project again.

Titan and time-sharing

By the end of the 1950s EDSAC 2 had nearly 200 regular users, and demand for computing was growing rapidly. To keep pace with this demand the Laboratory decided to acquire a commercially manufactured machine, for which the University Grants Committee (UGC) was beginning to provide funds to universities generally. Wilkes's preferred choice was the Atlas computer, then the most powerful in the world, designed by Manchester University and manufactured by Ferranti. The cost of the Atlas (more than £2 million), however, was far in excess of what Wilkes could muster from the UGC and the university.

To secure a sale, the head of Ferranti's computer division, Peter Hall, made an ingenious offer to the Laboratory. Ferranti would supply an Atlas of reduced specification, at a greatly reduced price, if the Laboratory would cooperate in the hardware and software design to develop a commercially saleable version of the computer, to be known as the Atlas 2—within the university the machine was known as the Titan. The offer was accepted and Wilkes assigned Wheeler as the design authority, with first David Barron and then Roger Needham (FRS 1985) leading software development. (Barron left the Laboratory in 1967 to become the founding professor of computer science at Southampton University. Needham, a research fellow appointed in 1962, succeeded Wilkes as head of the Laboratory in 1980.)

The initial plan was to provide a conventional batch operating system, by which users submitted their programs on paper tape or punched cards and collected the results some hours later. The operating system development was well under way when in September 1963 Wilkes returned from a long summer visit to MIT. There he had seen the recently developed Compatible Time-Sharing System (CTSS) in operation. This system, by multiplexing the resources of a large central computer, gave 30 users equipped with teletype terminals simultaneous use of the machine and provided results in real time. Wilkes was convinced that time-sharing was the way of the future and proposed this mode of operation for the Titan. Such a change of direction would entail additional hardware and a complete redesign of the operating system, and was opposed by ICT (which had acquired Ferranti's computer division in 1963) and by some in the Laboratory. Wilkes stood his ground and prevailed.

While the redesign was under way, Titan was pressed into service in 1964 with a temporary batch operating system written by Swinnerton-Dyer; EDSAC 2 was decommissioned in the following year. The time-sharing service finally began operation in 1967. The time-sharing mode of operation was ground-breaking and the first of its kind in the UK. It became the preferred mode of computer use in universities until the concept was rendered obsolete by the arrival of personal computers. For the remainder of the 1960s time-sharing was Wilkes's principal avocation, both as proselytizer and researcher. He gave numerous talks on the topic, wrote journal articles (29, 30), and a monograph, *Time-sharing computer systems*, first published in 1968 and which subsequently appeared in two further editions (31).

By the late 1960s, now in his mid-fifties, Wilkes was at the peak of his career. In 1965 the university—with extraordinary belatedness—had appointed him to a personal chair, for which he chose the title Professor of Computer Technology. The title was a characteristic swipe at the rising tide of self-important professors of computer science in lesser institutions. As Wilkes liked to say, he had been a scientist and he knew the difference. In 1967 he was the second recipient of the A. M. Turing Award of the United States' Association of Computing Machinery (ACM), computing's highest honour.

The chequered development of Titan brought home to Wilkes, and to computer users generally in the university, the unbridgeable gap between developing a computer as a research project and providing a user-focused computing service. The timing of Titan had been additionally unfortunate because it coincided with the rise of standards-based computing. For users, standards were needed to facilitate the easy interchange of programs and data between researchers in an international context. Because IBM had come to dominate the industry with a three-quarters market share worldwide, an IBM computer was what most users really wanted.

The resolution of this conflict was to separate the academic and research activities of the Laboratory from the provision of a computer service (Ahmed 2013, pp. 66–83). This separation occurred in practically every university worldwide during the late 1960s and early 1970s. It happened in Cambridge University in 1970. Wilkes handled the separation with his usual adroitness. First, David Hartley was appointed inaugural director of the University Computer Service. Wilkes, always a shrewd judge of character, saw that Hartley was a natural manager and that his talents should be encouraged in that direction. (In 1994 Hartley became chief executive of JANET, the organization for inter-university networking in the UK.) Second, the opportunity was taken to rename the 'Maths Lab' as the Computer Laboratory (the name originally proposed in 1937). Wilkes remained at its head.

Final decade in the computer laboratory

The reorganization of computing in the university and the demise of unifying computer-building projects meant that Wilkes had to redefine his role as head of the Laboratory.

By the early 1970s computer science had become a mainstream academic discipline, and computing departments were being established in universities worldwide. In 1975 the Science Museum reflected this surge of interest with a new gallery of computing, in which the EDSAC had its rightful place among the pioneering British developments (figure 5). Wilkes ensured that the Laboratory kept pace. He proceeded to broaden the academic base, develop computer science teaching and establish new research projects. New appointments were made, sometimes in areas such as theoretical computer science and information retrieval, which were

Figure 5. The first and sixteenth presidents of the British Computer Society in conversation. Maurice Wilkes (left) with Cecil Marks in 1975 at the opening of the Science Museum computer gallery. (Courtesy of Science Museum/Science & Society Picture Library, and by permission of the Master and Fellows of St John's College, Cambridge.)

well outside Wilkes's areas of expertise. Undergraduate courses in computer science were introduced, complementing the venerable Diploma in Numerical Analysis and Automatic Computing. The cumulative effect of these initiatives resulted in a department of exceptional breadth and depth for its size, and which punched well above its weight internationally.

Wilkes's character was formed between the wars, and by the standards of the 1970s he could appear somewhat remote; this earned him the not-unaffectionate soubriquet 'the old man' among junior staff and research students. However, Wilkes never distanced himself from the cutting edge of research and he was ever receptive to new ideas. His new role in the Laboratory gradually took the form of a technology scout, seeking out breaking technologies that could be the basis for Laboratory projects and, ideally, commercial exploitation.

To some degree he had already rehearsed this role a few years previously when—inspired by the computer graphics work at MIT—he established a CAD (computer-aided design) project. This work catalysed the government into sponsoring the CAD Centre at Cambridge in 1968, and that in turn spun off several entrepreneurial start-ups.

In 1970 Wilkes initiated the CAP computer project. While he had been engaged in time-sharing research in the late 1960s, Wilkes had encountered the concept of 'capabilities'. In a multi-user computer it was necessary to prevent one program from interfering with another and to ration resources. Capabilities offered an elegant solution to this problem that made use of 'tickets' or 'tokens' that controlled programs' shared access to computing resources. The idea had first been promulgated by E. C. van Horn and J. B. Dennis at MIT and was subsequently taken up by V. Yngve and R. Fabry at the University of Chicago (Levy 1984). Wilkes visited both MIT and Chicago in the summer of 1967, became enthused by the idea, and included a detailed account in his 1968 *Time-sharing computer systems* monograph. As it turned out, neither MIT nor Chicago succeeded with the idea, partly because they opted for software-based implementations that proved impracticably slow. Wilkes decided that a hardware-based, microprogrammed approach might work, and this became the basis of the CAP computer. The project was managed by Needham and Wheeler and was delivered in 1975. The system provided a regular computing service for the Laboratory and also served as a research platform for experimental computer architectures (34). Although the project won the BCS Technical Innovation Award in 1978, the capability concept itself never developed its full potential in a time-sharing context at Cambridge or anywhere else. By the late 1970s time-sharing was on the wane with the emergence of microcomputers.

Another of Wilkes's initiatives was the Cambridge Ring local area network. A local area network enabled several small computers, terminals and peripherals to be interconnected to provide an integrated, but shared, computing service. The Cambridge Ring was one of numerous networking projects around the world, although unique of its kind. Its genesis began with one of Wilkes's chance encounters. In January 1974 he had been giving a lecture tour in Switzerland for the British Council and happened to visit the Hasler telecommunications company in Berne. There he saw a novel experimental system for digital telephony that he could see might also work for a computer network.

The idea of the Cambridge Ring was that the various components of a networked computer system would be interconnected by means of a closed communications loop or ring. The ring contained several 'slots' that circulated continuously, and a device in the network could either remove data from a slot or place data in an empty slot for another device to collect (35). (A physical analogy of the Cambridge Ring would be a paternoster lift of the period.) As in previous collaborations, David Wheeler took up the challenge and with a research student, Andy Hopper (FRS 2006), designed suitable integrated-circuit electronics. (Hopper became head of the Laboratory in 2004.) The system was operational in 1977. The Cambridge Ring was a great technical success. It won the Laboratory's second BCS Technical Innovation Award in 1981 and became an ISO standard (ISO CR82), and several firms manufactured the system under licence. Sadly, because of the winner-takes-all economics of microelectronics, the Cambridge Ring was eclipsed by the Xerox Corporation's Ethernet system. The short life of the Cambridge Ring technology was the shape of things to come, not just at Cambridge but worldwide. Every emergent technology was leapt upon simultaneously by several research groups so that the chances of any one group marching ahead of the pack were slim. The legacy of the Cambridge Ring, however, lives on in 'Silicon Fen' companies such as ARM.

Within the Laboratory, the Cambridge Ring formed the backbone of the Cambridge Model Distributed System on which work began in 1978 (36) (Needham & Herbert 1982). This was a novel distributed architecture that provided very powerful facilities using a cluster of small computers. The Cambridge Distributed System (the 'Model' was subsequently dropped) continued to evolve after Wilkes's retirement and provided a computing facility for the Laboratory up to the late 1980s.

At the end of the 1980 academic year Wilkes reached the statuary retirement age of 67 years. A banquet was held in his honour at St John's College, which was attended by university colleagues, Laboratory staff and alumni, and many of computing's glitterati who had got their start at the summer schools in programming or in the Diploma in Numerical Analysis and Automatic Computing. It was an evening to remember.

RETIREMENT AND HISTORICAL WRITING

Wilkes's anointed successor as head of the Laboratory was Roger Needham, and Wilkes was determined that he would not overshadow him. This was not, however, the main reason that in 1980 he and Nina decided to leave Britain for several years to join the Digital Equipment Corporation (DEC) in Maynard, Massachusetts (figure 6). Ever since his first visit to the USA in 1946 he had loved the country and its people. Thereafter he had visited at least once a year, most frequently to MIT, which he considered his most valuable listening post. It was a mutual affection. Wilkes could charm his hosts and act the role of the English professor in a thoroughly disarming way. He was a master of the calculated understatement, and whereas in Cambridge he could seem stiff and reserved, in the USA he became visibly more relaxed and his occasional waspishness caused nothing more than wry amusement. He received all of the important awards from the American computer and electronics professional societies—starting with the ACM Turing Award in 1967 and culminating with the von Neumann Medal of the IEEE in 1997. He particularly valued receiving in 1982 the Harry Goode Memorial Award from the University of Pennsylvania, where had attended the original Moore School Lectures in the summer of 1946 (figure 7).

At DEC Wilkes held the rank of 'senior consulting engineer', an honorific title held by barely a dozen of the company's then 70 000 employees. His most important role was to serve on the Research and Advanced Development Committee, which acted as an interface between project engineers and upper management. In addition he managed several research projects in areas that included computer security and standards for floating-point arithmetic. Towards the end of his tenure he managed DEC's participation in the joint MIT–DEC Athena Project, a distributed computer system for education.

While he was in the USA, and after he returned to the UK in 1986, Wilkes spent more and more time exploring the history of his subject. He had a remarkable instinct for doing history, and in another life that is the path his academic career might have taken. His special interest was Charles Babbage, of whom he first learned from Hartree in 1946. It says much of Wilkes's commitment that in May 1949—the month in which EDSAC began to work—he found time to visit the Science Museum in London to study Babbage's scientific manuscripts. He was the first person of the computer era to go back to the primary sources. In 1971 he gave the principal address (33) at a memorial meeting marking the centenary of Babbage's death, in which he reflected:

> I was by no means prepared to find Babbage living in a world so recognizably like that into which I was plunged 25 years ago. ... So intimate is the impression created by Babbage's notebooks that one feels one has strayed into his laboratory and, while waiting for him to come in, has started to read the papers that are lying about. They are not wholly intelligible, but one is sure that when he does come in he will tell one about it.

Wilkes had a vivid lecturing and writing style, and never more so than on the subject of Babbage. He developed a strong friendship with Alan Bromley of Sydney University, the leading authority on Babbage's calculating machinery, and was greatly saddened by Bromley's untimely death in 2002. During his DEC sojourn Wilkes wrote a playlet 'Pray Mr Babbage', which was professionally acted and subsequently published (39). For many years Wilkes had enjoyed a correspondence with I. Bernard Cohen, Professor of the History of Science at Harvard University.

Figure 6. Maurice and Nina Wilkes at the Computer Museum, Digital Equipment Corporation, 1982.
(By permission of the Master and Fellows of St John's College, Cambridge.)

Figure 7. Maurice Wilkes (right) receiving the Harold Pender Award of the University of Pennsylvania in 1982. The award was presented by John Brainerd, emeritus Dean of the Moore School of Electrical Engineering, who organized the summer school in computer design that Wilkes attended in 1946. (By permission of the Master and Fellows of St John's College, Cambridge.)

During his time in the USA, this developed into a strong friendship, during the course of which Cohen encouraged Wilkes to write his memoirs and helped see them through the press (37).

Wilkes returned to England in 1986. Now aged 73 years he believed, like Rutherford, that he could only be truly happy spending his days in a laboratory. While he had been away in the USA, Acorn Computers—the Cambridge-based developer of the highly successful BBC Microcomputer—had been acquired by Olivetti and had transformed itself into the Cambridge Olivetti Research Laboratories (ORL), with Andy Hopper as its managing director. Wilkes joined up as a full-time staff advisor on research strategy, and stayed with the Laboratory for the next 16 years. As at DEC, Wilkes was able to find a distinctive, but not central, role in the organization. Where other 'big shots' might not have been able to accept the loss of status from having been captain of their own ship, this never troubled Wilkes. His role at ORL was part advisor and industry watcher, and part ambassador. He was a great asset for ORL—he was extraordinarily well connected, could open doors, and had a measured charm. He had a major role in negotiations when first DEC and then Oracle took part ownership of ORL. His knowledge of the computer and electronics industries remained completely up to date, and he lectured on this topic for the 1990 Royal Society Clifford Paterson Lecture (40).

Wilkes's eminence continued to advance with his age. In 1992 he received the Kyoto Prize; with the ACM Turing Award, he had now received the two most prestigious honours in computing. In the following year he received an honorary doctorate from Cambridge University; recognition by his alma mater was the honour that Wilkes valued above all, even above the knighthood conferred on him in 2000.

Wilkes loved the daily rhythm of mornings spent in the Laboratory, lunch at St John's College, and—as he got older—an afternoon nap in his college rooms. He continued to write on computer history, particularly on Charles Babbage and his milieu, and published several articles in *Notes and Records of the Royal Society* (see, for example, (38, 42)). He wrote a book, *Computer perspectives* (41), which consisted largely of historical reflections on the development of computing during his lifetime.

After its acquisition by AT&T, ORL was shut down in 2002. For what was to be the last time Wilkes had to find another workplace, and he returned to the Computer Laboratory as an emeritus professor. Rather like an aged *victor ludorum*, he was welcomed back by the diminishing number who had known him in his prime, and held in awe by the rising generation. The Laboratory had expanded and moved in his years of absence. Now located in the William Gates Building on the university's West Cambridge site, the Laboratory was a world away from the old anatomy building where he had started out in the 1937. As he entered his nineties, life was inevitably less joyful. He bore the infirmities of old age well, but he found himself somewhat isolated; he had outlived practically all of his contemporaries and many of his students. His life partner Nina died in 2010, but the practical care of his children ensured that he could continue to live in the family home in Huntingdon Road that he had occupied since 1952. He continued to be seen daily in the Laboratory and St John's College up to the last weeks of his life.

ACKNOWLEDGEMENTS

I thank Wilkes's former colleagues who read and commented on an early draft of the memoir and answered email enquiries: Don Gaubatz, David Hartley, Andrew Herbert and Andy Hopper FRS. My thanks go to the Laboratory's official historian, Haroon Ahmed, Wilkes's son, Anthony, and the computer historian Mary Croarken, who provided several valuable insights. I also thank Alex May of the *Dictionary of national biography*, who shared Wilkes's vital data and other information with me. I am most grateful to Kathryn McKee, who granted me early access to Wilkes's personal archive, now housed in St John's College Library.

The frontispiece photograph was taken in 1973 by Godfrey Argent and is reproduced with permission.

BIOGRAPHICAL SUMMARY

Academic degrees and appointments

1934	BA, Cambridge University
1937	PhD, Cambridge University
1937–39	University Demonstrator, Mathematical Laboratory, Cambridge University
1939–45	War service: Radar Engineering and Operational Research
1950	Fellow, St John's College, Cambridge University
1945–80	Head of Mathematical Laboratory and Computer Laboratory, Cambridge University
1965–80	Professor of Computer Technology; thereafter emeritus
1980–86	Senior Consulting Engineer, Digital Equipment Corporation, Maynard, Massachusetts
1981–85	Adjunct Professor of Electrical Engineering and Computer Science, MIT
1986–2002	Staff Member for Research Strategy: Olivetti Research Board (1986–89), Olivetti and Oracle Research Laboratory (1989–99), AT&T Laboratories (1999–2002)

Honours and appointments

1956	Fellow of the Royal Society
1957–60	President, British Computer Society; Distinguished Fellow 1973.
1967	A. M. Turing Award, Association for Computing Machinery
1968	Harry Goode Memorial Award, American Federation for Information Processing Societies
1974	Foreign Honorary Member, American Academy of Arts and Sciences
1976	Fellow, Royal Academy of Engineering
1977	Foreign Associate, US National Academy of Engineering
1979	Foreign Corresponding Member, Royal Spanish Academy of Sciences
1980	Eckert–Mauchly Award, Association for Computing Machinery and IEEE Computer Society
1980	Foreign Associate, US National Academy of Sciences
1980	IEEE Computer Society Pioneer Award
1981	McDowell Award, IEEE Computer Society
1981	Faraday Medal, Institution of Electrical Engineers
1982	Pender Award, University of Pennsylvania
1988	C&C Prize, Tokyo
1991	ITALGAS Prize for Computer Science, Turin
1991–94	Member of Council, Association for Computing Machinery
1992	Kyoto Prize, Japan
1994	Fellow of the Association for Computing Machinery
1997	Mountbatten Medal, National Electronics Council
1997	Von Neumann Medal, IEEE

1999	Foreign Corresponding Member, Spanish Academy of Engineering
2000	Honorary Freeman, The Worshipful Company of Scientific Instrument Makers
2000	Knighthood
2001	Hall of Fellows, Computer History Museum, Mountain View, California

Honorary degrees: Newcastle upon Tyne, Kingston upon Hull, Kent, City of London, Bath, Amsterdam, Munich, Linkoping, Cambridge University, University of Pennsylvania.

REFERENCES TO OTHER AUTHORS

Ahmed, H. 2013 *Cambridge computing: the first 75 years*. London: Third Millennium Publishing.

Croarken, M. 1990 *Early scientific computing in Britain*. Oxford University Press.

Ferry, G. 2003 *A computer called LEO: Lyons teashops and the world's first office computer.* London: Fourth Estate.

Gold, T. 1951 Design of an ultrasonic delay-line. *Phil. Mag.* **42**, 787–791.

Levy, H. M. 1984 *Capability-based computer systems*. Bedford, MA: Digital Press.

Huskey, H. D., Halstead, M. H. & McArthur, R. 1960 NELIAC—a dialect of Algol. *Commun. Assoc. Comput. Mach.* **3**, 463–468.

Kendrew, J. 1962 Myoglobin and the structure of proteins (Nobel lecture). (See http://www.nobelprize.org/nobel_prizes/chemistry/laureates/1962/kendrew-lecture.pdf.)

Mathematical Laboratory 1950*a Report of a conference on high speed automatic calculating-machines, 22–25 June 1949*. Cambridge: University Mathematical Laboratory.

Mathematical Laboratory 1950*b Report on the preparation of programmes for the EDSAC and the use of the library of sub-routines*. Cambridge: University Mathematical Laboratory.

Needham, R. M. & Herbert, A. J. 1982 *The Cambridge distributed computing system*. London: Addison-Wesley.

Pugh, E. W., Johnson, L. R. & Palmer, J. H. 1991 *IBM's 360 and early 370 systems*. Cambridge, MA: MIT Press.

BIBLIOGRAPHY

The following publications are those referred to directly in the text. A full bibliography is available as electronic supplementary material at http://dx.doi.org/10.1098/rsbm.2013.0020 or via http://rsbm.royalsocietypublishing.org or http://www.cl.cam.ac.uk/archive/mvw1/list-of-papers.txt.

(1) 1936 (With J. E. Best & J. A. Ratcliffe) Experimental investigations of very long wireless waves reflected from the ionosphere. *Proc. R. Soc. Lond.* A **156**, 614–633.

(2) 1939 (With K. G. Budden & J. A. Ratcliffe) Further investigations of very long waves reflected from the ionosphere. *Proc. R. Soc. Lond.* A **171**, 188–214.

(3) (With J. E. Lennard-Jones & J. B. Bratt) Design of a small differential analyser. *Proc. Camb. Phil. Soc.* **35**, 485–493.

(4) Theoretical ionization curves for the E region. *Proc. Phys. Soc.* **51**, 138–146.

(5) 1940 Theory of reflexion of very long wireless waves from the ionosphere. *Proc. R. Soc. Lond.* A **175**, 143–163.

(6) A method of solving second order simultaneous linear differential equations using the Mallock machine. *Proc. Camb. Phil. Soc.* **36**, 204–208.

(7) Region formation in the ionosphere according to an attachment theory. *Proc. Camb. Phil. Soc.* **36**, 479–484.

(8) 1947 Oblique reflexion of very long wireless waves from the ionosphere. *Proc. R. Soc. Lond.* A **189**, 130–147.

(9) (With J. A. Ramsay) Theory of the performance of radar on ship targets. *Proc. Camb. Phil. Soc.* **43**, 220–231.

(10)   The ENIAC—high-speed electronic calculating machine. *Electron. Engng* **19**, 104.

(11)   (With K. Weekes) Atmospheric oscillations and the resonance theory. *Proc. R. Soc. Lond.* A **192**, 80–99.

(12) 1948 (With W. Renwick) An ultrasonic memory unit for the EDSAC. *Electron. Engng* **20**, 208–213.

(13)   Design of a practical high-speed calculating machine: the EDSAC. *Proc. R. Soc. Lond.* A **195**, 274–279.

(14) 1949 Programme design for a high speed automatic calculating machine. *J. Scient. Instrum.* **26**, 217–220.

(15)   Electronic calculating machine development in Cambridge. *Nature* **164**, 557–558.

(16)   *Oscillations of the Earth's atmosphere.* Cambridge University Press.

(17) 1951 Thermal excitation of atmospheric oscillations. *Proc. R. Soc. Lond.* A **207**, 358–370.

(18)   (With D. J. Wheeler & S. Gill) *The preparation of programs for an electronic digital computer.* Cambridge, MA: Addison-Wesley. (2nd edition 1957.)

(19)   The best way to design an automatic computing machine. In *Report of Manchester University Computer Inaugural Conference, July 1951*, pp. 16–18. Computer Laboratory, Manchester University.

(20) 1952 World-wide oscillations in the Earth's atmosphere. *Q. J. R. Meteorol. Soc.* **78**, 321–336.

(21) 1953 The use of a 'floating address' system for orders in an automatic digital computer. *Proc. Camb. Phil. Soc.* **49**, 84–89.

(22)   (With J. B. Stringer) Microprogramming and the design of the control circuits of an electronic digital computer. *Proc. Camb. Phil. Soc.* **49**, 230–238.

(23) 1954 A table of Chapman's grazing incidence function. *Proc. Phys. Soc.* B **67** 304–308.

(24) 1956 *Automatic digital computers.* London: Methuen.

(25)   (With D. W. Willis) A magnetic tape storage system for the EDSAC. *Proc. Instn Elect. Engrs* **103B** (Suppl. 2), 337–345.

(26) 1958 (With W. Renwick & D. J. Wheeler) The design of the control unit of an electronic digital computer. *Proc. Instn Elect. Engrs* **105B**, 121–128.

(27) 1964 An experiment with a self-compiling compiler for a simple list-processing language. *Annu. Rev. Automatic Program.* **4**, 1–48.

(28) 1966 *A short introduction to numerical analysis.* Cambridge University Press.

(29) 1967 The design of multiple access systems. *Computer J.* **10**, 1–9.

(30) 1968 (With R. M. Needham) The design of multiple access computer systems, part 2. *Computer J.* **10**, 315–320.

(31)   *Time-sharing computer systems.* London: Macdonald. (2nd edition 1972, 3rd edition 1975.)

(32) 1969 The growth of interest in microprogramming. *Comput. Surv.* **1**, 139–145.

(33) 1971 Babbage as a computer pioneer. In *Report of Proceedings: Babbage Memorial Meeting, 18 October 1971*, pp. 1–18. London: British Computer Society and Royal Statistical Society. (Reprinted in *Historia Mathematica* **4**, 415–440 (1977).)

(34) 1979 (With Needham, R. M.) *The Cambridge CAP computer and its operating system.* New York: North-Holland.

(35)   (With D. J. Wheeler) The Cambridge digital communications ring. In *Local area communications network symposium, Boston, May* (ed. R. Rosenthal & N. B. Meisner), pp. 47–62. Washington DC: National Bureau of Standards.

(36) 1980 (With Needham, R. M.) The Cambridge Model Distributed System. *Assoc. Comput. Mach. Operat. Syst. Rev.* **14**, 21–29.

(37) 1985 *Memoirs of a computer pioneer.* Cambridge, MA: MIT Press.

(38) 1990 Herschel, Peacock, Babbage and the development of the Cambridge curriculum. *Notes Rec. R. Soc.* **44**, 205–219.

(39) 1991 Pray Mr Babbage … A character study in dramatic form. *Ann. Hist. Comput.* **13** (2), 147–154.

(40) 1992 Progress and research in the computer industry. (Clifford Paterson Lecture 1990.) *Phil. Trans. R. Soc. Lond.* A **334**, 173–184.

(41) 1995 *Computing perspectives.* San Francisco, CA: Morgan Kauffmann.

(42) 2002 Charles Babbage and his world. *Notes Rec. R. Soc. Lond.* **56**, 353–365.

ALLAN CHARLES WILSON

18 October 1934 — 21 July 1991

ALLAN CHARLES WILSON

18 October 1934 — 21 July 1991

Elected FRS 1986

By Rebecca L. Cann

Department of Cell and Molecular Biology, University of Hawaii at Manoa,
Biomedical Sciences Building T514, 1960 East–West Rd, Honolulu, HI 96822, USA

Allan Charles Wilson was born on 18 October 1934 at Ngaruawahia, New Zealand. He died in Seattle, Washington, on 21 July 1991 while undergoing treatment for leukaemia. Allan was known as a pioneering and highly innovative biochemist, helping to define the field of molecular evolution and establish the use of a molecular clock to measure evolutionary change between living species. The molecular clock, a method of measuring the timescale of evolutionary change between two organisms on the basis of the number of mutations that they have accumulated since last sharing a common genetic ancestor, was an idea initially championed by Émile Zuckerkandl and Linus Pauling (Zuckerkandl & Pauling 1962), on the basis of their observations that the number of changes in an amino acid sequence was roughly linear with time in the aligned haemoglobin proteins of animals. Although it is now not unusual to see the words 'molecular evolution' and 'molecular phylogeny' together, when Allan formed his own biochemistry laboratory in 1964 at the University of California, Berkeley, many scientists in the field of evolutionary biology considered these ideas complete heresy. Allan's death at the relatively young age of 56 years left behind his wife, Leona (deceased in 2009), a daughter, Ruth (b. 1961), and a son, David (b. 1964), as well his as mother, Eunice (deceased in 2002), a younger brother, Gary Wilson, and a sister, Colleen Macmillan, along with numerous nieces, nephews and cousins in New Zealand, Australia and the USA. In this short span of time, he trained more than 55 doctoral students and helped launch the careers of numerous postdoctoral fellows.

ALLAN'S NEW ZEALAND BEGINNINGS

Given his early family background, far from the centre of academic culture and university life, the appearance of his raw talent to emerge as New Zealand's first and—so far—only

http://dx.doi.org/10.1098/rsbm.2013.0006

MacArthur Fellow, would have been difficult to predict. Allan's father, Charles (1893–1960) was the son of immigrant farmers from Northern Ireland who came to New Zealand in 1879 on the *Adamant* from Portadown. Allan's paternal grandparents, the Wilsons (George and Judith) farmed Puriri Park, near the Paerata–Waiuki railway line. His mother, Eunice Boyce Wood (1908–2002) was a fourth-generation New Zealander whose father was a carpenter and whose brothers worked a nearby farm across the road from the Wilsons. She married Allan's father in 1928. Charlie was 34 years old at the time, and Eunice was 19. Neither of his parents attended secondary school. Even though the family had a petrol-driven milking machine by the 1930s, most other Depression-era work on a dairy farm required horse-power and hard manual labour.

These conditions, however, were ideal for nourishing Allan's intense curiosity and fierce independence of thought. There had been a local ostrich farm nearby, providing a contrast to the native flightless birds of New Zealand that he learned about in school, and provoking a lifelong interest in how anatomy and behaviour drives evolutionary change. The surrounding neighbourhood around the Wilson farm was once known for its abundant wildlife. Allan was the eldest of three siblings (birth order later became a topic that interested him when discussing behavioural evolution) who grew up on the Wilson family's North Island dairy farm at Helvetia, named after Swiss pioneers who had first settled in the area in the late nineteenth century. It is a little northwest of Pukekohe, which is about 31 miles south of Auckland. His early rural life helped Allan to develop a skill set that included close observation of the natural world, a love of birds, and a humorous sceptical approach to all things religious or philosophical.

Military personnel and equipment interrupted the bucolic Pukekohe neighbourhood with a sudden jolt during the 1940s, with the government setting up camps in nearby farm paddocks to accommodate both New Zealand tank divisions and US troops en route to nearby conflict zones. Such changes brought exposure to another slice of life that many New Zealanders had so far only seen in movies: real American soldiers. Allan's mother encouraged her own brood to engage with them as they trained in nearby camps, with Allan attributing his embrace of the unknown to this early example of her simple openness. Allan said (and this was later confirmed personally by his brother and sister both) that his mother saw the soldiers as mostly just lonely young men who had left youngsters and families of their own behind, and thought that having her children around them would help provide a reminder of what they were fighting to preserve.

Allan also learned to mimic an American accent from these soldiers, and learned American slang at a young age, eventually working out the meanings of strange expressions with his brother, Gary. As children they had the freedom to explore and participate in the daily cycle of a working farm, including patches of bush, with waterways rich in eel, trout and crawfish. The area is known today as Schlaepfer Park, with its waterfall and pools, timber and a waterfall with glow-worms; the park is now owned by Scouts New Zealand. Using local examples, Allan put together a collection of bird eggs from different species, blown to help preserve their shapes and colours. Plants and insects, especially common wetas (genus *Hemideina*), also attracted his attention. Other pastimes involved collecting used beer bottles and running errands for the soldiers to earn dollars. A shared bedroom next to a porch with Gary provided the means for quick escapes from official farm chores. Possums (genus *Trichosurus*) were abundant in the area during the 1940s, and Allan eventually took an interest in preparing their skins and skeletons for study. A local pond, known for being 'bottomless', also provided study specimens for a microscope that he somehow managed to acquire.

The Pukekohe Primary School drew in about 600 children from the surrounding area, and Allan was recognized as an excellent pupil and bright student, although he had a keen interest in rugby, or 'footy'. There is a strong Wilson family tradition of rugged physical exertion, promoted by both of his parents, who had been actively engaged in sports. This eventually carried over to Allan's usual weekend appearance in shorts and flip-flops during the height of northern California's foggy summer days of just 7 °C, with everyone else swaddled in fleece or down. He always attributed his extreme cold tolerance to a wild childhood running on the rugby field, and to his membership with the Selwyn College rugby team, playing in the sleet and snow.

As part of farm life, Allan entered calves in the competition of his school's calf club, which entailed taming and hand-feeding his animals, grooming them, and preparing for the spring event still celebrated in some New Zealand country schools even now. As he matured, he took a heightened interest in helping his father improve the dairy herd's breeding stock and was given a pedigreed heifer calf to raise by a family friend, who told him to bring it back for breeding to his prize bull when it was old enough. Charlie Wilson used the bull sired from this union to improve the Wilson's herd, and the farm produced a line that eventually won several prizes for the family. Allan kept the logbook for the family's cattle breeding programme, with entries including delightfully earthy names such as Tough Tit, Big Maori, Droopy, and Lame Leg. Allan's strong interest in animal husbandry led many to believe that he would eventually become a veterinarian, but he changed course. Drawn to biochemistry, the deep knowledge he had gained working in the farm helped fuel a strong interest in understanding the ruminant lifestyle: where did they acquire the bacterial ecosystem that survived stomach acids, and how was it that these microbes allowed a cow to extract essential nutrients unavailable to other mammals? He was to explore questions raised by commensal species for the rest of his life (9, 15–17, 19, 21)*.

His attachment to the farm also served as a flashpoint that we students learned to exploit, as we discovered the one sure way to get under his normally unflappable exterior. Most Americans associate New Zealand with sheep. One Monday we had an argument over some experiment during a laboratory group meeting. After lunch I posted a cartoon from the *New Yorker* magazine on his office door with a caption roughly rendered 'I'm from New Zealand, all I know is sheep'; Allan came barrelling into his lab demanding to know who had put such an insulting note up for everyone to see. I admitted I had done it and apologized for offending him. He became very quiet and then took me gently aside. I thought I was in for a major dressing down, but instead, he related to me the hard life on the farm and how his parents sacrificed, taking on extra jobs, to help send him and his brother to King's College secondary school, where he would lose his New Zealand accent and have opportunities that they could only imagine. My making fun of New Zealanders as colonial rubes with such a cruel animal joke was a sure sign of upper-class oppression. And it was a dairy, not a sheep ranch! I replied that my mother had been raised on a farm in the Midwest, the oldest girl of eight children, and I told him I fully understood his reaction, but that there were snobs at Berkeley as well, judging from the reactions I got when I said I was born in Iowa. From then on, the sheep jokes kept coming. Miniature sheep appeared mysteriously in the aspirin supply he kept in a desk drawer to help with migraine headaches. His office door would open and a small mechanical sheep herd would suddenly buzz across the floor. There were reprint requests from sheep stations in Australia. Returning from a meeting, he found an inflatable sheep sitting on his office chair.

* Numbers in this form refer to the bibliography at the end of the text.

Menus from restaurants specializing in whole roasted sheep (and sometimes goats) mysteriously appeared in his mailbox. Laminated pictures of sheep descended outside his fourth-floor office window, carefully anchored from the Biochemistry building's rooftop. The desensitizing seems ruthless when I now consider what we subjected him to.

In 1947, after the end of World War II, Eunice Wilson enrolled Allan as a day boy in King's College in Otahuhu, a little south of Auckland. The local Sunday school teacher, a vicar's wife, convinced Allan's mother that the world would open up for Allan if only he could be sent outside Pukekohe for secondary school. His mother took additional odd jobs, serving in local tea rooms, to cover the school fees for them. King's College drew boys from prominent, professional families, and although it is now coeducational, it still attracts the children of statesmen, business tycoons, medical professionals, well-known politicians, gentleman farmers, and lawyers. At King's he again made his skill in mathematics and, later, chemistry known to teachers. To get to school, Allan (and, later, Gary) had to ride their bicycles from the farm to the steam train station, then take a 20-mile trip to campus. The yellow, weathered train station was still standing in the winter of 2011, and Gary (now a journalist) graciously explained to me their experience of carefully timing their arrival on their bikes to the last possible second, then careering down a hill at top speed once they sighted the train from a nearby farm road. If they mistimed it, they had a slim chance of making it to the next station before the train stopped there to pick up more passengers. His description reminded me, more than anything else, of Allan's approach to catching an aeroplane, which usually entailed us making a last-minute run across the San Francisco Bay Bridge to the airport south of the city, with him in the passenger seat grinning and on the lookout for the California Highway Patrol the whole way. He hated waiting for anything.

Missing the train and an encounter with a professional scientist leads to a new direction

Allan's sister, Colleen (a former nurse), recalled in an interview broadcast in 1988 that Allan credited missing the train home one night with an event that changed his direction away from veterinary school. He spent that extra hour in the King's library reading a book that suggested a person would need to become familiar with the basic processes that produced biological diversity if they were to really understand biology, including the radiation of plants and animals around the planet. (She suggests that the book was 'Baldwin on biochemical evolution', I believe referring to Baldwin (1937).) If this is so, he was introduced to the idea that enzyme-catalysed metabolic dynamics were fundamental to all living systems, providing a unifying framework with which to study biodiversity. The second event that changed his life was his uncle's introduction to a local celebrity, Dr Campbell Percy McMeekan, the head of the Ruakura Animal Research Station, after being taken to a conference at which local farmers could learn about the ongoing research and new discoveries. McMeekan was a Cambridge-educated animal scientist who succeeded in getting the government-backed dairy unit on the station operational before the permission to build it was even granted! He encouraged Allan to go to Otago instead of veterinary school, and suggested that he study biochemistry, with which he could explore more fundamental processes essential to animal and plant life. Allan was picking up odd summer jobs at the time to help defray his education, often at a vegetable plant processing peas, the night shift at a dairy factory producing butter and powdered milk,

Figure 1. Allan (left) hitch-hiking home several hundred miles from Otago with a fellow student, Colwyn Trevarthen, in the early 1950s.

and working at a bakery; during holidays he was posted in a tent as a traffic monitor counting vehicles going though the local Glenbrook/Patumahoe intersection. The University of Otago at Dunedin was hundreds of miles away on the South Island, several days' travel by train, ferry, train again, and—if he was lucky—a few stints of hitching a ride (figure 1). It was not easy for him financially, but he enrolled as a 17-year-old in 1952 and finished his BSc with a double major in zoology and chemistry. He made a special return trip back to Otago in 1989, where he was awarded an honorary doctorate in science (figure 2).

His experience at Otago crystallized his thoughts into the formal sense that evolutionary biology was being crippled by overspecialization and a lack of communication. He expressed dismay that if you became expert in comparative anatomy and natural history of a set of organisms, you usually lacked the vocabulary and/or background to ask the right questions of a chemist or biochemist concerning some essential feature in the very adaptation whose morphology or behaviour you wanted to understand. Where were the hormones, the enzymes or the structural proteins that carried out the cell's business? And, if one understood the enzyme's kinetics, did you know where, when or how in what animal or plant the enzyme actually was synthesized and stored?

A MATURATION OF INTERESTS AND PROFESSIONAL FOCUS

While at Otago, Allan met the visiting American physiologist Dr Donald S. Farner, who encouraged him to apply to graduate school under his tutelage at Washington State University

Figure 2. Allan with his sister, Colleen, and mother, Eunice, after receiving an honorary DSc at Otago in 1989.
(Online version in colour.)

in Pullman, eastern Washington. He eventually went to work with Farner in the Laboratory of Zoophysiology for several years after completing his military service in New Zealand. His daughter, Ruth, has related that he routinely directed latrines to be dug in areas that he wished to explore for fossils, making the best of this break from formal science. It is difficult to imagine what went through his mind when he first saw this locale, isolated enough to be home to a major nuclear production facility, compared with green New Zealand.

With Farner, he studied white-crowned sparrows (genus *Zonorichia*) in the Snake River Canyon, and graduated from Washington State University with an MS in zoology in 1957. In his master's project he explored how hormones regulated the behavioural cycles of birds, including the onset of migratory restlessness, along with annual breeding and moult (1, 2). Linking behaviour to physiology became an important goal for him, leading to deeper questions about variation between closely related species. When it came time to begin his own research lab, he strongly supported students who attempted to do both things, bridging the gaps between organismal and molecular evolution. He formed strong collaborative research teams that can be reflected in the collection of experts he assembled for his publications covering mammals, amphibians, fish, birds, insects, plants and fungi. Throughout this time, he also continued to advise his father on cattle breeding operations, until Charlie died suddenly in 1960.

After graduation from Washington University he continued on to the University of California (UC), Berkeley, to study with Dr Arthur Pardee, and received his PhD in Biochemistry under Pardee's direction from Berkeley in 1961. Pardee was a former student of Linus Pauling's and had recently returned to Berkeley from a sabbatical in Paris with François Jacob and Jacques Monod. This was an exciting time to join the laboratory, given the flash of insight that Pardee had contributed to an awareness of how a bacterial gene could be controlled by a regulatory protein combining with a discrete site adjacent to it on the bacteria's chromosome, referring to the mechanism of gene control in the famous PaJaMo paper (Pardee *et al.* 1959). Allan explored gene regulation further with Pardee, authoring papers about metabolically important compounds that figured in the expansion of bacterial life on Earth, and searching for biochemical clues that would underlie the basis of why certain cells became irregular, leading to cancer (3, 4). These early publications from his thesis work demonstrate his versatility in moving from the eukaryotic systems he was most familiar with to the prokaryotic systems he would begin to exploit with greater regularity.

UNIVERSITY LIFE BEYOND THE LABORATORY

His early Berkeley interlude marked the period during which he met his future wife, Leona Greenbaum, who was a graduate of Hunter College and had also enrolled in a graduate programme at UC Berkeley (where she studied mycology and received an MS in botany in 1960). They shared an interest in social change movements, folk dancing and food. Leona and Allan were clearly a match made before eHarmony (an internet dating site claiming to match couples on the scientific basis of more than 50 variables), raising the eyebrows of friends and family. They differed greatly in height, in upbringing, in religion, in ease with the outdoors, and in artistic outlooks. However, they shared a love of travel, books, opera and the theatre and, more importantly, politics. They both also liked to cook, and made a point of searching out small, obscure restaurants serving delicious third-world cuisines. Leona was a little older, a New York City girl who learned to drive only in her sixties. She was as outspoken as Allan was reserved, and made a habit of striking up conversations with strangers on buses, in the market and waiting in line at the bank or post office. One thing Allan said he could count on from her was surprises, including having to pick his way in the dark across a living room floor over a visiting troop of Girl Scouts camped out there. Throughout their time together she remained an important source of intellectual stimulation for his work. Leona always encouraged him to think about broadening both his scientific and social perspectives, and on his next journey she accompanied him to Brandeis University in Boston and a postdoctoral fellowship with Dr Nathan Kaplan.

Nate Kaplan was a former member of the Manhattan Project, and a fellow biochemist with a doctorate from UC Berkeley (1943), who had been recruited to build a new graduate programme at Brandeis in 1957. Allan thrived in this Boston environment, where the enzyme lactate dehydrogenase was a model system and cancer was a continued focus for many. Several themes common to later graduate student training at Berkeley emerge in this context, namely Kaplan's institution of graduate research rotation projects as a formal part of the first-year graduate experience, and regular reporting of these research project results requiring formal presentations documenting student progress. His early publications in the collection with Kaplan and colleagues reveal a return to birds and an exploration of enzyme diversity between species in oxygen-'limiting' environments versus those experiencing less oxidative stress (5). There is also evidence of his growing awareness of gene duplication as a force directing molecular diversity, as well as complicating the correct reconstruction of taxonomic relationships between species. Working to identify forms of this enzyme specific to tissues such as muscle versus heart or liver, he also helped to stumble on a practical extension of these enzyme differences and also the need for truth in labelling. Boston fish markets sometimes mislabelled their products for sale, to justify higher prices for more sought-after species. Cod versus haddock provided an example, in which LDH isoforms (alternative forms of the protein lactate dehydrogenase) could be used to enforce truth in advertising. Later, Allan's lab in Berkeley began developing its expertise with mitochondrial DNA (mtDNA) sequencing, and several former postdoctoral fellows applied this lesson. Stephen Palumbi used it for detecting illegal whaling in Tokyo fish markets, and Rob De Salle unmasked fake Beluga caviar sources from upscale shops on the Upper East Side of New York!

BACK TO BERKELEY AS AN INDEPENDENT SCIENTIST

Allan returned to Berkeley in 1964 to set up his laboratory in the Biochemistry Department as an assistant professor. He remained at Berkeley during his entire academic career, promoted to associate in 1968 and full professor in 1972. Reflecting on his long career there with me after I took my own 'real' job at the University of Hawaii at Manoa, he related that beginnings were always hard, and how important it had been to him that early on he had had a stable family life, one that Leona kept steady and serene. In retrospect, after observing (and hearing) some stormy interactions with Leona, his use of the adjective 'serene' seems comical. He related that he was always sincerely grateful to return home at night to his wife and kids running up to him in the driveway as he parked the car and unloaded a briefcase of work. Interactions with fellow Berkeley faculty could apparently be perilous, given the expectations that some had of imminent Nobel prizes. His children later had to deal with schoolyard taunts of a classmate who bragged that her father was more famous than their own dad. But again, Allan balanced these situations with his gratitude to senior scientists such as Pardee and Barker, who organized the old Biochemistry Department to include a common stock room, a library with shared journals and reference materials, a lunchroom to facilitate informal get-togethers, and an annual retreat to encourage open, pre-publication communication of new research results. His appearance in a photograph taken in 1968 with Ruth and David at Yosemite National Park (figure 3) is a stark reminder to me of the inevitable passage of time.

I first met Allan in 1974, when he guest lectured on molecular anthropology in an anthropology class that I attended as a non-traditional postgraduate, taught by Vincent Sarich, his former PhD student, who was one of four professors of physical anthropology at that time in Berkeley (serving with Sherwood Washburn, Phyllis Dolhinow and F. Clark Howell). In contrast to the complicated and contrasting views of primate relationships presented by a patchy fossil record, ethology (or comparative anatomy), the approach that Allan and Vince took to illustrate primate relationships (6, 7), including the connection between humans, chimps and gorillas, seemed intuitively obvious to someone with a background in genetics and biochemistry. How could their conclusions of recent shared common ancestry have evoked such controversy? Even with all the new australopithecine fossils being described, I immediately knew I wanted to join their research team, and in the following year I was accepted into the anthropology graduate programme. For two years I mostly operated on the fringes of Allan's lab, learning polyacrylamide electrophoresis and everything I could about the systematics of macaques and baboons.

The Wilson lab at that point was a smoothly operating machine. In 1980 we female students kidded Allan about his prematurely grey hair and his usual mode of weekday dress, which was a white shirt, grey trousers and black Oxford shoes, earning him his codename 'Grey Eminence'.

Figure 3. Allan with his children, Ruth and David, on a camping trip to Yosemite National Park in the mid 1960s. Ruth eventually received her PhD in plant sciences before moving to Seattle. David now works and lives in France. (Online version in colour.)

It took little time to realize that some of that grey hair was probably due to his students. After getting up the nerve to ask him about why he always preferred to wear the same 'uniform', he replied that never having to waver in his clothing choices (except at weekends) meant never having to waste time on meaningless trivia. For him, it was enough of a challenge helping to get his kids up and fed, with homework done, and himself out of the door in the morning. He claimed that his best ideas came to him as he was brushing his teeth, and the rest of the day was downhill from there. Perhaps his experience as a young father helped him understand the stresses that his students with children of their own were undergoing as well, and I do not think it was an accident that several married students with toddlers gravitated to his lab. (The lab bench I inherited came with a lower drawer complete with teething marks, which I later learned from the lab's long-time dishwasher, Mrs Eudola Bradley, were courtesy of Linda Maxson's young son, whose mother used it as a temporary crib.) Allan showed remarkable patience with all of us, some more mature than others, and some more active in extracurricular activities. With the Berkeley campus in the centre of many political battles, his former student Tom White related years later that Allan had once bailed him and another labmate out of jail after a Black Panther demonstration! The lab had its share of drug raids, punk bands formed, gay and political activists, belly-dancer enthusiasts, mountain climbers and cave explorers, and Zen priests. How he endured the years of loyalty oaths for Berkeley faculty and kept his proud New Zealand citizenship throughout remains a mystery to me. Many of us were able to gather in Berkeley for a party organized to celebrate the 25th anniversary of his molecular clock. He took our personality quirks in his stride, calmly smiling and storing up blackmail material for later when he needed a favour, usually his request to take a very young student protégé into one's lab for the summer. Allan reserved his rare public expressions of ill-temper for people whom he judged intolerant racists, scientific creationists or

Figure 4. Allan 'in the field' in Hawaii en route to his mother's 80th birthday in New Zealand.
(Online version in colour.)

molecular-clock deniers. In later years, Allan was usually more at home behind a desk than collecting samples in the field, but he was such an avid birder that his final version of field work usually included a pair of binoculars and a good bird book (figure 4). Any visit to a wildlife sanctuary always prompted a string of new questions.

DAY TO DAY IN THE WILSON LAB

His fearsome lab manager and former student Dr Ellen Prager intimidated everyone new and was the enforcer of all regulations, written and unwritten. She was the gate-agent, eyeballing the traffic in and out of our fourth-floor labs, and a vigilant watchdog for keeping Allan to his scheduled appointments. Ellen was also a prolific co-author of many publications with Allan on bird lysozymes. She was so much more than a co-author, however, functioning as the historian of the lab, the keeper of his grant proposal and manuscript drafts, the overseer of research grants, and the custodian of freezers and/or cold-room space. She hated the fact that some of us insisted on playing loud rock and roll as we worked, although we did not disturb Allan because his office was a bit down the hall from the lab. The actual lab was made up of three adjoining rooms, so a demilitarized zone in the centre room eventually evolved to separate the incompatibles. Allan's approach to lab noise was simply to walk in and pull the plug on our radios and boom boxes if he wanted to talk, because he never bothered with on/off switches. When the original Sony Walkman was invented, it made a near-universal overnight appearance in our lab coat pockets.

It took those first few years to learn who had finished which previous theses, who had followed up on unfinished threads, and how the various projects interrelated. Samples were spread out between freezers and refrigerators by the yard, everyone with a designated shelf. Norman Arnheim, Allan's first postdoctoral fellow, was king of the freezer space for a very long time, judging by his accumulated lysozyme reagents. Eventually Allan was renting commercial meat-locker space to accommodate his collection of stomachs, bones, placentas, blood, antisera, cultured cells, and whole bodies. Road kills and zoo specimens, including a whole alligator, kept company together, tagged with a name and a collection site. One shudders to think now of the lab biosafety issues, but it was a different era then. By 1978 I was finally getting a grasp of the full scope of Allan's impact, just as the lab was making the transition from proteins and immunology to restriction enzyme analysis, recombinant DNA work and DNA sequencing.

Cross-fertilization between the Zoology Department's Museum of Vertebrate Zoology and Allan's lab provided ample intellectual stimulation, as students shared technologies and samples. There existed a subtle differentiation between those lab facilities, with the Museum of Vertebrate Zoology operating an efficient starch-gel electrophoretic laboratory for population genetic work (two classic examples with Galapagos tortoises and western salamanders are given in Feder *et al.* (1978) and Marlor & Patton (1981)), and Allan's lab specializing in applications of the micro-complement fixation method, using an indirect measure of protein divergence to reconstruct with immunology the relationships between species. This was the method made famous by Vince and Allan in their papers challenging the palaeoanthropology community over the correct timescale for the divergence of humans and apes. It was also the same method that led Allan, with Ellen, Linda Maxson, Susan Case, Lorraine Cherry and others to suggest that morphological evolution was more likely to be dependent on gene regulatory changes than on individual substitutions in protein-coding sequences (8, 10). A famous paper by Allan and Mary-Claire King highlighted this difference between humans and chimpanzees, using her electrophoretic data as well (11). Today the MorphoBank project, funded by the National Science Foundation and aimed at helping researchers determine what a common ancestor of a group of organisms might look like, would be a prime resource for his students. Allan had also just completed, with former students Tom White and Steve Carlson, his famous review of molecular evolution (12), and had established that a molecular clock, in the words of former student Steve Beverly, could keep 'damn good time!'

Allan used his appointment to the editorial board of *Journal of Molecular Evolution* to help keep abreast of the latest research in his field and to forge new alliances with international groups interested in the same problems as he was. This journal started in 1971, publishing a steady stream of papers on proteins and complex molecular interactions, including those between duplicate genes and gene families. This was a topic of particular interest to Allan, because he viewed gene duplication as the key to the acquisition of new functions in the cell. At the time of his death in 1991 he was an associate editor and quite an active contributor. The steady stream of illustrious scientists knocking on his office door to attend editorial meetings and discuss contributions included Linus Pauling, Masatoshi Nei, Francisco Ayala, Walter Fitch, Carl Woese, Émile Zuckerkandl, Tom Jukes, Harold Vargus, Mike Bishop, David Penny, Joe Felsenstein, Bob Selander, Oliver Ryder, Charles Sibley, Luca Cavalli-Sforza,

John Maynard Smith, Bill Hamilton, Peter Grant and Ernst Mayr. Some of his collaborators had gathered samples for biological research from New Guinea on a new exploration platform, R/V *Alpha Helix*, funded by the National Science Foundation and operated by the Scripps Institute of Oceanography. He also had samples from zoos and herbaria around the world, aquaria scattered far and wide, and private game farms. He himself secured materials from Africa and the Middle East as a result of sabbatical trips to the Weizmann Institute and Nairobi. Other collaborators were suggesting work with mummified tissues and samples preserved in amber. Publications, drafts, proposals, and correspondence with many of these scientists and their students, who went on to become famous for their own discoveries, has been assembled by Ellen and is now archived at UC Berkeley's Bancroft Library, accessed through 'Finding aid to the Allan Wilson papers, 1953–1998, bulk 1962–1991' (http://www.oac.cdlib.org/findaid/ark:/13030/kt958035w4/dsc/#c01-1.3.6.12).

Finding the sources to fund this work was a constant issue, because his lab was exploding in size, and the advent of recombinant DNA techniques required his acquisition of new equipment and supplies. His relationship with Bruce and Giovanna Ames, faculty members who operated in adjacent laboratory space, was especially helpful in bridging the lean years of transition: Bruce was able to pay for certain shared services when Allan could not. Allan talked often about his and Leona's warm interactions with the Ames duo over Giovanna's gourmet dinners, his discussions of oxidative stress and mutation rates with Bruce, and how changes in the human diet were putting mutational pressures on the human gene pool that would be interesting to follow over time (Ames *et al.* 1993). As Allan got deeper into mitochondrial genetics, these discussions intensified to involve his students and postdoctoral fellows, stimulating research questions about lifespan, copy number, metabolic rates and brain size. The relation between molecular evolution and the evolution of the brain was a problem that he kept returning to, and one could safely predict that, had he lived, he would today be investigating brain-specific regulatory RNAs.

Change the emphasis from proteins to DNAs

The transition in the Wilson lab to DNA technologies was eventually achieved by advances on two fronts, both with the help of valued collaborators in the person of haematologist Yuet Wai Kan, his former postdoctoral fellow Norm Arnheim, and Wesley M. Brown, an enterprising 'orphan' from Cal Tech who sought out Allan's help while publishing his thesis results on the isolation and analysis of mtDNA (Brown 1980), performed in Jerome Vinograd's lab at Cal Tech and brought to an abrupt end with Vinograd's sudden death. Allan encouraged his many graduate students to develop their own networks, and a very fruitful one fostered by Elizabeth Zimmer and the Kan laboratory at the University of California at San Francisco opened the door to globin gene family evolution for Sandra Martin, Karen Vincent, Barbara Chapman and William Davidson, among others. Working with Kan, they brought together Allan's interests in the processes of gene duplication, regulation at a distance from a structural gene locus, and complexity in using duplicate gene sequences to reconstruct phylogenetic relationships (13, 14). From a medical diagnostic lab came new techniques and an open window that transferred these back to work with the lysozyme systems of birds and mammals. The Arnheim lab provided further assistance for cloning and work with repetitive sequences. At the same time, Allan and Wes recruited a team in 1979 to begin exploring the use of his restriction mapping of human animal mtDNAs for population genetics. The first large-scale sequencing project for humans, the Sanger sequence of human mtDNA, which is now known as the Cambridge Reference Sequence (Anderson *et al.* 1981) was assisted by Wes's meticulous restriction endonuclease maps that helped place ambiguous fragments in the correct order, independently verifying the annotation of that genome. The ability to prepare, to biochemical purity, mtDNA from hundreds of different animals meant that entire populations could be analysed at a fraction of the cost and time required for cloning and sequencing a single nuclear gene at that time. In addition, the uniparental inheritance pattern of the mitochondrial genome in most animals meant that phylogenetic reconstruction depended on a simpler pattern, with genetic recombination largely eliminated as a consideration. A cherished memory of Wes and Allan's interactions comes from a presentation made by Wes at the annual Asilomar retreat, where a frustrated Allan pulled his headstrong postdoctoral fellow off the stage with a shepherd's crook after he had gone 20 minutes over his allotted time.

From my personal perspective, our papers on human mtDNA and the exploration of modern human origins tested Allan's ability to engage the public as well as his peers in scientific debate (18, 20). We struggled with graphics, with metaphors, and with each other as the media circus swirled around us. A fierce backlash in some anthropological circles carried personalized attacks that also stung. We were even accused of finding the right answer but for all the wrong reasons. The mother of us all had somehow morphed into the wicked witch, and the name Mitochondrial Eve stuck like nothing had before. Allan's advice through all of this was to wait, watch, and let the dust settle. We had published our data, for all to see, and we just might be wrong, but he did not think so and neither did I.

The Wilson lab publication record for papers in rodent, bird, fish, monkey and human mtDNAs during the 1980s and 1990s fostered a new team of scientists engaged in looking at biodiversity from a fresh perspective. It also placed additional pressure on all of us struggling with the least biased way of portraying molecular data in populations constantly exchanging genes, because the computer-assisted methodologies that we used to build phylogenetic trees were based largely on assumptions that populations were forever diverging into new species. If one added to that the fact that mtDNA is such a large part of the total DNA content of a eukaryotic cell, making it more likely to survive the degradation of time, the dream that these phylogenies would extend into history now became reality. First came a quagga, an extinct zebra (22), and the world of ancient DNA exploded. The Presley Institute of Fossil Biochemistry became more than just a velvet painting of Elvis on the wall in the lab middle room: we imagined it would be possible to fund ancient DNA research based on recovery of DNA from shed skin cells of clothing touched by dead celebrities. Some veterans of this era in the Wilson lab fanned out to help found centres of excellence in Natural History Museums and university institutes around the world. A DNA lab in a museum is now considered standard fare, thanks to Allan's impetus. A student's doctoral thesis on the systematics of an obscure group of plants or animals, without reference to a molecular phylogeny, is unheard of today. The debate to use a universal 'barcode' to formally describe biodiversity in groups for which no taxonomic expert can reasonably hope to study fully can be directly linked to his paper on universal polymerase chain reaction primers for mtDNA studies with Tom Kocher, Kelly Thomas, Axel Meyer, Scott Edwards, Svante Paabo and Frances Villiblanca (23). The fact that the '2% per million years of divergence' mantra attached to the rate of mtDNA evolution is a starting point for many is based on years of carefully sought specimens, calibration and recalibration, bootstrapping, and long nights in the lab when you finally had unlimited access to the thermocycler. The relatively simple mitochondrial

Figure 5. Eunice Wilson's 80th birthday celebration in New Zealand, in 1988. From the left: Allan, Eunice (his mother), Leona (his wife), Colleen (his sister) and Gary (his brother). Allan's mother was the epicentre of family life; she was active in all aspects of her community and was eventually awarded the Queen's Service Medal in 1995 for her lifetime contributions. (Online version in colour.)

genome had two major advantages in evolutionary reconstruction. First, it had a single-parent transmission pattern in most animals, with no genetic recombination to befuddle the construction of a shared ancestor. Second, while containing a limited number of essential genes, it also contained non-coding regions with a very high mutation rate, making it ideal for examining recently diverged species and geographically distinct populations.

HIS WARMTH AS A MENTOR MATCHED HIS SKILLS AS A RESEARCHER

Throughout this period of rapid lab expansion and increasing rate of publication, Allan stayed close to his family and long-time associates. Leona's initial diagnosis of breast cancer proved to be an event that disrupted some of his travel and speaking schedules, which had become quite demanding. Many of us experienced a phone call asking whether we would consider giving a paper at an invited conference, because he had declined to appear and suggested we were the more appropriate speaker anyway. This generosity no doubt irked some symposium organizers who were hoping to snare the 'big cheese', but it also reflected Allan's spirit in that his name was rarely first in author order, even if the idea had been his to begin with and he had largely written the paper. When I go through citations in texts, I am often struck by this pattern, in comparison with many other senior scientists. The fame accompanying his MacArthur Foundation award in 1986 surpassed his previous two Guggenheim Fellowships and his appointment as a university professor by the Berkeley campus, an achievement given only to their most prominent educators. What his family in New Zealand made of all the attention is unclear. Allan and Leona made the trip back to Pukekohe for his mother's 80th birthday party and family reunion (figure 5). They stopped to stay with me in Hawaii en route, bringing stories of old friends and new crazy ideas. As usual, Allan was eager to hear what progress I was making in setting up my own research programme, and we shared a final trip out to Kauai for some birding. Leona commented that she thought Allan had been losing too much weight.

Allan's story would not be complete without a footnote about the development of the polymerase chain reaction as a working tool, used today in all molecular genetic laboratories. A cadre of Allan's former colleagues and students eventually assembled in a biotechnology start-up in Alameda, California, with ties to the Berkeley Biochemistry Department. In the mid to late 1980s they needed a tested and well-understood proof-of-concept molecule to demonstrate the capability of Kerry Mullis's fledgling technology. Having a great idea is one thing; executing a controlled experiment is another. No one understood this more than Allan, and he quietly assisted their efforts to establish working protocols that would generate consistent and reliable results, especially for ancient DNA studies (24). Norm Arnheim, Russ Higuchi, Henry Erlich and Tom White were there in the trenches, using globin constructs, modern and ancient mtDNA fragments, and other bits and pieces from the Wilson lab. Fortunately, Allan lived long enough to enjoy the blossoming of this technology and to help direct its future use in molecular evolutionary studies. As recognition of his further achievements, he received the 3M Life Sciences Award from the Federation of American Societies for Experimental Biology in 1991.

The Allan Wilson Centre for Molecular Evolution was founded in New Zealand to carry on the work promoted by Allan's insistence that new insights into important biological and chemical processes essential to life on Earth would stem from seeing the natural world with a properly trained mind. He wanted young scientists to have access to multidisciplinary tools that would equip them to solve problems of use to all scientists, and to learn the communication skills that would engage the general public in the thirst for that knowledge. That training would include bioinformatics, breakthroughs in environmental sciences using molecular tools for disease ecology, and an appreciation of the wondrous species diversity evolving in isolation in their own backyards. Universities and institutes partner to form a core with a defined mission of education and outreach now, fostering science in a way that Allan envisaged would help provide a new future for the home that he really never left.

AWARDS AND HONOURS

1972   Guggenheim Fellow
1986   MacArthur Fellow
        Fellow of the Royal Society
1983   Fellow of the American Academy of Arts and Sciences
1989   Honorary DSc, Otago University
1984   Member of the Human Genome Organization
1971   Associate editor of *Journal of Molecular Evolution*
1990   College of Sciences and Arts Distinguished Achievement Award, Washington State University at Pullman
        Regents' Distinguished Alumnus Award, Washington State University at Pullman
1991   3M Life Sciences Award from the Federation of American Societies for Experimental Biology
1997   Distinguished New Zealand Biotechnologist Award, New Zealand Biotechnology Association

ACKNOWLEDGEMENTS

I thank Gary Wilson, Colleen Macmillan, Ruth Wilson, Charles Daugherty, Thomas White and Norman Arnheim for their detailed knowledge of the life and work of Allan Wilson. Vince Sarich died in 2012, before this biography noting his contributions to the groundbreaking work he performed with Allan could be published. Gary provided the family pictures. I am sorry for any inadvertent omissions to this biography.

The frontispiece photograph was taken in 1990 by Jane Scherr and is reproduced by courtesy of Washington State University, Pullman.

REFERENCES TO OTHER AUTHORS

Ames, B. N., Shigenaga, M. K. & Hagen, T. M. 1993. Oxidants, antioxidants, and the degenerative diseases of aging. *Proc. Natl Acad. Sci. USA* **90**, 7915–7922.

Anderson, S. (and 13 others) 1981 Sequence and organization of the human mitochondrial genome. *Nature* **290**, 457–465.

Baldwin, E. 1937 *An introduction to comparative biochemistry*. Cambridge University Press.

Brown, W. M. 1980 Polymorphism in mitochondrial DNA of humans as revealed by restriction endonuclease analysis. *Proc. Natl Acad. Sci. USA* **77**, 3605–3609.

Feder, J. H., Wurst G. Z. & Wake, D. B. 1978 Genetic variation in western salamaders of the genus *Plethodon*, and the status of *Plethodon gordoni*. *Herpetologia* **34**, 64–69.

Marlor, R. W. & Patton, J. L. 1981 Biochemical relationships of the Galapagos giant tortoises (*Geochelone elephatopus*). *J. Zool.* **195**, 413–422.

Pardee, A. B., Jacob, F. & Monod, J. 1959 The genetic control of cytoplasmic expression of 'inducibility' in the synthesis of β-galactosidase by *E. coli*. *J. Mol. Biol.* **1**, 165–178.

Zuckerkandl, É. & Pauling, L. B. 1962 Molecular disease, evolution and genic heterogeneity. In *Horizons in biochemistry* (ed. M. Kasha & B. Pullman), pp. 189–225. New York: Academic Press.

BIBLIOGRAPHY

The following publications are those referred to directly in the text. A full bibliography is available as electronic supplementary material at http://dx.doi.org/10.1098/rsbm.2013.0006 or via http://rsbm.royalsocietypublishing.org.

(1) 1957 (With D. S. Farner) A quantitative examination of testicular growth in the white-crowned sparrow. *Biol. Bull.* **113**, 254–267.

(2)   (With D. S. Farner & J. R. King) The development of vernal migratory behavior in caged individuals of several taxa of *Zonotricia*. *Anat. Rec.* **128**, 546.

(3) 1962 (With A. B. Pardee) Regulation of flavin synthesis by *Escherichia coli*. *J. Gen. Microbiol.* **28**, 283–303.

(4) 1963 (With A. B. Pardee) Control of enzyme activity in higher animals. *Cancer Res.* **23**, 1483–1490.

(5)   (With R. D. Cahn & N. O. Kaplan) Functions of the two forms of lactate dehydrogenase in the breast muscle of birds. *Nature* **197**, 331–334.

(6) 1967 (With V. M. Sarich) Immunological time scale for hominid evolution. *Science* **158**, 1200–1203.

(7) 1969 (With V. M. Sarich) A molecular time scale for human evolution. *Proc. Natl Acad. Sci. USA* **63**, 1088–1093.

(8) 1974 (With L. R. Maxson & V. M. Sarich) Two types of molecular evolution. Evidence from studies of interspecific hybridization. *Proc. Natl Acad. Sci. USA* **71**, 2843–2847.

(9)   Evolutionary importance of gene regulation. *Stadler Genet. Symp.* **7**, 117–134.

(10)   (With E. M. Prager) Slow evolutionary loss of the potential for interspecific hybridization in birds. A manifestation of slow regulatory evolution. *Proc. Natl Acad. Sci. USA* **72**, 200–204.

(11)   (With M.-C. King) Evolution at two levels in humans and chimpanzees. *Science* **188**, 107–116.

(12)   1977   (With S. S. Carlson & T. J. White) Biochemical evolution. *Annu. Rev. Biochem.* **46**, 573–639.

(13)   1980   (With E. A. Zimmer, S. L. Martin, S. M. Beverly & Y.-W. Kan) Rapid duplication and loss of genes coding for the α chains of hemoglobin. *Proc. Natl Acad. Sci. USA* **77**, 2158–2162.

(14)   (With S. L. Martin, E. A. Zimmer & Y.-W. Kan) Silent δ-globin gene in Old World monkeys. *Proc. Natl Acad. Sci. USA* **77**, 3563–3566.

(15)   1984   (With D. E. Dobson & E. M. Prager) Stomach lysozymes of ruminants. I. Distribution and catalytic properties. *J. Biol. Chem.* **259**, 11607–11616.

(16)   (With P. Jolles, F. Schoentgen, J. Jolles, D. E. Dobson & E. M. Prager) Stomach lysozymes of ruminants. II. Amino acid sequence of cow lysozyme 2 and immunological comparisons with other lysozymes. *J. Biol. Chem.* **259**, 11617–11625.

(17)   (With P. V. Hornbeck) Local effects of amino acid substitutions on the active site region of lysozyme: a comparison of physical and immunological results. *Biochemistry* **23**, 998–1002.

(18)   (With R. L. Cann & W. M. Brown) Polymorphic sites and the mechanism of evolution in human mitochondrial DNA. *Genetics* **106**, 479–499.

(19)   1986   (With L. S. Weisman & B. M. Krummel) Evolutionary shift in the site of cleavage of prelysozyme. *J. Biol. Chem.* **261**, 2309–2313.

(20)   1987   (With R. L. Cann & M. Stoneking) Mitochondrial DNA and human evolution. *Nature* **325**, 31–36.

(21)   (With M. F. Hammer, J. W. Schilling & E. M. Prager) Recruitment of lysozyme as a major enzyme in the mouse gut: duplication, divergence, and regulatory evolution. *J. Mol. Evol.* **24**, 272–279.

(22)   (With R. G. Higuchi, L. A. Wrischnik, E. Oakes, M. George Jr & B. Tong) Mitochondrial DNA of the extinct quagga: relatedness and extent of post-mortem change. *J. Mol. Evol.* **25**, 283–287.

(23)   1989   (With T. D. Kocher, W. K. Thomas, A. Meyer, S. V. Edwards, S. Pääbo & F. X. Villablanca) Dynamics of mitochondrial DNA evolution in animals: amplification and sequencing with conserved primers. *Proc. Natl Acad. Sci. USA* **86**, 6196–6200.

(24)   (With S. Pääbo & R. G. Higuchi) Ancient DNA and the polymerase chain reaction. *J. Biol. Chem.* **264**, 9709–9712.